Validation of Aseptic Pharmaceutical Processes

Validation of Aseptic Pharmaceutical Processes

edited by

Frederick J. Carleton

Pfizer Inc.
New York, New York

James P. Agalloco

E. R. Squibb & Sons, Inc.
New Brunswick, New Jersey

MARCEL DEKKER, INC. New York • Basel

Library of Congress Cataloging-in-Publication Data
Main entry under title:

Validation of aseptic pharmaceutical processes.

Includes index.
1. Sterilization. 2. Pharmaceutical technology.
I. Carleton, Frederick J., [date] II. Agalloco,
James P., [date] [DNLM: 1. Sterilization--
methods. 2. Technology, Pharmaceutical.
QV 778 V172]
RS199.S73V34   1986   615'.19   85-29325
ISBN 0-8247-7362-4

MARCEL DEKKER, INC.
270 Madison Avenue, New York, New York 10016

Current printing (last digit):
10   9   8   7   6   5   4   3

PRINTED IN THE UNITED STATES OF AMERICA

In writing this book we were helped and encouraged by a great many people who listened to our ideas and gave us the benefit of their thinking. Foremost among these were our wives, Helen Carleton and Linda Agalloco, as well as our children, Brant Carleton, and Stephen, Andrea, and Adam Agalloco, who, throughout these four years of preparation, encouraged us, pushed us to think harder, played devil's advocate and considered ideas and topics with us. Most of all, we are grateful for their love and understanding.

Preface

Innovative and creative scientists are confronted today with a period in which both the demands and the opportunities for innovation have never been greater. Approaches and procedures in the present environment must be designed to encourage satisfying opportunities for individuals in pharmaceutical operations in which the exchange and sharing of information is readily available.

Somerset Maugham once wrote that "perfection is nothing more than a complete adaptation to the environment; but the environment is constantly changing, so perfection can never be more than transitory." Technical limitations in the pharmaceutical manufacturing and control environment raise concerns and inspire new approaches and techniques when problems arise and threaten the stability of an otherwise satisfactory operation. To provide the information needed to respond to developing technology, the editors have assembled a treatise which will provide a source for both experienced and inexperienced practitioners in the pharmaceutical industry.

Validation of Aseptic Pharmaceutical Processes is designed as a reference book for use by managers, supervisors, and scientists in the pharmaceutical industry. The primary intent of this work is to guide the design engineers, the manufacturing personnel, the research and development scientists and quality control professionals in validating those processes needed for aseptic pharmaceutical production. It is also necessary to identify the obstacles that will be encountered not only in the initial validation attempts, but also during the subsequent phases of the validation program.

The purpose of this book is to meet the need for a text on the validation of aseptic pharmaceutical production and provide general information and guidelines. It is a compilation of various theories, sterilization variables, and engineering and microbial studies that can be used independently or in combination to validate equipment and processes. The concepts and methods presented in this book are not intended to serve as *standards* that must be followed for validation, but are submitted solely as a guide. Equivalent methods for achieving this purpose exist and should be considered and utilized, where appropriate.

The development of a subject as broad and complex as "validation" in the pharmaceutical industry has widespread application, affecting regulation, current Good Manufacturing Practices, development, quality assurance, manufacturing, and facilities. The idea of validation was conceived by the Food & Drug Administration in the mid-1970s as a means for improving drug product quality. For those of us who have pioneered during the early years of validation, the absence of a clear and concise summary of this subject has caused significant duplication of effort on the part of the pharmaceutical industry. This book, the editors believe, will help fill the information void we have all experienced.

We acknowledge, with thanks, the generous help we received from many sources: our colleagues for the chapters they contributed; the critical reviews from Stanley Sklar, Phil De Santis, Stella Reed, Raymond Shaw, Jr., Doris Conrad, Andrew Schmitz, Jr., Kevin Munnelly, Barbara Gordon, Joseph Robinson, Solomon Pflag, and John Kimmins; and the interest and assistance afforded to us by our many friends in the pharmaceutical industry. A special note of thanks is due to Mrs. Maureen Ocleppo, who survived the countless drafts, and to Sandra Beberman of Marcel Dekker, Inc., whose patience was remarkable.

Frederick J. Carleton
James P. Agalloco

Contributors

James P. Agalloco M.S., M.B.A. Department of Pharmaceutical Technology, E. R. Squibb & Sons, Inc., New Brunswick, New Jersey

David H. Artiss Artiss and Associates, Medfield, Massachusetts

Ralph Badagliacca M.S. Department of Quality Control, Pfizer Inc., Brooklyn, New York

Robert E. Bremmer P.E. Calibration and Consulting Services, Inc., Des Plaines, Illinois

Laurie A. Burns* Department of Pharmaceutical Technology, E. R. Squibb & Sons, Inc., New Brunswick, New Jersey

Theodore E. Byers Byers Enterprises, Alexandria, Virginia

Frederick J. Carleton M.S. Quality Control Division, Pfizer Inc., New York, New York

Phil De Santis M.S.Ch.E.† Department of Pharmaceutical Technology, E. R. Squibb & Sons, Inc., New Brunswick, New Jersey

Francisco DeVecchi VECO International, Inc., Farmington Hills, Michigan

George R. Dietz M.S. Isomedix, Inc., Whippany, New Jersey

Jeannine A. Der Bedrosian‡ Department of Pharmaceutical Technology, E. R. Squibb & Sons, Inc., New Brunswick, New Jersey

John J. Errico M.S.C.S., P.E.§ Penicillin Recovery Department, Pfizer Inc., Groton, Connecticut

---

Current affiliations:

*Department of Instrumentation and Controls, Stearns Catalytic Corporation, Philadelphia, Pennsylvania
†PACO Pharmaceutical Services, Lakewood, New Jersey
‡Independent consultant, East Brunswick, New Jersey
§Process Automation Group, Pfizer Inc., Groton, Connecticut

Barry D. Garfinkle M.S., Ph.D.* Department of Process Validation, Merck Sharp & Dohme, Inc., West Point, Pennsylvania

Carole S. Genovesi Department of Internal Environmental Control, Wyeth Laboratories, West Chester, Pennsylvania

John R. Gillis Ph.D. Skyland Scientific Services, Inc., Belgrade, Montana

Stephen W. Goodsir Parenteral Pilot Plant Section, Pharmacy Research and Development Division, Wyeth Laboratories, West Chester, Pennsylvania

Barbara M. Gordon M.S. Department of Pharmaceutical Technology, E. R. Squibb & Sons, Inc., New Brunswick, New Jersey

Gayle D. Heffernan R.Ph. Department of Pharmaceutical Technology, E. R. Squibb & Sons, Inc., New Brunswick, New Jersey

Robert A. Jacobs Wyeth Laboratories, Great Valley, Pennsylvania

J. Patrick Jeater M.S.Ch.E. † Process Validation Unit, Pilot Plant Subdivision, Wyeth Laboratories, Paoli, Pennsylvania

Thomas A. Jennings M.A., Ph.D. T. A. Jennings Associates, Inc., Bala Cynwyd, Pennsylvania

Clarence A. Kemper M.S., M.E., Ph.D. Kaye Instruments, Inc., Bedford, Massachusetts

Robert G. Kieffer Ph.D. Quality Assurance Department, Sterling International Group, Sterling Drug, Inc., New York, New York

Timothy J. Leahy Ph.D. Millipore Corporation, Bedford, Massachusetts

Charles S. Levine M.S. Quality Assurance Department, Astra Pharmaceutical Products, Inc., Westboro, Massachusetts

Alvin Lieberman M.S.Ch.E. HIAC/ROYCO Division, Pacific Scientific, Inc., Menlo Park, California

C. Kenneth Lovejoy M.S.M.E. Manufacturing Engineering Department, American McGaw, Division of American Hospital Supply Corporation, Irvine, California

Vincent S. Rudo R.Ph. Department of Pharmaceutical Technology, E. R. Squibb & Sons, Inc., New Brunswick, New Jersey

Ronald J. Simko M.B.A.‡ Department of Manufacturing Technical Support, Schering–Plough Corporation, Kenilworth, New Jersey

Current affiliations:

*Department of Sterile Process Project Engineering, Merck Sharp & Dohme, Inc., West Point, Pennsylvania
†Process Validation Department, ICI United Kingdom, Macclesfield, Cheshire, England
‡Department of Pharmaceutical Manufacturing, Schering–Plough Corporation, Union, New Jersey

Dominic A. Ventura M.S., Ph.D.* Pharmacy Research & Development Department, Wyeth Laboratories, West Chester, Pennsylvania

James D. Wilson† Division of Product Assurance Services, Abbott Laboratories, Abbott Park, Illinois

---

Current affiliations:

*Quality Control Division, Elkins—Sinn, Inc., Cherry Hill, New Jersey
†Scientific Affairs Support Services Department, Abbott Laboratories, North Chicago, Illinois

Contents

Validation of Aseptic Pharmaceutical Processes

1

Why Validation?

ROBERT G. KIEFFER

Sterling International Group, Sterling Drug, Inc., New York, New York

I. INTRODUCTION

The prime objective of anyone working in a pharmaceutical plant, whether in production or quality control, is to manufacture products of the requisite quality at the lowest possible cost. In this chapter it will be shown that process validation is essential for the achievement of this objective.

In June 1980, Theodore Byers defined validation as follows: "Validation is attaining and documentation of sufficient evidence to give reasonable assurance, given the current state of science, that the process under consideration does, and/or will do, what it purports to do."

There are three reasons why the pharmaceutical industry is concerned that their processes perform consistently as expected: (1) government regulation; (2) assurance of quality; and (3) cost reduction.

Government Regulation: The United States, Food and Drug Administration, current Good Manufacturing Practices (GMPs) do not talk specifically about process validation, but the concept of validation is strongly implied throughout the document [1]. Moreover, the concept of Good Manufacturing Practices is meaningless without process validation.

The implication of validation in the GMPs can be seen in Section 211.110:

> Such control procedures shall be established to *monitor* the output and to *validate* the performance of those manufacturing processes that may be responsible for causing variability in the characteristics of in-process material and the drug product.
>
> *Valid* in-process specifications for such characteristics shall be consistent with drug product final specifications and shall be derived from previous acceptable *process average and process variability estimates* where possible and determined by the application of suitable statistical procedures where appropriate.

And also in Section 211.113:

> Appropriate written procedures, *designed to prevent* objectionable microorganisms in drug products not required to be sterile, shall be established and followed.

The GMPs also speak of equipment of *appropriate* design (Section 211.63), *qualified* personnel (Section 211.25), production and control procedures *designed* to assure that the drug products have the characteristics they are represented to have (Section 211.101), etc.

The proposed GMPs for large volume parenterals (LVPs) contain very specific references to qualification and validation of processes and procedures [2]. For example, Section 212.243 cites the necessity of heat distribution and heat penetration studies in the validation of the sterilization process.

Assurance of Quality: Without process validation, which implies a process that is well understood and in a state of control, confidence in the quality of products manufactured is impossible. GMPs and Process Validation, two concepts that cannot be separated, are essential to quality assurance. Frequently, the validation of a process will lead to quality improvement, in addition to better quality consistency.

Cost Reduction: Experience and common sense indicate that a validated process is a more efficient process and a process that produces less reworks, rejects, wastage, etc. Process validation is fundamentally good business practice. Although compliance with government regulations is important, the principal reason for validating a process is assurance of quality at a reduced cost.

The term "validation" is a relative newcomer to the lexicon of the pharmaceutical industry. On the other hand, the concept of validation is not new to the pharmaceutical industry, since it has been validating processes for many years:

> All of us have validated our processes to some extent. It would not be economically feasible to use equipment not knowing if it will produce the product we want, not to employ people with no assurance that they can do the job, nor fail to implement in-process checks or examinations to assure that products meet specifications [3].

Although validation studies have been conducted in the pharmaceutical industry for a long time, there is an ever-increasing interest in process validation due to the industry's greater emphasis in recent years on quality assurance and productivity improvement. Process validation is a necessary part of a quality assurance program and fundamental to an efficient production operation.

Furthermore, the limitations of end-product testing to assure quality have become more clearly understood. The performance of sterility testing, 100% inspection for particulates, assay for the active ingredient, etc., cannot guarantee that each unit of the product meets specifications. Thus, the heavy emphasis on quality assurance, good manufacturing practices, "building quality in," and in-process control, all of which imply and require that processes be validated.

The pharmaceutical industry uses expensive materials, sophisticated facilities and equipment, and highly qualified personnel. The efficient use of these resources is necessary for the continued success of the pharmaceutical industry. The cost of product failures—rejects, reworks, recalls, complaints, etc.—is a significant part of the total production cost. Detailed study and control of the manufacturing process—validation—is necessary if failure costs are to be reduced and productivity improved.

II. DEFINITIONS

There have been many definitions of validation proposed, but at the present time there is no universally accepted definition. The definition given at the beginning of this chapter is excellent and widely used. For the purposes of this chapter a precise definition is not critical. It is intended that the reader of this chapter and of this book will obtain thereby a practical, working understanding of validation. Two additional, frequently used terms in the process validation literature are "qualification" and "challenge." Since there is confusion in terminology, the sense in which validation, qualification, and challenge are used in this chapter will be defined and described.

Process Validation: Process Validation is the scientific study of a process:

1. To prove that the process is doing what it is supposed to do, i.e., that the process is under control
2. To determine the process variables and acceptable limits for these variables, and to set up appropriate in-process controls

Process optimization—to optimize the process for maximum efficiency while maintaining quality standards—is a natural consequence of this scientific study of process variables and their control.

Validation lends itself to a variety of approaches. Two commonly used approaches are the review of historical data and a system challenge. Frequently a combination of these two is used. Also, there are acceptable variations within these two basic approaches. On occasion, there is no appropriate challenge test and, if the process is new, no historical data. In this case one studies the system design, tests the output of the system, installs appropriate controls, and monitors the system. An example of such a case is a Water-for-Injection system [4].

Validation essentially involves a determination of the critical variables and the acceptable range of these variables, followed by the continuous control of these variables. There are numerous ways to accomplish these objectives.

Qualification: "the performance of tests to determine if a component of a manufacturing process possesses the attributes required to obtain a specified quality of a product" [5].

Qualification deals with components or elements of a process, while validation deals with an entire manufacturing process for a product (see Fig. 1). In Section III of this chapter some of the typical components of a process are described.

Challenge: "the performance of tests to determine the limits of capability for a component of a manufacturing process. Limits of capability does not necessarily mean challenging until destruction, but limits of variation within which a defined level of quality can be assured" [5].

III. COMPONENTS OF VALIDATION

The validation of a process requires the qualification of each of the important elements of that process. The relative importance of an element may vary

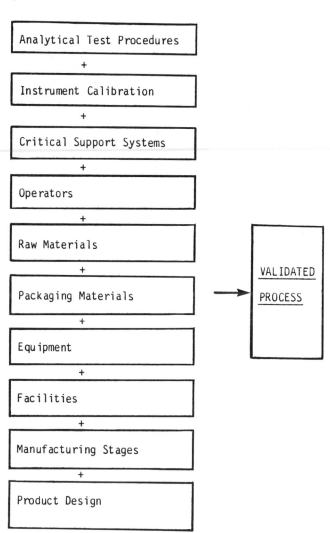

FIGURE 1   Qualification of each of the components of a process results in a validated process.

from process to process. Some of the components commonly considered in a process validation study include:

    Analytical test procedures
    Instrument calibration
    Critical support systems
    Operator qualification
    Raw and packaging materials
    Equipment
    Facilities
    Manufacturing stages
    Product design

A. Analytical Test Procedures

Analytical test procedures are used to determine potency of the active ingredient, levels of impurities or degradation products, etc. The qualification of an analytical test procedure requires demonstration of suitable accuracy, precision, specificity, sensitivity, and ruggedness of the method. Criteria of suitability depend on the purpose of the method. The assay of a potent active ingredient must be more precise and more accurate than the determination of a nontoxic degradation product. Since analytical test procedures are used in the qualification of other components of the process, their qualification is one of the first tasks performed.

B. Instrument Calibration

A pharmaceutical process uses many measuring devices to control the process. This control is accomplished either automatically by an appropriate feedback mechanism or through manual adjustments by an operator. In either case, the proper calibration of the measuring device is critical to the process. Some devices that need calibration are thermometers, pressure gauges, relative humidity meters, conductivity meters, timers, alarms, etc.

Calibration can be defined as the comparison of a measurement standard or instrument of known accuracy with another standard or instrument to detect, correlate, report, and/or eliminate by adjustment any variation in the accuracy of the item being compared.

Validation means controlling the variables. One variable is equipment, instrument, and measuring device accuracy. This variable is controlled through calibration. Some laboratory instruments that need to be calibrated are balances, spectrophotometers, chromatographs, calculators, computers, pH meters, rheometers, etc.

Before further validation studies can be attempted, the dependability and accuracy of the equipment used to monitor, control, and evaluate the process must be assured. Thus calibration is carried out early in the validation program. The specifications and frequency of calibration must be related to the use of the device or instrument in the context of the overall process. (Metrology will be discussed in a later chapter.)

C. Critical Support Systems

A support system is any general system that the plant needs to operate daily. These include air systems, electrical network, vacuum for cleaning, water supply and others. For purposes of validation we are concerned with *critical* support systems. These are systems that must operate at a certain level in order to maintain the required level of quality of the final product. It is evident, for example, that inadequate air filtration could result in a contaminated product, especially when performing an aseptic fill.

Some examples of critical support systems are

HVAC—heating, ventilation, and air conditioning
Water—Water for Injection, Purified Water, Potable Water
Steam
Compressed air
Nitrogen
Drainage system

The qualification of a critical plant support system consists of three phases:

1. Design
2. Installation and challenge
3. Monitoring

Designing the system, or for an existing system defining it, is the first phase. Technical data on system components (filters, deionizers, compressors, valves, etc.) must be located, reviewed, and collated. Distribution drawings of the HVAC, water, and drainage systems have to be prepared. While defining an existing system, it is likely that system deficiencies will be identified that must be corrected (plumbing dead legs, incorrect pressure gradients, inadequate filtration, etc.). The second phase involves making sure that the installed system performs as designed and, if possible, challenging the system to make sure that for normal and reasonable inputs the system output is acceptable. Finally, the system must be monitored at regular intervals to make sure that it continues to function properly. For example, a HEPA filter is usually challenged using the standard DOP test and frequently monitored for leaks with a particle counter.

D. Operator Qualification

The operation is the most important component in a process. Thus the qualification of the operator by training and experience is absolutely essential to the success of the whole validation program. An untrained operator can negate the work done in qualifying the other components of the process. The qualified operator is trained in all aspects of the job—technical, supervisory, productivity, good manufacturing practices, etc. It is important in the training program to emphasize the necessity of not making changes in a validated process without considering the consequences of the change, such as the need to revalidate the process if the change is significant. Frequently, the problems and failures that occur are caused by changes made in a thoroughly studied, validated system, by well-intentioned personnel.

E. Raw Materials and Packaging Materials

Qualification of materials involves the setting of specifications for all critical parameters of these materials. These specifications must be set in light of their purpose in the product and the end use of the product. Frequently the materials will have specifications in addition to those found in an official pharmacopeia, such as a particle size specification for an ingredient in a suspension formulation. Second, vendors must be qualified. Vendor qualification usually includes testing of samples and an audit of the vendor's facilities.

For a parenteral product, the container/closure system is especially important. Special care needs to be taken to assure the compatability of the container/closure with the product and that the closure is capable of maintaining the integrity of the product.

F. Equipment

The qualification of equipment starts with the design or selection process, followed by installation and verification that the equipment functions as desired. Qualification of equipment also requires the development of written procedures that describe the proper operation of the equipment, the development of a preventive maintenance program, the validation of cleaning procedures, and the training of personnel using or supervising the use of the equipment. Cleaning procedures must be shown to adequately remove product or dirt and to leave acceptably low levels of cleaning agents, solvents, etc. If the equipment must be sterile or pyrogen-free, the procedures used to accomplish this have to be shown to be effective.

Computers are being used with greater frequency as process control equipment. Computers are commonly used to control sterilizers. Qualification of a computer is in most respects similar to the qualification of other process equipment. The computer-controlled system must be challenged to make sure that the system will function properly under a variety of conditions and with various inputs. Normally the equipment vendor will supply software programs to check out the system. The security of the system relative to inadvertent program modifications, power failures, etc., must be considered. Periodically the computer system must be checked to assure that it is still performing as expected.

G. Facilities

The qualification of a facility includes four phases: design, construction, verification, and ongoing maintenance and monitoring. At the design or planning phase, the purpose of the facility, the product(s) to be manufactured, GMP and efficiency requirements, as well as cost, must be considered. The design of the critical systems (HVAC, water, etc.) is most important. Flow of material and personnel to avoid crossovers and turnbacks has to be studied. This leads to room and equipment layout. Room surfaces, especially in aseptic areas, have to be designed to be easily sanitized. Finally, everything needs to be documented—drawings, written specifications, etc.

The construction phase requires careful supervision to make sure that all the design specifications are being met. The process of verifying that the constructed facility meets all the established requirements starts when construction commences and ends with the installation and qualification of the equipment and critical systems. The verification phase should be documented and design specifications and engineering drawings modified if necessary. The last phase of qualifying a facility consists in establishing appropriate ongoing preventive maintenance, cleaning, sanitation, and environmental monitoring procedures.

H. Qualification of Manufacturing Stages

For each type of pharmaceutical dosage form there are various distinct stages in the manufacturing process that need to be qualified in order to validate the complete process. For a typical parenteral product, such as a small-volume parenteral, the stages are

1. Dispensing
2. Component preparation
3. Compounding
4. Sterile filtration
5. Filling
6. Terminal sterilization
7. Particulate inspection

8. Leak testing
9. Packaging

Additional stages would have to be qualified for aseptic bulk manufacture and filling, or for a lyophilized product.

I. Product Design

The product design consists of the formulation, container/closure system, basic manufacturing procedure, and quality control specifications and methodology. Chronologically, product design is the first component of validation to be studied. Although product design is normally the responsibility of the Research and Development function, it is wise to involve plant personnel, since their experience and knowledge of the plant's capabilities can be very valuable. A poorly designed product can make it impossible to validate and control a process. Consider the consequences of a formulation that is inherently unstable or inadequately preserved, specifications that are too tight, or analytical methodology that is not rugged.

IV. ORGANIZATION

The setting up of a validation program starts with the commitment of top management. Senior management support is necessary, since considerable resources will be necessary in order to carry out the program. It is the aim of this chapter to furnish the reader with material that can be used to show management the value of a validation program.

The composition of the validation team will depend on the component of the process being studied and the technical disciplines available (this will generally vary with the size of the company). Normally the following disciplines are involved in the plant validation program:

1. Quality Control
    a. Chemical testing
    b. Microbiology
    c. Quality assurance
2. Production
3. Engineering
4. Product Development (Research and Development)

Other functions that frequently are involved are

1. Training—for qualification of personnel
2. Statistics—for experimental design and evaluation of data
3. Safety
4. Purchasing—qualification of vendors of raw and packaging materials
5. Drug Regulatory Affairs

Since process validation is a plant-wide operation, the program is ultimately the responsibility of the plant manager. The plant manager will usually appoint a validation coordinator to lead the validation team or in a small plant take on this task himself.

The role of Research and Product Development is important. For a new product R&D should provide the plant with the following:

1. A product design whose components—formulation, manufacturing procedure, analytical methodology, and material and product specifications—have been validated. The manufacturing procedure should be validated by R&D at least on a pilot-batch basis.
2. Identification of the critical variables in the product and process.
3. Tentative limits for these variables. The limits may have to be modified as a result of the process validation studies done by the plant, since many components of the process will be different than those used in R&D studies.
4. Methodology to measure, monitor, and control the critical variables.

The validation coordinator, with the help of a team, will set up the qualification program for each component of the process to be validated, make sure that the program is executed properly and on schedule, and coordinate the evaluation of the results obtained. The qualification program will consist of the following:

1. Flow diagram and description of the system
2. Qualification protocol, which includes:
   a. Parameters to be validated
   b. Methods to be used
   c. How results will be analyzed
3. Writing of standard operating procedures (SOPs) for the system, including in-process controls and monitoring procedures
4. Documentation of the qualification program

V. VALIDATION AND IN-PROCESS CONTROL

The purpose of validation is to identify the critical process parameters, establish an acceptable range for these parameters, and provide a means of controlling them. Ongoing, daily, batch, in-process control and monitoring emanates from the validation study. Without in-process control, the validation work becomes meaningless, an academic study. Consider, for example, a validated autoclave being used without monitoring the temperature, or a still without monitoring conductivity. Furthermore, adequate in-process control frequently can eliminate the need for costly periodic revalidation of the process.

The role and importance of in-process control can be seen by examining its place in a total quality assurance program. A total quality assurance program has four stages:

1. *Development*: This is the product design phase and also includes the initial validation studies.
2. *In-process control/monitoring*: Consists of the ongoing, daily control and monitoring of the process.
3. *Auditing*: A periodic process audit verifies that procedures established during validation are being complied with and that these procedures are still adequate. "Putting a program in writing does not

ensure that it will be followed, nor does it, in and of itself, provide the feedback necessary to correct and update programs and processes" [6].

4. *Modification*: There are a variety of reasons for changing a system— productivity improvement, lower costs, revised quality requirements, new equipment, new processes, etc. Sometimes we find that a process can change imperceptibly with small modifications, so that the resulting system is considerably different than the original. Changes in the process require that it be *revalidated*.

In-process control is too important to be left to chance or to be handled in an arbitrary manner. Control charts are a very useful, statistically based tool for in-process control. In its simplest form, the control chart consists of a plot of the variable being monitored vs. time, with action levels established at plus or minus 2 and/or 3 standard deviations. This technique provides the operator with the means of determining whether the process is under control and whether the product resulting from the process is likely to meet specifications. For a parenteral operation a control chart is useful for control of filling, for analysis of environmental control data, for accumulation and analysis of assay data, microbial counts of water, etc.

VI. VALUE OF VALIDATION

As indicated earlier, the main advantages to be obtained from validating a process are cost reduction, process optimization, and assurance of quality, with compliance with regulatory requirements as an added bonus. This is not to imply that compliance with regulations is unimportant; however, more is to be gained and perhaps a better job done by looking at the more positive aspects of validation, i.e., those aspects that affect the bottom line of an operation. In this section some of the potential returns that can be expected from a company's investment in validation will be reviewed.

A. Reduction of Quality Costs

Traditionally, quality costs are divided into prevention, appraisal, internal failure, and external failure costs. These costs are defined in Table 1.

There is little published data on total quality costs [7]. The author is not aware of any data published for the pharmaceutical or parenteral industry. However, that is not to say that the pharmaceutical industry has not studied quality costs, and some information is available at least on an informal basis. A conservative estimate is that quality costs for the pharmaceutical industry in general are about 10–15% of the total manufacturing costs. The quality costs for the parenteral industry are undoubtedly higher, because parenteral products generally involve more sophisticated technology and special requirements (sterility, for example) due to the nature of their use involve higher prevention and appraisal costs. Also, failure costs in the parenteral industry are generally higher due to the high costs of materials and processing.

While these measurable costs are high, the hidden costs can be greater. Consider the cost of recalls, complaints, and law suits. A recall can ruin a product or company at worst and at best tarnish the product and the

TABLE 1   Quality Costs

---

1. *Preventive costs* are costs incurred in order to prevent failures and/or reduce the appraisal costs.

   a. Quality planning
   b. Vendor approval system
   c. Training
   d. Documentation—SOPs, monographs
   e. Preventative maintenance
   f. Calibration
   g. Sanitation
   h. Process validation
   i. Quality assurance auditing and self-inspections
   j. Annual review of data or trend analysis

2. *Appraisal costs* are costs of inspection, testing, and quality evaluation. Some examples of appraisal costs are

   a. Inspection/testing of raw and packaging materials
   b. Inspection/testing of in-process materials
   c. Inspection/testing of finished products
   d. Stability testing

3. *Internal failure costs* are costs associated with nonconforming material—material that does not meet quality standards—still in the company's possession. Some examples of internal failure costs are

   a. Rejects
   b. Reworks
   c. Reinspections
   d. Retests
   e. Wastage/scrap
   f. Troubleshooting
   g. Sorting substandard material

4. *External failure costs* are costs associated with a nonconformance condition after the product has left the company's ownership. Some examples of external failure costs are

   a. Recalls
   b. Complaints
   c. Returns due to quality-related problems

---

company's reputation, resulting in decreased sales and profit. Persistent failure problems in a plant can adversely affect morale and create friction between departments, and between management and the workers.

It is obvious that a validated and controlled process, as defined in this chapter, will result in fewer internal failures—fewer rejects, reworks, retests, reinspections, and wastage. Validation makes it possible to do the job right the first time. Also, a scientifically studied and controlled process makes it unlikely that defective products will be shipped to the consumer—thus, no recalls or complaints.

Spending resources on prevention (validation) will also enable the pharmaceutical manufacturer to decrease appraisal (testing and inspection) costs. Theoretically, for a validated process for which we have absolute control of all variables, there should be no need to perform any inspections or testing on the finished product. As this ideal is approached, Quality Control department testing can be decreased correspondingly. Some examples include

1. Sterility testing of terminally sterilized products given a validated/controlled autoclave
2. Inspection for particulates given control of the sources of particulate contamination
3. Components testing from suppliers with validated/controlled processes

In those cases where testing cannot be completely eliminated, validation should allow us to reduce the frequency of testing or reduce the number of samples tested.

Training is one of the components of validation and prevention cost.

"The goal of every manufacturer is to produce a quality product in a reasonable amount of time at a minimum cost. The cost of training is minimal when one compares it to the loss of revenue that may occur as a result of inadequate training. Remember the adage: 'If you think education is expensive, try ignorance.'
Properly trained employees help reduce errors in the manufacturing process. Training helps to reduce the time a company spends correcting errors in documentation and the money it spends reworking a product. A company minimizes the possibility of costly recalls by developing a good method of manufacturing and by training its employees to perform according to that method. Training helps to place the responsibility of protecting the company's revenues in the employees hands" [8].

B. Process Optimization

When a process is thoroughly studied, some way of optimizing it is inevitably found. The optimization of a process for maximum efficiency while maintaining quality standards is a consequence of validation. The dictionary defines "to optimize" as "to make as effective, perfect or useful as possible"; we would add "at the lowest cost." The optimization of the facility, equipment, systems, closures, etc., results in a product that meets quality requirements at the lowest cost. Trained, qualified people are a key element in any process and thus have the greatest impact on improving efficiency and productivity. In this context GMP training cannot be separated from a total training program that includes how to do the job correctly, easily, and rapidly.
Some areas where experience shows that optimization is possible as a result of validation studies are the following:

1. Optimum batch sizes relative to availability of equipment and personnel and size of facility.
2. Decreased downtime of equipment due to programmed preventative maintenance based on thorough understanding of equipment and process.
3. Reduced sterilization times due to studies of bioburden, validation and control of autoclave, etc.

4. Reduced mixing times.
5. Reduced overfill of liquids due to knowing limits/capabilities of filling equipment.
6. Faster and more accurate analytical test procedures.
7. Development of standards for the process—standards for labor, equipment, yields, etc.—that results in better production control and resource allocation.
8. Better product or component specifications due to challenging the specifications. Are they reasonable and appropriate in light of the use of the product?
9. Reduced energy costs. Properly calibrated temperature gauges, for example, can prevent the overheating of a Water-for-Injection storage vessel, sterilizer, etc., which would result in a wastage of energy.

An example of the optimization resulting from instrument calibration is given by Bremmer:

"We have had two clearly documented cases where Calibration information identified poor instrument performance in a fermentation process. In one case, subsequent instrument replacement led to improved yields, attributable to improved instrument accuracy. In the other case, improved yields and improved fermentor turnaround times were realized. At this point it should be noted that it is not always the Calibration Program itself that improves instrument performance, yields or quality. The Calibration, however, often provides hints which allow qualified people to find solutions" [9].

C. Assurance of Quality

"Validation is an extension of the concepts of quality assurance since close control of the process is necessary to assure product quality and it is not possible to control a process properly without thorough knowledge of the capabilities of that process" [10].

In other words, validation and process control are at the heart of GMPs. Without validated and controlled processes it is impossible to produce quality products consistently.

In the past, control of quality consisted largely of end-product testing and inspection. End-product testing and inspection have inherent deficiencies relative to assurance of quality. Process validation and in-process control are far superior methods of quality assurance.

The limitations of product testing and the value of validation for assuring quality of a batch is officially recognized by the U.S. Pharmacopeia (USP):

"However, it is not to be inferred that application of every analytical procedure in the monograph to samples from every production batch is necessarily a prerequisite for assuring compliance with Pharmacopeial standards before the batch is released for distribution. Data derived from manufacturing *process validation* studies and from *in-process controls* sometimes may provide greater assurance that a batch meets a particular monograph requirement than analytical data derived from an examination of finished units drawn from that batch" [11].

Inspection procedures fall into two categories: 100% inspection or inspection of a statistical sample. Obviously, inspecting a statistical sample does not give absolute assurance that each unit produced will meet specifications. For a given level of defects and a given sampling plan, the probability of a defective item not being discovered can be calculated. Even 100% inspection may not be better: "Yet research shows that, even in 100% inspection, up to 15% of defective items are not detected" [12].

An example of the fact that *one can't inspect quality into a product* is that 100% inspection of parenterals for visible particulates has not resulted in particulate-free products on the market. The quality of parenterals, from the point of view of absence of visible particulates, is better today than 10 years ago, because the pharmaceutical industry has located the sources of particulates, improved the process, and has better process control.

Similarly, end-product testing, in the absence of validation, gives little assurance of quality for a number of reasons, among which are

1. Very limited sample size.
2. The limited number of tests performed on a sample. For example, it is impractical to test for all possible impurities or contaminants.
3. The limited sensitivity of the test.

Although these limitations apply to all product testing, they are most dramatically illustrated with respect to sterility testing.

"The production of sterile products is probably the best example to illustrate the importance of proper manufacturing conditions and practices (Process Validation, GMPs) over end testing. Consider the use of an end product sterility test, for instance, to demonstrate sterility assurance of a production lot. This particular end product testing approach is flawed in several ways. First of all, the nature of the test is such that a finding of no growth in a *limited test sample* cannot be extrapolated with much certainty to characterize the nature of the entire lot. This is because the contamination which the test is intended to detect, is not necessarily distributed uniformly throughout the entire lot. A more significant flaw, however, is the *inherent insensitivity of sterility tests*. For example, the sampling requirements of the USP Sterility Test are such that it can only detect (with a 90% confidence level) a lot in which 10% of the units are contaminated. 10% is a rather high level of contamination; and at only a 90% confidence level, that means that for one out of every 10 tests, you may not be able to detect even this level of contamination" [13].

Again the USP recognizes the limitations of the sterility test and the importance of process controls:

"It is recognized that sterility tests may not detect microbial contamination of a low order of magnitude in a lot of product. . . . The statistical limitations of the sampling requirements . . . are clear. . . . Negative results from a valid sterility test are indicative of the sterility of the lot only if the records of all pertinent sterilization and microbiological decontamination procedures and aseptic processing stages subsequent to sterilization indicate that these processes have been carried out in complete accordance with the written standard operating procedures in the manufacturer's files, and that these are in compliance with current compendial and regulatory requirements and principles for the production of Pharmacopeial products" [14].

It can be concluded that assurance of product sterility should rely more on manufacturing controls, especially a validated and controlled steam sterilizer, than on sterility testing.

D. Safety

Validation can also result in increased operator safety. For example, gauges used on equipment that is designed to operate at certain temperatures and pressures must be reliable, i.e., they must be calibrated.

VII. LIMITATIONS

There are no inherent limitations in the concept of validation relative to its ability to assure quality and reduce costs, but on the practical side, validation is not an absolute cure-all. Some of the practical limitations are people, availability of facilities and equipment, cost, inadequate technology, etc.

People, while being a company's greatest asset, are also the cause of many problems with a process. A validated process, in order to function properly, requires that people follow procedures, do their job conscientiously and without error, do not modify the system, etc. People deficiencies that affect product quality and productivity are not confined to operators; generally, the deficiencies of supervisors and management are more significant. An operator can do little if management does not provide adequate tools to do the job and control the process—adequate equipment, facilities, systems, and procedures.

This leads to the consideration of costs—costs of process validation. Management must allocate resources to a validation program, and since resources are always limited, this necessarily leads to some compromises in the validation program. One can always spend more money on facilities, equipment, system development, in-process controls, and validation studies. A 100% assurance of quality is impossible. A definition of validation that illustrates this is "the documentation and evaluation of evidence to provide a *high degree of assurance* that the process with proper controls delivers a product of predetermined quality" [15].

A high degree of assurance is all that can practically be expected from validation. The degree of assurance to be attained is a balancing act between cost and benefit. The quality standard must be examined relative to the use of the product and what the consumer expects and requires of the product. Specifications need to be challenged in this light, as the manufacturing process is challenged. From the consumer's point of view, too much quality assurance (at a higher cost) may be as undesirable as too little. Does the consumer obtain any real benefit from a sterility confidence level of 10^9 vs 10^6, or in other words, "Does it make sense to employ aseptic filling operations for a terminally sterilized product?" [16]. Absolute assurance of sterility is unattainable; a high level of confidence is possible. Complete assurance of the absence of all impurities is not feasible.

Validation can provide a high assurance of quality and can assist in reducing manufacturing costs, but there will still be some risk to product quality, and medicines will still cost money.

VIII. SUMMARY

Process validation is a concept that is fundamental to GMPs and any Quality Assurance program. There is no effective Quality Assurance program without validation.

    Validation studies inevitably lead to process optimization, better productivity, and lower manufacturing costs. The investment made in validation, like the investment made in qualified people, can only provide an excellent return.

REFERENCES

1. *Fed. Reg.*, 43, No. 190, September 29, 1978.
2. *Fed. Reg.*, 41, No. 106, June 1, 1976.
3. Broker, C. G. 1980. *Pharm. Eng,* 1(1):18.
4. Kieffer, R. G. et al., 1983. *Design Concepts for the Validation of a Water for Injection System,* Parenteral Drug Association Technical Report No. 4.
5. 4th European Seminar of Quality Control in the Pharmaceutical and Cosmetic Industries, September 25/26, 1980, University of Geneva, Switzerland, p. 72.
6. Marash, S. A. 1982. *MD&DI,* October, p. 57.
7. O'Neill, H. 1981. The quest for quality, 1: How to remove rejects. *Management Today,* July, pp. 71—74.
8. Hall, P., Eates, G. K., Fleming, T. C., and Linton, E. 1982. *Pharm. Technol,* April, pp. 68ff.
9. Bremmer, R. E. 1982. *J. Parenteral Sci. Technol.* 36(5), pp. 193ff.
10. 4th European Seminar on Quality Control in the Pharmaceutical and Cosmetic Industries, September 25/26, 1980, University of Geneva, Switzerland, p. 16.
11. *The United States Pharmacopeia,* XX. 1980, p. 5.
12. Lockyer, K. and Oakland, J. 1981. The quest for quality, 2: How to sample success. *Management Today,* July, pp. 75—77.
13. Broker, C. G. 1980. *Pharm. Eng.* (1): pp. 18ff.
14. *The United States Pharmacopeia,* XX., 1980, p. 1039.
15. Elliott, R. L., Sterling Drug, Inc. *Personal communication.*
16. Kladko, M., 1982. *Pharm. Technol,* May, pp. 72ff.

2
Organizing for Validation

RONALD J. SIMKO*

Schering-Plough Corporation, Kenilworth, New Jersey

I. INTRODUCTION

The formal aspects associated with organizing for validation are many and varied. In 1980 several papers describing specific organizational strategies for validation organizations were presented at a Pharmaceutical Manufacturing Association (PMA) seminar [1–4]. This chapter is intended to help the reader sort through these alternatives. Various department missions employed for validation in the pharmaceutical industry, and the impact of each specific mission will be discussed. Methods of building validation awareness within the company will be reviewed. Finally, the benefits to the organization of maintaining a strong validation unit will be defined.

In general, challenges associated with validation organizations can be divided into three basic areas:

1. Establishing the organization
2. Operating it from a quality and cost-effectiveness basis
3. Maintaining a functioning organization

In any discussion of validation, semantics plays a key role in the understanding of terms. Therefore, a common approach to the definition of validation terms is documented in the following lexicon [5].

Process validation: establishing documented evidence that a process does what it purports to do.
Prospective validation: establishing documented evidence prior to process implementation that a system does what it purports to do based on a preplanned protocol.
Concurrent validation: establishing documented evidence that a process does what it purports to do based on information generated during actual implementation of the process.
Retrospective validation: establishing documented evidence that a system does what it purports to do based on review and analysis of historical information.

Current affiliation: Schering-Plough Corporation, Union, New Jersey.

Validation change control: a formal monitoring system by which qualified representatives of appropriate disciplines review proposed or actual changes that might affect validated status and cause corrective action to be taken that will ensure that the system retains its validated state of control.

Revalidation: repetition of the validation process or a specific portion of it.

Calibration: demonstrating that a measuring device produces results within specified limits of those produced by a reference standard device over an appropriate range of measurements. This process results in corrections that may be applied if maximum accuracy is required.

Validation protocol: a prospective or concurrent experimental plan that, when executed, is intended to produce documented evidence that the system has been validated.

Sterilization process: a treatment process from which probability of any microorganism survival is less than 10^{-6}, or one in a million.

Nonsterilization process: any treatment process that purports to do something other than to sterilize. It may be a method associated with, or even, integral to, one that sterilizes.

Control parameters: those operating variables that can be assigned values that are used as control levels.

Operating variables: all factors, including control parameters, that may potentially affect process state of control and/or fitness for use of the end product.

State of control: a condition in which all operating variables that can affect performance remain within such ranges that the system or process performs consistently and as intended.

Installation qualification: documented verification that all key aspects of the installation adhere to appropriate codes and approved design and that manufacturer's recommendations are suitably considered.

Operational qualification: documented verification that the system or subsystem performs as intended throughout all anticipated operating ranges.

II. ESTABLISHING THE ORGANIZATION

A. Mission

Formulating a department mission is essential to ensuring proper definition of a department role in the organization. This is necessary so that not only Process Validation staff members understand the breadth of their job, but that other corporate groups with whom there is interaction also understand.

In some organizations senior staff members representing the Process Validation, R&D, Quality Assurance, Production, and Engineering functions convene to form advisory or steering committees for the validation program. This committee can prove extremely valuable to the validation program by defining the mission, as well as by making decisions on specific issues of concern. To ensure that these decisions are made with sufficient information, though, it is necessary that the validation professionals provide sufficient technical information to this committee. Once developed, the documentation of the approved policies then allows all involved in the program to be aware of priorities as well as the general framework for the validation efforts. This common understanding is then clear to both levels of management. Both are aware of what is expected and the efforts being undertaken.

Although there is fairly broad diversity of validation department missions within the pharmaceutical industry, the mission that is germane to all companies' Validation departments is the satisfying of regulatory requirements to have one's processes validated. Since the publication of the Good Manufacturing Practices (GMPs) in 1978, satisfying this regulatory issue has been the fundamental mission of validation departments.

This regulatory compliance mission can be achieved in two basic ways. It can be accomplished by a direct, "hands-on" group charged with validation responsibilities, or by a coordinating unit, that oversees the hands-on operation performed by others. In this case, the "hands-on" work may be performed either by other company personnel or by consultants or subcontracted firms.

B. "Hands-on" Functions

This "hands-on" group may function in any number of operating departments. Thomas Primm described the accomplishment of validation objectives within the Engineering division [1]. By incorporating Process Validation within the Process Engineering structure, the validation efforts of verifying process performance and determining equipment capabilities are merged into the Process Engineering objective of ensuring that the manufacturing processes employed are the best possible.

G. J. Papariello [2], justified the inclusion of the validation function within the Research and Development sphere, since it is that organization which is responsible for new product introductions. Certainly, the most efficient way to validate a new product or process is to incorporate this concern during the development and scale-up phases, and then carry through the program into the production environment.

William Greer [4] illustrated a structure that incorporated Validation into the Quality Control unit known as Process Control Services, while Jean—Yves Guillemoteau [3] described a matrix validation organization existing within the Manufacturing division. Others have structured entities known as Pharmaceutical Process Validation or Pharmaceutical Engineering, which are self-contained departments designed to accomplish the goals of validation.

The common theme running through each of these validation structures is that the accomplishment of the validation mission is a shared one. Only with cooperation between the Process Validation, Production, Quality Assurance (QA), Engineering, and R&D staffs can the validation objectives be met. It begins with the joint establishment of the validation mission by a steering committee and then continues during the day-to-day accomplishment of the objectives.

C. "Hands-off" Functions

Many larger firms have facilities in different geographical locations. Validation organizations may exist at each of the sites and can be supported by a corporate coordinator, who promotes consistency between the sites. This is important because close communication is necessary for the discussion of common problems and can prevent one group from reinventing the wheel, as previously discovered by a sister group. The corporate coordinator, in his or her "hands-off" validation role, then can have significant impact on the success of the program.

Pat Jeater [6] discussed another validation organization option, the use of a consultant. The advantages (e.g., technical expertise, not part of permanent organization) and the disadvantages (cost overruns, training of the consultant) are the same for validation efforts as they are when a consultant is used on other projects. To maximize the return from a consultant, the assignment of a "coordinator" who is an employee of the company is necessary.

D. Validation Perspectives

The validation mission can be looked at from one of these perspectives: prospective, concurrent, and retrospective. The prospective approach is based on a preapproved validation protocol. Based on the strategy outlined in the protocol, the study is undertaken, and the results documented and approved prior to acceptance of the process. The concurrent approach is also based on a preapproved protocol. However, the data gathered are generated during the actual implementation of the process. Retrospective validation evaluates the process differently. In this case historical data are evaluated to support the validity of the process in question. Each of these perspectives or combinations of them are used in industry.

The validation mission is also influenced by the product lines supported. Typically, validation studies in sterile product facilities have been process-oriented. This is generally in contrast to "product-specific" studies employed in nonsterile product facilities. What may be the ideal is to blend each of these approaches. When a FDA investigator requests validation data for a sterile facility, the request is usually by product. Consequently, it would be desirable to pull together all the process validation data compiled (sterilization, depyrogenation, media fills, etc.) into product files. This not only makes discussions with the investigator more straightforward, but also assures that each critical step of the manufacturing process has received validation scrutiny.

On the other hand, product validation data for a nonsterile product can be strengthened by applying a process orientation. This may involve a detailed review of each piece of process equipment used on a periodic basis to ensure proper performance. This is not unlike the periodic sterilizer revalidations employed in sterile-product validation efforts.

Since these validation efforts, when complete, form the basis for subsequent troubleshooting activities, and can also reveal process improvement opportunities, some firms have expanded the role of validation units to include these functions.

Whether the objectives are solely of regulatory defense, or whether they also include process improvement and troubleshooting, the validation unit is dependent on several other organizations for assistance. These include the metrology group and the testing laboratories. Because of these dependence relationships, validation organizations, on some occasions, have been structured to perform these support services themselves.

The dependence of validation on the successful calibration of process recorders/controllers provides justification for the inclusion of a metrology function within the validation umbrella. It is not necessary, however, if a close working arrangement exists with those charged with this function. At the very least, the validation group should satisfy itself that the calibrators are doing their job correctly. Ignoring this could mean considerable wasted effort expended on supposed validation studies. An extension of this involves the advent of new technology and its application to pharmaceutical processing. Among new applications which are elaborated in a later chapter is the ever-increasing use of computers to monitor and control processes. The validation of the computer, as a result, cannot be ignored. Thus, the validation organization can be a natural home for this activity as well.

One function on which the Validation unit depends to a large extent is the laboratory function. Both the microbiological lab for sterile products testing and analytical labs for physical product testing support the validation effort. On most occasions the labs used are the Quality Control (QC) Labs. However, in some instances, Validation units have established their own minilabs to support their efforts. A captive lab has certain obvious benefits in that validation testing does not need to wait in queue with production-or research-requested testing. Establishing a captive lab, however, brings a myriad of other complications to the department. Now the validation of all lab procedures utilized must be validated by this group rather than a QC group supporting the validation testing. This includes analytical procedures and process equipment such as sterilizers used in lab procedures.

E. Staffing

When staffing a validation group, the mission and the organization do exert a degree of influence, primarily in the academic backgrounds of the members. Because of the aforementioned diversity, a considerable variety of academic backgrounds are usually found among validation professionals, with members having degrees in Chemistry, Microbiology, Pharmacy, Statistics, and Computer Science, as well as a variety of Engineering disciplines.

More important than the actual area of academic background are these three skills: problem-solving capability, interpersonal skills, and oral and written communication abilities. The technical talent to recognize and solve problems is fundamental to validation. Because of its pivotal role in the company, considerable interactions develop with others. Strong interpersonal skills allow this to be of maximum effectiveness. Finally, unless validation objectives and concerns are effectively expressed both orally and in written form, the best of "hands-on" efforts may be wasted. What emanates from the fieldwork must be attractive written documentation. By presenting the documentation well in written form, a well-thought-out and organized effort will be conveyed. If the validation professional can sucessfully communicate orally, especially during an FDA visit, the strength of the validation package is even greater.

A position that can also be used effectively and provide substantial benefits is that of Validation Technician. These individuals are usually experienced production operators who have been promoted to the next job classification. Certainly the position provides the technician an opportunity to contribute to problem solving, etc., which may have been inhibited in a production environment. Conversely, to the department, it provides a work force of competent people who provide stability while others in the department may be in more dynamic career paths. These technicians additionally provide validation professionals with the opportunity to develop their supervisory skills.

III. OPERATING THE ORGANIZATION

Once department missions have been formalized and the validation operation organized, the challenge is to implement the plan. To achieve its objectives, the validation organization needs to interact with many peer groups. Within the company those other departments include:

> *Research operations*: involved with new product introductions as well as existing process improvements
> *Engineering*: when involved with new or modified equipment or facilities
> *Production*: whose processes require validation
> *Maintenance*: concerning change control
> *Quality Control/Quality Assurance Operations*: including testing labs, administrators, and regulatory compliance specialists

A. Research

The research organization is involved with new product introduction and existing process improvements. It should be the Validation department's key objective in this area to ensure the acceptability (and thus validatability) of new products or "improved" processes in the manufacturing area. Certainly all firms have "older" products or processes that perform at a less than optimum level. A successful accomplishment of validation objectives ensures that new products or processes do not receive the same fate.

Communication is critical in accomplishing this. The R&D organization must be made aware of the validation plan and resulting acceptance criteria. The awareness of these expectations should prompt an R&D testing regimen that will enhance the probability of acceptance of the product (or process) to Manufacturing. It also affords the analytical laboratories the opportunity to develop and validate analytical methods during the development phase rather than the hectic early days of production. Clearly what will result are products or processes that are expected to be validatable in a production setting. There can always be surprises, though, specifically when a product does not scale up as expected. In this situation, Validation, Manufacturing, Quality Assurance, and R&D must work out a suitable solution, since the product should not be introduced to production if it cannot first be validated in the pilot plant.

B. Engineering

The relationship that, along with R&D, possesses the greatest potential for long-term validation benefits is with engineering groups involved with new facility or equipment start-ups. In the initial stages of capital projects there exists the ideal opportunity to ensure the acceptability of processes later on. The concern of validation must be built in at the design phase, and continued during construction. It is one thing for a Water-For-Injection system to be designed properly, and another thing for it to be constructed properly. Thus, in this example, it is necessary for the validation effort to include activities such as the documentation of weld quality and distribution piping slope verification.

Once construction is complete, the qualification phase can begin. Qualification protocols defining design and operating criteria need to be developed and signed off by all parties involved. This ensures that there are no

misunderstandings as to what is expected of the facility. Production, Quality
Assurance, Project Engineering, and Validation all need to approve this plan
in writing.

C. Production

Interactions with production personnel should stress the benefits of a validation program. If the benefits are really understood, production personnel
will be supportive of these efforts rather than skeptical. After all, a validation process is one in which there is confidence, and this confidence has
cost-savings implications. What results from a validated process is a higher-
quality product (fewer rejects, retests, reworks—meaning monetary savings)
that is produced more efficiently (tighter schedules leading to less work-in
process inventory-yielding monetary savings). A conscientious validation
program supported by a proper change control program ensures that the
above scenario is not fiction. These positive effects of a well-conceived validation program justify the efforts for economic reasons rather than just
regulatory compliance. As a result, the validation effort need not be an
expense of doing business in the pharmaceutical industry.

Upon completion of a validation study, the results are presented in a
written report which is then approved by all protocol signatories. Signed-off
reports should then be distributed to all affected operations so that procedural
changes and/or acceptable process parameter ranges discerned from the validation report can be incorporated into standard operating procedures
(SOPs). This procedure further ensures that production SOPs reflect
validated conditions. To protect against future process changes being implemented without validation scrutiny, the validation operation should review all
change authorizations impacting on product or process. Their approval ensures that validation issues are addressed for each change.

D. Maintenance

Without the support and cooperation of the maintenance organization, the best-
designed and implemented validation study will soon be rendered worthless.
This will occur the instant that an undocumented change is made to a validated
piece of equipment. As a result, an education program is essential to make
Maintenance personnel understand the impact of their preventative or emergency maintenance activities. Once this is understood, the documentation of
any changes made to a system must be communicated back to Validation so that
an assessment of the impact can be made. Realize that changing a belt on a
dry heat sterilizer fan motor could affect air flow within the sterilizer and
thus change "cold spot" locations and perhaps sterilizing capabilities within
the oven.

E. Quality Assurance

Since most validation organizations rely on existing Quality Control laboratories
for testing support, effective communication here is also important. Certainly
validation protocols that require lab support should include lab management
sign-off. This ensures that lab personnel know not only the number and
type of tests required for the study, but also how the testing fits into
the overall validation program. This affords them the opportunity to understand how the data will be used and avoid situations where the lab personnel's

tests invalidate the validator's intent. Additionally, validation staff members should acquire an understanding of lab testing procedures. What results is two-way communication that ensures good understanding of both organizations' intentions.

Significant interactions also occur with those Quality Assurance groups that have regulatory compliance responsibilities. These interactions should be cooperative ventures designed to ensure a firm's regulatory compliance. Through the technical competency of the validation staff and the GMP compliance expertise existing within Quality Assurance, these efforts should be successful. The key point is to communicate so that the regulatory compliance objective of validation is met.

F. Professional Associations

Interactions of validation professionals with counterparts at other pharmaceutical firms prove extremely valuable. Most frequently this is accomplished through meetings sponsored by societies, universities, or seminar organizations. These gatherings are extremely beneficial, not only because of the knowledge imparted during the structured presentations, but because of the opportunities available for informal discussions of problems and concerns. In the New York-Philadelphia pharmaceutical belt [7] validation professionals from the regional firms convene on a regular basis in informal and loosely structured sessions to discuss current validation issues. Conversations and discussions held at these sessions have in fact been the source of much of the information contained in this chapter.

G. FDA

No discussion of interactions of validation personnel can be complete without the inclusion of the FDA investigator. These interactions are a part of any validation professional's work experience. Although heightened anticipation exists when an FDA investigator is in the plant, the potential is certainly there for a valuable learning experience. The interactions during these investigations frequently prove challenging and can be constructive both for the firm as well as for the individual defending the validation package.

H. Communication

Up to this point only the formal roles that validation departments have in the corporate organization have been discussed. These are the roles defined by the department mission and, as has been seen, are also affected by the organizational structure and the various interdepartmental interactions that exist. Beyond this formal role is an additional critical responsibility, and that is one of education. By implementing a validation awareness program through which various levels of people within the corporate hierarchy are informed of validation and its benefits, the importance of validation in the overall business plan can be made clear. Further, providing others with this awareness strengthens the validation department's role and elevates it to a position of equality with those departments with whom they interact.

To the hourly employees, an education program can build professionalism into their work career [8]. Such a program could stress the whys and wherefores of a process. This understanding can also aid in GMP compliance and job enrichment.

Communication or education sessions to any of the peer groups—Production, R&D, etc.—foster the cooperative spirit essential to the validation effort. It cannot be stressed enough that each of these organizations has a dependent relationship with Validation. With Production, this dialogue may take the form of regularly scheduled project status meetings. These clearly inform production management of ongoing validation issues related to their operation. With QA, Engineering, and R&D, such meetings can also be regularly held to ensure that there is continuing dialogue on interacted projects.

Upper management must also be supportive of Validation and its role in the organization. The key for validation management is to get their support. This will come with success. Informational sessions and/or project status meetings can also be used to elicit this support. This backing of management is necessary. Without it, staff additions, capital project approvals, etc., will not come and the organization will not thrive. Further, this will be evident to the peer groups, diminishing the validation organization to something less than a peer group. The effectiveness of the program is thereby placed in jeopardy. Consequently, the status of the validation organization must be maintained equal to the other operations previously spoken of, and it is the Validation management's responsibility to see that this occurs.

This issue of education is at the heart of a successful validation program. Validation needs the help of its peer groups. To accomplish this it needs the support of upper management as well as demonstrated success. Advertising these successes and the merits of the validation program strengthen the program and allow the validation organization to function on an equal footing with other groups. A cooperative climate develops, and this success breeds continued success. The benefits of the validation program become a reality.

IV. MAINTAINING THE ORGANIZATION

A. Continuing Education

For the continued realization of validation objectives, the quality of the staff must be maintained. A program of continuing education is critical to achieving this. It is necessary for the organization to provide staff members with opportunities to take courses that can aid them in remaining current technologically. At the same time, it is the employees' responsibility to avail themselves of those opportunities made available. Since there is no shortage of organizations that sponsor technical education courses, one must choose wisely. Directly job-related courses and seminars are frequently sponsored by various trade associations, such as the Parenteral Drug Association, the Pharmaceutical Manufacturing Association, the American Institute of Chemical Engineers, the Instrument Society of America, and the American Pharmaceutical Association. Courses offered by these organizations are frequently held in conjunction with meetings and are designed to keep their membership technically current in their related fields. Universities and professional seminar organizations also add to the complement of technical education courses available.

In general, courses should be chosen to bring staff members to a basic level of understanding of skills needed to do the job. The most effective learning experience, though, is found on the job. If, for example, a validation professional is assigned to do sterile products validation, then a course on the microbiology and engineering of sterilization processes would be appropriate. It is probably best scheduled, though, after several months of on-the-job training. This would then set the stage for the course to have maximum effectiveness.

Beyond those specific training courses are general courses of study that should be made available on a broader scale to Validation staff members. All nonpharmacy majors should be exposed to a short course on pharmaceutics. These are typically offered by pharmacy schools and provide attendees with a general overview of the subject. The proliferation of computers in the industry may necessitate computer education courses for all. This should be supplemented by providing staff members opportunities to practice learned skills on a computer. Since Validation staff members are asked to solve problems and make decisions, a course that teaches those logical thought processes may also provide benefits. Finally, educational opportunities are made easier and less costly by showing video-taped courses in in-plant training rooms. A whole course in statistics, for example, could be offered via videotape.

Since continuing education is a necessary aspect of anyone's job, it must be treated as such and used to supplement on-the-job learning. The opportunities are varied and have been enhanced by technologies now available. Computer systems, interactive video learning centers, and also videotaped courses, now bring these learning opportunities to the workplace, where the skills necessary for success are made available to all.

B. Organizational Transfers

Another way of building the technical strength of the entire organization is through interdepartmental personnel transfers. Validation professionals are conscientiously aware of quality manufacturing procedures and can apply these concepts in a Production or Quality Assurance organization. Technical areas within Engineering or R&D may also find validation talent helpful in filling openings. Because the validation operation interacts so closely with all these other areas, smooth transition to other assignments can be achieved. Certainly situations like this are a two-way street, as professionals from other departments within the company can come to the Validation department in an attempt to broaden their own career path. Additionally, existing validation staff members may be given different validation assignments. This can provide the staff greater depth and strengthens each person's ability to qualify for promotional opportunities.

V. SUMMARY

Validation is essential if a company is to comply with FDA guidelines. The way that the unit charged with those responsibilities is organized, and the role played by the unit, may allow the department to do much more than just establish regulatory compliance. Validation need not be an expense of doing business in the pharmaceutical industry. It has the potential for being a key contributor to a cost-efficient business strategy.

Accomplishing process validation objectives can be a real bonanza. At the forefront of these objectives is gaining the support of management. If this happens, an organization can emerge in which validation concepts are among the key issues discussed. This is true not only when new products are formulated and new facilities are designed, but also in full-scale manufacturing.

The challenges are many for the validation organization; the benefits are real. Not only can a strong "business-oriented and regulatory-complying" group emerge, but further, it can be a driving force to quality improvements, operating efficiencies, and a strengthened technical organization.

REFERENCES

1. Primm, T. M. 1980. Organizing for validation—Engineering Division. Presented at the PMA Seminar on Validation of Solid Dosage Form Products, Atlanta, Ga., May.

2. Papariello, G. J. 1980. Organizing for validation—Process Development. Presented at the PMA Seminar on Validation of Solid Dosage Form Products, Atlanta, Ga., May.

3. Guillemoteau, J. Y. 1980. Validation of solid dosage forms—An organization within the manufacturing division. Presented at the PMA Seminar on Validation of Solid Dosage Form Products, Atlanta, Ga., May.

4. Green, W. 1980. Organizing for validation—Quality assurance viewpoint. Presented at the PMA Seminar on Validation of Solid Dosage Form Products, Atlanta, Ga., May.

5. Chapman, K. G. 1983. A suggested validation lexicon, *Pharm. Technol*, August.

6. Jeater, P. 1983. Organizing for Process Validation.

7. Simko, R. 1981—1984. Notes from Validation Discussion group meetings.

8. Lehecka, E. 1984. Pharmaceutical professionalism—Bridging the gap to high tech. Presented at SME Conference, Philadelphia, Pa., May.

3
Validation and Facility Design

C. KENNETH LOVEJOY

American McGaw, Division of American Hospital Supply Corporation, Irvine, California

I. INTRODUCTION

The process of validating a pharmaceutical facility for the aseptic production of drugs for human consumption is the final step in a long chain of events. Validation starts with the design phase of the facility and its related equipment because it is here, at the beginning of the project, that ground rules must be established and the project scope be committed to writing. It is necessary to have a thorough understanding of what must be accomplished in order to determine the correct procedure. This should in turn be followed by supportive evidence that this procedure has been performed correctly.

First ask yourself the why, what, where, and who questions, as well as the usual when and how questions. Examine why you are building this project in the first place. If your reason is to gain new market share, be creative and work in the realm of the state of the art. If you are in the business to contract-package, make cost a prime consideration. Have a clear reason why you are in the game in the first place, and then work the rules to your advantage.

Next answer the question of what you are planning to build. Will the design be dedicated to one product, or does it have to be versatile? Is the product bulk packaged or unit packaged? Is terminal sterilization needed? What about office space needs? Will lab work be done on site or contracted out? Answers to such questions will provide the basic foundation for the project scope; however, plans must be finalized by the time it is necessary to commit to a viable project.

The location of a facility is vitally important. There are several links between location and validation that must be considered. For instance, your process may need to be near a consistently high-quality water source. The amount of available water could also be a concern; restrictions on its use would mean production limitations, and special washing procedures may have to be validated. The available labor pool is an important factor, in terms of quality as well as quantity. Adequate training programs will have to be established and validated, so the availability of good trainers and facilities should be considered. Weather may be an important factor in some cases; for instance, constant high humidity creates special cleaning and air conditioning needs that must be validated. A location with good vendor support can be easier to validate than a remote location, simply because the machinery and equipment will be better prepared. These are some of the things to look for in selecting a location. The important point is to recognize your needs and how they relate to your choice of a manufacturing site.

The question of the personnel required to build the facility and install the equipment is too often overlooked. Decide on the key people needed to start the project and get it through to validation, but be sure to make plans for them when production starts. Careful planning here assures you of a coordinated project effort to achieve validation without key people leaving before it is completed. The latter often happens because these employees cannot see where they fit in after the FDA visit. A suggestion is to hire contract engineers from a job shop specializing in pharmaceutical-type projects and supervise them with a very small salaried staff.

The when and how questions must be answered too, of course. How long the project will take (i.e., when it will be completed), and how it will be paid for are germaine to the validation cause. Regardless of how many people are on the salaried staff and how large the contract is, the project manager must maintain a firm control over the schedule and the budget.

The thought that goes into answering these questions lays a strong foundation for a successful validation. What you test for proof of operation has its base in what you planned for it to achieve and how you planned for it to be built, back at the beginning of the project. On the other hand, if you didn't plan for much, that is what you will get.

Before proceeding to a detailed description of the validation process, it is necessary to define some of the more commonly used terms in this field.

II. DEFINITIONS

Webster's Seventh New Collegiate Dictionary (1976) gives the origin of the word "valid" as meaning "sound." To *validate* something is to make or declare it legally binding, to support it by facts. Thus, *validation* is defined in this context as the process of testing (fact gathering) to prove that a manufacturing system meets its preestablished requirements, giving it strength to stand up to a legal challenge (FDA inspection).

When the system has completed the validation process, it can be called *qualified*. This means that it is fit or competent to do the task it was designed to accomplish and that it has complied with certain preestablished conditions. Therefore, validation is the process that leads up to the point when a system is declared qualified.

These preestablished conditions are called *specifications*. They are a detailed statement of particulars that thoroughly describe the item or process in question. They leave little doubt about what is expected when the end product appears. Each part of the manufacturing system—equipment, product, component, and facility—needs specifications so that when it is time for validation, the inspection team knows what ground rules have been established.

There is one particular type of specification known as a *procedure*. This is a predefined method of doing things, or a detailed set of steps to be followed to reach a certain goal. Procedures are needed, for instance, to guide machine operators in the correct use of their equipment so that they can produce consistent quality parts that meet the validated specifications.

Another type of specification is the *Quality Acceptance Criteria,* or "QAC." These documents are usually written by the Quality Assurance group in concert with Engineering and Production in order to give the manufacturing group limits and guidelines that must be met in the performance of the operation. They are vital to the design of proper test procedures to validate the process. As the name states, the QAC define the criteria that an operation must meet in order for it to be accepted.

Finally, there is a document that ties all of these terms together. It is known as a *protocol,* and it is a signed document containing a record of the points on which agreement has been reached by negotiating parties (usually the Production, Engineering, and Quality Control people). The important words here are "signed," "agreement," and "negotiate." The protocols contain a list of what is expected to result from the project, how it relates to the other parts of the project, and how it will be specified and tested to see that it conforms to expectations. Protocols are generally negotiated by Production, Engineering, and Quality Control leaders, and signed by each representative to document agreement. They provide an excellent reference source for the FDA (or other authorities) to use in order to understand the process, where it originated, and what it is intended to accomplish. The protocols carry the procedures to validate the process so that it can be proven qualified to produce goods that meet the specifications.

These definitions will help in understanding the entire validation process. It is important to have a firm understanding of these basics in order to proceed through the four key steps toward the ultimate goal, a qualified operation.

III. VALIDATION STEPS

There are four basic steps that lead from project initiation to project validation. These are, in order,

    Planning
    Documentation
    Construction
    Testing

Although they are listed in sequence, they obviously overlap. Documentation occurs throughout all phases of the project, as it is a necessary ingredient of the ultimate goal, the validation of the facility and equipment. Construction cannot start until basic layouts are completed and agreed to, but layout and planning will continue well into the construction phase. Testing can commence before construction is complete, in order to save valuable time on the project. See Figure 1.

These four steps will be addressed individually in the following sections.

A. Planning

Planning is the most important of the four steps. It is the foundation of the project, and as such, it is expected to support its entire weight. Initially, the plan is flexible, subject to review and modification to ensure that the

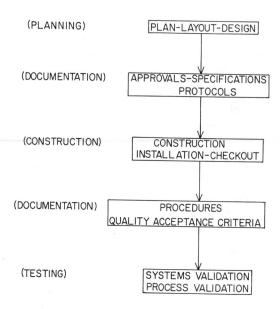

FIGURE 1   Validation flow chart.

best design is achieved. Once established, however, it must withstand any forces that would try to change it for whatever reasons. It must cope with sudden additions to the project scope, or attempts to change its direction. The physical layout must be *thoroughly* understood by all parties, especially the Production and Quality Control groups, and agreed to in writing before any serious construction can start. Any potential changes that arise must be assessed against a firm layout base, reasoned out by rational experts, and agreed to unanimously. This means that it is necessary to be thoroughly knowledgeable about the reasons for building; there are no wrong reasons, only poorly planned ones.

There are many important elements of the planning process. These include the following.

1. Site Selection

There are good pharmaceutical sites and bad ones, depending on the needs of the operation. After getting by the basic considerations that apply to any facility, such as flood plain location, municipal tax structure, available transportation, capacity for future growth, access, cost of land, etc., consider the following questions.

> Is the water of sufficient quality? Can it be properly and economically treated so that it can be used?
> Does the local labor pool fit the technological needs?
> Will the local environment pose a problem to product quality?
> Do local zoning laws inhibit the development of future biological products?
> Where is the water table located? Will it interfere with specialized sewer drain needs?
> If the site contains an existing facility, does this facility *really* fit your needs, or are you using it just because it is existing?

What compromises are you electing to recognize up front with operations, with product quality, with cost? Acknowledge them, but eliminate any compromises with quality. Assess the level of risk with the other compromises, then proceed with the design work.

2. Design Staff

The design staff is the group that will lay out the facility, specify the equipment, direct the documentation, perform the testing, and validate the project. They are obviously a key group in the validation program, and cannot be taken for granted. They must work well with other groups in the plant, yet maintain a purposeful direction that will see the project through to a swift and successful validation. The decision to be made here is how much of the project to contract out and how much to keep inhouse. If you have an existing engineering staff capable of making layouts and understanding all of the ramifications of building codes, Good Manufacturing Practices (GMP) regulations, industry standards, and so on, then make your own designs and let them out to bid. If not, think twice before building up that staff, because there are architectural and design/build firms that can work with representatives of the customer (you) to prepare full and detailed layout plans using purchased expertise. Remember, if you build up a staff for this project, you have to find something for them to do when the project is complete, and that may prove very difficult.

Another way around building a permanent engineering staff is to use consultants and contract engineers. These people will be on your payroll for the duration of the project only, and you will have exactly the expertise you need when you need it. When the project is complete, these "employees" will leave you with a validated process and a fully traceable history, but no personnel problems. Of course, it is possible that you may decide to hire one or two of the people as permanent staff. The match should be excellent, since you both have had ample time to see how well you can work together.

3. Project Scope

Validation will be much easier if you define in the beginning what it is you are going to validate, then build toward that goal. The scope of the project must be carefully and completely defined. How far are you going to go? What products are going to be produced? What production and quality control methods will be used? How much capacity are you allowing for? These questions and others like them need to be answered in detail before the actual layout of walls and equipment can begin.

4. Individual Protocols

Once the scope is established, each functional area can be addressed in a protocol. This describes the area (such as "Water Treatment," or "Receiving and Stores," or "Aseptic Filling") and lists its particular requirements for facility, utilities, staffing, documentation, etc. This is a good place to develop a complete understanding of what goes on in that area, why it is needed, and what it will take to make it completely functional. Each protocol also provides an excellent index of information on the subject, and a convenient tool to help the FDA inspector understand why and how the operation was done the way it was.

Table 1 gives a list of individual protocols that can be used to describe a new parenteral facility and manufacturing operation. It may not be necessary to include all of these areas in a simpler project.

TABLE 1   Validation Protocol Titles

I. *General Facility Support Systems*

   1. Definitions
   2. Personnel training
   3. Plant design
   4. Materials management
   5. Quality control
   6. Quality assurance
   7. Documentation
   8. Engineering
   9. Metrology
   10. Systems certification

II. *Manufacturing Support Systems*

   1. Environmental control
   2. Water
   3. Steam
   4. Compressed air
   5. Sanitation

III. *Manufacturing*

   1. Receiving and stores
   2. Component preparation
   3. Component sterilization
   4. Solution formulation
   5. Solution filling
   6. Terminal sterilization
   7. Inspection/labeling/packaging
   8. Quarantine/warehouse/shipping

Each protocol can contain sections on the following subjects as a base. Other headings can be added to fit the needs of particular protocol subjects.

   Introduction
   Description (facility or equipment or method)
   History (why and how the current system evolved)
   Material flow
   Documentation (list of applicable procedures and drawings)

5. *Capacity Calculations*

The size of the project has to be determined, and that is usually based on a product forecast. A strong word of caution is due here, however, because forecasts are often changed. It is imperative to start with a reasonable forecast that has the written approval of top management. Then it must be reviewed by the people in charge of the project. The forecast should be questioned if it does not seem reasonable. A forecast that is too large is as dangerous as one too small; in either case, you end up with equipment that cannot do the job efficiently. Too large a boiler will not produce steam reliably and will be a constant source of problems. Too large a mixing tank cannot be used to make small batches. Too small a receiving area makes for costly off-site storage and delays in daily production schedules. Proper capacity calculations should reflect what is needed to get through the first 2 to 4 years of production, and the operation should be designed for expansion through added shifts or modular add-ons for the next 5 to 10 years.

Production capacities will need to be validated as a system to show that product can be mixed, released, and aseptically filled within the GMP time limit. This will require that the size of the mix be coordinated with the speed of the filling line so that no product is left over to be wasted. Inspection and packaging facilities will likewise have to be sized to handle the flow of product smoothly, avoiding log-jams and confusion that could raise questions during a validation attempt.

6. *Flow Path Considerations*

This is where the traditional layout process begins. The facility should be laid out so that raw materials enter at one end and finished product flows out the other. Crossovers and turnbacks should not be allowed; they only invite cross-contamination. People should interface with the operation from the side of the flow path. Consideration should be given to whether upper or lower floors or mezzanines, are warranted. Careful planning here will result in construction of a logical facility that can be readily validated because cross-contamination and confusion have been eliminated (see Figure 2).

7. *Room Layout*

Room layout is a logical extension of the flow path. The key here is to decide what type of layout is desired. The concentric zone concept has been used effectively where the inner core is the critical manufacturing area. Here

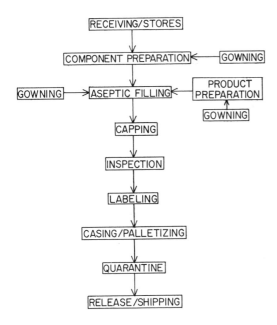

FIGURE 2   Material flow path.

would be contained the aseptic filling rooms, and only sterilized components
and product would be allowed in. Strict environmental controls govern this
zone, such as full gowning, separate HEPA air conditioning systems, etc.
This core is surrounded by support areas where there is a lesser degree of
control, but it is still required. Some gowning would be necessary, such as
hair coverings and lab coats, and access would still be restricted. An example of rooms in this zone would be component cleaning rooms or final packaging rooms. Finally, the outer region contains offices, laboratories, and other
areas requiring minimal or no control. See Figure 3.

If this layout is not possible or preferable, the same result can be achieved
by layering the control levels down the length (or height) of a building. This
sometimes permits support areas to be located closer to user points. The idea
is that critical manufacturing areas have to be isolated and protected from
unwanted disturbances such as vibrations from air conditioning machinery,
or dirt from a warehouse operation, so their arrangement with respect to
adjacent operations is important.

The component preparation rooms are the transition from the stores/staging
area to the sterile core. These rooms should be laid out so that they can
easily take product from the uncontrolled warehouse area, clean and prepare
it, and pass it into the filling area without passing on any contamination.
This is most easily done with airlocks and positive-pressure air conditioning
systems. The layout should provide a means of passing clean and sterilized
parts directly into the filling room through double-door sterilizers (gas,
steam, or dry heat), using them as an airlock. Dirty parts can come back
into the preparation area by way of pass-throughs and/or airlocks with inter-
locking doors. See Figure 4.

The key to this layout, and its importance to the validation effort, is to
be able to show that unsterilized goods cannot be brought into the sterile
core. Airlocks and double-door sterilizers must be interlocked to prevent

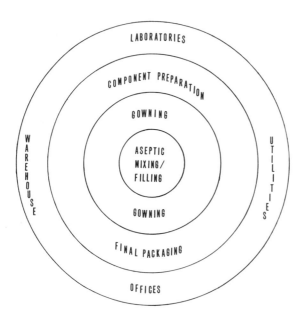

FIGURE 3   Room layout: zone concept.

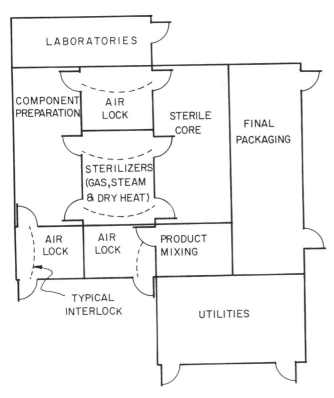

FIGURE 4 Room layout: door interlock.

having both doors open at the same time. Sterilizers must be further controlled so that the clean-side door cannot be opened until after a cycle has
been run. Procedures must be validated for control of the personnel using
the area, to be sure that they do not cause the sterile core to be violated.

The other major interface with the sterile core, the mixing tank room,
must be given similar considerations. Once mixed and released, however,
the product can be piped into the filling room. Actual contact between the
two rooms is not necessary. It only remains to prove through validation
testing that the design of the transport lines assures the clean, smooth flow
of product from mixing tank to filler without fear of making the wrong hookup. The cleaning system must also be validated, whether it is a clean-in-
place method or a hand disassembly-and-rebuild.

8. Equipment

Now that the process has been organized and the rooms arranged, the next
step is to lay in the equipment. This includes process and utility pieces.
Again the straight-line flow concept is important, to minimize the handling of
product from one operation to another. Excessive handling can be a source
of contamination and damage.

If possible, the parts washers should feed the filling and assembly areas
directly, if not by a continuous oven, then by specially made sterilizer racks
and baskets. It is easier to validate if handling is held to a minimum.

Laminar-flow hoods should be used over all product contact areas, i.e., until the product is sealed in the container. Cap crimping, however, should be done *outside* the sterile area. It is a dirty process, and once the container is plugged it can be moved into a separate adjoining room, still under laminar flow, where the final cap can be put on.

9. Environmental Control System Layout

With the equipment in place and room usages allocated, the air conditioning ductwork can be laid out. Ceiling inlets should be located where they can support and feed the laminar-flow modules. Any layout that covers all areas and helps to sweep the room with clean air will do. Returns should be located along the walls at floor level, especially near corners and where they are not blocked by equipment. Again, the sweeping of the room is what is important, not geometry. It works well to space inlets and returns around the equipment to sweep the room, then use laminar-flow modules or booths for critical operations. Do not lay out inlet and return grills before all equipment is placed, because some of them could become blocked as a result (see Figure 5).

True laminar-flow rooms with grill-work floors, such as might be found in a NASA clean-room facility, have been considered for pharmaceutical use. However, the floor pits are very difficult to keep microbiologically clean, especially when the manufacturing process is wet. This type of installation is not recommended for aseptic pharmaceutical production facilities.

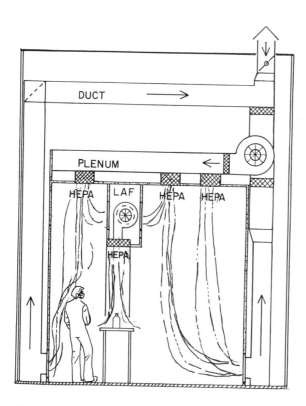

FIGURE 5 Environmental control system: filters and ductwork.

The question of air conditioning ductwork and plenums must be answered at this time. Return ducts can often be run up inside walls to a blower inlet, and the blower can discharge into a plenum over the ceiling. This reduces ductwork, but it means that the layout will have to minimize overhead activity in order to keep the plenum free of dust. Roughing filters should be installed at the inlet to the blowers, and box-type filters can be installed in the blower discharge as additional protection to the HEPA units.

10. Support Clusters

In addition to the environmental control system, there are numerous other systems required for the support of an aseptic production facility. They need to be located outside the critical zone but near enough to minimize transfer cost and time. Water treatment plants, for instance, need to be near mixing and packaging operations. Clean steam is necessary for sanitizing production mix and fill areas. You will have to validate that the steam is sufficiently hot and clean to do the job, so the boiler or still should be fairly close to the core. Clean (even sterile) compressed air will be used at many locations, so the compressor and receiving tanks should be nearby to minimize the line lengths through which the air must pass. Laboratories should be on the periphery of the central core, near mixing and packaging operations. Receiving and stores areas need to be at the beginning of the process, whereas shipping should be at the other end, and so on. Maintenance rooms need to be located conveniently near the lines that are being serviced. In a large facility, several small satellite rooms can be serviced by one remote master maintenance shop.

11. Consultations with FDA

When the layout process is complete, it is time to consult with the local FDA office (the one that will be doing the inspection) for the review of the plans. Don't expect the FDA people to stamp the plans approved, but do open up a line of communication with them about your project. They can be very helpful in uncovering potential trouble spots and sharing some of their experiences with you. Visit them when you have something concrete to share, but before it is too late to make any changes.

Now that it has been firmly established what is to be built and it has been committed to plans and writing, a giant step has been taken toward completing the validation process. Everything discussed so far has a bearing on that process, and following those steps will smooth out the road to validation immensely.

B. Documentation

It is undeniable that much of what is done serves to document the process and its progress. There is also no question that this is a time-consuming process. However, it must be done in order to avoid the consequences of a hopelessly confused validation attempt. Good documentation shows the FDA that you know what is being done and why. It gives the Quality Assurance (QA) group the material needed to do their job, and it makes good common sense.

The important documents have already been mentioned. By way of review:

Specifications are very important so that all parties will know exactly what is to be built and what results are expected. Note the emphasis on

what, not how. Specifications should address the result, not how to
get there. They are particularly important for pieces of machinery
and equipment that will be built by outside manufacturers. Specifications give a clear list of the features desired, which can be compared
to what is available, so it will be known exactly what compromises may
have to be accepted.

Procedures are required for each piece of equipment and each system.
Their methods of operation need to be spelled out in order to remove
any doubt in the line operator's mind about how to do the job. They
will be used in the employee training programs required by GMPs.
Procedures for laboratory tests and off-line operations such as metrology are also needed.

Validation protocols are necessary so that all parties can agree on exactly
how the process will be tested to demonstrate that it does what it has
been designed to do. The FDA also likes to use these protocols to
help them understand the process and the rationale behind it. In
addition, they make an excellent index of features, procedures, technical data, historical information, and reasoning for each selected
area.

Additional documents that will greatly ease the burden of validation include
the following:

Engineering Drawing Control: A program is necessary to control physical
changes throughout the facility. One way is to formulate a procedure requiring an approved engineering drawing prior to any changes to production
(or production-related) items. When the need for a change (a new leg on the
distilled water loop, for instance) is recognized and the change has been
sketched up, it can be discussed by representatives from Production, Quality
Control, Engineering, and other interested parties that will be involved in
the validation. They should agree on the need for the change and its method
of implementation. A sign-off by these three groups will give some assurance
that all implications of the change have been understood and accepted.

The approval process might take the following form, once the concept
sketch of the change has been reviewed:

1. The change request is filled out in sufficient detail such that the
    three key parties can approve it for implementation. The change re-
    quest should be a numbered, traceable document that is kept and
    cross-filed with the applicable drawing number. Therefore, the level
    of detail used in filling out the change request should be sufficient to
    provide a history of the drawing.
2. The approved change request is put into the Drafting department's
    workload. This could be a contractor's drafting group, or it could
    be an in-house group if the work is being done by your own mainten-
    ance staff. In any event, unless the drawing is actually needed in
    order to perform the work, it does not have to be drawn up right
    away.
3. Simultaneously, a copy of the approved change request is given to
    the party who will actually make the change, and work is begun.
4. When the work is complete and validated for use, the engineering
    drawings are brought up to date to reflect the "as-built" condition
    (it may not look exactly like the change request form showed it).

5.   The engineering drawings are signed off by Production, Engineering, and Quality Control as approved, and filed for future retrieval (see Figure 6).

Maintenance Work Order: In the case of a remodeled facility, where some or all of the work may be done by an in-house maintenance crew, Maintenance Work Orders (MWOs) can be used to document the changes. These go along with a drawing control policy in assuring that seemingly innocent changes cannot be authorized and made without the proper departmental approvals. These work orders can also be used to check the drawing changes to see that both agree. (It is advisable to set up a work order review, however, so that truly innocent work orders and emergency needs can be acted on without undue delay and waste.)

Engineering Tests: Records must be kept of those tests that establish the limits of equipment operation, or prove that a process is functioning correctly. These tests are a vital and necessary part of the validation process, and must be recorded in a clear, easily retrieved format. The first part (made up by the responsible engineer) "requests" the test and informs interested parties about the purpose and nature of the test. Those reviewing this first part can request modifications to the test so that full value can be gained from the work. The second part of the form reports on the test itself—how it was conducted and what results were obtained. This summary is reviewed and approved (or disapproved if necessary) by the triumverate of Engineering, Production, and Quality Control. This form provides the validation process with a record of test results to which all parties have agreed.

Quality Acceptance Criteria: These have been mentioned previously, but their development is very important. Established during the planning segment, they can tell you in advance what types of tests will be needed, how

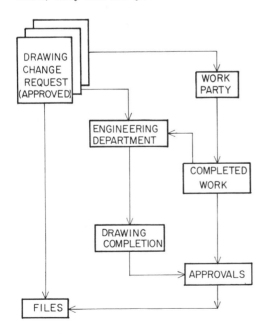

FIGURE 6   Drawing.

many and how often, and what kind of data will be expected. Agreement on this by all concerned parties is crucial to a successful validation attempt.

Construction Progress: An often-overlooked source of information during a validation review is the wealth of history that can be collected during construction. One suggestion is that a diary be kept, and that a scrapbook be set up and filled with photographs taken every few days of wall erections, piping runs, equipment installations, etc. Once the final coat of paint is put on, it is difficult to convince an FDA inspector how something was built unless there is a good photographic history. If the project is fairly large, with extensive piping runs and ductwork, a construction model can be very useful. This scale layout will uncover problems, such as a compressed air line running through the center of an air conditioning duct. Models can also be put on computers with three-dimensional graphics to achieve a similar effect.

Another record of construction progress can be kept in the form of weld samples—sections of the welded stainless steel distilled water tubing, for instance, taken at random during the fabrication process. They will show the quality of the piping system. Along with the weld samples, frequent transit sightings should be taken of the drain pitch built into these different transmission lines. These will show compliance with the GMPs.

There are undoubtedly other forms of documentation that you will find useful in structuring your validation approach. Keep them all up to date and prepared for immediate presentation: They will be required.

C. Construction/Installation

Now it is time to spend money on making all the plans and preparations into a full-fledged pharmaceutical facility. There is more to this, however, than just constructing walls and setting equipment in place. It is usually preferable to start on the outside and work in, in order to understand more fully how closely this phase relates to the validation process.

1. Construction

Grounds: The actual construction work starts with the site preparation. The validation presentation can be enhanced if it can be shown that care was taken to seal off and/or treat the soil under and around the facility to prevent moisture, insects, and bacteria from invading the structure. Carefully document all of this for later use in proving your intent to provide a clean, professional atmosphere for the production process.

Shell: The outer shell should provide protection from the elements, and from animals and insects. Depending on what is inside, the judicious use of knockout panels should be considered for purposes of access and/or expansion.

Rooms: Once the layout has been decided, interior rooms can be prepared. The zone will dictate the schedule of finishes to be used. Here the GMP regulations will provide some direction. Floors must be impervious and easily cleaned. Walls and ceilings should be smooth and free of ledges, pockets, etc. Wood should not be used, as it can rot when wet and harbor insects. There are ample metal and plastic materials available to the builder to take the place of wood products.

Epoxy is often the choice in paints, especially in the sterile core area. It is hard and smooth, impervious, and easily cleaned. It can be painted over cinder block, plaster, dry wall, or other bases. It can be troweled on to make a floor, and epoxy can be mixed with sand to make a nonskid surface. Other coverings have also been used successfully, such as vinyl, urethane, or even stainless steel sheet sealed with a flexible caulking. All of these materials can be easily validated as meeting GMP requirements.

Attic and mezzanine areas should be carefully constructed so that vibrations from their activities do not disturb operations beneath them. Solid flooring and continuous walls help in this respect. Suspended catwalks also help.

Sewers: Sewers and drains are critical items that are addressed in the GMPs. Process lines must be kept separate from facility lines, traps are necessary, and air breaks should be used to assure that sewer backups cannot flood the process areas. It may be advisable not to locate any drains in aseptic clean rooms because of the concern over microbiological growth in the trap. At the minimum, a sealed cover over the drain outlet should be considered in these critical instances.

Ductwork: Air conditioning ductwork is sometimes taken for granted, but that can be a mistake. Poorly constructed and sealed HEPA filter ducting can destroy an otherwise perfect validation program. The ducting should be carefully specified to be stainless steel or high-quality galvenized steel, have locked and sealed joints, and a nonvibrating installation. Filter mounts must be firm and leakproof (100% in the case of HEPA filter mounts). Fiberglass insulation should not be used anywhere in the air conditioning system.

Piping: Process piping construction and installation deserves special attention, particularly distilled water and liquid product lines. These welded stainless steel lines must be assembled clean and free of pits and contamination traps. Heliarc welding is recommended, with frequent samples being taken to show consistent weld quality. These systems must be sloped to a drain so that they can be acid-cleaned and passivated after installation. Many a validation has been delayed due to lack of attention to this important detail.

Other lines whose contents come in contact with the product or product-contact surfaces (such as steam and compressed air) should be sloped also. The direction of slope should be back to the source, or to a planned low-point drain. This makes them easy to clean and keep clean, and eliminates any "dead legs" (areas where moisture or product can pool and start a bacteria colony). Records of these slopes (such as transit sightings) can be put right on the piping drawings so the FDA inspector can see that you have followed the regulations.

Landscaping: An often-overlooked area that can go a long way toward helping the validation process is the exterior landscaping. The first impression an inspector gets of the plant being reviewed is the exterior views. If this is neat and well kept, the inspector may feel that the effort carries over to the inside. Additionally, it is known that certain plants and flowers can alter insect infestation. Thus, these types of vegetation, planted in open earth beds around the periphery, serve a twofold purpose: They aid in the reduction of possible contaminants (e.g., insects), and they are esthetically pleasing to the eye. Other aspects of proper landscaping have to do with plantings that will not clog roof drains with big leaves, produce pollen or particulates that can contaminate the product, or whose root structure will not plug underground drains.

Punch List: Finally, make up a contractor's punch list to cover all unsatisfactory conditions. This will serve to verify that all specifications
have been met and that the facility is ready for validation. As the punch
list is worked through, the time draws closer to accepting the facility from
the contractor. This should be done only when all specifications have been
acknowledged and when it is certain that the facility can be successfully
validated.

2. Installation

Equipment: How equipment is installed can have a direct influence on
how easily it can be validated for the process it is designed to do. For
instance, it may be difficult to convince anyone that a parts washing area
can produce clean parts when the stainless steel washers and driers are
mounted with rusty angle iron and carbon steel bolts. And how many
times have we seen an impressive array of filling equipment marred by the
excessive use of silicone sealant on control box mountings and piping sup-
ports? Pay attention to detail here, where it can be readily seen, and
many validation questions will never even be asked. A good installation
leaves a good first impression that you know what you are doing.

Equipment installation may begin right after the rough framing is up,
or after the last coat of paint is on the walls, or anytime in between. It
all depends on how completely the equipment is built into the structure
and how it is to be moved into the room. If the equipment will not fit
through standard doors or passageways, make special allowances. Remember that what goes in will eventually come out, so knock-out panels or
special door openings may be needed. Verify that corridors and passageways are large enough to permit moving the equipment through them, and
provide some means of getting equipment onto mezzanines and upper floors.
Fork lift access can be important, so leave a work platform and floor space
for maneuvering. Helicopters have even been used for lifting exceptionally
large pieces into confined areas.

Check-out: When the equipment has been hooked up, it needs to be
checked out. This is an engineering process whereby the pieces are
started up one by one according to the manufacturers' instructions and
often with their personnel on hand. Most companies provide a startup
service, and it is advisable to take advantage of this. They can find problems before they happen, and provide ready solutions to the problems that
are bound to occur during start-up. Documentation during this process
need be only enough to satisfy the engineering department's needs.

After each piece has been started up and made to run smoothly by the
engineers and the manufacturer's representatives, all pieces can be run
together. Again, this is an engineering process to verify that the systems can be made operative without blowing up or tearing apart. This is
not yet the time to worry about limits, tests, or qualifications. Since the
facility has not been cleaned up and qualified, the engineers have the
option to use garden hoses for water lines, not to gown up, to cut and
trim as necessary to make things fit and work, and to override automatic
systems as needed.

D. Testing

The installation phase is concluded when all equipment is operating in such
a manner that documented testing can begin. This means that all switches

are set, all guides and guards are in place, all interlocks are operational, and the pieces will operate as a system when required. This final phase in the facility design/validation process takes place in two steps:

Step 1. *System validation*, or testing, to prove that the equipment functions safely and properly per the equipment specifications

Step 2. *Process validation*, or challenging, to prove that the equipment systems operate in the manner required to meet the stated objectives in the Quality Acceptance Criteria and are capable of making an acceptable product

These are both structured test series, well documented, and carefully planned. They should not begin until all start-up, debugging, and checkout tests are complete.

1. System Validation

The system validations make an excellent training ground for future production operators. Under the guidance of the engineers, the operators and their QC counterparts can learn the manufacturing processes they will have to follow in order to produce good product. At the same time, they can be putting the equipment through a series of limits tests, documenting the settings and techniques that work for them.

You now have a new facility, with new equipment operated by new personnel with new procedures, possibly to produce a new product. Everything has to be proven to the mutual satisfaction of the Manufacturing and Quality groups. The systems tests are designed to do just that. They are run by Production personnel in training with the help of engineers, and they utilize prepared procedures in attempts to produce nonsaleable goods that will meet the preestablished specifications. This is the "rehearsal" phase, where all involved learn how to do their part of the process. It is not done with saleable product, so tests must be carefully structured to minimize waste.

It should be kept in mind that it is not always necessary to verify everything by testing. Be selective. For instance, do not run a capping machine as fast as it can go just to prove that it will do it, if your line speed is only half that rate. It can always be revalidated at a higher speed later. But *do* run a test series on the capper to find out at what setting the closures come loose during sterilization or subsequent handling. That kind of information will allow the establishment of an operating band within which good product will always be produced, and within which the operation is taking place at a safe distance from the failure point.

System validations have to be performed on all phases of the manufacturing process, and sometimes on the laboratory processes. Air conditioning systems and room air pressure balances have to be tested with all heat loads and room activities present. Sterilizers have to be validated for proper functional and mechanical operations. Machines on assembly lines have to be run through their paces both individually and together to see that a cohesive, interacting system exists. Washing procedures, laboratory procedures, metrology operations, inspection systems, etc., all have to be tested to determine their safe bands of operation.

2. Process Validation

Once these experiments have been run and carefully documented, it is time to put the whole operation together and run the process validation. This is done under full manufacturing and quality group supervision, using the specifications and procedures that have been documented as workable. Usually this validation produces saleable product which becomes the first released goods, thus verifying that the entire manufacturing operation is a success. These tests are the final steps in the validation process to produce an operation that can be safely promoted to the FDA as "being in a state of readiness called qualified."

IV. CONCLUSION

This entire process, from initial design layouts through documentation, construction, and final testing, is defined as validation. Each step is important in bringing about a complete understanding of the manufacturing system. All that remains is to convey this understanding to the FDA inspectors when they visit.

4
Calibration and Certification

ROBERT E. BREMMER

Calibration and Consulting Services, Inc., Des Plaines, Illinois

I. INTRODUCTION

Can there be a valid process or product certification without the measurement assurance of a comprehensive Calibration Program?

In order to answer this question, an understanding as to what constitutes a comprehensive Calibration Program and how that program interacts with Certification must be developed. That understanding will first require definitions of some commonly misunderstood activities and terms.

Many people consider the activity of adjusting an instrument and the calibration of an instrument to be the same activity. The differences between these activities can readily be identified if one considers the calibration of an etched-glass liquid-in-glass thermometer. There is no readily available adjusting screw to return the liquid level to the proper marking if the temperature indicated by the thermometer does not correspond to a known temperature it is measuring. From another perspective, another key (economic) difference between adjustment and calibration is that, for an effective Calibration Program, measurement instruments that have an adjustment feature should require adjustment (during the calibration activity) only about 5--10% of the time. It is clear, then, that calibration is not adjustment, but is rather:

> The comparison of a measurement standard or instrument of known accuracy with another standard or instrument of lesser accuracy in order to confirm, detect, correlate, report or eliminate by adjustment any variation in the accuracy of the item being compared.

Instrument calibration is only one component of those activities that are referred to as a Calibration Program. Those activities that comprise a comprehensive Calibration Program will be described later in this chapter, but a clearer understanding of the objective of the program will be gained if the reader considers a Measurement Assurance Program as a more appropriate title for the activities of this program. (Because historically these activities have been referred to as a calibration program, this terminology will continue to be used in this presentation.)

This chapter will:

1. Define the components and activities of a comprehensive Calibration Program/Measurement Assurance Program.
2. Define and describe certification/validation from a Measurement Assurance perspective.
3. Review calibration and Calibration Programs from an FDA perspective.
4. Review several specific Certification/Calibration Program interface examples.
5. Identify some specific areas of risk associated with some of the presently established Certification Programs. And then—
6. Answer the initial question posed in this introduction: Can there be a valid process or product certification without the measurement assurance of a comprehensive Calibration Program?

II. COMPONENTS OF A COMPREHENSIVE CALIBRATION PROGRAM

Components of a comprehensive Calibration Program are identified in Table 1. The details necessary to establish the type of program needed by a specific firm, how to implement that program initially, and how to maintain/upgrade that initially established program are described in *A Systems Approach to an Effective Calibration Program* [1]. This section (and the remainder of this chapter) will highlight those aspects of a comprehensive Calibration

TABLE 1   Components of a Comprehensive Calibration Program

The inclusion decision

Instrument selection

Instrument installation

Standards and Standards laboratory

Instrument calibration

Training

Documentation

Long-range planning

Calibration control:

    Policies and procedures

    Scheduling system

    Performance measurement

    Outside calibration agencies

    Out-of-tolerance response system (product-oriented)

    Audit system

    Corrective action

Program that are especially important to the certification activity. Those important aspects are

1. Instrument selection
2. Standards and Standards laboratory
3. Calibration control
    a. Policies and Procedures (calibration procedures only)
    b. Scheduling system
    c. Documentation
    d. Outside calibration agencies
    e. Out-of-tolerance response systems (product)

A. Instrument Selection

1. General

Although the Calibration Program should generally be operated by the engineering department of a company, the Quality Assurance organization should take an active role in many aspects of the program, in addition to audit and use of the Calibration Program measurement instruments. One of those areas where the preventive-oriented philosophies associated with many Quality Assurance organizations can be most effective is in new instrument selection. Just as with production processes, it is often an economically sound approach to utilize more labor in the design of the manufacturing process in order to produce only good product (rather than to attempt to inspect quality into the product). It is also appropriate to utilize prevention-oriented philosophies in initially purchasing quality into measurement instruments. This will help assure ongoing measurement accuracy when the instrument is used.

A philosophy that addresses instrument reliability and instrument adequacy (with respect to the accuracy of the measurement that must be made) can help assure the success of a Certification Program and the economic returns associated with appropriate measurement instruments.

2. Instrument Adequacy

When reference is made to instrument adequacy, consideration is given to whether the measurement system (Fig. 1) is "sufficiently accurate" to meet the measurement needs of the product, process, or measurement traceability. "Sufficiently accurate" can be further defined through the use of the *uncertainty ratio* (U_R), which is the ratio of the accuracy of the measurement system (or standard) compared to the product, process, or measurement instrument (system) that it measures or adjusts. Uncertainty ratios (U_R) of 1/3 to 1/4 are generally considered to be a minimum, and smaller ratios (1/5, etc.) provide a higher confidence of adequacy.

$$U_R = \frac{\pm 2s \text{ accuracy of instrument}}{\pm \text{tolerance on product, process, or measurement instrument under calibration}}$$

where S = the instrument standard deviation obtained from similar instrument past performance or valid manufacturer's information, and the tolerance is associated with acceptance limits (see Fig. 2).

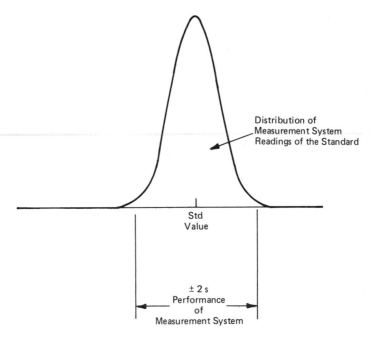

FIGURE 1   Ability of a measurement system to measure a standard.

Figure 2 depicts an adequate measurement system with a U_R of 1/4.

The basis for considering the performance of a measurement system as a statistical distribution is described in the introduction of Instrument Society of America Recommended Practice 55.1 [2] as "It is only by controlling a process, be it a manufacturing process or a measurement process, that a statistical population arises."

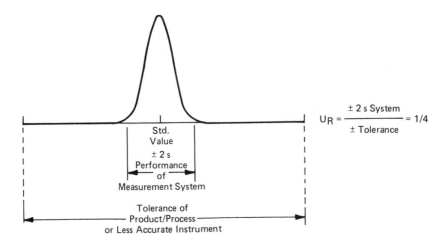

FIGURE 2   Measurement system with 1/4 uncertainty ratio.

Regardless of whether a specific measurement system or a family of instruments/systems follows a normal distribution, the consistency of the thought process that develops from a statistical approach applied to instrument performance, system measurements, and the Calibration Program itself, provides a basis for program evaluation, decision making, and eventually measurement accuracy improvement.

3. Selection of New Instruments

Inclusion of Calibration Program considerations in the selection of new instruments may appear, to some, as overstepping the traditional Calibration Program boundaries. In considering the adequacy of our measurement system as an integral part of the quality of our products, we will soon develop a rationale similar to the subject of a talk given several years ago by the author, "You Can't Inspect Quality into Test, Measurement and Control Equipment" [3]: You have to buy it in, install it in, calibrate it in, and keep it in on an ongoing basis. In effect, new instrument selection on Calibration Program principles is a prevention-oriented quality approach to a principally prevention-oriented system (Calibration).

Instrument Accuracy and System Interaction: There are certain inherent inaccuracies associated with any measurement system, and the instrument specifier should understand the magnitude of these inaccuracies prior to selecting an instrument. Some of these inaccuracies are in the sensor (thermocouple, bourdon tube, etc.) or the sensor-instrument connecting lines and connections, and some of them are in the instruments themselves, including electrical component aging/temperature stability, wear of mechanical linkages, friction (at moving connections and pen stick), recording paper slippage, or paper expansion with temperature/humidity.

Other inaccuracies result from improper sampling, or a temperature bulb located at a position that does not give a valid representation of the temperature—in fact, there may be no representative temperature due to poor temperature distribution. In many cases, for simplicity, it is acceptable to treat all of these inaccuracies by lumping them (adding their standard deviations) together to obtain a system standard deviation:

$$s_{system} = (s^2_{instrument} + s^2_{environment} + s^2_{variable\ distribution} + s^2_{sensor} + \cdots)^{1/2}$$

The instrument measurement inaccuracy is usually the greatest inaccuracy or, if not, the outside inaccuracies may be decreased to acceptable levels by various techniques (such as profiling of an autoclave for different size bottles at different loading patterns).

General Instrument Cost and Maintainability Considerations: While it is generally recommended that one use an instrument similar to those that are already successfully meeting your needs, in many cases this is not possible. When it is necessary to purchase a new (to the plant) type of instrument, the higher costs associated with more accurate instruments must be understood. Some of these potentially higher cost factors include:

1. Basic initial cost of the instrument (one-time cost).
2. Increased cost associated with better standards and transfer standards to calibrate this equipment (one-time cost).
3. Calibration will invariably take more time, not only because of the newness of the standards and measurement equipment, but also because more care must be exercised in the use and adjustment of most of this equipment (ongoing cost).
4. Increased accuracy of equipment usually means increased complexity of equipment. Thus, more time and skill is often needed to repair the equipment (an ongoing cost).
5. New calibration procedures will likely have to be written (one-time cost).

If a new type of instrument is required, however, the following priority format is suggested in selecting a manufacturer:

1. Initially target for an approximate 1/4 (or lower) uncertainty ratio (previously discussed) and consider, as appropriate, the risk factor at the extremes of the acceptance limits.
2. Use demonstrated quality manufacturers and instruments with which your plant personnel are already familiar.
3. If plant instruments have not demonstrated quality operation (and it is traceable to the instruments), standardize on another manufacturer using criteria described above and inputs from other sources. These inputs could include:
    a. Infrequency of repair, ease of repair, and calibration
    b. Instrument stability with time and ambient conditions
    c. A cost analysis for the standardization and the possibility of negotiating a plant-wide or corporate-wide pricing arrangement with a quality supplier
    d. Training offered by the manufacturer and cost of this training

Specific Application Considerations: Along with the primary consideration in instrument selection (appropriate uncertainty ratio), the following other aspects should also be addressed in the selection process:

1. *Recorder and controller range and quality*: The recorder, which may or may not be a part of the control system, may nevertheless be the primary tool for the acceptance or rejection of product, process quality and, occasionally, research data. For these critical application instruments, the following requirements should hold:
    a. The range of the instrument shall be as narrow as practical around the operating conditions so that instrument resolution is as large as practical. This could include the purchase of special charts.
    b. Quality of the instrument (repeatability, resolution, potential high-wear features, maintainability).
    c. Adaptability for use in programmable systems.
2. *Instrument installation environment*: In addition, critical recording instruments should be located with sufficient accessibility to allow calibrations to be performed to required accuracies. Consideration

should also be given to instrument use environment (humidity, temperature variation, excessive heat, steam, etc.) for those instruments affected by these conditions.

3. *Calibration costs*: Yearly calibration costs often exceed the initial cost of an instrument, especially for simple instruments such as pressure gauges, thermometers, and some recorder/controllers.

4. *Calibration procedure*: The specific calibration procedure should be set up and tested prior to operational startup of any critical instrument.

5. *Nonprocess instruments*: Although the above provisions deal principally with process instruments, similar consideration should be given to the selection of such devices as micrometers, calipers, scales, etc., when these are to be used for critical measurements on products or components.

To further aid in selection, a checklist similar to Table 2 can be used. The use of this type of checklist in instrument selection is an especially simple matter if the Calibration Program has been effectively implemented into the Research and Development and specification-setting areas of a company. Under this situation, operating limits and product/process acceptance limits could be clearly differentiated.

TABLE 2   New Transferred Instrument Checklist

A. Instrument service and location (plant)_____
    Instrument No._____Project No._____

B. Is this instrument to be included in the Calibration Program_____
    If B is yes, please fill out the following:

    1. Variable to be measured_____
    2. Range of variable of interest to be measured_____
    3. Acceptance limits (specification range) of the product for this variable
       (most severe conditions if multi-use instrument)_____
    4. Suggested range of instrument and ±2s accuracy (for uncertainty
       ratio greater than 1/4 see Calibration Coordinator) _____
       _____
    5. Instrument and manufacturer recommended _____
    6. Are calibration instructions and standards available for this instrument?
       _____
    7. Anticipated date of operational use _____
    8. Is the instrument installation environment compatible with the instrument needs?_____

C. Have you included in the purchase requisition provisions to ensure that operating and installation instructions will be sent sufficiently early to obtain their full benefit?_____

By:_____   _____   _____
          Name   Dept   Date

          _____
          Company (if outside designer)

B. Standards and Standards Laboratory

A standards laboratory, as a minimum, is a designated area where:

1. Company standards are maintained.
2. Transfer standards (see Fig. 3) are calibrated against plant or company standards.
3. Appropriate environmental conditions (consistent with the needs of the standards and transfer standards) are maintained. The standards utilized in the Standards laboratory should be of appropriate accuracy (U_R) and should be traceable to the NBS, or some other recognizable standards source. Traceability is described in Figure 4.

Other important physical requirements associated with a Standards laboratory (space adequacy, appropriate environment) and with the management requirements of a Standards laboratory (documentation, training, planning) are identified in Chapter 6 of *A Systems Approach to an Effective Calibration Program* [1].

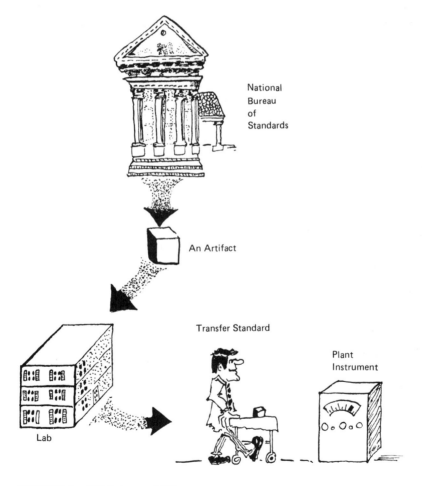

National
Bureau
of
Standards

An Artifact

Transfer Standard

Plant
Instrument

Lab

FIGURE 3   NBS traceability.

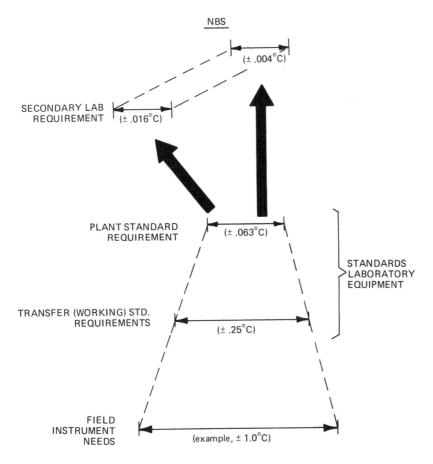

FIGURE 4 Typical minimum temperature accuracy relationships for a small plant calibration program.

C. Calibration Control

These components of a comprehensive Calibration Program represent the systems and controls that maintain the ongoing adequacy and viability of the program.

1. Calibration Procedures

Each instrument should be calibrated according to a written procedure. In addition to the instrument adjustment and identification requirements contained in a procedure, documentation and paperwork requirements should also be included. A major documentation requirement is the recording of "as-found" data prior to any adjustment of the instrument.

2. Scheduling System

The periodic calibration of Calibration Program instruments is a clear requirement of the Drug (CFR 21, Part 211) and the Device (CFR 21, Part 820)

Good Manufacturing Practices (GMPs) (see Sec. IV). Whatever mechanisms and procedures are used for scheduling purposes, a key regulatory issue, with respect to scheduling, is whether a company follows its own scheduling procedures.

3. Documentation

Documentation is the double-edged sword of the program. While documentation provides the opportunity to analyze documented calibration results in order to improve the program, it also provides the opportunity for outside and inside auditors to make an in-depth review of a program.

Failure to document may result in an FD-483 observation item.

4. Outside Calibration Agencies

Outside calibration agencies are firms, not internally employed, that are hired to perform maintenance and/or calibration on Calibration Program instruments. Under these circumstances, the plant remains responsible to assure that their plant Calibration Program requirements are met. This issue is addressed in Appendix 1 "Validation of Outside Calibration Services."

5. Out-of-Tolerance Response System (Product)

From a product quality assurance viewpoint, product review systems initiated when instruments are found to be out of tolerance represents a significant product protection system (albeit after the fact). Heavy reliance is placed on the recording of "as-found" data (prior to instrument adjustment) by the Calibration technician. Quality Assurance then uses this data, production records, and actual product (as necessary) to assess possible product risk.

All of the above systems are described in greater detail by Bremmer [1].

III. CERTIFICATION/VALIDATION FROM A MEASUREMENT ASSURANCE PERSPECTIVE

The objective of a product or process certification program is not to demonstrate, on a one-time basis, that acceptable product can be manufactured. Rather, the objective of a Certification Program is to assure that acceptable product will be delivered on an ongoing basis.

Ideally, a Certification Program should build a level of reliability into the certified process such that final product inspection is not necessary to ensure product adequacy—controlling the raw material inputs and processing variables while sampling the output variables (where possible) assures product conformity to requirements. Thus, the Certification Program should include not only those specific requirements associated with a particular manufacturing process or equipment, but also those ongoing systems and controls (including audit) that will assure ongoing product adequacy. Table 3 shows just a few of the components of such a system. Measurement assurance impact on these major components is addressed in the remainder of this section.

A. General Comments on the Certification/Calibration Program Interface

It is possible to challenge the adequacy of a company's entire product specification and product release system through the Certification/Calibration

TABLE 3   Certification Program Components

There are four major aspects to this program:

1. Qualification (equipment)

    a. Equipment
    b. Installation
    c. Operational

2. Validation (product/process)

    a. Protocol developed and met

3. Ongoing systems

    a. Calibration, change control, maintenance, training, etc.

4. Certification

    a. Management confirmation that the other aspects were completed
       and that there is a commitment to maintain the ongoing systems

---

Program interface (some of the risks associated with these areas are discussed in Sec. VI). The intent of this section, however, is to limit the historical scope of the Certification/Calibration Program impact to that time frame which starts with equipment qualification.

A well-implemented Certification Program will begin to affect a new plant or processing change in the research and development stage, and will play an important role in equipment (and instrument) selection. In addition, it will include the necessary planning aspects at an early phase in a project to assure that time, skilled labor, and sufficient funds are available to implement successfully the certification program that is developed. A program that lacks any of these three resource commitments has a high risk of undesirable results regardless of the adequacy of the technical planning that went into the program.

B. Qualification

1. Equipment Qualification

The equipment qualification phase of certification involves the assessment of the equipment that will be involved in the certification against the purchase specifications or any other equipment requirements that exist. This phase should include not only the major pieces of processing equipment, but also those measurement instruments that could have an effect on the process equipment, on those measurements made during certification runs, and on those raw materials, products, or product tests that are assessed by measurement instruments.

The equipment qualification phase of this instrument measurement review should include the following:

Are those measurement instruments (which are required to make key
    measurements) actually there?
Are they a part of the Calibration Program?

Are they sufficiently accurate to meet the accuracy requirements of the process, tests, and certification measurements (see Sec. II and Sec. VI, Sec. B).

In considering which instruments should be included in the certification activity, one must consider the obvious instrument as well as the obscure instrument that is located in the internals of our control panel. Appendix 2, "What Is a Calibration Program Instrument?" covers this topic in greater depth.

2. Equipment Installation

The equipment installation phase of certification deals with whether the processing equipment, piping, and power are installed as per the drawings. In some cases, to accomplish this activity successfully, it is necessary that installation qualification begin at an early phase, before the installation of some piping that might be buried in walls (e.g., when pitched lines are necessary as part of a specific processing requirement). Installation qualification, when performed by a skilled individual, can also serve as a preoperational check on the adequacy of the engineering design.

The installation qualification phase of certification takes on an entirely new dimension when Calibration Program considerations are included, because instrument installation details are usually not included as part of facility or process design. In addition, since few engineers or field installation personnel are sensitive to many of the factors that can affect measurement accuracy, there is a high likelihood of inappropriate instrument installation.

Just a few of those measurement instrument installation factors that should be addressed as part of an effective Certification Program include the following:

1. *Environment*: Is the instrument affected by the environment in which it is installed or the environment through which its sensor signals are transmitted? The potential effects associated with temperature/temperature change, humidity, electrical noise, and vibration can all affect some types of measurement instruments.
2. *Sanitary/cleanability aspects*: Is the instrument and associated sensors installed in such a way that they are cleanable, removable, or sanitizable in such a way as not to cause damage when those activities are being accomplished? Can the instrument be located in an area where the cleanliness and gowning requirements of the calibration technician or maintenance personnel and their tools are minimized? Does the instrument installation cause "dead pockets"?
3. *Calibration*: Whenever possible, instruments should be calibrated in place so that:
    a. The calibration will be performed in the environment in which the instrument will operate.
    b. Potential damage to the instrument is minimized when it is being dismounted, moved, and reinstalled.
    c. Downtime is minimized.
4. *Properly sensing the variable of interest*: Is the instrument sensor accurately measuring the parameter of interest? Temperature distribution factors associated with convection currents, insulation factors, and heat radiation loss (or gain) can, for example, produce erroneous temperature readings.

5. *Accessibility*: Accessibility considerations include more than mounting the instrument in a safe and noncramped location (so that calibration technicians or maintenance personnel can devote their full attention to the accurate comparison and/or adjustment of the instrument). Accessibility can also include providing sufficient space, electrical power, and an air supply close to the instrument so that measurement standards can be properly utilized.

3. Operational Qualification

Operational qualification addresses such questions as:

Does the equipment actually perform according to the specifications?
Does it deliver the designated flow rates (under "no load" conditions)?
Does it turn at 1800 revolutions per minute?
Can it heat to the design temperature?

In addressing Calibration Program considerations during the operational qualification phase, the first opportunity occurs to determine if the measurement instrument will actually measure a processing parameter. In addition, this is normally the time when measurement instruments associated with process equipment will first be calibrated. These calibrations should be performed to written procedures, against appropriate standards, by qualified calibration technicians.

Documentation of the calibration, and the affixing of dated calibration stickers on Calibration Program instruments, should also be accomplished.

C. Validation (Product/Process)

In the validation phase of the Certification Program, the opportunity now exists to confirm that many of the engineering judgments made during design have the proper affect on the manufacturing process or product. In addition, the validation phase also provides the opportunity to address the actual distribution impact on the certification and process control measurements. Ideally, validation allows a judgment as to whether there is a measurement difference between the various exposure conditions of the process/product and the condition that is sensed by the process control instrument. An example of distribution effect that could be determined in a validation is shown in Appendix 3, "Process Temperature Distribution Impact on Instrument Accuracy Requirements."

The key to a successful validation phase is the development of an appropriate protocol that will challenge the effects on the product or process of changes to key variables throughout the normal range of operating conditions that will be experienced.

D. Ongoing Systems

As described earlier in this section, ongoing systems provide the assurance that acceptable product or materials will be delivered on an ongoing basis. Some of these systems that affect certification of a clean room are identified in Table 4. Ongoing systems that have Calibration Program interaction include the following:

1. *The Calibration Program*: Those program aspects that address documentation of instrument range changes, adjustments required to return

TABLE 4   Some Typical Ongoing Systems That Affect
Certification (for a Clean Room)

Calibration Program

Change control (equipment, procedures, specifications)

Maintenance

Housekeeping

Environmental monitoring

Audit

Training

Incoming inspection

Recertification

Others

---

an instrument to tolerance, product risk reviews for out-of-tolerance
instruments, calibrator training, Calibration Program audit, etc.,
should all be an active and functioning part of the Calibration
Program.

2. *Change control*: Changes in instrument use should be addressed from
    an adequacy and installation viewpoint prior to instrument substitution.
    As an alternative, the Calibration Program itself can be relied upon to
    control changes that take place to an individual measurement system.

3. *Maintenance*: Instruments involved in control of a certified process
    should be calibrated before and after preventive maintenance (which
    may affect their measurements) is accomplished.

4. *Environmental monitoring*: Those instruments that can affect the va-
    lidity of ongoing environmental monitoring systems of a certified proc-
    ess should be included in the Calibration Program. Such instruments
    can include:
    a. Particle counters (use: clean room particulate counting)
    b. Temperature control instruments in incubators, on autoclaves, in
        stability rooms
    c. Photometers (use: HEPA filter challenges)
    d. Thermo-anemometers (use: HEPA filter or room velocity measure-
        ment)

5. *Audit*: Audit should include the Calibration Program, training of the
    calibration technicians and the personnel who analyze product risk
    associated with out-of-tolerance instruments. Audits should also chal-
    lenge the rationale by which instruments have been included in the
    Calibration Program.

6. *Training*: Along with the training requirements previously identified,
    training should include Calibration Program training for the auditors,
    as well as appropriate user training for those individuals who will ac-
    tually use the measurement instruments.

7. *Incoming inspection*: Instruments that measure the conformance to
    specification of the incoming raw materials used with a certified proc-
    ess should be included in the Calibration Program. An even better

approval procedure would be to assess as well the adequacy of the supplier's measurement instruments and their Calibration Program.

8. *Others*: Some firms, as an aspect of their Certification Program, require the recalibration of process control and measurement instruments at the completion of validation in order to assure that the entire validation was done by properly functioning instruments. This, of course, is an economic decision based on the costs associated with this additional calibration (weighed against the risk of an out-of-tolerance condition severe enough to "decertify" the process and the cost of recertification).

E. Certification

Certification represents sign-off by appropriate levels of management that the components of the Certification Program have been accomplished, and that systems are in place to assure ongoing adequacy of the certification. The existence of an appropriate Calibration Program must represent one of those components.

IV. CALIBRATION/CALIBRATION PROGRAMS FROM THE FDA VIEWPOINT

In the early 1980s, several years after the FDA requirement for Calibration Programs had been clearly mandated in the Drug (Title 21, Part 211) and in the Device (Title 21, Part 820) Good Manufacturing Practices, calibration deficiency items still ranked as the second most recurring deficiency found by the Bureau of Medical Devices. The specific deficiency cited in 1981 FDA Audits (from *The GMP Newsletter*) was the lack of "calibration of production and quality assurance equipment," along with an indication that calibration would be given close attention in future years.

The Bureau's apparent intent is to place emphasis on voluntary compliance and to continue to provide small device manufacturers with assistance by offering free courses in GMP requirements. Such programs include calibration program requirements that can serve as an excellent "starter" for the manufacturer.

This section will identify calibration requirements defined by the GMP regulations, some of the components of the Bureau of Medical Devices GMP Calibration Training, provide some analysis of FD-483 observations/excerpts from *GMP Trends* (and other documents), and some pertinent calibration observations.

A. GMP Calibration Regulations

Some specific GMP calibration regulations that address the Pharmaceutical and Device industries are the following:

CFR 21 Part 58—Good Laboratory Practice for Nonclinical Laboratory Studies

Section 58.63—Maintenance and Calibration of Equipment

(a) Equipment shall be adequately inspected, cleaned, and maintained. Equipment used for the generation, measurement, or assessment of data shall be adequately tested, calibrated and/or standardized.

(b) The written standard operating procedures required under Section 58.81(b) (11) shall set forth in sufficient detail the methods, materials, and schedules to be used in the routine inspection, cleaning, maintenance, testing, calibration and/or standardization of equipment, and shall specify remedial action to be taken in the event of failure or malfunction of equipment. The written standard operating procedures shall designate the person responsible for the performance of each operation, and copies of the standard operating procedures shall be made available to laboratory personnel.

(c) Written records shall be maintained of all inspection, maintenance, testing, calibrating and/or standardizing operations. These records, containing the date of the operation, shall describe whether the maintenance operations were routine and followed the written standard operating procedures. Written records shall be kept of non routine repairs performed on equipment as a result of failure and malfunction. Such records shall document the nature of the defect, how and when the defect was discovered and any remedial action taken in response to the defect.

* * * * *

Current Good Manufacturing Practices for Finished Pharmaceuticals

Section 211.25—Personnel Qualifications

(a) Each person engaged in the manufacture, processing, packing, or holding of a drug product shall have the education, training, and experience, or any combination thereof, to enable that person to perform the assigned functions. Training shall be in the particular operations that the employee performs and in Current Good Manufacturing Practice (including the Current Good Manufacturing Practice regulations in this chapter and written procedures required by these regulations) as they relate to the employee's functions. Training in Current Good Manufacturing Practice shall be conducted by qualified individuals on a continuing basis and with sufficient frequency to assure that employees remain familiar with CGMP requirements applicable to them.

Section 211.68—Automatic, Mechanical, and Electronic Equipment

(a) Automatic, mechanical, or electronic equipment or other types of equipment, including computers, or related systems that will perform a function satisfactorily, may be used in the manufacture, processing, packing, or holding of a drug product. If such equipment is so used, it shall be routinely calibrated, inspected, or checked according to a written program designed to assure proper performance. Written records of those calibration checks and inspections shall be maintained.

(b) Appropriate controls shall be exercised over computer or related systems to assure that changes in master production and control records or other records are instituted only by authorized personnel. Input to and output from the computer or related system of formulas or other records or data shall be checked for accuracy. A backup file of data entered into the computer or related system shall be maintained except where certain data, such as calculations performed in connection with laboratory analysis, are eliminated by computerization, or other automated processes. In such instances, a written record of the program shall be maintained along with appropriate validation data. Hard copy or alternative systems, such as duplicates, tapes, or microfilm, designed to assure that backup data are exact and complete and that it is secure from alteration, inadvertent erasures, or loss shall be maintained.

Section 211.160—General Requirements

(a) The establishment of any specification, standards, sampling plans, test procedures, or other laboratory control mechanisms required by this subpart, including any change in such specifications, standards, sampling plans, test procedures, or other laboratory control mechanisms, shall be drafted by the appropriate organizational unit and reviewed and approved by the quality control unit. The requirements in this subpart shall be followed and shall be documented at the time of performance. Any deviation from the written specifications, standards, sampling plans, test procedures, or other laboratory control mechanisms shall be recorded and justified.

(b) Laboratory controls shall include the establishment of scientifically sound and appropriate specifications, standards, sampling plans, and test procedures designed to assure that components, drug product containers, closures, in-process materials, labeling and drug products conform to appropriate standards of identity, strength, quality and purity. Laboratory controls shall include:

(4) The calibration of instruments, apparatus, gauges and recording devices at suitable intervals in accordance with an established written program containing specific directions, schedules, limits for accuracy and precision, and provisions for remedial action in the event accuracy and/or precision limits are not met. Instruments, apparatus, gauges, and recording devices not meeting established specifications shall not be used.

* * * * *

CFR 21 Part 820—Good Manufacturing Practices for Medical Devices: General

Section 820.61—Measurement Equipment

All production and quality assurance measurement equipment, such as mechanical, automated, or electronic equipment, shall be suitable for its intended purposes and shall be capable of producing valid results. Such equipment shall be routinely calibrated, inspected, and checked according to written procedures. Records documenting these activities shall be maintained. When computers are used as part of an automated production or quality assurance system, the computer software programs shall be validated by adequate and documented testing. All program changes shall be made by a designated individual(s) through a formal approval procedure.

(a) Calibration

Calibration procedures shall include specific directions and limits for accuracy and precision. There shall be provisions for remedial action when accuracy and precision limits are not met. Calibration shall be performed by personnel having the necessary education, training, background, and experience.

(b) Calibration Standards

Where practical, the calibration standards used for production and quality assurance measurement equipment shall be traceable to the national standards of the National Bureau of Standards, Department of Commerce. If national standards are not practical for the parameter being measured, an independent reproducible standard shall be used. If no applicable standard exists, an in-house standard shall be developed and used.

(c) Calibration Records

The calibration date, the calibrator, and the next calibration date shall be recorded and displayed, or records containing such information shall be readily available for each piece of equipment requiring calibration. A designated individual(s) shall maintain a record of calibration dates and of the individual performing each calibration.

The last GMP included in this listing is the original document that identified Calibration Program requirements (but was never formally issued).

CFR 21 Part 212—Good Manufacturing Practices for Drugs

Section 212.68—Equipment Calibration

(a) Procedures shall be written and followed designating schedules and assigning responsibility for testing or monitoring the performance or accuracy of automatic or continuously operating equipment, devices, apparatus, or mechanisms such as, but not limited to, the following:

(1) Temperature-recording devices on sterilizing equipment.
(2) Temperature-recording devices on sterilizers.
(3) Pressure gauges.
(4) Mechanisms for maintaining sterilizing medium uniformity.
(5) Chain speed recorder.
(6) Heat exchanger pressure differential monitor.
(7) Mercury-in-glass thermometer.

(b) Written records of such calibrations, checks, examinations, or inspections shall be maintained, as specified in Section 212.183.

Section 212.183—Equipment Calibration and Monitoring Logs

Written records of calibration and monitoring tests and readings performed shall be maintained for at least 2 years after the expiration date of each batch of drug product produced by the equipment.

(a) Calibration records shall include:

(1) A description of the equipment.
(2) The date the equipment was purchased.
(3) The operating limits of the equipment.
(4) The date, time, and type of each test.
(5) The results of each test.
(6) The signature of each person performing a test.

(b) Monitoring records shall include:

(1) A description of the equipment.
(2) The date the equipment was installed.
(3) The date the equipment was last calibrated, if appropriate.
(4) The operating limits of the equipment.
(5) The date and time of the recording.
(6) The reading.
(7) The signature of each person performing the monitoring.

(c) Corrective measures employed to bring the equipment into compliance with its operating specifications shall be:

(1) Recorded in the appropriate equipment log.
(2) Noted in the calibration and/or monitoring record.
(3) Immediately followed by testing to assure that the corrective measures were adequate to restore the required operating characteristics.

Section 212.192—Production Record Review

The review and approval of production and control records by the quality control unit shall extend to those records not directly related to the manufacture, processing, packing, or holding of a specific batch of large volume parenteral drug product but which have a bearing on the quality of batches being produced. Such indirectly related records shall include:

(a) Those dealing with equipment calibration or standardization.

B. Bureau of Medical Devices GMP Calibration Training

In the early 1980s, the Bureau of Medical Devices began GMP Training Programs for small device manufacturers as a means to improve understanding (and thus compliance) to regulations. That training was partically accomplished through a "draft" handout entitled "Calibration" (GMP Section 820.61), which stated:

General

Each medical device manufacturer must implement a calibration program that is at least as stringent as that required by the GMP. The intent of the GMP calibration requirements is to assure adequate measurement equipment performance, i.e., accuracy, precision, etc. The individual program decided upon can be as simple or as sophisticated as required for the measurements to be made. Some instruments need only be checked to see that their performance is within specified limits, while others may require calibration to a specification.

Quality Assurance should determine which measurements are necessary to assure that the finished product meets approved specifications, and make sure that the instruments used to make these measurements are included in the Calibration Program. When measurement equipment which is part of the calibration system, is located in the same areas as equipment which is not part of the system, the system equipment should be identified by label, tag, color code, etc., to ensure it is the only equipment used in determining compliance of a component or product with specifications. Equipment used only for monitoring (voltage or waveform exists, but exact value or shape not important) need not be calibrated, but it should be identified (e.g., for monitoring).

The GMP requires that equipment be calibrated according to *written procedures* and that these include specific directions and limits for accuracy and precision.

Accuracy is the measure of an instrument's capability to approach a true or absolute value. Since different manufacturers may have different accuracy requirements, each manufacturer must decide what accuracy is required for each measurement and provide equipment to achieve that accuracy. Proper calibration will assure that the selected equipment has the accuracy desired.

Precision has no unit of measure and only indicates a relative degree of repeatability. Repeatability is the result of resolution, and stability.

There are a number of sources where information can be obtained from which calibration procedures can be developed. Instrumentation manufacturers often include calibration procedures with their instruction manuals. While these procedures alone are not adequate to meet the GMP requirement, they can usually be used for the actual calibration process. In some cases voluntary standards exist (ASTM, ANSI, IEEE, etc.).

Information contained in calibration procedures should be adequate to enable qualified personnel to properly perform the calibrations. A typical equipment calibration procedures includes:

    Purpose and scope
    Frequency of calibration
    Equipment and standards required
    Preliminary examinations and operations
    Calibration process
    Remedial action when out of tolerance conditions are found
    Documentation requirements including data forms

Remedial action is required by the GMP. Remedial action includes not only recalibration but also an evaluation of the impact of out-of-tolerance measurement on product quality and appropriate corrective action.

Also covered in this document are the following:

    Personnel Requirements
    Documentation
    Calibration Schedules

Standards
Equipment Environment
Audit of the Calibration System
Contract Calibration
Integrating Measurements into the Quality Assurance System

Additionally, an overview of the Bureau of Medical Devices (BMD) position
on Calibration (Measurement Assurance and Medical Devices) is also included
in the program. This position paper is included as Appendix 4.

C. Analysis of FD-483 Observations

Form FD-483 is used by the FDA to document apparent observations of a
firm's failure to follow GMPs. Unfortunately, many firms may assess the
present adequacy of their Calibration Programs by the results of an FDA inspection. They view that by "passing" an inspection with no or minimal calibration observations, their program is sound.

In drawing conclusions from FDA inspections, it is important to keep in
mind that the major thrust of these inspections is to "audit against the firm's
own procedures." A particular firm may pass an inspection of their Calibration Program (even if their program is inadequate) because the FDA may not
be sufficiently knowledgeable of the product requirements or an individual
inspector may not be aware of what constitutes an appropriate Calibration
Program.

A better understanding of the adequacy of a firm's Calibration Program
can be gained by assessing one's own program from the perspective of:

The information that the FDA presents in their BMD Small Manufacturer's
Assistance Programs (Sec. IV, Sec. B).
Significant FD-483 observations of other firms (Sec. IV, Sec. D).
Analysis of FD-483 observations from an overall viewpoint similar to the
approach shown in Table 5. This type of approach can help to assess
those areas that may provide the greatest risks.

D. Pertinent FD-483 Observations

Past FD-483 observations can be used to assess Calibration Program require-
ments/measurement requirements for a specific type of manufacturer. The
following list of some pertinent FD-483 observations have been divided by
operational type. In addition, only those observations that have potential
far-reaching technical impact have been selected:

Manufacturing—Sterile Product Controls

. . . The firm lacks written procedures for in-process test methodologies and sample collections, such as in the case of pH measurements.
. . . The method of calibrating thermocouples was of questionable accuracy due to fluctuations in oil bath used as reference.
. . . The dry heat oven temperature recorder was calibrated at
about 187°F but its operating temperature is to be 320 to 325°F.
. . . The method currently in use for monitoring the temperature
of the refrigerator, which was used to store the biological indicator
spore suspension, is inadequate. The firm used a single thermometer which measured the air temperature.

TABLE 5   Analysis of 483 Observations from GMP Trends

Type of observation	Type of operation			
	Sterile products	Critical medical devices	Manufacturing controls	Laboratory controls
Not traceable (NBS or other)	2			
Standard not confirmed	2	1		
Critical instrument/ parameter not in calibration program	5	6	1	
No calibration procedures		1	1	1
No or inadequate calibration records		3	1	
Improper calibration	1			
No calibration program			1	
Noncalibration *negated* validation	1			
User-standardized instrument citation	1			
Calibrated at nonoptimal condition	1			
No listing of calibration program instruments		2		
Instrument not of sufficient accuracy or tolerances too great	3			
Calibration interval not followed			1	

FDA-483 citations addressing calibration items from September 1, 1980, to August 15, 1981. *GMP Trends* (bi-monthly newsletter that edits FDA-483 inspection observations and reports) have been extracted and analyzed. These observations have begun to show an increased sophistication on the part of FDA inspectors, and several specific observations have been included that might interest the reader.

. . . No established specifications for temperature tolerances or set point for interpreting qualification data, nor for a given time at desired temperature.

. . . The slit-to-agar air sampler was not sterilized prior to operation within the sterile areas and the exhaust of the vacuum pump did not have a bacterial retentive filter.

. . . Pressure switches on WFL tank number . . . were not tagged to show date of calibration, date of recalibration, accuracy of the instrument, signature of person who performed calibration as required by the firm's SOP.

. . . An improper calibration correction factor was applied to the HIAC Solution Particle Tester used for particulate measurement of sterile solution samples.

Manufacturing Controls

. . . The computer controlled automatic coating pans used in coating . . . tablets lack of a program for routine calibration and inspection to assure proper performance. In addition, there is no written documentation of the validation of this equipment.

. . . Departmental procedures for instrument calibration do not provide calibration methods or limits for all of the firm's instruments.

. . . The . . . scale used to monitor the average tablet weights in the tableting area was accurate to only 0.1 gm, while some tablet specifications call for an average weight such as 3.45–3.64 gm/10, an accuracy to 0.01 gm.

. . . That the floor scale . . . was being used to weigh bulk tablets to determine yield although it had been found to be in error during its last calibration on . . . and also during previous calibrations.

Laboratory Controls

. . . There were no written specifications on acceptable and *non-acceptable limits for weights used in checking calibrations*. There were no written procedures for frequency of checking these weights which were used in checking calibrations. Written instructions on corrective action to be taken if the weights used for checking calibrations were out of limits were not available.

. . . Few records were maintained at the . . . regarding maintenance and calibration of scientific equipment.

. . . There were no written SOPs or records in the microbiology section covering equipment maintenance and calibration.

. . . Review of laboratory records showed the results obtained from laboratory standard solutions of active ingredients prepared for ultraviolet spectra analysis of manufactured products are not reproducible. The absorbance values and concentration of the standard, in the same solvent, showed significant percentage differences when compared to other values of the same standard.

. . . Throughout the laboratory records reviewed, it was found that the lot numbers of the primary or secondary standard used in preparing the standard solutions were not recorded in any laboratory record. Therefore, there was no adequate history of what had been used to prepare the standard solutions.

. . . Limits of acceptance are frequently used which have not been validated.

Critical Medical Devices

. . . Written calibration schedules for the load cells, weight belt feeders, hygrometers, pressure flow transmitters, and temperature transmitters are set up to begin on the next calendar year and not from the date of initial calibration.

. . . Calibration of all mechanical, and electrical equipment is not conducted according to written procedures. Where possible, calibration is performed in accordance with the equipment manufacturer's technical manual. However, we observed some measurement equipment such as calipers, micrometers, balances, and oven are calibrated in the absence of written calibration procedures.

. . . We observed the lack of equipment calibration procedures to include specific limits for accuracy and precision. Additionally, we noted the lack of documented provisions for remedial action when accuracy and precision limits are not met.

. . . The . . . oven is equipped with a non-calibrated . . . thermometer providing the only means for manufacturing personnel to monitor temperature.

V. CERTIFICATION/CALIBRATION PROGRAM INTERFACE EXAMPLES

A. New Plant

In planning the certification of a new "grass roots" manufacturing facility (from a Calibration Program perspective), the first step is to establish confidence in the certification program measurements. There are three key general areas that must be included as initial targets for establishing measurement confidence:

1. Plant calibration program measurements (initial and ongoing)
2. Materials, support, and product testing measurements
3. Adequacy of instruments associated with the certification activity *and* the adequacy of the process measurement and control instruments associated with each particular product/process or system to be certified

1. *Plant Calibration Program Measurements*

Technical Component: The technical component of this concept is established by a thorough review and documentation of significant factors of the plant Calibration Program. This review will, of necessity, be phased since not all components of the system will be in place at the time review should begin (e.g., the adequacy of the standards ordered for the laboratory and the environmental design requirements should be reviewed long before calibration technician training is completed). Those components that should be reviewed can be taken from Table 1 in Sec. II.

In order to establish confidence in the measurement system, it is important to keep in mind that ongoing measurement confidence is established through the Calibration Program's ongoing systems (including audit of these systems).

Personal Credibility: While not considered a normal part of a certification program, the personal credibility of the Standards laboratory management and technicians/calibrators can expand a technically sound Calibration Program from a scheduled resource to a pervasive plant-wide component of a measurement assurance program for R&D areas as well as design and production.

2. *Materials, Support, and Product Testing Measurements*

Confidence in these measurements (and thus the measurements on which product validation judgments are made) relates to the (a) skills of the laboratory personnel making these tests, (b) adequacy (appropriate U_R) of the instruments making those measurements, and (c) whether those instruments are included in the new plant Calibration Program.

As was noted in the plant Calibration Program, measurement approach, phased review by qualified personnel is one way to establish confidence in test measurements. Instrument adequacy can be reviewed long before an assessment can be made on laboratory personnel skills or as to whether the test measurement instruments are included in the plant Calibration Program.

3. *Adequacy of Certification and Process Measurement/Control Instruments*

The ability of operating personnel to use the measurement and control instruments, the adequacy (U_R) of the instruments themselves, and whether they are calibrated before use and/or are on the plant Calibration Program are again key factors. Phasing of this activity is usually synchronized with a specific process or product certification activity.

Appendix 5, "Calibration Program Certification Checklist," can be used as a guide in establishing a new plant certification/Calibration Program activity.

B. New Process in an Existing Plant

If an effective audit program exists and effective change control procedures also exist for previously reviewed measurement assurance and support/testing measurement activities, it will not be necessary to completely reassess those aspects identified in Section V, Sections A.1 and A.2 of this section. New process measurement requirements and new instruments, however, should cause a review of those portions of these sections that they may affect.

VI. MEASUREMENT ADEQUACY RISK ASSOCIATED WITH SOME CERTIFICATION PROGRAMS

This section addresses certification program risk from two aspects, instrument adequacy and operation at specific limits. Recommendations are then made as to how that risk can be decreased.

A. Instrument Adequacy

1. *Uncertainty Ratio Perspective*

As described earlier, adequacy deals with the relative relationship (U_R) between the instrument accuracy and the use of the instrument. Since adequacy does not connote a precise condition, it is often necessary that we

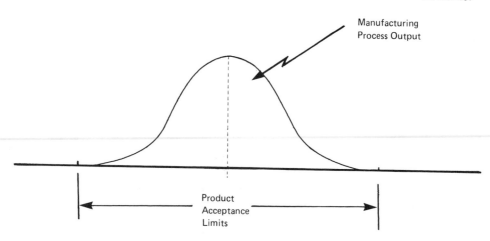

FIGURE 5   Manufacturing process output variability.

deal with some firmer concepts than a rule of thumb $1/4$ U_R when considering a specific application.   The following examples depict conditions of adequacy and inadequacy.

Figure 5 represents the output of a manufacturing process, and the acceptance limits for product manufactured by that process.

Figure 6 represents the measurement variability of an instrument that accepts/rejects product.

The actual measurement of product with characteristic "A" is represented by Figure 7.   The representation indicates that there is virtually no likelihood of rejecting product with characteristic "A" when the measurement instrument is operating properly.

Figure 8 represents measurement of characteristic "A" by a less accurate instrument.   In this situation, the probability of rejecting material with characteristic "A" is shown by the darkened area within the instrument's distribution representation.   For the conditions of this example, that probability is about .05 (or about 5%).   This would be representative of an inadequate

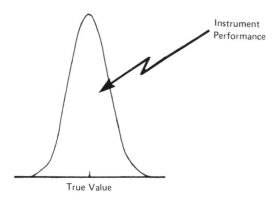

FIGURE 6   Measurement system variability.

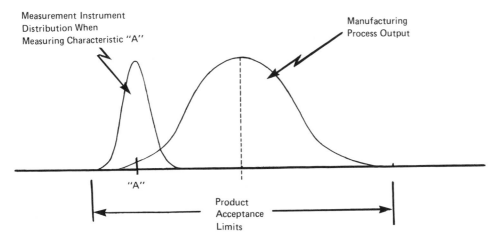

FIGURE 7 A process measurement made by an "adequate" instrument.

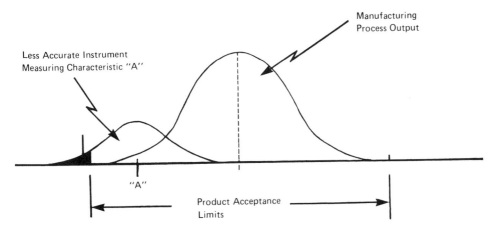

FIGURE 8 A process measurement made by an "inadequate" instrument.

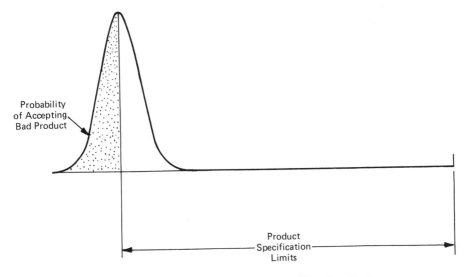

FIGURE 9 Measurement variability at the specification limit.

instrument. In this example, we are rejecting product because of a need-
lessly inaccurate instrument.

As a general rule, adequacy should be addressed from two perspectives:

1. *Economic perspective*: Will the more accurate instrument allow us to
   increase the firm's profitability (considering instrument, recalibration,
   procedure writing, and training cost compared to lower rejects of good
   product/improved quality)?
2. *Risk perspective*: Will there be an unacceptable risk of producing
   harmful product, damaging company reputation, or operating in an
   unsafe condition because of insufficient instrument accuracy?

Since these perspectives are difficult to address for each specific instrument
application, the general 1/4 rule ratio should be used, along with a clear
understanding of the differences between specification limits (go/no-go limits)
and operating limits. For applications involving risk perspectives, even
higher uncertainty ratios may be warranted (unless the specifications have
already been tightened to reflect the risk concerns). These situations are
addressed in Section VI, Section B.

B. Specification Limits

If a measurement instrument performs acceptance measurements at the go/no-
go specification limit of a product or process, the instrument will indicate an
erroneous decision about 50% of the time. This risk condition is shown in
Figure 9.

In order to minimize the possibility of erroneous decisions, it is often desirable to establish operating limits that are different (more restrictive) than
the specification limits. An example follows.

1. A Risk Example

In order to assess this risk example, we must first begin with some basic
assumptions that, unfortunately, are not usually true:

Assumption 1. We are aware of the actual product specification levels that
will cause product problems or poor quality.
Assumption 2. The process operates at some level between these product
problem bounds.
Assumption 3. The accuracy characteristics of our instrument are known.
Assumption 4. We have production instrument records that allow us to
determine which instruments we used to make which products.

For our example, we will consider a single measurement made by an instrument as representing only one reading from its distribution of potential accuracy readings. This condition is indicated in Figure 10.

By establishing (and clearly defining) target operating levels different
from the go/no-go specification limits, rational decisions on product measurement risk can then be made. Figure 11 indicates one potential relationship
between operating levels and go/no-go specification limits.

When the instrument is functioning properly and the process is operating
within its normal operating range, we would expect a normal "worst-case" condition at the lower operating level as shown in Figure 12.

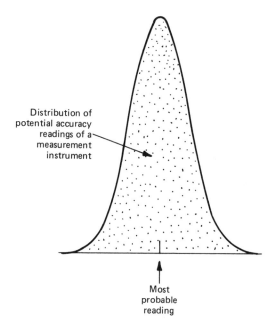

FIGURE 10   Most probable instrument measurement.

As an example, consider a condition where a ±0.1 accuracy (±2 s) measurement instrument is found to be reading 2.5 standard deviations high while measuring at the lower operating limit (a bias of +0.25* with no other instrument system inaccuracy observed). We could then envision the condition shown in Figure 13.

Statistical quantification of the risk can be made by using areas under the normal curve, as shown in Fig. 14 and in the sample calculation:

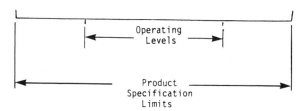

FIGURE 11   Typical production specification limits and operating levels.

---

*All measurements would be +0.25 unit higher than the most probable "correct" value. We would thus have to subtract 0.25 unit from the production instrument records.

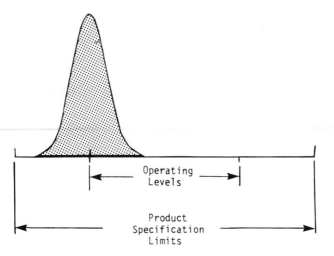

FIGURE 12   Instrument operating properly at lower operating levels.

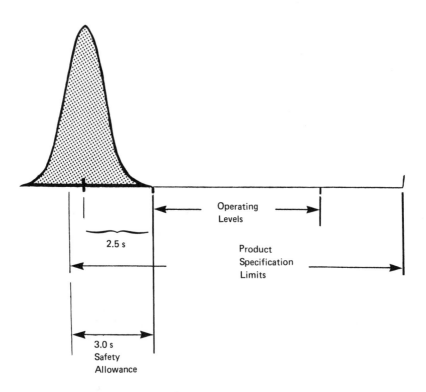

FIGURE 13   Measurement distribution of an instrument reading 2.5 s high
when operating at the lower operating level.

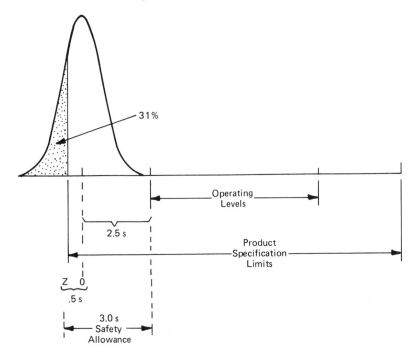

FIGURE 14   Probability of rejecting good product made at the lower operating level (or accepting bad product made at the upper product specification limit).

Sample risk calculation: Fraction of the area under the normal curve between 0 and 0.5 s (Z) = 0.19 (19%).   Fraction of the area smaller than Z =
0.50 − 0.19 = 0.31 (31%).

By knowing (and using) the "real" go/no-go specification limits and separately establishing operating levels that allow for

Process measurement distribution characteristics
Instrument variability
Actual instrument out-of-tolerance conditions

a measurement and product assurance system can be established based on
quantifiable risks.   A brief description of such as system is contained in [7].
A more detailed description is contained in Chapters 8 and 9 of [1].

VII.   CONCLUSION

This chapter has identified the dependency of the certification program on
the existence of a comprehensive Calibration Program.

With further consideration, one can realize that validation approaches
based on the use of historical data are equally dependent on the existence of
many aspects (instrument adequacy, scheduled recalibration, documentation,
calibration procedures, etc.) of a comprehensive Calibration Program during
the period for which historical data is being evaluated.   If this is not the
case, there is no assurance of the validity of the proposed retrospective
certification data.

APPENDIX 1: VALIDATION OF OUTSIDE CALIBRATION SERVICES*

One of the most frequent calibration concerns that has been identified to me by personnel from small firms/plants is the adequacy of the calibrations performed by outside contractors. Some of the comments that were expressed to me are

> I don't know if their standards or their instrument calibrations are traceable.
> They don't send the data.
> I'm not satisfied that their personnel are trained, especially with respect to GMP training.
> I can't obtain a copy of their instrument calibration procedures.
> They don't follow my internal Calibration Program procedures.
> Their approach is to adjust instruments rather than calibrate them and they don't recognize the difference.
> They want too much money to send as-found data, etc.
> My documentation is weak when I use outside services.
> Outside services are better able to perform electrical and lineal calibrations than those related to my needs.

These types of difficulties, and the apparently overwhelming task of a small firm/plant to instill an appropriate quality commitment into an outside calibration organization with many clients (who have not addressed this commitment), has caused many small plants to abrogate their responsibilities in this area. This responsibility was recently emphasized in the *GMP Newsletter*, where the FDA responded to a question:

The Question: We have our measurement equipment calibrated by an outside lab. The lab gives us certification that the calibration was conducted and that the standards are traceable to NBS. Is that adequate documentation for the FDA inspector?

The Answer: FDA says yes—you need, however, to get data showing the accuracy of the equipment before and after calibration and the conditions under which it was calibrated. The lab should notify you if the equipment is out-of-calibration when they receive it, so you can decide whether remedial action, such as retesting or recall, is called for. You should also keep the calibration records and schedule. Since the lab is an extension of your own quality assurance program, you should audit its procedures, if possible, as part of your own quality audit.

It is my belief that there are many responsible outside calibration organizations that can meet the calibration needs of our specific industries. During the next year my firm, Calibration & Consulting Services, Inc. (C&CSI), will attempt to determine whether we can creditably evaluate (and validate periodically) some of these outside services (for specific measurement parameters).

APPENDIX 2: WHAT IS A CALIBRATION PROGRAM INSTRUMENT?*

What do you think about when it is necessary to determine which "measurement" instruments will be included in your Calibration Program?

---

*Excerpted from [4].

Let us help a little in that determination. *Webster's New World Diction-*
ary defines an instrument (from a measurement context) as "A tool or implement, especially one used for delicate work or for scientific or artistic
purposes," and "any of various devices for indicating or measuring conditions, performance, position, direction, etc., or something for controlling
operations, especially in aircraft or rocket flight."

In 1978 the Food and Drug Administration also helped in that definition
when Title 21, Food and Drugs Section, Human and Veterinary Drugs
Current Good Manufacturing Practice in Manufacturing, Processing, Packing or Holding (Drug GMP) was issued. Specifically:

211.68 Automatic, Mechanical, and Electronic Equipment

   (a)   Automatic, mechanical, or electronic equipment or other types
         of equipment, including computers or related systems that will
         perform a function satisfactorily, may be used in the manufac-
         ture, processing, packing, and holding of a drug product. If
         such equipment is so used, it shall be routinely calibrated, in-
         spected, or checked according to a written program designed
         to assure proper performance. Written records of those cali-
         bration checks and inspections shall be maintained.

In addition, comments 183, 191, and 192 of the Preamble to that document
gives us some further insight:

Equipment Calibration

   183   One comment requested that proposed 211.2(a) be modified to per-
         mit use of equipment other than types listed. One comment argued
         that the use of computers should be allowed. Several comments
         suggested deletion of the word "precision" since it is superfluous
         and redundant.
         "The intent of this paragraph is to allow the use of any equip-
         ment that will perform a function satisfactorily in accordance with
         the requirements in Part 211. The Commissioner is, therefore,
         revising this paragraph in the final regulation (now 211.68Aa) to
         permit the use of any automatic, mechanical, electronic, or other
         types of equipment, including computers or related systems, that
         will achieve this goal. Use of modifying word "precision" is not
         necessary because the paragraph requires that any equipment
         perform a function satisfactorily."

   191   A comment said the intent of 211.68(a) is not clear as to the use
         and type of equipment that is applicable. The comment further
         said precision equipment that has no effect on the drug product
         quality should be exempted from written program requirements.
         "The paragraph refers to equipment which is used in the manu-
         facture, processing, packing, and holding of drugs and may,
         therefore, have an effect on drug product quality. No examples
         of equipment which did not have an effect on drug product quality
         were offered."

   192   A comment requested that the term "precision automatic equipment" be
         defined. The respondent said it could, for example, include tablet

counters and liquid fillers which are checked on a routine in-process basis where there is no need for routine calibration or inspection.

"The Commissioner believes that tablet counters and liquid fillers are examples of precision automatic equipment. When routine in-process checks are made, regardless of the time interval, such checks should be performed according to prescribed procedures and records kept in accordance with the requirements of this paragraph.

In most cases the inclusion/exclusion determination with respect to potential Calibration Program instruments is clear.

Some examples of instruments falling in the "excluded" category include:

1. A pressure gauge on a steam line to a reactor when product parameters are controlled by other instruments (such as a temperature controller with a well-agitated vessel). The pressure gauge, in this case, simply tells us if there is steam available.
2. A temperature measurement of the discharge of cooling water from a heat exchanger when the temperature is used only occasionally for heat balance calculations.
3. A thermostat in an office area.
4. A thermostat in a production area when temperature, within reasonable ranges, has no product effect.

	Determination	
Measurement instrument used to	Include	Exclude
Measure final product quality	X	
Control product quality	X	
Certify product/equipment	X	
Control environment that could impact product quality or test results (e.g., incubators, stability areas, "required" controlled environment storage)	X	
Generate IND, NDA, etc., data	X	
Make measurements under GMP applications	X	
Calibrate or control any of the above, or, if included in your Calibration Program scope	X	
Measure pollutant levels, exposure levels	X	
Measure/control energy use levels where economics may dictate Calibration Program discipline (air leaving cooling coil in air handling unit)	X	
Develop new products (research and pilot plant)	X	
All others		X

There are some decisions, however, that should require some in-depth considerations by measurement-sensitive personnel. A sampling of just a few that should lead to an inclusion decision includes:

1. Thermostats/humidistats in rooms where humidity or temperature affect the test, but no one asks you to consider whether the room instruments should be on the program. One such example would be the environmental recording/controlling instruments on an Instron (plastic test) room where, in some cases, test results are directly affected by room humidity/temperature changes.

2. An incoming testing area for chemicals or plastics where particle size (as measured by screening) is important. "Standard gauge" screen sizes used to assess these materials should be initially checked (calibrated) upon receipt and rechecked periodically to determine if abuse/use have changed their characteristics.

3. The "standards" used to adjust/standardize pH meters, user-checked scales and balances, etc.

4. The process temperature/pressure/etc. switch that actually controls a pressure, a temperature, or starts to time a cycle. In some cases, the process switches within ethylene oxide control panels are actually the instruments whose accuracy determines length of cycle and ethylene oxide pressure.

5. Fill volume control may depend on the relative accuracy/precision of the volumetric cylinder used initially to set up (and periodically assess) the filler. Have we at least initially confirmed that the volumetric cylinder, when new, was within specification requirements or if, in fact, its accuracy was even specified?

Involving personnel in the inclusion/exclusion decision who have an understanding of the measurement and manufacturing/testing processes is the way to ensure that an appropriate decision is made. This is best accomplished by including personnel with a wide array of job responsibilities in your Calibration Program.

APPENDIX 3: PROCESS TEMPERATURE DISTRIBUTION IMPACT ON INSTRUMENT ACCURACY REQUIREMENTS*

It is often necessary to consider process distribution variations in order to appropriately select or analyze a measurement instrument. Many examples where distribution should be considered relate to regulatory requirements.

A. Incubators Associated with the USP Sterility Test

Incubation temperature requirements associated with USP Sterility Testing for Soybein-Casein Digest Medium call for a 20–25°C range.† Most people interpret this range as meaning that the incubated material (not necessarily the air temperature in the incubator) in the room shall not be below 20.0°C or above 25.0°C.

---

*Excerpted from [5].

†Other media have other temperature requirements.

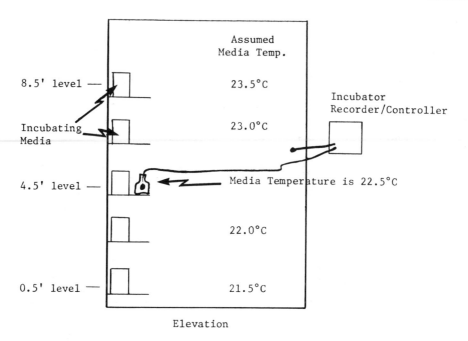

FIGURE 15   Hypothetical 20−25°C incubator stored media temperature distribution.

Most incubator rooms do not make use of internal air recirculation fans to distribute air (which would tend to equalize temperature) and thus experience temperature variation/stratification. This temperature variation can be significant—for the following example, the variation is assumed to be ±0.5°C for each 2 ft of elevation difference. Actual certification of the incubator room should address the actual temperature variations in the room.

Consider the example of Figure 15. While all incubated material must be at 22.5 ±2.5°C (20−25°C), ±1.0°C of this allowed variability is removed because of the temperature distribution inherent in the room. Thus, the actual allowed operating range of the media temperature recorder* (which will satisfy the temperature requirements of all the media in the incubator) is 22.5 ±1.5°C.

The instrument selected to record and control this incubator would have a recommended uncertainty ratio of 1/4.

$$U_R = \frac{\text{instrument accuracy}}{\text{process requirement}}$$

$$1/4 = \frac{\text{instrument accuracy}}{\pm 1.5°C}$$

instrument accuracy = ±0.375°C

---

*The incubator recorder controller average air reading with the door closed should also be 22.5 ±1.5°C, although the air temperature reading may fluctuate to as high as 24.5°C or as low as 20.5°C.

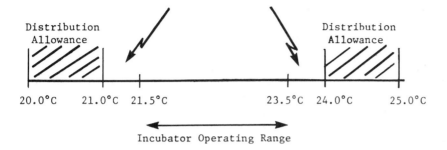

FIGURE 16   Process and instrument inaccuracy allowances.

Assumption: While the media temperatures are stabilized at their assumed values, the incubator recorder/controller (which measures air temperature) records an average air temperature of 22.5°C but cycles between 22.0 and 23.0°C with the door closed.

Recommendations

1. A 1% accuracy instrument with a span of 30°C (say, 10–40°C range) would meet the instrument accuracy requirement-instrument tolerance (±2 s accuracy ±0.3°C).
2. The temperature should be set such that the recorder operating limits are between 21.5 and 23.5°C.
3. Instrument 'Out-of-Tolerance' *allowances* and inaccuracy should be set at ±0.5°C. Thus, if the recorder indicates operation between 21.5 and 23.5°C, an 'out-of-tolerance' review is not made unless the instrument is more than +0.5°C out of tolerance.

Figure 16 graphically describes the incubator recommendations.

Some other examples where measurement instrument analysis should consider process variability include:

1. Temperature distribution in an ethylene oxide autoclave
2. Temperature and humidity in a prehumidification room
3. Temperature in an autoclave
4. Temperature and humidity variation between the sensor location and the product exposure areas for low-humidity tableting/powder filling
5. Temperature in an ultrasonic bath
6. Temperature in a mold or heating platen
7. Temperature in cold-room storage
8. Temperature in a stability room
9. Temperature in a water bath

As previously noted, for critical process control/measurement operations, a distribution study should be completed after instrument (and facility) start-up to confirm the initial judgments and estimates made in instrument selection.

APPENDIX 4: MEASUREMENT ASSURANCE AND MEDICAL DEVICES

The medical device GMP regulation describes Good Manufacturing Practices for methods used in, and the facilities and controls used for, the manufacture, packing, storage, and installation of all finished medical devices intended for human use. The regulation is intended to assure that such devices will be safe and effective, and in compliance with the Federal Food, Drug, and Cosmetic Act.

The medical device GMP equipment requirements are based on MIL-STD-45662 and were written to assure that production and quality assurance measurement equipment (mechanical, electronic, automated) used in the manufacture of medical devices is suitable for its intended use. The GMP requires:

> Routine calibration according to written procedures
> Documentation of the calibration of each piece of equipment requiring calibration
> Documented validation of the software programs used in automated production or quality assurance equipment
> Specification of accuracy and precision limits
> Provisions for remedial action to in-process or finished devices
> Training of calibration personnel
> Use of standards traceable to NBS, or other recognizable standards

Although not listed here, the GMPs also include requirements for equipment maintenance.

In March 1980, the BMD did an evaluation of 807 medical device GMP inspections accomplished from February 1, 1979, to September 30, 1979. The BMD found that approximately 60% of the manufacturers were in compliance with the calibration requirements of the GMP. The major calibration deficiencies were a lack of written calibration procedures and documentation of calibration.

Many manufacturers and laboratories utilize contract calibration labs to calibrate their measurement and test equipment. When this method is used, the FDA views the contract laboratory as an extension of the manufacturer's quality assurance program. Normally the FDA would not inspect a contractor's facilities, but we would expect the manufacturer or nonclinical lab to audit the contractor to verify that proper procedures are being used. If problems occurred due to inadequate calibration procedures and the FDA needed to determine where the problems existed, the FDA could visit the contractor. Either the contractor or the manufacturers might be held responsible for inadequate procedures leading to a defective, unsafe device or false data. Generally, the manufacturer of the device is responsible for assuring that the device is manufactured under acceptable GMPs.

When a medical device manufacturer utilizes a contractor, the FDA expects the manufacturer to provide evidence that the equipment was calibrated according to GMP requirements. The manufacturer can do this by:

> Requiring and receiving certification that the equipment was calibrated under controlled conditions using traceable standards. Certification should include accuracy of equipment when received by the lab (to facilitate remedial action if necessary), accuracy after calibration by the lab, standards used, and environmental conditions under which calibrated. Certification should be signed and dated by a responsible individual.
> Maintaining an adequate calibration schedule.
> Maintaining records of calibration.
> Periodically auditing the contractor to assure that appropriate and adequate GMP procedures are being followed.

The contractor should have in place the applicable controls called for in the GMP regulation. For example, the contractor should have:

Written calibration procedures
Records of calibration
Trained calibration personnel
Standards traceable to NBS, or other independent reproducible standards

The device manufacturer must meet the GMP requirements; the contractor should also comply with the applicable requirements, so that the manufacturer may fully comply.

APPENDIX 5: CALIBRATION PROGRAM CERTIFICATION CHECKLIST

At least three separate groupings of measurement and control instruments have a direct bearing on certification validity: (a) laboratory support and product test instruments, (b) qualification/validation measurement instruments, and (c) process control instruments. In addition to these measurement instruments, initial and ongoing certification validity depends on the adequacy of the standards, the Standards laboratory, and the Calibration Program. This appendix identifies, in a chronological implementation framework, many of the instrument aspects that should be addressed in a process certification program in order to assure system integrity.

Phase I. Support facility and equipment qualification and certification

A. Standards laboratory

1. Is the laboratory appropriate (cleanliness, temperature, humidity, etc.) to meet environmental requirements of the standards and test equipment?
2. Is space sufficient for segregation of instrument activities and access to instruments?
3. Are laboratory personnel qualified for their specific activities; are they knowledgeable about GMP requirements, are they motivated to accuracy, and is their training documented?
4. Are there systems in place (including an audit-type function*) to assure the ongoing adequacy of the laboratory and standards system? These systems should include a documentation system.
5. Is the laboratory management appropriately trained, and is that training documented?

---

*An appropriate audit system may allow a one-time certification of the Standards laboratory, standards, and Calibration Program. Future certifications could then be based on confirmation of the certification status by the audit function.

B. Standards and transfer standards

1. Are the standards (and transfer standards as necessary) of suffi-
    cient accuracy to meet process control/test equipment needs
    (e.g., uncertainty ratios of 1/4 or smaller*).
2. Are the instruments in an appropriate calibration status, and are
    they so labeled?
3. Are the transfer standards (or standards, if necessary) appro-
    priate for field calibration? *Note*: Will these instruments be
    affected by field environment?
4. Are the standards traceable to a recognized accurate source (such
    as the NBS), and is the uncertainty ratio to that source 1/4 or
    smaller (e.g., 1/5, etc.)?
5. Is there demonstrated stability of the standards and/or a cross-
    check mechanism that assures their ongoing measurement accuracy?
6. Are manufacturers' maintenance/troubleshooting manuals and
    critical spare parts available?

C. Calibration Program

1. Are there written instrument calibration procedures for all instru-
    ments on the Calibration Program that will be used in certification
    activity?
2. Are instrument calibration technicians appropriately trained, and
    is that training documented?
3. Are there systems in place (scheduling, deliquency and in-toler-
    ance reporting, analysis of out-of-tolerances from a product and
    instrument systems viewpoint, training, audit, etc.)?

Phase II. Instrument qualification

A. Laboratory support and product test instruments

1. Are measurement instrument uncertainty ratios 1/4 or smaller?

$$\frac{\pm \text{ accuracy capability of the measurement instrument}}{\pm \text{ tolerance on product measurement}}$$

and

$$\frac{\pm \text{ standards accuracy or } \pm \text{ transfer standard accuracy}}{\pm \text{ accuracy capability of the measurement instrument}}$$

2. Does an appropriately controlled Calibration Program exist?
3. Have the instruments exhibited reliable past performance?
4. Is the environment adequate to meet accuracy needs of the
    measurement equipment?

B. Qualification/validation measurement instruments (the instruments
    that are not a usual part of the ongoing process control or product
    test instruments)

$$*\frac{\pm \text{ accuracy capability of standards/transfer standards}}{\pm \text{ accuracy capability of measurement instruments}}$$

1. Are uncertainty ratios 1/4 or smaller? See Phase II, Section A.
2. Is the instrument calibrated in an environment that will not affect the instrument's accuracy readings?
3. Is the installation appropriate (instrument, sensor, lead wires, etc.)?
4. Does an appropriately controlled Calibration Program exist?
5. Have the instruments exhibited reliable past performance?
6. Are manufacturer's maintenance/troubleshooting manuals and critical spare parts available?

C. Process control instruments (those instruments associated with the process on an ongoing basis)

1. The same considerations that apply to Phase II, Section B, apply to these instruments.
2. Are the user and maintenance personnel aware that these instruments are on the Calibration Program, and do they understand their responsibilities with respect to these instruments?

Phase III. Process qualification/validation phase

A. Qualification/validation measurement instruments

1. Calibrate in use environment before each validation run*
2. Calibrate in use environment after each validation run*

B. Process control instruments

1. Same program as Phase III, Section A.

Phase IV. Process certification

1. Documentation of Phase I, Phase II, and Phase III activity.
2. Documentation that there is a change control system.
3. Sign-off.

Phase V. Recertification

1. Documentation that the change control system is functioning properly.
2. Pre-post-run calibration documentation.
3. Sign-off.

---

*Calibrating before and after each run is an economic decision based on length of run, time between runs, stability of instruments, and costs of repeating runs if the instrument is subsequently found to be out-of-tolerance.

APPENDIX 6: TYPICAL CERTIFICATION SYSTEM FORMS

Page _____ of _____

Instrumentation System Certification

Process or product_____   /____/ Initial certification

Date _____   /____/ Recertification

Certification engineer _____

The following instruments are associated with this process or products or
with the certification of same.

Instrument number	Type instrument	Specific use	Included in calibration program?	Data on Adequacy (Pg)	Calib. (Pg)

Calibration Review for Instruments on the Calibration Program or Involved with Certification

Inst. number	Initial calibration date	Date of validation tests	Subsequent calibration date	Condition found (in or out of tolerance)	Date standard calibrated	Remarks

Certification Engineer _____

Date _____

Adequacy Review for Instruments on the Calibration Program or Involved with Certification

Inst. number	Inst. range	Est. inst. accur. (± 2 s)	Process/ product range	Process/product $\pm$ spec. limits	U_R (± 2 s inst./$\pm$ tol. prod.)	Assoc. std. no.	Std. ± 2 s accuracy	Std. U_R (± 2 s std./ ± 2 s inst.)	Remarks

Certification Engineer _____

Date _____

90

REFERENCES

1. Bremmer, R. E. 1983. *A Systems Approach to an Effective Calibration Program*. Calibration and Consulting Services, Inc., Des Plaines, Ill.
2. Instrument Society of America. Recommended Practice RP 55.1, Hardware testing of digital process computers.
3. Bremmer, R. E. 1981. You can't inspect quality into test, measurement and control equipment. 1981 Pharm. Tech. Conf., September 22–24.
4. Bremmer, R. E. 1982. *Calibration Newsletter 3*:1.
5. Bremmer, R. E. 1980. *Calibration Q. 13.*
6. Bremmer, R. E. 1982. *Calibration Q. 14.*
7. Bremmer, R. E. 1982. Establishing an effective calibration program. *Medical Device and Diagnostic Magazine*, May.

5
Design, Installation, and Calibration of Thermocouple Measuring Systems

CLARENCE A. KEMPER

Kaye Instruments, Inc., Bedford, Massachusetts

I. INTRODUCTION

The purpose of calibrating any measuring instrument is to assure that it will indicate the correct value of the property being measured. For a self-contained temperature sensor, such as a liquid-in-glass thermometer, calibration can be defined as the process of determining correction factors for the sensor by comparing its indicated output to that of an accepted standard when both are at the same temperature. Verification of proper operation may be accomplished by checking a single point, but calibration must be done at two or more points.

A thermocouple is a simple, reliable, and versatile temperature sensor constructed by joining two wires of different composition to form a "thermocouple junction." When a thermocouple is connected to a well-designed reference and measuring system, the indicated output is a unique function of the junction temperature. It will be shown that the total output of a thermocouple circuit is not just a sensor characteristic, however, so the entire measuring system must be considered in a proper calibration procedure.

The discussions of this chapter will address the broader issue of assuring that the indicated value of temperature is an accurate representation of the value being measured. Although many of the basic considerations apply to any temperature sensor, only thermocouples will be discussed in detail. Thermocouples are the most satisfactory sensors for conducting heat penetration and temperature distribution studies in validation, while resistance temperature detectors (RTDs) are the most satisfactory transfer standards for temperature calibration. Some of the reasons for selecting those sensors will be discussed in conjunction with overall system calibration and accuracy.

Temperature is the most frequently measured property in industrial processes, and thermocouples are the most frequently used sensors when temperature is to be recorded or controlled. The primary reasons for selecting thermocouples are that they are more reliable and less expensive than other temperature sensors having an electrical output. Other excellent reasons for using thermocouples in the measurement of temperatures are that RTDs or thermistors are inherently less repeatable and less inter-changeable.

The inaccuracies in most thermocouple systems do not occur in the sensors; they occur in the instrumentation used to measure the outputs and in the circuitry connecting the thermocouple sensors to the measuring systems. A simplified explanation of thermoelectric theory is included in this chapter as a guide to proper installation of thermocouple circuits. By understanding the source of thermoelectric output, it is easier to avoid the mistakes most often encountered in the use of thermocouples, thereby assuring better measurement accuracy.

II. THERMOELECTRIC THEORY

During the 160 years since T. J. Seebeck discovered that current flows in a circuit of two dissimilar conductors whenever the junctions of the conductors are at different temperatures, many investigators have developed theories to explain thermoelectric phenomena. Some, such as Thomson and Bridgman, have based their explanations on thermodynamic considerations; others, such as Mott and Jones, have employed the electron theory of solids [1,2]. The following explanation of thermoelectric phenomena might be objectionable to both thermodynamicists and atomic physicists, but it is a concept that can be understood easily and employed to avoid many of the errors encountered in thermocouple circuits.

1. The energy level of an electron in any conductor increases as the temperature of the conductor increases.
2. The amount of energy change for a given temperature change depends on the composition and molecular structure of the conductor.

The material property that expresses the amount of energy increase for a given temperature increase is called the thermoelectric power. The value of thermoelectric power is given in units of microvolts of energy increase for each degree Celsius of temperature increase in the material.

Figure 1 depicts a simple thermocouple circuit consisting of two external conductors, A and B, which are connected at a junction where the temperature is T_2. For simplicity, it is assumed that the entire circuit of the voltage-measuring device is at a uniform temperature, T_1. It will be shown that under this assumption the net thermoelectric potential difference is generated only in the external circuit. If the temperature of the voltage measuring device is equal to T_1 throughout, the two terminals to which the conductors A and B are connected must also be at the temperature T_1.

The lower portion of Figure 1 gives a graphical representation of the thermoelectric potential of the circuit shown in the upper position. The horizontal ordinate is the temperature at a given location in the circuit and the vertical ordinate is the corresponding electrical potential at that location. Since the thermoelectric power is the amount of energy increase for a given temperature increase, the slope of each line is equal to the thermoelectric power of that conductor. If the thermoelectric powers are different, the slopes of the two lines will be different. Since the potential at the junction where the two conductors are joined together must have a singular value,

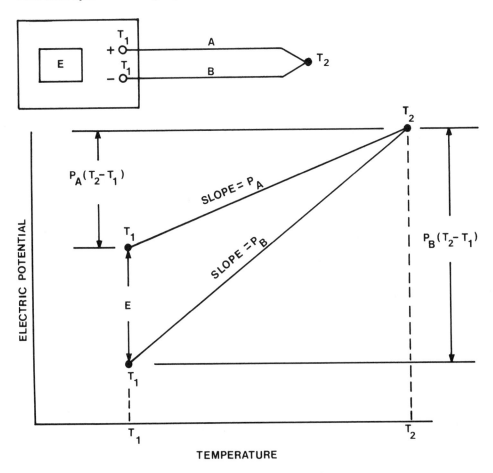

FIGURE 1   Basic thermocouple.

Figure 1 shows that there will be a net potential difference between the two terminals of the voltage-measuring device.

Consider the energy levels of the electrons in the conductors as the circuit is traversed in a clockwise direction starting at the terminal where material A is connected to the voltage-measuring device. Assuming that the temperature T_2 is greater than the temperature T_1, the energy level of the electrons in material A will increase as the junction with material B is approached because the temperature of the material is increasing. Assuming that the thermoelectric power of the conductor is constant, the amount by which the energy increases is equal to the thermoelectric power of material A, P_A, multiplied by the change in temperature, $(T_2 - T_1)$. As the circuit is traversed from the junction of the two conductors to the terminal where material B is connected to the voltage-measuring device, the energy level of the electrons will decrease by an amount equal to thermoelectric power of material B, P_B, multiplied by the change in temperature, $(T_1 - T_2)$.

In this example, the thermoelectric power of material B is greater than that of material A, so the change of energy level in B will be greater than that in A for the same change in temperature. This simple circuit illustrates a characteristic of thermocouple materials that causes some confusion. When the temperature of the external junction is greater than that of the junctions at the voltage-measuring device, the material having the greater thermoelectric power will be the negative lead. Since material B is assumed to have the greater thermoelectric power in the following examples, the terminal to which it is connected will be the negative terminal. The circuit summations are expressed starting at the terminal to which material B is connected and traversing the circuit in a counterclockwise direction in order to yield a positive potential difference.

If P is the thermoelectric power and T is the temperature at any location in the circuit, the "gradient" explanation of thermoelectric output states that the net potential generated by the circuit is equal to the cyclic integral of the product of the thermoelectric power and the differential change of temperature [3,4]. That statement is expressed mathematically by Eq. (1), in which E is the net electric potential difference generated by the circuit:

$$E = \oint P \, dT \tag{1}$$

Although the thermoelectric powers of all conductors change slightly with a change in temperature, for the purposes of this discussion the thermoelectric powers are assumed to be constant within any length of homogeneous conductor. In reality, the lines in Figure 1 would be curved slightly, rather than being straight as they are when it is assumed that each homogeneous conductor has a constant thermoelectric power. If the internal circuits of the measuring instrument are uniform in temperature and the thermoelectric power of each conductor is a constant, the integral of Eq. (1) can be evaluated by Eqs. (2) and (3), where P_A is the thermoelectric power of conductor A, P_B is that of conductor B, and P_I is that of the internal circuit.

Equation (2) represents the "conductor" explanation of thermocouple output, which states that the net electrical potential difference generated by each conductor in the circuit is equal to the thermoelectric power of the conductor multiplied by the temperature difference between the ends of the conductor. The net electrical potential difference generated by the total circuit is equal to the sum of the differences of each conductor. The "conductor" explanation is a simplified form of the "gradient" explanation.

$$E = P_B(T_2 - T_1) + P_A(T_1 - T_2) + P_I(T_1 - T_1) \tag{2}$$

It is obvious that the last term in Eq. (2) is zero and the contribution of the internal circuit is zero if the temperature is uniform. The net output of the entire circuit under these assumptions is given by Eq. (3):

$$E = P_B(T_2 - T_1) + P_A(T_1 - T_2) \tag{3}$$

An alternative to the "gradient" or "conductor" explanation of thermoelectric output is the "junction" explanation [1,2]. It states that the electrical output of each junction of two conductors is equal to the product of the temperature of the junction and the difference between the thermoelectric powers of the two conductors. The net electrical potential difference generated by the total circuit is equal to the sum of the outputs of all junctions in the circuit. Equation (4) is the mathematical expression of the "junction" explanation for the circuit of Figure 1:

$$E = T_1(P_I - P_B) + T_2(P_B - P_A) + T_1(P_A - P_I) \qquad (4)$$

It is not quite as obvious in Eq. (4) that the contribution of the internal circuit is zero, but the two terms containing P_I do cancel and the other terms may be rearranged to yield Eq. (5). It is also not obvious that the substraction of the thermoelectric powers at each junction must be performed in a direction consistent with cyclic integration. Thus, the difference of thermoelectric powers in the second term in Eq. (5) is the negative of that in the first term. This requirement is often confusing to the inexperienced investigator applying the "junction" explanation.

$$E = T_2(P_B - P_A) + T_1(P_A - P_B) \qquad (5)$$

Both Eq. (3) and Eq. (5) may be rewritten to yield Eq. (6), showing that, for this simple circuit of homogeneous conductors having constant thermoelectric powers, the output predicted by either explanation is the same. It is equal to the difference of thermoelectric powers of the two conductors multiplied by the difference between the temperatures at their junctions.

$$E = (P_B - P_A)(T_2 - T_1) \qquad (6)$$

Many people focus on the junctions in evaluating thermocouple circuits, so they often fail to recognize phenomena such as regions of stress within a conductor. When wires are flexed repetitively at one location, the resulting cold-working can create regions of nonhomogeneous thermoelectric power, thereby changing the net electric output of the circuit. By using the "gradient" or "conductor" explanation to evaluate a circuit, it will be seen that the electrical output is generated where temperature gradients exist in the conductors and that the thermoelectric power of the conductors in those regions must be known [4]. This is particularly important where thermocouples are used to measure the temperatures of elements within a chamber in which the temperature is different from the surrounding ambient.

Figure 2 depicts a slightly more complex thermocouple circuit which adds a third conductor, C, between the voltage-measuring instrument and each of the other conductors. Since most thermocouple circuits are constructed of duplex wire with the two conductors in close physical proximity, the error introduced by assuming that both conductors are at the same temperature, at any location in the circuit, will be negligible. Thus, in the circuit of Figure 2, it is assumed that both of the junctions to the C conductors are at a reference temperature, T_r. Since the internal circuit of the voltage-measuring device will have no net output if the temperature is equal to T_1 throughout, the output of the circuit of Figure 2 is given by Eq. (7):

$$E = P_C(T_r - T_1) + P_B(T_m - T_r) + P_A(T_r - T_m) + P_C(T_1 - T_r) \qquad (7)$$

The terms containing P_C cancel, illustrating an important characteristic of thermocouple circuits: If at all points along the length of a duplex thermocouple pair the temperature is the same in both conductors, the output of that portion of the circuit will be zero if the thermoelectric powers of the two conductors are the same. Duplex copper leads do not contribute to the net output of a circuit if they are made of pure, instrument-grade copper and

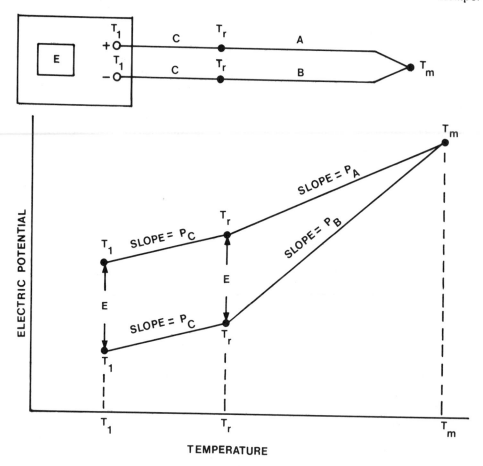

FIGURE 2   Simple thermocouple circuit.

have not been stressed to create cold-worked regions. Equation (7) can be rewritten to yield Eq. (8):

$$E = (P_B - P_A)(T_m - T_r) \qquad (8)$$

The fact that the C portion of the circuit makes no net contribution to the output is also shown graphically in the lower portion of Figure 2. Since the slope of each line is equal to the thermoelectric power of the conductor, the output curves of the two C conductors are parallel. Therefore, even though the temperature changes from T_r to T_1 in that portion of the circuit, there is no change in the net potential difference.

From Eq. (8) it may be observed that if the temperature T_r is maintained at some known reference value, and the thermoelectric powers of conductors A and B are known, the electrical output of the circuit is proportional to the temperature of the measuring junction, T_m. It should be remembered that the thermoelectric powers of conductors vary slightly with temperature, thereby giving all thermocouples a nonlinear output versus temperature rather than the linear output of this simplified explanation. For the purpose of understanding how to avoid circuit errors, however, the linear assumption is adequate.

The fact that the duplex conductors, C, make no net contribution to the electrical output is important, because this allows duplex copper leads to be used in connecting the voltage-measuring device to the junctions at the reference temperature, T_r. Then the temperature of the terminals on the voltage-measuring device can be any value without changing the net electrical output of the circuit. It is relatively easy to maintain the junction of two conductors at a constant, known temperature, but it would be extremely difficult to do so at the terminals of a voltage-measuring device.

The value that has been chosen universally as the standard reference temperature for thermocouple circuits is the equilibrium temperature between ice and air-saturated water, or 0.00°C. A few instruments are sold with oven-controlled reference temperatures of higher values, but all standard tables give the output of thermocouples as a function of the measured temperature, T_m, on the assumption that the reference temperature, T_r, is at 0.00°C [5].

Figure 3 depicts a thermocouple circuit composed of several lengths of duplex thermocouple wire. This is the type of circuit that might be used in a typical validation study. Section 1 could be the length of thermocouple wire that goes from the measuring system to a connector outside the autoclave; section 2 could be the connector; section 3 could be the length of thermocouple wire that goes from the external connector, through the wall of the autoclave, to the measuring junction inside the autoclave. Since the circuit from the reference junctions to the voltage-measuring device makes no net contribution, the electrical output of the circuit in Figure 3 is given by Eq. (9):

$$E = P_{B1}(T_1 - T_r) + P_{B2}(T_2 - T_1) + P_{B3}(T_m - T_2) + P_{A3}(T_2 - T_m)$$
$$+ P_{A2}(T_1 - T_2) + P_{A1}(T_r - T_1) \tag{9}$$

Equation (9) may be rewritten to yield Eq. (10):

$$E = (P_{B1} - P_{A1})(T_1 - T_r) + (P_{B2} - P_{A2})(T_2 - T_1)$$
$$+ (P_{B3} - P_{A3})(T_m - T_2) \tag{10}$$

It may be observed from Eq. (10), and the graphical representation of the output in Figure 3, that when at all points along the length of a thermocouple the temperature is the same in both conductors, the output of that portion of the circuit depends only on the difference between the thermoelectric powers of the two conductors and the temperature change along their length. The difference between the thermoelectric powers of two conductors is known as the Seebeck coefficient of the pair [4,5].

The Seebeck coefficient of a single material is always given relative to some reference material. The early evaluations by Peltier, Seebeck, and others were done relative to lead, and recent evaluations are relative to platinum-67. Table 1 gives the approximate Seebeck coefficients of the most common thermocouple materials relative to Pt-67, and Table 2 gives the corresponding values of the most frequently used thermocouple pairs at temperatures near the ice point. The Seebeck coefficient of any pair

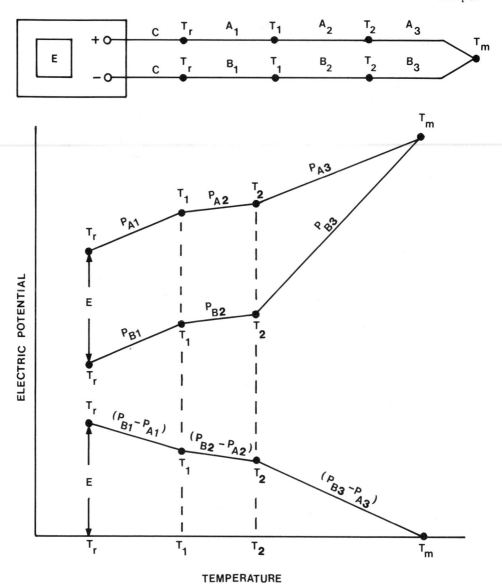

FIGURE 3   Typical thermocouple circuit.

TABLE 1 Approximate Seebeck Coefficients of Common Thermocouple Materials Relative to Platinum-67 at 0.0°C

Material name	ASTM E-20 Letter code	Approximate composition	Seebeck coefficient (μV/°C)
Chromel	EP and KP	90% Ni, 10% Cr	25.8
Iron	JP	99.5% Fe	17.9
Copper	TP	100% Cu	5.9
^{90}Pt^{10}Rh	SP	90% Pt, 10% Rh	5.4
^{87}Pt^{13}Rh	RP	87% Pt, 13% Rh	5.3
Alumel	KN	95% Ni, 2% Al, 2% Mn, 1% Si	−13.6
Constantan	JN[a]	55% Cu, 45% Ni	−32.5
Constantan	EN and TN	55% Cu, 45% Ni	−32.9

[a]JN is similar to EN and TN but will generally have a slightly different output.
Source: Ref. 5.

of conductors is equal to the difference of the Seebeck coefficients of each conductor relative to a standard material. If the Seebeck coefficient of copper relative to Pt-67 is +5.9 μV/°C and that of constantan is −32.9 μV/°C, the Seebeck Coefficient of a copper-constantan duplex pair (type T thermocouple) is 38.8 μV/°C. The material having the most positive Seebeck coefficient relative to Pt-67 will be the positive lead, which is the copper lead in the previous example.

TABLE 2 Approximate Seebeck Coefficients of the Common Thermocouple Pairs at 0.0°C

Thermocouple name	ASTM E-20 Letter code	Seebeck coefficient (μV/°C)
Chromel-Constantan	E	58.7
Iron-Constantan	J	50.4
Chromel-Alumel	K	39.4
Copper-Constantan	T	38.8
Platinum-^{90}Pt^{10}Rh	S	5.4
Platinum-^{87}Pt^{13}Rh	R	5.3

Source: Ref. 5.

If the Seebeck coefficient, S, is substituted for the difference in thermo-electric power, $P_A - P_B$, throughout the circuit of Figure 3, Eq. (10) can be rewritten to yield Eq. (11):

$$E = S_1(T_1 - T_r) + S_2(T_2 - T_1) + S_3(T_m - T_2) \tag{11}$$

Figure 4 depicts a typical thermocouple circuit of duplex leads where the output is expressed in terms of the Seebeck coefficients of the conductor pairs. If the thermocouple wire in every section of the circuit is obtained from a single homogeneous length of wire, the Seebeck coefficient in every section will be the same. That condition is expressed by Eq. (12):

$$S_1 = S_2 = S_3 = S \tag{12}$$

Substituting the condition of Eq. (12) into Eq. (11) yields Eq. (13):

$$E = S(T_m - T_r) \tag{13}$$

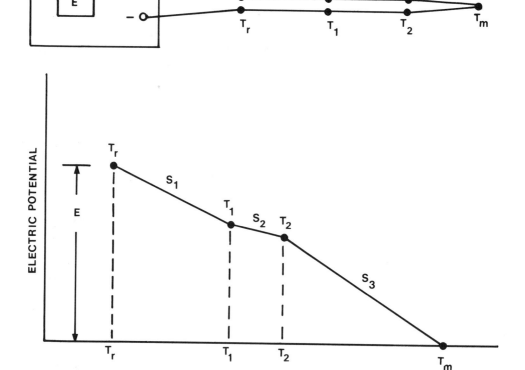

FIGURE 4   Typical duplex-lead thermocouple circuit.

If the temperature is expressed in degrees Celsius and the temperature of the reference junctions is maintained at 0.00°C, T_r in Eq. (13) is equal to zero and the net output of the circuit is given by Eq. (14):

$$E = ST_m \tag{14}$$

Equation (14) is valid only when the Seebeck coefficient is constant. The Seebeck coefficient of any pair of thermocouple wires changes slightly with temperature, but in a homogeneous length of wire it is a unique function of temperature. Therefore, when the temperature is expressed in degrees Celsius and the reference junctions are at 0.00°C, the true output of a homogeneous thermocouple is a unique function of the measured temperature as given by Eq. (15):

$$E = \int_0^{T_m} S(T) \, dT \tag{15}$$

Standard values of voltage output as a function of measuring junction temperature, with the reference junctions at 0.00°C, have been developed for all commonly used thermocouple pairs. Those values are given by NBS Circular 125 in the United States [5] and by DIN standards in Europe.

III. THERMOCOUPLE REFERENCE TEMPERATURE

Equation (13) shows the importance of establishing an accurate reference junction temperature. Any difference between the actual reference temperature and the standard value produces an error that is equal to the temperature difference multiplied by the Seebeck coefficient at the reference temperature. The ice point has been chosen as the "standard" thermocouple reference temperature because it is a known value of temperature that can be established quite accurately with relatively little effort.

A. Ice Bath References

Figure 5 depicts an ideal thermocouple circuit where a pair of continuous, homogenous conductors extend from the measuring junction to their junctions with copper. The junctions to copper are immersed in an ice bath and are called the reference junctions of the circuit. The reference junctions must be inserted to a sufficient depth in the bath to avoid conduction errors [6].

The temperature of the ice bath will be 0.00 ± 0.01°C if the following procedures are followed:

1. Use a Dewar flask that is at least 10 in. deep and 4 in. in diameter.
2. Make ice using distilled water and crush it finely.
3. Fill the Dewar flask completely with the crushed ice and fill the voids between the ice particles with distilled water.
4. Insert the thermocouple leads into the central portion of the bath to a depth of at least 4–8 in., depending on the size of wire.
5. Allow approximately 30 min for the ice and water to reach thermal equilibrium.

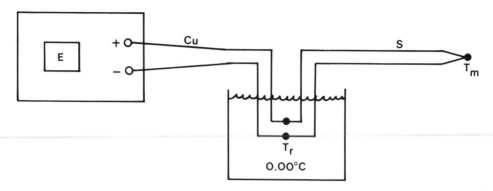

FIGURE 5   Thermocouple circuit with ideal reference.

6. Pack the ice down into the Dewar flask, removing the excess water and adding additional crushed ice to maintain a solidly packed bed of ice with the voids filled by water.
7. Repeat step 6 as required.

B. Automatic References

While the mixture of ice and water in a Dewar flask is an ideal reference, it is not very practical outside the Standards laboratory. An excellent alternative to the Dewar flask is an automatic ice bath that maintains a mixture of ice and water in a sealed chamber by means of thermoelectric cooling. Immersion wells extend into the chamber and the reference junctions of the thermocouple circuit are inserted to the bottom of the wells. When used in accordance with the manufacturer's operating instructions, the reference temperature provided by automatic ice bath is typically $0.00 \pm 0.3°C$ [7]. The output of the circuit depicted in Figure 5 is given by Eq. (14).

In many applications it is not convenient to construct reference junctions on each lead of a thermocouple. Automatic ice baths are available with built-in reference thermocouples attached to terminals to which the external thermocouple leads are connected [7]. Figure 6 depicts a circuit using this type of

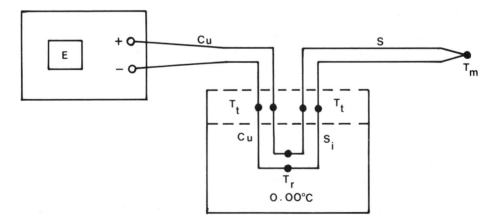

FIGURE 6   Thermocouple circuit with reference having internal thermocouples.

reference. Each pair of "input" terminals is for a specific thermocouple type. Internal wires of the same type form reference junctions to copper that are maintained at 0.0°C in the ice bath. The copper leads from the reference junctions are connected to the "output" terminals of the reference.

The output of the circuit depicted in Figure 6 is given by Eq. (16). T_t is the temperature of the terminals, S is the Seebeck coefficient of the external thermocouple, and S_i is the Seebeck coefficient of the internal thermocouple. Even though the internal thermocouple is made of the same type of material as that in the external portion of the circuit, its Seebeck coefficient may be slightly different because it may be from a different production lot of wire.

$$E = S(T_m - T_t) + S_i(T_t - T_r) \tag{16}$$

The external thermocouple produces a voltage equal to $S(T_m - T_t)$ and the internal thermocouple produces a voltage equal to $S_i(T_t - T_r)$. The total voltage is the sum of the two. Since T_r is equal to 0.0°C, Eq. (16) can be rewritten to yield Eq. (17):

$$E = ST_m + T_t(S_i - S) \tag{17}$$

The second term of Eq. (17) may be considered an error term. If the Seebeck coefficient of the internal thermocouple is exactly equal to that of the external thermocouple, the second term of Eq. (17) is zero and the output is the same as that of the ideal circuit of Figure 5 and Eq. (14).

C. Thermocouple Compensators

In many industrial temperature-measuring applications, even an automatic ice bath with built-in reference thermocouples may not be practical. Automatic ice baths are expensive and do not operate reliably in ambient temperatures below 0.0°C or above 40.0°C. All instruments and systems being sold today for thermocouple temperature measurement provide an electronic circuit for determining the temperature of the terminals to which the thermocouples are attached. An appropriate reference voltage is added by the system to that produced by the external thermocouple. Early versions of such circuits were called compensators, because they compensated for the fact that the terminals to which the thermocouples were connected were not at the ice-point temperature. Figure 7 depicts such a circuit.

The compensator produces a voltage that is a function of the terminal temperature. A typical compensator is a resistance bridge with the temperature-

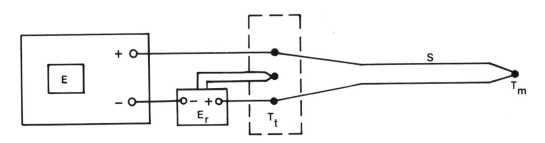

FIGURE 7   Thermocouple circuit with compensator.

sensitive resistor installed near the thermocouple terminals. The bridge is adjusted to have a zero output when the temperature of the resistor is 0.0°C and to produce the proper voltage for the specified thermocouple type at a normal ambient temperature [8]. The compensator voltage is added to the voltage produced by the thermocouple and the total voltage is measured by the voltage-measuring device. Equation (18) gives the output of the circuit depicted in Figure 7:

$$E = S(T_m - T_t) + E_r \tag{18}$$

The perfect compensator would have an output equal to that which would be produced by the external thermocouple when its reference junctions were at ice point and its measuring junction was at the terminal temperature. That characteristic is expressed by Eq. (19):

$$E_r = S(T_t - T_r) \tag{19}$$

Substituting this ideal compensator output into Eq. (18) and setting T_r equal to zero yields the same total output as that given by Eq. (14) for the ideal circuit.

D. Multichannel Thermocouple Systems

In older multichannel systems, the compensation voltage is added electrically as depicted in Figure 8. When the compensation voltage is added electrically to the output of a multiple-point scanner, all of the thermocouples in the group must be the same type. The compensator must be designed to produce the output required for a given thermocouple type, and its output should be

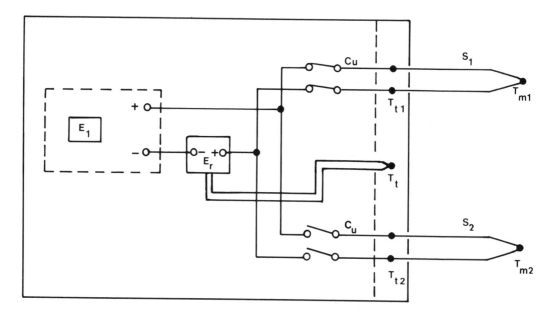

FIGURE 8   Multichannel thermocouple system with internal compensator.

adjustable in calibration to match the Seebeck coefficient of the external thermocouples.

Modern multichannel thermocouple measuring systems use digital computing capability to add the proper compensation voltage to the measured thermocouple output as depicted in Figure 9. Rather than adding a compensation voltage electrically, the temperature of the terminals is measured by the system and the value stored in memory. When a channel is programmed to be a thermocouple input, the system automatically computes the appropriate compensation voltage for that type of thermocouple, adds it to the measured voltage, and converts the total voltage to the corresponding temperature.

Whether the system reference voltage is added electrically as in Figure 8, or mathematically as in Figure 9, it is based on a single measurement of the terminal temperature, which may be different from the temperature of each individual pair of terminals in the group. The total voltage output of the first thermocouple in Figure 9 is given by Eq. (20):

$$E_1 = S(T_{m1} - T_{t1}) + S(T_t) \qquad (20)$$

The first term of Eq. (20) is the measured voltage produced by the external thermocouple and the second term is computed by the system based on the measured value of terminal temperature. Equation (20) may be rewritten to yield Eq. (21):

$$E_1 = S(T_{m1}) + S(T_t - T_{t1}) \qquad (21)$$

The second term of Eq. (21) is an error term. If the actual temperature of the terminals to which a thermocouple is attached is different from the

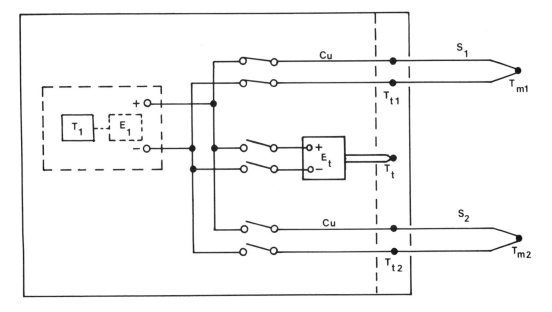

FIGURE 9   Multichannel thermocouple system with computer and internal reference.

terminal temperature measured by the system, an error is introduced that is equal to the temperature difference multiplied by the Seebeck coefficient at the terminal temperature.

In some installations it is not possible, or desirable, to run thermocouple wire from the measuring junction to the recording system. Figure 10 depicts one solution that is similar to the multichannel computer system of Figure 9. In this case, however, the conversion to copper is at the terminals of a remote uniform temperature reference whose temperature is measured by some independent means [7]. If the logic of the multichannel data system is designed to operate with a remote reference, the output of each thermocouple is computed in the same fashion as when an internal reference is provided. Equations (20) and (21) apply to this type of installation as well.

IV. SOURCES AND TYPES OF ERROR

The dictionary defines accuracy as the absence of error, but accuracy is a term that has many different meanings. Any discussion of temperature measurement accuracy must focus on the various sources and types of errors. In a typical thermocouple installation, the three primary sources of error are the thermocouple sensors, the circuit that connects the thermocouple sensors to the measuring system, and the measuring system [9,10].

In discussing errors and accuracy it is important to distinguish between relative accuracy and absolute accuracy. Relative accuracy is the degree to which temperature measurements at different locations can be compared or the degree to which the measurement of a single temperature is repeated. Absolute accuracy is the degree to which a measurement gives the absolute thermodynamic value of temperature. In many processes relative accuracy is sufficient, but in thermal sterilization processes absolute accuracy is essential.

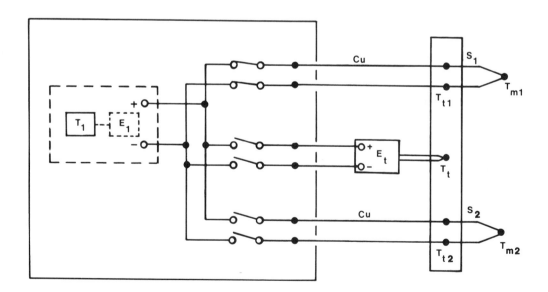

FIGURE 10   Multichannel thermocouple system with computer and external UTR reference.

The rate at which microorganisms are destroyed is a strong function of the temperature, so the time required to produce a sterile product depends on the temperature of the product. If the true value of temperature is less than the indicated value, improper sterilization may result.

Another important distinction to make is that of systematic errors and random errors. Systematic errors can be eliminated from the final results by calibration, but random errors can be minimized only by proper selection and installation of the measuring instrumentation. The lack of interchangeability, conformity, and uniformity produce systematic errors; most nonhomogeneous regions in the circuit and the lack of repeatability produce random errors.

A. Sensor and Circuit Errors

In thermocouple systems it is difficult to draw a clear distinction between sensor errors and circuit errors, because a thermocouple is a total integrator of the temperature change from the measuring junction to the reference junction. Conformity and interchangeability are characteristics generally attributed to the sensors; nonhomogeneous effects are attributed to the circuit.

1. Conformity to Standard

Conformity error is the difference between the actual voltage produced by a thermocouple and the standard output voltage for that thermocouple type at the same measured temperature. The reference junctions of the thermocouple circuit are assumed to be at 0.00°C. One specification that is often quoted for thermocouples is the maximum conformity error that thermocouples can have and still meet accepted industrial standards. For standard-grade type T (copper-constantan) thermocouples, that error is the greater of ±1.0°C or ±0.75%. For special-grade type T thermocouples it is the greater of ±0.5°C or ±0.4% [11]. Selected grade thermocouples supplied by Kaye Instruments have a maximum conformity error of ±0.25°C or ±0.2% at 120°C [12].

It must be emphasized that the conformity error is not indicative of the total measurement error in any particular installation. Conformity errors can be eliminated by calibration at a number of temperatures over the operating range, and there are many other system errors that may be larger than the conformity error.

2. Interchangeability

The degree to which a number of thermocouples all have the same output at the same measured temperature is known as the interchangeability of the thermocouples. Interchangeability is important when comparing two temperatures in an uncalibrated system. When a number of thermocouples are made from the same production lot of wire, the maximum interchangeability error is typically the greater of ±0.1°C or ±0.1%.

As with conformity errors, interchangeability errors can be eliminated by calibration. In both cases it is often sufficient to calibrate the sensors at the two extreme temperatures of the operating range and apply a linear correction to the measurements. If the measuring system does not provide the capability of applying individual calibration corrections to each input, interchangeability error becomes an important consideration and all thermocouples used at one time should be made from the same production lot of wire.

3. Nonhomogeneous Regions

The thermoelectric power of a conductor is a function of the composition and structure of the material. Most thermocouple conductors are alloys of several elements. Among the commonly used thermocouple materials, only copper and platinum are essentially pure elements; even copper wire must be checked to be sure it has the proper characteristics. The Seebeck coefficients of thermocouples will vary slightly between production lots of wire because of variations in composition and annealing. Annealing affects the thermoelectric power because it alters the grain structure of the conductor. Similarly, the thermoelectric power of a conductor can be changed slightly if it is stressed to the point of permanent distortion. The phenomenon known as cold working changes the thermoelectric power as well as the physical characteristics of a metal [13].

When a thermocouple circuit is constructed of continuous, homogeneous wire from the measuring junction to the terminals of the measuring system, calibration can eliminate most errors associated with the sensor and the circuit. Tests have shown conclusively that the output of a homogeneous length of thermocouple wire depends only on the total change in temperature from one end to the other; the location of the change within the wire does not matter. This characteristic is extremely important in calibrated systems, because the location of the gradient in the wire during operation will generally be different from the location of the gradient during calibration.

Connectors introduce a section of nonhomogeneous conductors in a thermocouple circuit. When they must be used, connectors should be made of the same materials as the wire and located away from regions of large temperature gradients. Even though the materials of thermocouple connectors are essentially the same as the wire, the annealing process used to make a rigid connector pin must be different from that used to make flexible wire. The resulting Seebeck coefficient is almost always slightly different.

Repetitive flexing of thermocouple wire at one location can also cause a nonhomogeneous region due to cold working. In the validation process, thermocouples are normally installed through fittings in the walls of sterilizers where they are clamped rigidly. In placing the thermocouples at different locations within the sterilizer, some amount of flexing at the fitting is unavoidable. Since solid wire is much more susceptible to cold working than stranded wire of the same size, only stranded wire should be used in this application and great care should be exercised to avoid flexing the wire more than necessary. The sterilizer wall is the region of maximum temperature gradient during operation, so even a small change in Seebeck coefficient in that region can cause a significant error.

The effect of nonhomogeneous regions in a circuit is illustrated in Figure 11 and the following example. All of the wire in the circuit has a Seebeck coefficient S, but the connector in the circuit has a Seebeck coefficient S_c. The temperatures at the ends of the connector are T_1 and T_2.

The output of the circuit shown in Figure 11 is given by Eq. (22):

$$E = S(T_m - T_2) + S_c(T_2 - T_1) + S(T_1 - T_r) \tag{22}$$

Equation (22) can be rewritten to yield Eq. (23):

$$E = S(T_m - T_r) + (S_c - S)(T_2 - T_1) \tag{23}$$

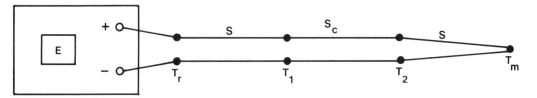

FIGURE 11   Thermocouple circuit with connector.

The second term of Eq. (23) is the error caused by having a connector in the circuit. The error will be zero if the Seebeck coefficient of the connector is equal to that of the wire or if there is no temperature difference across the connector. It is unlikely that the Seebeck coefficient of a connector will match that of the wire exactly, so it is important to avoid using connectors where they will have large temperature differences imposed on them.

To illustrate the error that would be caused by installing a connector in the wall of a sterilizer, assume the following values for the circuit of Figure 11 and Eq. (23):

$$T_m = 120.0°C \quad T_2 = 100.0°C \quad T_1 = 50.0°C \quad T_r = 0.00°C$$

$$S = 40.0 \ \mu V/°C \quad S_c = 42.0 \ \mu V/°C$$

The output according to Eq. (23) is

$$E = 40.0(120.0 - 0.0) + (42.0 - 40.0)(100.0 - 50.0)$$

$$= 4800 \ \mu V + 100 \ \mu V = 4900 \ \mu V$$

Error = 100 μV or 2.5°C

The values employed in this example are typical of those that would be experienced if a connector in a type T (copper-constantan) thermocouple circuit were installed in the wall of a steam autoclave. The error is 100 μV, or about 2.5°C. A similar error could be caused by a cold worked region at the wall, but the magnitude of the error would be less. For a connector to have a Seebeck coefficient 5% greater than the wire it is designed to match is typical, but the change due to cold working will be much less.

A second type of nonhomogeneous circuit is illustrated by Figure 12. Many thermocouple probes are constructed using lengths of thermocouple wire swaged into stainless steel tubes. This type of material may be purchased in

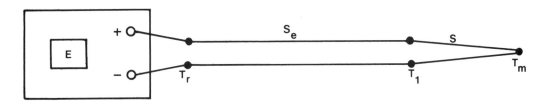

FIGURE 12   Thermocouple circuit with two sections.

long sections and cut to form stainless steel thermocouple probes of the desired length. One end is welded to form the measuring junction and the two wires at the other end are attached to extension leads of matching thermocouple wire. The wire in the stainless tip has a Seebeck coefficient S and the extension wire has a Seebeck coefficient S_e.

The output of this circuit is given by Eq. (24):

$$E = S(T_m - T_1) + S_e(T_1 - T_r) \tag{24}$$

Adding and subtracting the term ST_r and rewriting Eq. (24) yields Eq. (25):

$$E = S(T_m - T_r) + (S_e - S)(T_1 - T_r) \tag{25}$$

The second term of Eq. (25) is an error term. The error will be zero if the Seebeck coefficient of the extension wire is equal to that of the wire in the tip or if the junction between the two is maintained at the reference temperature.

This type of probe should be avoided, unless it can be calibrated under the same conditions encountered in normal operation. Specifically, the value of T_1 must be the same during both calibration and operation or an unrecognized error will be introduced. Assume the following values for the circuit of Figure 12 and Eq. (25) when the probe is calibrated in a laboratory:

$$T_m = 120.0°C \quad T_1 = 30.0°C \quad T_r = 0.0°C$$

$$S = 40.0 \ \mu V/°C \quad S_e = 40.2 \ \mu V/°C$$

The output of the circuit according to Eq. (25) is

$$E = 40.0(120.0 - 0.0) + (40.2 - 40.0)(30.0 - 0.0)$$

$$= 4800 + 6 = 4806 \ \mu V$$

Assuming that the standard Seebeck coefficient is 40.0 $\mu V/°C$, the calibration correction is 6 μV or 0.15°C when the probe is measuring 120.0°C.

When this probe is used inside a steam autoclave, the temperature of the junction between the tip and the extension wire will be at autoclave temperature. Assume that all other values are the same as in the calibration example, but the value of T_1 is 120.0°C. The output will be

$$E = 40.0(120.0 - 0.0) + (40.2 - 40.0)(120.0 - 0.0)$$

$$= 4800 + 24 = 4824 \ \mu V$$

Applying the calibration correction of 6 μV still leaves an error of 18 μV, or almost 0.5°C. This example, even more than the previous one, shows the importance of using thermocouples that have a continuous length of homogeneous wire from the measuring junction to the region outside the autoclave.

4. Diffusion of Steam

All insulating materials are permeable to steam after extended exposure. When stranded wire is installed through the wall of an autoclave, steam

will eventually diffuse through the insulation, flow to the lower pressure outside the autoclave through the small passages formed between the strands of
wire, and condense to form drops of moisture where the insulation ends. This
diffusion of moisture along the wire will not cause an error in the output of
a thermocouple, but it should be prevented from collecting on terminals or
connectors where corrosion could cause problems. Diffusion of moisture along
the wire to the outside of the autoclave will not occur if solid wire is used instead of stranded wire, but solid wire is more susceptible to cold working.
The flexing of solid wire at the wall of an autoclave may introduce a serious
error, whereas moisture dripping from stranded wire is only an inconvenience.

Some thermocouple assemblies are constructed using flexible hose to protect the thermocouple wire inside the autoclave. One end of the flexible hose
fits over a length of stainless steel tubing that forms the thermocouple probe
and the other end of the flexible hose connects to a stainless steel tube that
provides a pressure seal at the wall of the autoclave. This design guarantees
that there will be no cold working of the homogeneous wire that runs continuously from the measuring junction to a connector outside the autoclave.

Unfortunately, the steam that diffuses through the flexible hose will condense inside when the assembly is cooled down. If some of the moisture collects in the stainless steel probe near the measuring junction, it will cause an
error if the probe is used subsequently to measure temperatures above 100°C.
Since the passage from the inside of the probe through the hose is open to
the atmosphere, any moisture in the probe will boil at 100°C, absorbing energy
from the surrounding material and reducing the temperature of the probe tip.
Depending on the amount of moisture, the distance of the moisture from the
measuring junction, and the rate of heating at the outer surface of the probe
tip, the magnitude of the error caused by moisture in this type of probe can
vary from a few tenths of a degree to several degrees.

The presence of moisture in a probe tip is detected readily in calibration,
so it should never cause an error in a validation run if the probes are calibrated before each run. If a large amount of moisture is present it will prevent the tip from ever reaching the calibration temperature, and the steam
condensing inside will make the portion of the probe that extends above the
calibration bath extremely hot. If a small amount of moisture is present it will
boil away, permitting the tip to achieve the proper temperature, but it will
retard the rate of heating during the time it is boiling. A probe with moisture
will take a noticeably longer time to reach the calibration temperature than a
dry one. If a maximum acceptable time to reach calibration temperature is
specified, the presence of moisture in a probe will be detected.

Attempts to fill the probe tip with a solid material to prevent moisture
from collecting near the measuring junction can cause cold working of the
wire due to differential thermal expansion of the wire and the filling material.
The resulting errors are more serious than the presence of moisture. Recent tests with a new filling technique indicate that moisture errors may be
eliminated in future probes without causing other problems [12].

5. Circuit Resistance

The resistance of a thermocouple circuit has no effect on the voltage generated. The indicated outputs of early industrial thermocouple meters were
inversely proportional to the resistance of the external circuits because gal-
vanometers were used to measure the current flowing in the circuits rather
than the voltage potential. Null-balance potentiometers generate a balancing
potential so no current flows in the circuit, and modern thermocouple meters

have measuring circuits with extremely large input impedances compared to that of the circuit. When using either of the latter types of instrumentation, normal levels of thermocouple circuit resistance will not affect the indicated temperature.

Cracked wire or poor electrical contact at connectors can introduce extremely high resistance in a circuit, affecting the accuracy of the voltage-measuring device and giving erratic values of the indicated temperatures. The wire in a circuit can be broken but held together by the insulation. When the wire is stretched, the ends come apart and cause an open circuit; when it is relaxed the ends of the wire may touch, again completing the circuit but with a high resistance at the point of contact. The surface of the copper contacts in a copper-constantan connector can become oxidized, thereby creating a high resistance. If an ohmmeter is used to measure the contact resistance, it may indicate a fraction of an ohm because the excitation voltage of the ohmmeter can break through the oxide film. With only the small potential generated by a thermocouple imposed, however, the resistance may be thousands of ohms. If erratic readings are experienced in a thermocouple circuit having a connector, cleaning the connector contacts may solve the problem. Oxidation of copper contacts can be prevented by plating them with gold [12].

B. Measuring System Errors

The accuracies of thermocouple measuring systems are stated in different fashions by different manufacturers. Some give detailed breakdowns of the error sources; some simply state total error when operating within a limited range of ambient temperatures. Changes in ambient temperatures are the most significant sources of error in thermocouple measuring systems, particularly in multichannel systems with internal references.

1. Resolution

The resolution of a measuring system is the ability to read the output. In analog chart recorders, resolution is determined by the width of the chart paper and the temperature range corresponding to the total width. Since the width of the chart is fixed, a smaller temperature range must be set if better resolution is required. This type of recorder can be purchased with plug-in cards to set the temperature range.

In digital systems, resolution is the value of the least significant digit. The resolution of temperature measurements may be 0.01, 0.1, or 1.° Fahrenheit or Celsius. Some meters even give a resolution of 0.001°. Measurement accuracy can be no better than the resolution, but it should never be assumed that the accuracy of a measuring instrument is as good as its resolution.

2. Conformity to Standard

All modern thermocouple measuring systems use microcomputers to add compensation voltage to the measured voltage generated by the external thermocouple and to convert the resulting total voltage to the corresponding temperature for that type of thermocouple. The conversion from voltage to temperature typically utilizes a series of straight lines or polynomial functions that approximates the standard tables.

The difference between the calculated temperature and the standard temperature at a given voltage is the conformity error at that temperature. At any given measured temperature the conformity error will always be the same. Maximum conformity error ranges from ±0.02°C in high-accuracy systems to as large as ±1.0°C in some systems.

3. Uniformity

Uniformity is the degree to which the measuring system indicates the same value when exactly the same input is applied to different channels of a multichannel system. The largest error in most multichannel thermocouple systems is the uniformity error caused by differences in the temperatures of the terminals to which the thermocouples are attached. It is not unusual to have terminal temperatures differ by 1.0°C. A difference in terminal temperature causes an error equal to the temperature difference multiplied by the ratio of the Seebeck coefficient at the terminal temperature to that at the measured temperature. Even when the terminals are insulated to protect them from external heating and cooling effects, they will be heated nonuniformly by the internal electronics of the measuring system.

Once a system has warmed up completely in a steady ambient temperature, the terminal temperatures will be stable. If each thermocouple is calibrated at the ice point (0.00°C), the uniformity error due to the terminal temperature difference will be included in the calibration correction. If the ambient temperature subsequently changes, the terminal temperature difference may also change. Even though the systematic uniformity error was eliminated by calibration, an additional random uniformity error may be introduced by a subsequent ambient temperature change.

4. Repeatability

Repeatability is the degree to which the measuring system will indicate the same output over a period of time when exactly the same input is being measured. Repeatability errors can be classified as short-term (seconds), medium-term (minutes), and long-term (weeks).

Short-term errors in the indicated output are caused by electrical phenomena. Continuous fluctuations in the output are usually caused by instabilities in the measuring circuit of the system. Sudden jumps of brief duration in the output are usually caused by common-mode voltage differences. The common-mode voltage difference is the potential difference between the sensor and the ground of the measuring system. In steam autoclaves, large static potential differences can be created between ungrounded probes and the ground of the measuring system, particularly when the probes are installed in plastic containers. Proper grounding of the probes can minimize the error caused by this phenomenon. The ratio of the maximum measurement error to the common-mode voltage difference is called the common mode rejection of the system and is expressed in decibels. A decibel is a measure of voltage ratio or current ratio equal to 20 times the common logarithm of the ratio. The common mode rejection varies from better than 140 db (10 million to 1) in high-accuracy systems to less than 100 db (100,000 to 1) in some systems.

Medium-term errors in the indicated output are caused by thermal phenomena. Temperature changes in the measuring circuit, in the thermocouple reference, and in the input terminals all cause errors in the indicated output. The magnitude of the measurement error caused by a change in ambient temperature is given by the temperature coefficient of the system. All manufacturers specify the temperature coefficient based on the system being stable before and after the change in ambient temperature; transient errors that occur during the temperature change may be much larger. Temperature coefficients vary from 0.01°C/°C for high-accuracy systems to 0.1°C/°C in some systems.

Long-term errors in the indicated output result from component aging. In validation studies this type of error is not important, because the system is calibrated with sufficient frequency to account for any long-term variations.

V. CALIBRATION PROCEDURE

Thermocouple systems used to measure temperatures in the validation process should be calibrated before and after each use. Typically, neither the measuring system nor the thermocouples will change their characteristics between calibrations, but the calibration process assures proper operation of the entire system. Because corrections applied to each thermocouple also include the uniformity error of the measuring system, each thermocouple should be connected to the same channel in calibration as in operation. To the extent possible, the entire system should be calibrated under the same ambient temperature and other conditions as it will experience during operation.

A. Calibration Basics

There are a few basic rules that should be followed in any calibration procedure.

1. Challenge all results. No single measurement should be accepted as being correct unless it is verified by other results. The transfer standard used to determine the temperature of the calibration bath could have an error. If two standards agree, the probability that they both have the same error is extremely low.

2. Be patient. A frequent mistake in calibrating instrumentation is to take measurements and make adjustments before conditions have stabilized. It may take much longer than expected for a system to become completely stable, because thermal errors decay exponentially and the output may seem to be stable even though it is still changing slowly.

3. The accuracy of the transfer standard must be better than that of the instrument being calibrated. This would seem obvious, but it is amazing how often a voltage calibrator is used that has a greater error than the system being calibrated. Rules such as being 10 times as accurate or even twice as accurate are not absolute: It is only important to recognize that the accuracy of the calibration can be no better than the standard used, and that it is a mistake to change the adjustment of a measuring system if it is already more accurate than the standard.

4. The characteristics of the transfer standard must have been determined by a procedure that is traceable to accepted primary standards [14]. In the United States, the National Bureau of Standards (NBS) is the accepted source of primary standards. The transfer standards used should have been calibrated by the NBS relative to their primary standards or by a qualified Standards laboratory relative to standards that they have had calibrated by the NBS. In either case, the test results and test numbers should be known so the calibration procedure can be traced back to the primary standards.

5. The transfer standard must be independent of the measuring system. Because the output of a thermocouple depends on the entire circuit, it is not a desirable temperature transfer standard. A resistance temperature detector (RTD) is a device that indicates changes of temperature by a change of resistance. Because the resistance of an RTD is only a function of its temperature, and the resistance can be measured independently of the system being calibrated, RTDs are ideal temperature transfer standards.

6. The characteristics of the transfer standard must be stable in shipment and other handling. As its name implies, the purpose of the transfer standard is to transfer a measured characteristic from one laboratory to another. The characteristics of the standard must be the same when received from the NBS as when it was calibrated relative to their standards. Because liquid-in-glass thermometers may be damaged or develop small voids in the liquid during shipment, they are not reliable temperature transfer standards. RTDs are fairly rugged devices that maintain their characteristics in normal handling and shipment.

B. Measuring System Calibration

The first step in calibrating a thermocouple system is to check the operation of the measuring system in the voltage mode and adjust it if necessary. Each manufacturer has a recommended procedure, which should be followed. A precision low-level dc voltage source having an accuracy better than ±1.0 μV ± 0.01% in the range of 0.0 μV to 20,000 μV should be employed in the voltage calibration. The measuring system should be turned on several hours before starting the calibration process to be sure that it has become completely stable. If the system is to be used for important voltage measurements, a second voltage source should be used to check the results of the adjustments. If the only important measurements are thermocouple temperature measurements, the calibration of the sensors will correct for any small voltage errors.

Once the voltage-measuring circuits have been adjusted, the thermocouple reference of the system should be checked by connecting thermocouples to the proper input terminals and placing several of their measuring junctions in an ice bath. If a crushed ice bath is used, it should be made and maintained as described in Section III, Section A. If an automatic ice bath is used, the measuring junctions should be inserted to the bottom of the wells. In either case, allow 10 or 15 min for the temperature to stabilize before making any adjustments.

The operation of the thermocouple reference in a multichannel, computer-based system is discussed in Section III, Section D. When the input terminal temperature of the system is above 0.0°C, a thermocouple with its measuring junction in an ice bath will generate a negative voltage. If the internal reference is adjusted until the indicated temperature is 0.0°C (32.0°F), the output of the internal reference is adjusted to equal the output that is generated by the external thermocouple when its reference junction is at 0.0°C and its measuring junction is at the temperature of the input terminals. The external thermocouple is generating a negative voltage of the same magnitude. As discussed in Section III, Section C and shown by Eqs. (18) and (19), this procedure provides the perfect internal reference or compensation voltage for that external thermocouple.

Since the input terminal temperatures and the Seebeck coefficients of each thermocouple in a multichannel system may be slightly different, other thermocouples connected to the measuring system may not indicate exactly 0.0°C when the internal reference is adjusted as described in the previous paragraph. For best overall accuracy, the internal reference should be adjusted until the average of the indicated temperatures of all thermocouples in the ice bath is 0.0°C. If the measuring system can be programmed to compute the average of the outputs of a group of thermocouples, that value can be used directly in the calibration procedure. It should be emphasized that calibration of the internal reference is a measuring system calibration and not a calibration of the external thermocouples.

C. Thermocouple Calibration

In order to assure absolute accuracy of every temperature measurement, each thermocouple must be calibrated by determining its output when its measuring junction is at two or more known temperatures. Electronic thermocouple calibrators are quite useful in checking systems for proper operation, but they do not provide temperature calibration of the thermocouples being used with the systems.

All temperature sensors should be calibrated at the ice point if 0.0°C is within their normal range of operation. As was discussed in Section III, Section A, the ice point is a known temperature that can be established quite accurately with relatively little effort. Measuring the ice-point temperature is an ideal check for any temperature indicator. It is also important to calibrate a temperature sensor at, or near, the maximum and minimum temperatures to be measured.

In steam autoclave measurements, the ice point is the recommended minimum calibration temperature and the normal process temperature is the recommended maximum calibration temperature. When selected-grade thermocouple wire [12] is calibrated at 0.0 and 121.0°C, and a linear correction is applied between those temperatures, the maximum conformity error relative to the NBS standard output [5] will be less than ±0.1°C over the entire range 0.0−121.0°C. This result has been verified by thousands of calibrations of the selected-grade wire [12] and is consistent with data in Ref. 5.

Typical operating temperatures in hot air ovens are in the vicinity of 200°C, and depyrogenation tunnels may be operated at temperatures above 300°C. In validating those processes, the thermocouples should be calibrated at a temperature near the maximum expected operating temperature of the process. If the ice point is used as the second temperature of a two-point calibration of selected-grade thermocouple wire and a linear correction is applied, the maximum conformity error relative to the NBS standard output may be as large as ±0.3°C between 0.0 and 200.0°C and as large as ±0.5°C between 0.0 and 300.0°C. This level of error is normally acceptable in these higher-temperature processes, and the error becomes much smaller near the maximum calibration temperature, which is also the normal operating temperature.

If better accuracy is required at higher temperatures, the thermocouples must be calibrated at intermediate points. The maximum expected error in any temperature measurement increases at higher temperatures. When a thermocouple is calibrated at two temperatures and a linear correction is applied between the two temperatures, the maximum expected error due to the thermocouple's characteristics is less than ±0.05°C between 100.0 and 150.0°C, approximately ±0.1°C between 150.0 and 200.0°C, and approximately ±0.2°C between 250.0 and 300.0°C.

Some thermocouple measuring systems provide a feature that permits the automatic application of a two-point correction on each thermocouple. When 0.0°C is one of the points, the calibration of the thermocouple not only corrects for the small differences in Seebeck coefficient between 0.0°C and the terminal temperature, it also corrects for any differences between the measured value of terminal temperature and the actual temperature of the terminals to which each thermocouple is connected. In this type of system it is desirable to use 0.0°C as the lower calibration temperature if the accuracy at higher temperatures is acceptable. If higher temperatures such as 150.0 and 200.0°C are used for the two calibration points, the accuracy in the range 150.0–200.0°C will be better, but rather large errors may be introduced at 0.0°C.

The type of equipment and instrumentation that must be used in a temperature calibration facility, and the amount of personnel training required to operate it, depend on the level of accuracy desired. To achieve calibration accuracies of ±0.01°C requires very expensive, elaborate instrumentation and highly trained personnel. Calibration accuracies of better than ±0.1°C can be achieved with relatively inexpensive instrumentation and simple procedures [15]. The less elaborate calibration facility is actually preferred in most validation processes because the level of accuracy is better than required and it is less likely that an error will be introduced by faulty procedure.

The following equipment and instrumentation is required in a basic temperature calibration facility to achieve total calibration accuracy of better than ±0.1°C at temperatures up to 150°C and ±0.2°C at temperatures between 150 and 300°C:

1. An automatic ice bath [7] or a Dewar flask filled with crushed ice and distilled water as described in Section III, Section A.
2. A high-temperature reference block [15] or a stirred oil bath with temperature uniformity better than ±0.03°C in the working region.
3. At least three RTDs that have been calibrated traceable to NBS standards to an accuracy of ±0.03°C at the minimum and maximum temperatures in the calibration range, and at intervals no larger than 50°C if ±0.1°C accuracy is required or 100°C if ±0.2°C accuracy is required.
4. An independent instrument to measure the resistance of the RTDs to an accuracy corresponding to ±0.03°C.
5. A precision resistor with calibration traceable to NBS standards to calibrate the resistance-measuring instrument.

The RTDs should be of a four-wire design, which provides independent leads for the excitation current and for measuring the voltage difference across the resistor. The same excitation current must be used in transfer calibrations as was used in the original calibration of the RTD, because the self-heating error of an RTD is a function of the current. The most common excitation current for a 100-Ω RTD is 1 mA. At least three RTD transfer standards should be available, because two standards must agree at each calibration temperature, and the third is required to determine which of the first two is correct if they do not agree.

A 25-Ω platinum RTD is the primary standard temperature sensor used by all primary calibration laboratories. It is quite expensive and also quite delicate. An industrial-grade, 100-Ω, platinum RTD is quite acceptable as a transfer standard, and its resistance can be measured to an accuracy of

±0.01 Ω with relatively inexpensive instrumentation [15]. A resistance change
of 0.01 Ω corresponds to a temperature change of approximately 0.025°C.

The resistance-measuring instrument must be calibrated at two values in
the range to be measured. One of the values can be zero resistance, or a
shorted input, and the second value should be approximately equal to the
maximum RTD resistance to be measured. When 100-Ω RTDs are used to
measure temperatures between 0.0 and 300°C, a 150-Ω precision resistor is
recommended as the second point. The resistor calibrations should be independently traceable to NBS standards and accurate to ±0.005 Ω.

The resistance-measuring instrument should be capable of measuring the
resistance of up to three RTDs and the precision resistor at the same time.
The current leads of the precision resistor and the RTDs should be connected
in series, so that the same excitation current passes through the precision
resistor and the RTD whose resistance is being measured. Adjusting the
current to make the instrument indicate the proper value of the precision
resistor automatically calibrates it for the RTD reading. In effect, the instrument compares the resistance of the RTD to that of the precision resistor.

The following detailed procedure is recommended for calibrating thermocouples to be used with multichannel measuring system in a validation
procedure.

1. Connect all thermocouples to the channels of the measuring system to
    which they will be connected in the validation run. Each thermocouple
    must be labeled clearly and a record made of the channel to which
    each is connected.
2. Turn on the measuring system and the resistance measuring instru-
    ment at least 2 hr before taking any measurements. If an automatic
    ice bath and a high-temperature reference block are to be used, they
    should be turned on at the same time. If a crushed-ice and distilled-
    water bath is to be used, it should be prepared at least 1/2 hr before
    being used. Most stirred-oil baths require about 15 to 20 min to
    stabilize. Because oil baths give off particulates that can cause prob-
    lems in clean air systems, they should be run as briefly as possible.
3. Once the measuring system has stabilized, it should be calibrated
    according to the procedures of Section V, Section B.
4. Place two RTD transfer standards in the wells of an automatic ice
    bath or in a crushed-ice bath. If an automatic ice bath is used, the
    RTDs should be inserted to the bottom of the wells and the wells filled
    with water. At least one manufacturer of automatic ice baths recom-
    mends filling the wells with a silicone oil having a specific gravity
    greater than unity [7]. Oil is recommended to prevent the possibility
    of ice forming in the wells, but water is much more convenient and
    the formation of ice in such units is an extremely rare occurrence.
    The temperature accuracy is the same in either case. If a crushed-ice
    bath is used, the RTDs should be inserted to a depth of approximately
    30 probe diameters. A 3/16-in.-diameter RTD should be inserted to
    a depth of 6 in. and a 1/4-in.-diameter RTD to a depth of 8 in. After
    the probes have been inserted for a few minutes, all excess water
    should be removed and additional crushed ice added to create a solidly
    packed bed of ice with the voids filled by water.
5. After the RTDs have reached equilibrium, check the calibration of the
    resistance-measuring instrument by measuring the value of the pre-
    cision resistor and make an adjustment if necessary. Then measure

the resistance of each RTD and compare the measured value to the
calibrated value of resistance at 0.0°C. The measured resistance of
a 100-Ω RTD should agree with the calibrated value to within ±0.01 Ω
at 0.0°C. If the RTDs indicate the same temperature, but both indicate that the ice bath is not 0.00 ± 0.03°C, check the ice bath. If
one of the RTDs has a resistance more than 0.01 Ω different from the
calibrated value, it should be removed from service or recalibrated
by a Standards laboratory.

6. Place both RTD transfer standards in the high-temperature reference
    block, or oil bath, and adjust the temperature to the desired value.
    Allow at least 10—15 min to stabilize if a reference block is used and
    about 5 min when using an oil bath. Measure the resistance of each
    RTD and determine the corresponding temperature of each from the
    appropriate calibration tables or equations. The RTDs should in-
    dicate the same temperature to within ±0.05°C if the temperature is
    below 150°C and to within ±0.1°C if the temperature is between 150
    and 300°C. If they do not, a third RTD should be used to determine
    which of the other RTDs is in error, and the faulty RTD should be
    removed from service or recalibrated by a Standards laboratory.
    When proper operation of both transfer standards has been verified,
    continue to monitor the high-temperature reference with one of the
    standards.

7. Place the thermocouples in the ice bath and allow at least 10 min for them
    them to stabilize. This part of the procedure can be done at the same
    time as step 6. Once step 6 is complete and the thermocouples have
    become stable at the ice-point temperature, their values at 0.0°C
    should be recorded for future correction. If the measuring system
    provides the capability to incorporate calibration corrections in the
    indicated output, the correction at the first point should be entered.
    In some systems this can be done automatically by pressing the
    appropriate keys on the operator's panel.

8. Place the thermocouples in the high-temperature reference and allow
    sufficient time for them to stabilize at the new temperature. The
    stabilization time will be approximately 10 min if a reference block is
    used and about 5 min in an oil bath. Once the indicated temperatures
    have become stable, the difference of each from the temperature in-
    dicated by the standard should be recorded for future corrections.
    If the measuring system provides the capability of incorporating cal-
    ibration corrections in the indicated output, the correction at the
    second point should be entered.

9. If more than a two-point calibration is to be employed, steps 6 and 8
    should be repeated for each calibration temperature.

Documentation is an important aspect of any calibration procedure. A
record must be made of the probe number attached to each channel and the
location of each probe in the autoclave or oven during the validation test.
The calibration corrections for each thermocouple must be recorded even
when they are applied automatically by the measuring system. The calibration
certificates of each RTD transfer standard and the precision resistor must
include the actual data values obtained. If the calibrations were performed
by the NBS, the certificates will contain a test number. If the calibrations
were performed by another Standards laboratory, the certificates must contain the NBS test numbers of the instrumentation used by that laboratory to

provide traceable calibrations of the transfer standards. Every transfer calibration must be documented in order to provide traceability to the primary standard and proof of the accuracy of the final measurement.

VI. SUMMARY

One of the most important steps in obtaining accurate temperature measurements with thermocouples is the proper design and installation of the thermocouple circuit. If possible, a continuous length of stranded homogeneous wire should be used from the measuring junction to the terminals of the measuring system. When two or more sections of wire are required by operational considerations, the connections between the sections must be in locations where the temperature in the circuit does not change significantly along its length. Ideally, each section of wire should be from the same production lot. If that is not practical, the wire should be selected to have the best interchangeability possible.

The measuring system must be designed specifically for high-accuracy thermocouple measurements. The input terminal section should provide a uniform temperature of all terminals and a means of measuring that temperature accurately. The system's voltage measuring accuracy must be ± 1.0 μV or better, and the computation of temperature from the measured voltage should deviate from the standard value by no more than $\pm 0.06°C$ over the entire measurement range. Most important, the thermocouple reference must track changes in ambient temperature accurately and the voltage measurement must not be affected by such changes, so that the calibration factors determined in the laboratory will still be valid on the production floor.

Finally, the entire system must be calibrated before each use. While it is not necessary to do a full calibration after each use, it is good practice to verify proper operation by calibrating the system at the process temperature after the validation run. When a properly designed and installed thermocouple system is calibrated by the procedures described in this chapter, the total measurement accuracy should be better than $\pm 0.1°C$ at $120°C$, $\pm 0.2°C$ at $200°C$, and $\pm 0.4°C$ at $300°C$.

VII. GLOSSARY

Cold working	Cold working is a phenomenon caused by stressing a metal beyond the yield point, which increases the hardness of the metal and changes the thermoelectric power.
Compensator	A compensator is an electronic circuit that measures the temperature of a set of terminals and produces a voltage approximately equal to that which would be produced by a thermocouple with an ice-point reference measuring the terminal temperature.
RTD	A resistance temperature detector is a temperature-measuring device containing a resistor whose value changes with temperature in a known manner.

Thermocouple	A thermocouple is a temperature-measuring device constructed by joining two wires of different composition.
Thermoelectric power	The thermoelectric power of a conductor is the property that expresses the change in electrical potential for a specified change in temperature.
Seebeck coefficient	The Seebeck coefficient is the difference between the thermoelectric powers of two conductors.
Thermistor	A thermistor is a solid-state, resistive temperature-measuring device.

VIII. NOMENCLATURE

E Net electric potential generated by a circuit or a portion of a circuit, in μV.

P The thermoelectric power of a conductor, in μV/°C.

S The Seebeck coefficient of a pair of conductors, in μV/°C.

T The temperature at a location in the circuit, in degrees Celsius.

Subscripts

A Refers to material A.

B Refers to material B.

C Refers to material C.

c Refers to a connector in the circuit.

e Refers to extension leads in a circuit.

I Refers to the internal circuit of the voltage-measuring device.

i Refers to the internal circuit of a reference with built-in thermocouples.

m Refers to the measuring junction in a thermocouple circuit.

r Refers to the referenced junctions in a thermocouple circuit.

1 Refers to location or section 1 in a circuit or to the first channel in a multichannel system.

2 Refers to location or section 2 in a circuit.

3 Refers to location or section 3 in a circuit.

REFERENCES

1. Finch, D. I. 1969. *General Principles of Thermoelectric Thermometry*, Publication D1.1000. Leeds & Northrup Company, North Wales, Pa.
2. Roeser, W. F. 1940. Thermoelectric thermometry. *J. Appl. Phys. II (6)*.

3. Moffat, R. J. 1962. The gradient approach to thermocouple circuitry, in *Temperature, Its Measurement and Control in Science and Industry*, Vol. 3, Part 2. Reinhold Pub. Co., New York.

4. Bentley, Robin E. 1982. The distributed nature of EMF in thermo-couples and its consequences. *Aust. J. Instrument. Control*, December.

5. Powell, R. L., et al. 1974. *Thermocouple Reference Tables Based on the IPTS-68*, NBS Monograph 125. U.S. Department of Commerce, Washington, D.C.

6. Caldwell, Frank R. 1965. Temperatures of thermocouple reference junctions in an ice bath. *J. Res. Natl. Bur. Std. 69C (2)*, April–June.

7. *Thermocouple Reference Systems*. 1980. Kaye Instruments, Inc., Bedford, Mass.

8. Muth, Stephen, Jr. 1967. Reference junctions, in *Instruments and Control Systems*, Vol. 40, No. 5, Reinbach Publications Division of Chilton Company, Philadelphia, Pa.

9. Gray, W. T., and Finch, D. I. 1972. Accuracy of temperature measurement, in *Temperature, Its Measurement and Control in Science and Industry*, Vol. 4, Part 2. Instrument Society of America, Pittsburg, Pa.

10. Howard, J. Lawrence. 1972. Error accumulation in thermocouple thermometry, in *Temperature, Its Measurement and Control in Science and Industry*, Vol. 4, Part 3. Instrument Society of America, Pittsburgh, Pa.

11. *American National Standard for Temperature Measurement Thermocouples*, ANSI–MC96.1. 1975. Instrument Society of America, Pittsburgh, Pa.

12. *Copper–Constantan Thermocouple Wire, Probes, and Accessories*. 1983. Kaye Instruments, Inc., Bedford, Mass.

13. Fenton, A. W. 1972. The traveling gradient approach to thermocouple research, in *Temperature, Its Measurement and Control in Science and Industry*, Vol. 4, Part 3. Instrument Society of America, Pittsburgh, Pa.

14. Cooper, M. H., Jr., and Johnston, W. W., Jr. 1972. Traceability, what and how, relating temperature measurements at ORNL, in *Temperature, Its Measurement and Control in Science and Industry*, Vol. 4, Part 2. Instrument Society of America, Pittsburgh, Pa.

15. *Practical Temperature Calibration Standards*. 1983. Kaye Instruments, Inc., Bedford, Mass.

6

Validation of Air Systems Used in Parenteral Drug Manufacturing Facilities

FRANCISCO DeVECCHI

VECO International, Inc., Farmington Hills, Michigan

I. INTRODUCTION

A. Objective

The importance of air as a contamination carrier or vector has been determined by many studies. Perhaps the most conclusive were the ones conducted by the National Aeronautics and Space Administration (NASA) during the early days of the space age. Shortly thereafter, the pharmaceutical industry—a leader in production of sterile products—recognized the need to use air systems to prevent airborne contamination. The advent of the absolute air filter (HEPA) with its high efficiency in cleansing the air (99.97% and up in the retention of particles of 0.3 μm) changed the airborne contamination control process. With the use of this device it is possible to reduce airborne contamination to a level where the air is no longer a critical factor in causing contamination.

As the use of absolute air filters became more popular, new techniques for handling air with HEPA filters were developed. One such case was the use of laminar air-flow systems, which were introduced in the manufacturing process of parenteral drugs in the early 1960s.

With the laminar-flow systems, the air supplied to an aseptic environment is no longer used solely as an element for clean-room pressurization or life support, but is used as a cleansing agent as well. Laminar-flow systems provide a continuous mass of clean air to the product and container. This mass is continuously moving in the same direction, displacing any contaminants released during the manufacturing process encountered along the path and eliminating them from the critical environment.

As air systems became more complex, their scope was enlarged to include the preservation of environmental quality. Consequently, a defective performance from the air system now has an effect on the overall quality of a product. Therefore, the need to improve the adequacy and proper performance of environmental control systems used in parenteral drug manufacturing has become paramount in recent years. Good Manufacturing Practices (GMPs) demand suitable contamination control procedures. These procedures should be reflected in the design, construction, and operation of an environmental control system, and specifically in the air handling, filtering, and distribution systems, building design, and construction features.

The central idea in the Good Manufacturing Practices concept is to "build in quality along the entire manufacturing process." Although this applies to pharmaceutical product manufacturing, the concept can be extended to any system related to or interacting with the production of a pharmaceutical drug. An environmental control system is designed for a specific reason in pharmaceutical production. The interaction of the system with the process must be determined to establish to what degree this interaction could alter the final quality of the product. For example, inadequately designed air systems for critical sterile filling areas represent a serious threat to the final quality of the product. The air acts as a carrier and distributor of undesirable elements from viable and nonviable origins that could alter the product in various degrees, making it unacceptable under current manufacturing standards. The degree and importance of this system-product interaction will vary along the process, depending on the location at which the operation is performed and the type, size, and quantity of products manufactured. To apply the concept of "building in quality" along with design, construction, and operation of an environmental control system, a thorough knowledge of the process, personnel, and material flow as well as quality is required.

With proper knowledge of the process and system-product interactions, it is possible to establish a quality control procedure at every stage of production. These procedures form part of the basis for the validation of the system.

The validation procedure, in this case, is intended to assure the adequacy and continuous performance of the environmental control system during each manufacturing stage of a pharmaceutical product.

There are three primary components in a validation procedure:

1. Input or design parameters—with knowledge of the process and the product-system interaction, certain design parameters are defined for the system by carefully selected personnel. If all the conditions are met during construction, these parameters should be attained after completion of the system.
2. Output or actual environmental parameters—these should be the ones obtained after completion of the system and should be the same as the input or design parameters.
3. Feedback or input/output comparison—once the system is completed, a comparison between input and output parameters is obtained by testing the system under various operational and nonoperational conditions.

In a validated system, output parameters, aside from being equal or better than the original design parameters, must be maintained continuously during environmental control system operation. To determine this, the system must be challenged or put in situations representing the possible standard and nonstandard operating conditions that may be encountered during everyday operation. The idea of challenging the system under unlikely but possible conditions is to determine the degree of change in the environmental parameters, and its recovery capabilities. A fundamental aspect of the validation process is to substantiate the constant and sustained operation of every component of the environmental control system at all times within the specified parameters. The testing and measuring procedures of environmental control parameters are universal; nevertheless, every system is unique and creates a need for specific challenges to assure that system's proper and continuous operation. The type of system will affect the testing methodology.

Air systems used in pharmaceutical manufacturing vary depending on the process; this chapter will consider those systems used for parenteral drug manufacturing, divided into two basic groups, (a) critically controlled environments, and (b) controlled environments.

Critically controlled environments can be divided by the air system used as follows:

1. Laminar air-flow rooms
2. Conventional rooms equipped with terminal filtration
3. Conventional rooms with remote filtration

Validation procedures, tests to be performed, and methodology vary depending on the phase in which they are performed. These phases are

1. Preconstruction phase—including design, engineering, and contractor selection
2. Construction phase—including every phase of the construction process
3. Postconstruction—at rest facility phase
4. Postconstruction dynamic test

Validation procedures require materials, workmanship verification, and performance tests at each of the phases described above.

The degree, intensity, and accuracy of the tests and checks are related to the impact the portion has on the final performance of the system. Obviously, final performance tests carry the most weight for acceptance of the total system, but the idea is to "build quality" into design, construction, and operation of the system, to assure proper and continuous performance of every one of the parts of the system.

B. Standard Operating Procedures

Validation of an environmental control system should include verification of the hardware used to create the environment as well as the software designed to support it. Major failures in an environmental control system are rarely related to inadequate performance of the hardware. Most of the time, failures are related to inadequate methods and procedures used by personnel working within the facility. Clear, specific, and current standard operating procedures are part of the support software needed for an environmental control system.

Standard operating procedures (SOPs) can be defined as part of the environmental control system. Preparation and writing of SOPs must be followed by adequate facilities design, operational and quality control programs. The scope of this will be of such a nature that it will cover all possible operational and testing conditions within the facility. The software portion should be in place at the design stage of the facility; this will assure the conditions indicated above. SOPs must be challenged during the validations procedures whenever possible.

The software portion of the environmental control system, unlike the hardware portion which does not normally change after construction, is dynamic and must be reviewed from time to time. These reviews will pinpoint the need for upgrading, changing, and making the software current if new procedures have been implemented or manufacturing demands dictate. These are referred to as software revalidation procedures. Revalidation intervals are determined by changes in manufacturing or control procedures.

C. Definitions

The following are definitions of some of the hardware and software components of the validation process.

HEPA (High-Efficiency Particulate Air) Filter: A throwaway, extended-medium, dry-type filter in a rigid frame having minimum particle-collection efficiency of 99.97% for 0.3-μm thermally generated dioctyl phthalate (DOP) particles, and a maximum clean-filter pressure drop of 1.0 in. water gate, when tested at rated air-flow capacity.

HEPA Filter Efficiency: The particle-removal efficiency of the individual filter unit as tested with thermally generated DOP aerosol and an aerosol penetrometer per Mil. Std. 282.

HEPA Filter Installation Leak Test: An in-place test of the bypass leakage of the HEPA filter system due to inadequate filters. The leakage rate is determined with air-generated DOP aerosol and an aerosol photometer.

Thermally Generated DOP: An aerosol generated by quenching (condensing) vapor that has been evaporated from liquid dioctyl phthalate by heat. The aerosol mean particle diameter is between 0.2 and 0.4 μm with a geometric standard deviation of 1.3.

Air-Generated DOP: An aerosol generated by blowing air through liquid dioctyl phthalate at room temperature. When generated with a Laskin-type nozzle, the approximate light-scattering mean droplet size distribution is as follows:

    99+% less than 3.0 μm
    50+% less than 0.7 μm
    10+% less than 0.4 μm

Optical Particle Counter: A light-scattering instrument with display or recording means to count and size discrete particles in air, as defined by American Society for Testing Materials Standard F50–69:

1. Instruments of this type having a sampling flow rate of at least 0.1 cfm, (and preferably 1.0 cfm), and with size discrimination capability to detect total particle concentrations >0.5 μm size and >5.0 μm size are suitable for leak testing and particle counting per paragraphs 5, 7, 8, and 11.
2. Instruments of this type having a sampling flow rate of at least 0.0067 cfm and with size discrimination capability equal to that in paragraph 3.10.1 are suitable for particle counting per paragraphs 7 and 11.

Aerosol Photometer: A light-scattering mass concentration indicator. Instruments of this type with a threshold sensitivity of at least 10^{-3} mg/liter for 0.3-μm-diameter DOP particles, capable of measuring concentration in the range of 80 to 120 mg/liter, and having a sample flow rate of 1 cfm + 10% of air are suitable for leak testing per paragraphs 5, 6, and 8.

1. *Linear readout photometer*—A photometer having a linear reading scale graduated from 0 to 100 with a range switch to vary the full-scale response in multiples of 10, through at least four decades of response. The instrument shall be capable of indicating 0.001% of a concentration that registers 100% on the highest range.
2. *Logarithmic readout photometer*—A photometer having a logarithmic response scale graduated 0, 1, 2, 3, 4, 5 covering the full range of instrument sensitivity without range switches. For this type of photometer, "one scale division" means the first intermediate scale division following the zero.

Thermoanemometer: An instrument for measuring air velocities based on the convective cooling effect of air flow on a heated wire. Instruments of this type designed specifically for low air speeds ranging from about 25 to 300 ft/min are suitable for velocity measurements.

Pitot Tube: A device for measuring total, velocity, and static pressures of flowing fluid streams. Pitot tubes for use with this standard shall conform to the proportions of Figure 7, AMCA Standard 210–67.

Air Pressure Gauge: An inclined manometer or magehelic gauge capable of measuring 0.01 to 2.0 in water gauge static pressure.

DbA Weighted-Scale Sound Meter: Sound-level meter referenced to 0.0002 μbar sound pressure level with an "A" weighted response curve per ANSI Standard S1.4–1971.

Wet/Dry Bulb Thermometers: Instruments used to measure moisture in the air so that the accurate dew point can be found.

Smoke Generator: Ventilation smoke tube pencil for generating visible smoke filament for air tracer studies.

As-Built Facility: An as-built facility is a clean room that is complete and ready for operation, with all services connected and functional, but without operating equipment or personnel.

At-Rest Facility: An at-rest facility is a clean room that is complete and has the operating equipment installed, but without personnel.

Operational Facility: An operational facility is a clean room in normal operation with all services functional and with operating equipment and personnel present.

Types of manufacturing environments and their corresponding air filtration systems include the following:

1. No controlled environment—rooms with no contamination control requirements where the environmental control requirements are based solely on personnel comfort. This condition is usually met with a simple central heating, ventilation, and air conditioning system with a low-efficiency air filtration system. Most frequently this type of system is used for general office space in pharmaceutical plants.
2. Controlled environments—rooms with moderate contamination control requirements. These are areas where the level of airborne contaminants

is specifically defined either by size, range, nature, or concentration, but where there is no need for strict control over contaminants generated by personnel, materials, equipment, etc. Comfort conditions are provided for operations personnel.

3. Critically controlled environments—rooms with strict contamination control requirements, in which air supply, materials, equipment, and personnel are regulated to control airborne contamination within a defined cleanliness level; in general, this type of room is defined as a "clean room."

Laminar Air-flow Clean Rooms: A clean room in which the absolute filtered air makes a single pass through the enclosure in a layered, parallel-flow pattern and in which absolute filters cover 80% of the ceiling (vertical flow) or one wall (horizontal flow) and air velocities are uniform.

Conventional Clean Rooms: A room in which the air is supplied to the enclosure through terminal absolute filter modules in the ceiling or walls, and covering less than 80% of the cross-sectional area. Air delivered to the room is of a turbulent nature.

Combination of Conventional Terminal Absolute Filtration Filter Modules and Dedicated or Portable Laminar-Flow Work Benches or Modules: In this system the absolute air is supplied by a terminal absolute filter to the room in a turbulent manner. Laminar-flow units are placed directly above or in front of a critical part of the process. The critical areas are at least 80% covered with absolute (HEPA) air filters.

Air Handling Systems: These rooms have certain common equipment: central heating, ventilation, and air conditioning plant, and a duct network or air supply; return air ducts and a self-contained air handling system used for air recirculation through HEPA filters exclusively (usually at the laminar flow units). A central air handling system is generally defined as the primary air handling system and the self-contained system or the laminar-flow units are the secondary system.

II. HEATING, VENTILATION, AND AIR CONDITIONING SYSTEMS

The primary purpose of an air conditioning, heating, and ventilation system is to provide a specific set of environmental conditions required for the manufacturing process. The established requirements can be met by several combinations of equipment and systems. An important point during the design stages is to match the equipment and systems claims with the actual performance desired for that combination.

The validation task force should therefore obtain enough information to verify that the equipment performance equates with the system performance—a situation that may not always hold true, especially in large and complex systems. To proceed in an organized and logical way, all the critical elements of the system should be defined, with their expected operational performance listed. A design-actual comparison can be made at the time of testing or verification. The relative importance of each of the environmental parameters should be established as the components vary within the facility. The adequacy of the selected equipment components is determined during system qualification after risk-effect analysis. Knowledge of the qualification criteria is fundamental for implementing proper validation protocols and to verify present conditions.

Hardware for environmental control systems includes:

Air moving equipment (blowers, fans, etc.)
Air cooling and heating systems
The air distribution network
Air filtration equipment
Temperature and humidity control devices
Pressurization control devices
Control systems

A. The Air Handling Unit

An air handling unit can be described as the core of the heating, ventilation, and air conditioning central system. This piece of hardware houses the supply and return fans, the heating and cooling coils, humidifiers, and some stages of air filtration as well as control devices to regulate the performance of each of the components.

Central systems used for controlled areas normally operate in the format defined as air-to-air or air-to-water cooling systems. Design generalizations are almost impossible to make because of the many types of systems and facilities in use. As a rule, however, most critical environments have a dedicated air handling system (including all the components required for humidity, temperature, air cleaning, and pressurization control), although the heating and cooling media may not be centrally generated. One of the reasons for this prevalent concept is the fact that critical areas are generally in isolated spaces within a larger building in which requirements for cleanliness and other environmental control parameters have been established, so heating and cooling requirements within the controlled environment are not affected in a serious manner by outside conditions, allowing better and more precise environmental control.

Heating and cooling requirements are calculated based on the future use of the controlled environment. These parameters determine the size, type, and nature of the hardware in the air handling unit.

Air handling units designed to service a clean environment must meet some requirements, in addition to those used in commercial systems. For one, the control systems that govern the air-flow temperature and humidity usually are designed within closer tolerances. Insulation materials are carefully selected and installed to prevent cross-contamination. Fresh-air filtration devices are selected and installed to provide a low-particulate burden to the system, regardless of the type of terminal filtration used.

All the design specifications are a result of an equipment qualification process and response to the process needs. Therefore, in this component, as in any other part of the system, a verification is required that the components meet the established criteria, to comply with the qualification requirements.

B. The Air Distribution Network

"A duct system is a structural assembly whose primary function is to convey air between specific points," according to the Sheet Metal and Air Conditioning Contractors, National Association (SMACCNA). These distribution systems are designed to fulfill certain specific functions at specific locations. These determine the criteria to be used in the design of it in terms of operational performance and construction.

In terms of operational pressure and velocity, air ducts are classified as follows:

High pressure: 3 in.w.g. (inches water gauge) and up (positive)
Low pressure: 0–3 in.w.g. (positive or negative)

The operational pressure is determined by the frictional drag losses caused by the air in motion as well as the losses caused by obstacles to the free path, such as grills, air filters, coils, etc.

Design of elements such as seals, sheet metal thickness, gauge, reinforcements, etc., is based on the operational pressure of the system.

Systems can have a combination of high- /and low-pressure components depending on the point of delivery along the system.

As part of the adequacy of design for an air ductwork distribution system, the limits are determined for:

1. Dimensional stability
2. Integrity at specified air volumes and pressures
3. Vibration
4. Noise, transmission and generation
5. Exposure to damage
6. Support

If all of these limits are not met, there is a potential for problems to the adequacy and integrity of a controlled environment, so qualification specifications should be verified, and testing for integrity of seals should be documented during construction, especially in those cases where a failure could cause pressurization of a nonclean environment.

1. Insulation

Particle-releasing materials are not allowable on the air path. Insulation and acoustical lines are to be applied only on the exterior of the ductwork. If inner lines are used, as in some air handling units, they should be totally sealed and the nature and qualifications of the procedure should be documented. No asbestos-containing insulation is permitted either as insulation, sealing, or adhesive agent.

2. Flexible Ducts

Certain applications require the advantages and versatility of flexible ducting. Integrity of the ducting system is a major concern in the selection of adequate material. Factory-fabricated ducts for air conditioning applications are available in the following types:

1. Spiral wire reinforced fabric
2. Spiral band reinforced fabric
3. Flexible metal
4. Factory insulated and acoustical types

The preferred type for controlled environment applications is flexible metal with an insulated jacket and a vapor barrier. Fabric ducts are not an adequate choice because of the risk of damage and their particle-releasing action.

Flexible ductwork is limited to short distances to minimize problems involving air tightness and continuity of the vapor barrier. Selection of these materials should be consistent with the overall design of the ductwork; generally speaking, these types of materials are suitable only for low-pressure systems.

3. Air Diffusers

The air can be delivered to the controlled environment from the duct network by a diffuser, the function of which is to distribute the air throughout the room. Air delivery can be at low or high velocities and with or without a terminal filtration. Low velocities are recommended for environments in which turbulence is considered a potential threat, generally those rooms working at levels not exceeding 10,000 particles of 0.5 µm and larger per cubic foot of air.

This type of low-velocity unit has an air absolute filter and is known as an absolute filter terminal unit. In this case there is no control over the directionality of the air delivered. High-speed differences are used mostly for comfort, and installation should create a turbulent environment to favor heat exchange for proper temperature control. Turbulence is generated by delivering air at high speeds in a directional fashion, creating eddy currents along the direct air path. This type of diffuser is usually avoided in controlled spaces because turbulence represents a cross-contamination potential. Also, the construction of this diffuser does not offer possibilities for adequate cleaning and sanitizing.

4. Louvers and Return Grills

Louvers and return grills are used to return the air back into the duct network. The adequate selection for locations will depend on various factors, such as:

1. Interaction with architectural components
2. Interaction with machinery and equipment
3. Volume of air to be removed
4. Ideal air-flow patterns
5. Nature and type of sanitizing procedures

An air return has limited influence in terms of air directionality. Velocities at short distances from the exhaust part drop dramatically, 90% at one time. The distance is equivalent to the diameter of the opening (Fig. 1). Low and uniformly distributed openings along the base of the controlled environment are preferred to minimize the effects of turbulence created by frictional drag from the air contact at floor level. Return grills include options to house prefilters designed to prevent contaminants in the ductwork and to control the undesired effects of back-flow, potentially present in some installations when the system is not fully operatonal. (If no exhaust is used, the airborne contaminant can reenter the clean space, moved by the changes in internal pressure.)

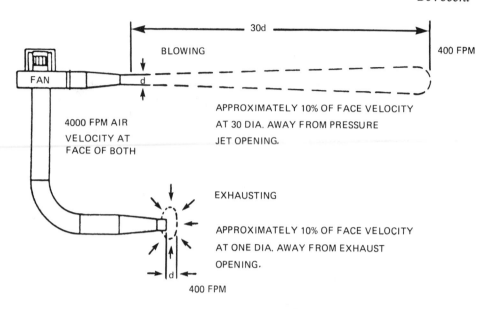

FIGURE 1   Air return.

Obstructions to air returns caused by equipment or personnel could alter the air-flow patterns, so layouts used during the design and qualification stages must be maintained during the validation procedures. This is particularly important in those installations equipped with partial or total laminar-flow equipment to assure proper usage of the laminar-flow properties.

Construction of grills and diffusers should assure adequate cleaning and sanitation procedures. The installation should guarantee the integrity and continuity of the ductwork as well as the controlled environment. Leaks at joints at the connecting points of diffusers of return grills potentially represent a problem for adequate, continuous operation.

C. Air Filtration

Various types of air filter designs, construction, and efficiency are available. The evaluation of airborne contamination levels in environments surrounding the facility is necessary for proper filter selection.

A great number of small particles (0.5 µm) are found in a typical air volume sample. These particles represent about 2% of the weight in a representative air sample, but they account for 59% of the number of particles in the air. Larger particles (10 µm) are not found as frequently in the environment or suspended in the air; because of their heavy weight and gravitational forces, they tend to settle down.

1. Filter Efficiency

In general, filter *efficiency* is defined as a filter's ability to retain a certain percentage of the particles that reach it (also known as *collection efficiency*), although, for high-efficiency filters, the percentage passing through the filter (penetration) is used as the measurement.

2. Functions of Air Filters

Air filters can be divided into two types according to function:

1. Filters for the separation and collection of contaminants in those areas where they are generated. These filters are generally employed in areas where the density of the dust is very high. These filters are usually water scrubbers, separators, vibratory filters, bag filters, bag filters with cyclonic collection systems, or electrostatic precipitators.
2. Filters used to provide clean air to a confined environment, to prevent outside contamination. This kind of filter is used most by the pharmaceutical industry.

To select the proper filtration system, the following operative characteristics of each filter must be determined: (a) collection efficiency and rating method; (b) air-flow resistance (pressure drop) at specified air volume; (c) service life; and (d) arrestance or dust-loading capacity.

3. Evaluation of Air Filtration Systems

Methods That Use Synthetic Dust Composed of Precise Mixtures of Different Types of Particles of Different Sizes: These particles are air-streamed to the filter, which is weighed before and after particles have gone through. By calculating the original weight of the synthetic dust, the original weight of the filter, and the new weight of the filter, the weight retained on the filter can be determined. Weight efficiency is expressed as a percentage. Examples of this method are the ASHRAE and AFI tests. This type of test is normally used for filters that work in extremely contaminated air. These filters, known generally as coarse filters, have very low efficiency. Most of the metal media filters are included in this group.

Tests That Use Atmospheric Air Without Addition of Dust: The purpose of this test is to measure the reduction of soiling properties of ventilation air, assuming that this is one of the major objectives in air cleaning. It is a more rigorous test than the weight method. Samples of cleaned and uncleaned air are drawn simultaneously through white paper sampling filters, and the sampling filters, and the sampling rate of the cleaned air is adjusted until the two white sampling filters discolor at the same rate. Dust collection efficiency is determined from the ratio of the two sampling rates. Discoloration of the test filter papers is measured with a photocell by noting the decrease in intensity of a standard illumination source shining through the paper. Atmospheric dust is commonly used as the test material for electrostatic precipitators and more efficient types of fibrous filters. The atmospheric and decoloration tests are used for filters intended to control the soiling properties of dirty air. Today's in-use standard is set by the American Society of Heating and Refrigeration Engineers (ASHRAE) No. 52–68 and is widely used in efficiency evaluation of intermediate air filters.

Methods Employing Particles of Uniform Size and Weight: These particles are thermally generated by an aerosol system and are blown in known percentage into the airstream. The difference between the percentage of particles in the air downstream of the filter face (calculated electronically), and the percentage in the air upstream of the filter face is the filter efficiency. This method, used on absolute filters, is known as DOP. The DOP Test is used for evaluating high-efficiency filters. It is an accurate and continuous method ensuring the quality of a very critical filter for a very critical environment.

4. Types of Air Filters

1. *Filters with static media.* These filters have nonrenewable media. Once saturated, they have to be replaced. This group includes most of the absolute filters and the intermediate-efficiency bag filters for dust control.
2. *Filters with an automatic change of the media.* These filters are similar to the static media filters; once the medium has been saturated, the filter medium is rewound, keeping the filter in continuous operation. These filters use the principle of inertial collection of prefilters.
3. *Electrostatic filters.* These filters operate by electrically charging the particles in the airstream, collecting them on oppositely charged elements afterwards. Their filter capacity is renewed by means of washing the elements or switching charges on the collecting elements. These filters are operated with a power source and high voltage.

5. HEPA Filters

A HEPA filter is a high-efficiency filter capable of retaining particles as small as 0.3 μm. The HEPA filter or absolute filter was developed by the U.S. Chemical Corps for use in air masks used for chemical warfare. The filter medium is composed of extremely fine (0.1-μm) glass fibers. The glass fibers make up as much as 99% of the medium, leaving about 1% for binders. Most of the microglass filter media in the market have fire-retardant and waterproof properties.

These superfine glass media provide several filtration capabilities to the HEPA or absolute filter. The retention of small particles is achieved by Brownian diffusion, of intermediate-size particles by the interception or inertial effect (impacted against the fiber by means of sudden changes of air directionality) and also by way of the sieving effect, the most elementary form of air filtration.

HEPA Filter Construction: To form an absolute filter, the glass medium is pleated in an accordion fashion. Each pleat is separated by using a corrugated separator firmly bonded to a frame (Fig. 2).

The basic components of a HEPA filter are

1. Frame
2. Filter medium
3. Separators
4. Adhesive
5. Gasket

Construction materials for filter frames include:

1. Particle board
2. Steel (galvanized or cadmium-plated)
3. Anodized aluminum
4. Plastic
5. Stainless steel

FIGURE 2   HEPA filter.

Frame selection is based on filter application. Particle board has been used widely by the industry with good results. Some argue the possibility of particle release, but if the filter passes the DOP test and provides class 100 air, it can be safely said that the filter will operate safely during its service life. Only defective filter frames are unsafe relative to particle emissions.

Frame selection in general is based on chemical or fire resistance requirements, since the particle emission and the strength of any of the above-mentioned materials offer satisfactory results.

Most of the media in use today are manufactured with glass microfibers, asbestos-glass and cellulose-asbestos having been discontinued. Filtration velocities are in the range 5–12 fpm. Dust-loading capacities of these media are in the range 0.0001–0.001 grains per cubic foot of air. Media can be made to sustain temperatures from below 0 to 750°F.

Separators are used primarily to space the filter media and allow a free passage of air, and secondarily to provide air directionality. Materials used for separators include:

1. Heavy Kraft paper
2. Aluminum alloy
3. Plastic
4. Glass
5. Asbestos

Because of their mechanical resistance and appearance, aluminum and plastic separators are preferred by the pharmaceutical industry.

Contaminated aluminum separators will show particles more readily than Kraft paper separators. Minipleat absolute filters and "separatorless" (TM) filters use molded-glass filter media, absolute paper ribbon, or glass strings as separators. The elimination or reduction of the number of separators will increase the air flow while maintaining the same pressure drop. Applications not requiring the use of separators for air directionality are suitable for this type of filter.

Adhesives: Adhesives are used in HEPA filters to bond the frame and the glass media. The ideal adhesive has a high solid content. Any adhesive that could potentially trap solvent or air bubbles could in time create a leakage problem not evident at the time of factory testing.

Rubber-base adhesives in general have a low solids content (30% max.). Before testing it is necessary to verify that the flue has cured—meaning that the solvent (MKT, generally) has evaporated.

Hot-melt adhesives and urethane foams are good alternatives, since their solids content is high.

Special adhesives are good for high-temperature applications, but they should be carefully selected to assure that there is no particle release with time.

Gaskets: Most of the gaskets currently in use are closed-cell Neoprene and have a durometer range from 9 to 15. Alternative materials such as Teflon gaskets, molded urethanes, etc., may be used, but they should assure a resilience equivalent to or better than that of closed-cell neoprene.

Handling of HEPA Filters: HEPA filters are designed to operate at a high efficiency level. Careful selection of materials and thorough testing by the manufacturer does not guarantee the performance at the user's plant. Improper handling by shippers and the user's employees can damage the filters permanently. Therefore, it is important to have proper shipping inspection, handling, and testing methods.

6. Air Filtration Systems

Air filter combinations used in pharmaceutical facilities vary according with the areas where the air systems are used. Each area has specific requirements that should be met by a specific filtration and air handliing system. The following are the most commonly used combinations:

Area	Absolute 99.97%	Intermediate 95% DOP	Prefiltration 85% ASHRAE, 30% ASHRAE
Clean room	Required	Optional	Recommended
Preparation	Optional	Recommended	Recommended
Washing	Optional	Recommended	Recommended
QC Labs, Chemical	Not required	Not required	Recommended
QC Labs, Microbiological	Recommended	Not required	Recommended
General packaging	Not required	Not required	Recommended

	Absolute	Intermediate	Prefiltration
Area	99.97%	95% DOP	85% ASHRAE, 30% ASHRAE
Research, general	Optional	Optional	Recommended
Animal rooms	Optional	Recommended	Recommended
Dust-generating operation	Optional	Recommended	Recommended

D. Controls

The combination of equipment designed to provide the necessary balance of environmental conditions must be continuously monitored, as well as the particular environment in question and control as well as the particular environment in question and control functions to assure continuous adequate operation. A control function is a feed back operation consisting, in this case, of the continuous analysis of the conditions provided by the hardware and those prevailing in the controlled environment. The continuous comparison of the input, provided conditions, and the output conditions at the room with the expected, preestablished conditions, triggers the feedback function requirement for proper and adequate balance.

The degree and complexity of the control system is based on the type of process, the size of the facility, the type of system used for energy conservation, the safety devices required for the process, and local or federal authorities.

Control devices can be activated and the control reaction transmitted by pneumatic or electrical energy. Selection is based on cost, reactive speed, availability, service precision, performance, etc.

The most common control devices used in a clean room are thermostats and humidistats. One aims to control all of the heating and cooling devices and the second to control humidity. Sensing of temperature and humidity by these devices varies from the use of thermocouples, mercury-operated devices, hot-wired thermosensors, gold-plated mirrors, etc. The cost and type most times is related to accuracy and performance, conditions determined again by the process.

1. Pressurization and Air Volume Controls

Pressure and air volume are critical for maintaining the integrity of a critical environment. Devices used for controlling pressure and air volumes work closely with the equipment and hardware used for environmental control, such as ductwork, dampers, and air handling devices. Depending on the type of system, several sensing stations are located within the room and up- and downstream of the air distribution network to assure the proper pressure differentials among the various rooms. The speed of reaction of these controls determine in many instances the recovery time of a critical enclosure, i.e., if a pressurization control takes a long time to react after a depressurization action, such as opening a door, is taken, the integrity of the enclosure could be put in jeopardy. The control complexity and price of pressurization and volume control devices vary with, among other things, the air volumes handled, accuracy, reactive speed control, and type of operation controls (electromechanical, electropneumatic, or electronic).

Control devices should be carefully validated prior to beginning operations. Control sequence and calibration are customary procedures in any new installation, and verification of the procedures, equipment, and recording methods is part of validation.

III. QUALIFICATION AND VALIDATION METHODS AND PROCEDURES

The phases of a project where specialized environmental control is required include the following (Chart I):

    Conceptual design
    Equipment and materials selection
    Design and engineering
    Selection of supplier and contractor
    Construction
    Testing and acceptance

The flow of personnel and materials dictates the conceptual design of the facility. Adequate operational parameters as well as process and equipment compatibility are defined at the detailed design and engineering stages. Early participation of those involved in the validation process favors a clear understanding of the design parameters to be validated and certified later.

Qualification is the determination made by a group of experts by which equipment, methods, or systems used are deemed adequate for the manufacturing process.

Those involved in validating a system should obtain sufficient documentation to prove the qualifications of those involved in the qualification process. The use of unqualified personnel cannot lead to a qualified system.

Qualification of materials, construction methods, personnel, etc., takes place during the stages of design, engineering, and selection of contractors and suppliers; validation personnel should be involved to ensure that the proper documentation is kept and proper recording procedures are set.

The validation process must be a team effort involving Design, Construction, Manufacturing, Maintenance, Quality Control and Quality Assurance groups. This process will ensure that the facility is properly programed, designed, and constructed under the required conditions imposed by the product or process.

This task is accomplished by a group of experts defined as the Validation Task Force (Chart II).

A. Personnel Qualifications

In order to have a valid and qualified system it must be designed, built, and operated by qualified individuals. The same applies for validation of the system. Therefore, all members of the task force should be qualified. Individuals can be qualified by their academic training, experience, or

TASK FORCE FORMATION

CONCEPTUAL DESIGN STUDY

DESIGN AND ENGINEERING
SPECIFICATIONS STUDY

SELECTION OF CHECK POINTS
BASED ON FINAL SPECIFICATIONS
AND CONTRACTUAL DOCUMENTS

VALIDATION CHECK POINTS
DURING CONSTRUCTION

VALIDATION CHECK POINTS DURING
QUALIFICATION AND COMMISSIONING

TESTING AND CHALLENGING
FOR VALIDATION

PREPARATION OF FINAL
VALIDATION DOCUMENTATION

FACILITY CERTIFICATION AND
PREPARATION OF
REVALIDATION SCHEDULE

CHART I   Environmental systems validation process.

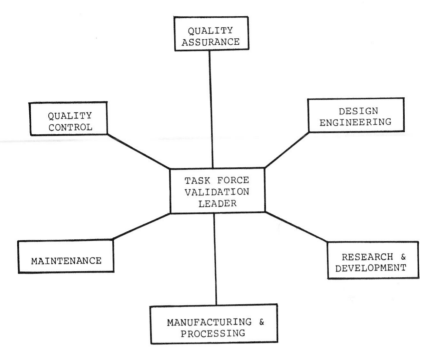

CHART II   Validation task force for environmental control system.

developmental work. Certain aspects of facility construction and product
manufacturing require academic board certification or official certification.
If this is the case, individuals participating in those disciplines must comply
with this requirement. Careful records must be kept to document the selection and qualification of the members of the task force. The more comprehensive the information is on each individual, the better. A statement signed
by the selected members attesting to the authenticity of the recorded information is advisable. Once the task force has been formed, every member should
convey the scope of participation to their represented groups. Coordination
of the task force can be assumed by any of the qualified individuals on the
force, but preferably the person selected should have a good overall knowledge of the manufacturing process as well as those aspects related to facilities construction and environmental control (Charts III and IV).

B. Organization and Coordination

The task force will remain active at every phase of the process, starting with
conceptual facility design. The process requirements are clearly identified
before the design process starts. Changes will follow the original analysis,
but before the task force formally accepts the validation parameters, a final
acceptance must be forwarded by groups involved in specifications. Any
further changes should have supporting documentation and must be forwarded
to the validation task force as well.

   With the parameters defined at the conceptual design level, the task force
will determine the prevalidation checks required along with the final design
and engineering. Chart IV shows a typical breakdown of the design and

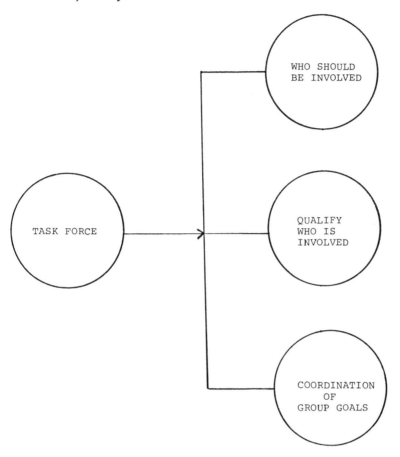

CHART III   Personnel qualifications.

engineering activities. Some of these activities have no relationship to the
validation process, but others, such as specifications for contractual documents, could be linked to it. Some of the validation checks and tests are
the contractor's responsibilities; therefore, the language, methodology, and
reporting methods should be reviewed and approved by the task force so
that they fulfill the validation requirements in the area of concern. Another
area in the same category is the specifications for construction logs and the
documentation related to the validation aspects. These are the open logs and
documents that are used during facilities construction to record activities related to the validation of the system, and any changes that may have an effect
on the original design parameters. The logs and forms designed for this
purpose should include spaces for the activity date, type of activity or test
performed, individuals involved, methodology used or document reference,
reporting form number, and distribution schedules.

It is always advisable for the task force to review the rest of the specifications and related engineering documentation prior to releasing them for
bidding purposes. This review will probably bring to light some items required for the proper functioning of the environmental control system. The

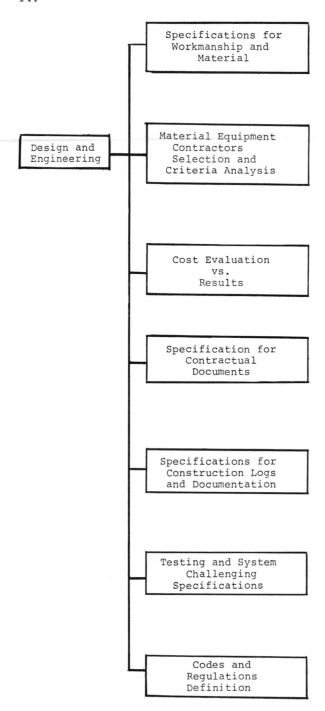

CHART IV   Validation check points definition.

experience of the individuals in this task force is extremely important, as this is one of the most critical stages in a new facility's construction and their input can mean the difference between the facility's success and failure.

C. Protocols

A protocol is a document in which a specific check or validation procedure is outlined. These documents are written by the task force and should reflect the philosophy of the validation process. They should assure the system's continuous performance within the specified parameters. Any deviation from the agreed protocols must be justified and approved by the task force. The justifications and any changes are to be carefully recorded and logged for further references.

A protocol should clearly define the scope, equipment, methodology, acceptance, and rejection levels, and recording methods required in each case. The calibration requirements and recalibration intervals for the equipment used should also be recorded. Sequential numbering and information such as author or authors, publication date, location, and referenced documents, as required, are advisable for future referencing and use. Verification protocols are also written to verify one or more of the following procedures for each component of the system during construction as part of a quality assurance process:

Reception
Storage
Handling
Acceptance
Rejection
Contamination control
Identification
Cleaning
Testing, etc.

Protocols are also employed to verify the appropriateness of the equipment design, size, and location, as well as the related process specifications such as construction materials (materials used in the equipment should not react, add or absorb, or in any way affect the raw materials or process equipment). Protocols should include written procedures to assign responsibilities for verification, cleaning, testing, and calibration during validation to qualified personnel.

1. Records

The reporting methods during the validation process can take as many forms as individuals and companies involved in the process; there is no universal or generally accepted practice. However, in most cases, reports can be divided into two groups:

Those related to verifying specifications, materials, or workmanship
Those that report the performance of a system or a component of a system

Because of their nature, those in the first group are part of the construction process and can be documented using the same forms and procedures devised for the construction engineers. This is generally done in the form of a logbook or similar device in which copies of engineering verification reports required for validation are kept. As indicated, these check points or verification points are predetermined by the task force and communicated to involved parties.

The second group of reports requires a more formal and structured reporting method, so specific forms must be designed following the outline suggested in the related protocol. These reports, along with the "validation logbook," which includes "as-built" drawings, will form a central part of the final validation file.

It is important to stress that all records should have the date, time, equipment description and calibration dates, signatures and names of personnel involved, and the location at which a protocoled procedure has been performed.

Deviation reports and information routing must be distributed along with the corresponding protocols.

IV. ENVIRONMENTAL PERFORMANCE TEST PROTOCOLS

Controlled environments should generally be subjected to the following set of performance tests related to environmental control:

1. Air flow, volume, and distribution test (also designated as postbalancing verification)
2. Temperature test
3. Humidity test
4. Pressurization Control test
5. Airborn particle count test
6. Enclosure induction test
7. Particle dispersion and recovery test
8. Main air supply and make-up supply volume and reserve capacity
9. Lighting level test
10. Microbial level assessment test

Most of these are performance tests required for the final certification and validation of the environment. The test sequencing indicated in Table 1 is the one typically used. Some of the tests are to be repeated at least two times, to verify the ability of the system(s) to operate continuously within the specified parameters. A final performance test must be executed when all the construction work has been finished, with the rooms "at rest" and under simulated operating conditions (sometimes defined as "static" and "dynamic" conditions). The instruments used for these tests should be in perfect conditions, and current calibration reports should be included with the report. Following is a summary of protocols used to determine the performance of an environmental control system.

A. HEPA Filter Leak Test

1. Purpose

To ensure against HEPA filter failure due to damage during installation or operation.

TABLE 1   Pressure Differential Stress Testing Matrix

	Test 1	Test 2	Test 3	Test 4
Gowning	Closed	Open	Closed	Closed
Ancillary	Closed	Closed	Open	Closed
Primary (room)	Closed	Open	Open	Open
Corridor	Closed	Closed	Open	Closed

2. Equipment

DOP polydisperse aerosol generated by blowing air through liquid dioctyl phthalate (DOP) at room temperature. The approximate light-scattering mean droplet size distribution of the aerosol is

99% + less than 3.0 μm
95% + less than 1.5 μm
92% + less than 1.0 μm
50% + less than 0.72 μm
25% + less than 0.45 μm
11% + less than 0.35 μm

DOP aerosol generator—compressed-air operated, equipped with Laskin-type nozzles as described in USA Standard N-5.11.

Aerosol photometer—light-scattering type with a threshold sensitivity of at least 10^{-3} mg/liter. Capable of measuring concentrations in the range of 80–120 mg/liter, and with air sample flow rate of 1 ft^3 ± 10% per minute. This instrument is to be calibrated by the manufacturer after every 100 hr of use.

3. Method

1. This test is performed only by certified personnel who introduce DOP aerosol upstream of the filter through a test port and search for leaks downstream with an aerosol photometer.
2. Filter testing is performed after operational air velocities have been verified and adjusted where necessary.
3. Align the aerosol photometer as follows:
4. Position the smoke generator so the DOP aerosol will be introduced into the airstream ahead of the HEPA filters.
5. Open the appropriate number of nozzles until a DOP challenge concentration of 100 mg/liter of air is reached. This challenge concentration is measured upstream of the HEPA filter, and is evidenced by a reading between 4 and 5 on the logarithmic scale of the aerosol photometer.

6. Scan each filter by holding the photometer probe approximately 1 in. from the filter face and passing the probe in slightly over-lapping strokes, at a traverse rate of not more than 10 ft/min, so that the entire face is sampled.

7. Make separate passes with the photometer probe around the entire pheriphery of the filter, along the bond between the filter medium and the frame, and along all other joints in the installation through which leakage might bypass the filter medium.

4. Acceptance Criteria

1. An unacceptable leak is defined as 0.01% of the reference calibra-tion curve.

2. Leaks are sealed using silicone sealant (DOW or 3M Weatherstrip Adhesive) by caulking a 1-in. to 2-in. area around the leak par-allel to the medium and between the separators. The sealant is forced over the filter medium between the separators and smoothed flush with the separators. The filter is then rechecked for leaks as specified above.

3. The extent of filter face obscured at any point by patching ma-terials is limited to 5% of the filter area so that the resulting void in the air stream will be filled in before reaching the work area. If more is sealed, the filter must be rejected and a new one installed.

B. Temperature Control Test

1. Purpose

To demonstrate the ability of the air handling system to control tem-perature at 72°F ± 10% all year round.

2. Equipment

Calibrated dry-bulb thermometer, thermoanemometer, or thermocouples and recorder.

3. Method

1. Air conditioning systems are to be in continuous operation for at least 24 hr prior to performing these tests. All lights in the sterile core are to be on during the testing as well as during the 24-hr preconditioning period.

2. Measure and record temperatures at 15-min intervals for a period of 2 hr at each of the indicated locations for each room. (See room reporting form.)

3. The test should be repeated for at-rest and dynamic conditions.

4. Acceptance Criteria

The system shall be capable of maintaining a dry-bulb temperature of 72°F ± 10% all year round, with the specified occupancy and heat-genera-tion design levels.

C. Humidity Control Test

1. Purpose

To demonstrate the capability of the air handling system to control humidity at the specified level for each room.

2. Equipment

Dry-bulb and wet-bulb thermometers; automatic humidity recorder.

3. Method

1. Execute this test after all the balancing procedures have been concluded.
2. Measure and record humidities for the conditions and locations specified for every room under "at-rest" and dynamic conditions.
3. Operate the system for at least 6 hr prior to the start of the test.
4. Record water temperatures at the beginning and end of the test, if possible.

4. Acceptance Criteria

The relative humidity at each grid point shall be equal to the specified levels and tolerance limits, indicated on each recording form. If these levels are attained, the system is accepted.

D. Air Flow and Uniformity Test

1. Purpose

1. To demonstrate that the air system is balanced and capable of delivering sufficient air volumes to maintain a minimum cross-sectional velocity under the absolute terminal/filter modules of at least 90 fpm measured 6 in. downstream of the filters.
2. To verify air velocities before the air encounters an obstruction; this should be conducted when new filters are installed in the system.
3. To verify horizontal and vertical air velocity components at the point the clean air reaches an obstacle or a surface 40 in. above the floor, whichever occurs first.

2. Equipment

Hot-wire anemometer and stand.

3. Method

1. These tests are to be executed in every room where an absolute terminal filter module is installed by approved personnel.
2. Draw a grid on the floor as indicated in the room diagram.
3. Measure and record the velocity at the center of each grid at the specified heights.
4. Allow no objects within 10 ft of the anemometer, except for built-in equipment. Minimize the number of people during the "at-rest" testing.

5. Measurements should be taken for a minimum of 15 sec.
6. Record the pressure readings (in inches) from the manometer connected to the module's plenum.

4. *Acceptance Criteria*

Average measured clean air velocity shall be higher than 90 fpm and not exceeding 150 fpm at 6 in. downstream from the filter face. Velocity differences within the same plenum should not vary more than 25%.

E. Pressure Control Test

1. *Purpose*

To demonstrate the capability of the system to control pressure levels within the specified limits.

2. *Equipment*

Inclined pressure gauge with resolution of 0.01 in. of water.

3. *Method*

1. All HVAC and laminar-flow systems are to be in continuous operation when performing these tests.
2. To avoid unexpected changes in pressure and to establish a baseline, all doors in the sterile facility must be closed and no traffic is to be allowed through the facility during the test.
3. Pressure readings are taken with the high- and low-pressure tubing at the following locations: (Refer to each room's diagram.)
4. The following stress conditions as indicated in Table 1 should be simulated while monitoring pressures at the locations delineated in step 3.

4. *Acceptance Criteria*

1. Pressure differentials should be as indicated in the design conditions at all times under static conditions.
2. Pressure differentials should be maintained as indicated in the design conditions under standard simulated operating conditions.
3. Pressure differentials should be above 0.02 at the primary environments when stress conditions occur.
4. The system will not be acceptable if, at any time during normal dynamic, static, or stress conditions, the pressure in the primary environments become less than zero or netative.

5. *Recording*

The final balancing report will become a part of the validation documentation.

F. Particle Count Test

   1. Purpose

   To establish that at critical work locations within clean rooms, a count of less than 100 particles per cubic foot of air, 0.5 μm in diameter or larger, is maintained.

   2. Equipment

   Light-scattering particle counter, as described in American Society for Testing Materials Standard F50−69.

   3. Method

   1. These tests are performed by authorized personnel after the HEPA filter leak tests and air velocity tests are completed.
   2. To obtain baseline data with the room in static conditions, perform the following tests with operational personnel absent and the equipment at rest:
      a. Using the particle analyzer, count particles greater than or equal to 0.5 μm in diameter at heights of 40 in. in the center of each grid shown on the test report.
      b. If the particle count in the 0.5 μm range is less than 50 per cubic foot of air, four additional counts at this location are taken to place these particle counts within a 50% confidence interval.
   3. After completion of these tests, if the absolute air filtration modules are operating within accepted limits, repeat steps 2a and 2b with operational personnel present and the fill equipment running. If at any time there is a deviation from accepted parameters, the various components of the systems in operation are reviewed, repaired, or adjusted until the desired conditions are achieved.

   4. Acceptance Criteria

   1. The air system can be considered validated when the results of three consecutive sets of tests are within accepted operational parameters.
   2. At any of the designated critical locations, a critical location being where any sterilized product or material is exposed to the working environment, the particulate count shall not exceed 100 particles 0.5 μm in diameter and larger per cubic foot of air.

   5. Ancillary Environment Acceptance Criteria

   The same test should be repeated at ancillary environments. Ancillary environment shall not exceed a particle count of 100,000 particles 0.5 μm in diameter and larger per cubic foot of air in order to be considered acceptable by current regulations. It is common practice to design and operate ancillary environments at levels not exceeding 10,000 particles of 0.5 μm per cubic foot of air. This is to provide additional protection to the final product while it is being processed at the critical area.

Table 2 summarizes the contamination sources and the suggested control methods. Review of this table prior to executing the above procedures is recommended.

TABLE 2   Contamination Sources and Control

Source	Control
People	Total body covering on critical areas and partial in noncritical areas
	Adequate personnel flow and restricted access to aseptic and critical environments
	Adequate equipment location to avoid excess handling of materials and minimum movement of personnel
	Limiting number of personnel working in critical environments
	Adequate operating procedures for personnel
Process	Adequate cleaning and sterilization procedures and equipment
	Barriers and separation from high-risk to low-risk operations
	Protective laminar-flow equipment
	Adequate process equipment designed for operation in critical areas; proper covers and barriers to contain contamination from moving parts
	Adequate operating procedures to assure proper handling, cleaning, sterilization of machinery and equipment
	Adequate standards for equipment and construction material selection
	Adequate selection of manufacturing environments
	Adequate vacuum cleaning devices for powder or contaminant-generating operations
Materials	Adequate materials control and selection
	Adequate sterilization and filtration procedures
	Adequate handling of materials procedures and equipment
	Adequate control and testing methods to assure cleanliness levels and sterility
Air	Adequate air filtration systems
	Adequate air cleanliness levels monitoring
	Adequate air systems validation procedures
	Adequate maintenance procedures

Table 3 provides the cleanliness class definition as established in Federal Standard 209-B.

Table 4 provides a guideline of cleanliness levels required for a typical manufacturing operation.

G. Induction Leak Test

1. Purpose

To determine if there is intrusion of unfiltered air into the clean work areas from outside the clean-room enclosure through joints and cracks in the walls, ceiling, etc., other than from the pressurized air supply system, and to determine unfiltered air intrusion into the clean room through open entrance doorways.

2. Equipment

Optical particle counter.

3. Method

1. Measure the concentration outside the clean-room enclosure immediately adjacent to the surface or doorway to be evaluated. This concentration should be at least 100,000 particles per cubic foot of a size equal to and greater than 0.5 μm. If the concentration is less, generate an aerosol to increase the concentration.
2. To check for construction joint leakage, scan all joint areas from a distance of 6 in. at a speed of approximately 10 in./min.
3. To check for intrusion of open doorways, measure the concentration inside the enclosure at 10 in. from the open door.
4. Repeat the same test in front of any openings, i.e., passthroughs, electrical outlets, and any opening connecting with the outside.
5. Repeat this test while opening and closing clean-room entrance doors.

4. Acceptance Criteria

No construction joint leaks or intrusion through open doors should exceed 0.1% of the measured external concentration.

TABLE 3   Air Cleanliness Level: Definition of Classes

| | Maximum number of particles | | | |
| | 0.5 μm | | 5 μm | |
Class	Per cubic foot	Per cubic meter	Per cubic foot	Per cubic meter
100	100	3.5	—	—
10,000	10,000	350	65	2.3
100,000	100,000	3,500	700	25

TABLE 4   Guidelines for Cleanliness Levels Required During Manufacturing of a Parenteral Drug

Operation	Class	Cleanliness level (particles 0.5 µm and larger)
Warehousing	—	—
Preparation	100,000	No more than 100,000
Filtration	100,000	No more than 100,000
Filling area	100,000 or better	No more than 100,000
Filling line (point of use)	100	No more than 100

H. Test for Air Flow Patterns

1. Scope

To determine air-flow interaction with machinery and equipment in a critical area protected with a laminar-flow clean air system.

2. Purpose

To determine the air-flow patterns during fill-line operation; to select and improve the flow pattern that generates the minimum turbulence and best washing capabilities.

3. Equipment

White visible or yellow smoke generator, anemometer, 35-mm camera or videotape recorder.

4. Method

1. Verify that the laminar-flow devices in the sterile core are operational.
2. Check air velocities at 6 in. from the filter face to ensure that the device is operating within the specified laminar-flow velocity (90 ft/min or more).
3. Verify that the ventilation and air conditioning systems are operating and balanced.
4. If the system operates according to the specified operating parameters, begin to generate white visible smoke at the critical locations. A critical location is defined as any area where sterilized product or material is exposed to the working environment.
5. Generate white smoke inside and over each component that forms part of the line. (To avoid damage to the materials or equipment, cover them tightly with plastic.) Film the smoke as it travels through each critical area of the machine.
6. Smoke should flow through these critical areas. If the air does return (back-flows) due to turbulence, the system cannot be

accepted and must be rebalanced or adjusted. Slight turbulence, due to equipment configuration, is not significant as long as the air does not return to the critical areas.

7. If the system passes the test in step 6, continue to film while the smoke is generated and an operator enters the protected area. If the smoke back-flows to the critical working area at any point during this operation, procedures must be established to prevent cross-contamination and reentry into these areas. If the unit passes, proceed to step 8.

8. Determine if the generated turbulence can carry contaminants from other areas to critical points of the line. If so, adjust the air flow to ensure a minimum of turbulence and rapid cleaning. If the turbulence cannot be stopped, a different aerodynamic pattern must be found. (Covers and diffusers can be used over the filling equipment.) If turbulence carries contaminants from any area to the critical areas, the system should be reevaluated and analyzed in terms of the filling, capping, and laminar-flow equipment.

5. Acceptance Criteria

If the results of steps 6, 7, and 8 are unsatisfactory, the laminar-flow system cannot be validated and the rest of the validation tests should not be carried out until a satisfactory operation has been reached. Otherwise, the system is valid and can be certified.

Should corrective changes be necessary, the changes are made, recorded, and the validation process repeated.

I. Recovery Test

1. Purpose

To determine the capabilities of the system to recover from internally generated contamination.

2. Equipment

Visual smoke generator, particle counter, hot-wire anemometer.

3. Method

1. With smoke generation output tube located at a predesignated location, generate smoke for 1—2 min and shut off.

2. Wait 2 min and then advance the sample tube of the particle counter to a point directly under the smoke source and at the level of the work zone. Record the particle count. If it is not 100 per cubic foot or less, repeat the test with the wait interval increased in steps of 1/2 min until counts are less than 100 per cubic foot.

3. Repeat for all grid areas, recording recovery time for each grid area.

4. Acceptance Criteria

The recovery time should be not more than 2 min.

H. Particle Dispersion Test

1. *Purpose*

To verify the parallelism of air flow throughout the work zone and the capability of the clean room to limit the dispersion.

These tests may be applied at the discretion of the buyer when deemed necessary.

2. *Equipment*

Visual smoke generator, particle counter, hot-wire anemometer.

3. *Method*

1. Perform this test after completion of the air-velocity uniformity tests.
2. Divide the work zone into 2 X 2 ft grids of equal area.
3. Set up the smoke generator, with outlet tube pointing in the direction of air flow and located at the center of a grid area at the work zone entrance plane.
4. If smoke is introduced with air pressure, adjust it to provide a smoke outlet velocity equal to the room air velocity at that point.
5. Operate the particle counter with the sample tube at the normal work level and at a point remote from the smoke source. Verify that the counter indicates particle concentrations less than 100 particles of 0.5 μm or greater.
6. Move the sample tube in toward the smoke source from all directions at this level to the point where particle counts show a sudden and rapid rise to high levels (10^6 per cubic foot). This defines the envelope of dispersion away from the smoke source and demonstrates the air-flow parallelism control of the room.
7. Repeat for all grid areas. Prepare a diagram showing grid areas and corresponding dispersion envelopes.

4. *Acceptance Criteria*

The degree to which dispersion away from the smoke source is confined and the regularity of the pattern (indication of directional drift in one direction) is a matter of the configuration of the line. It is recommended that dispersion should not extend beyond 2 ft radially from the point of smoke source; i.e., at 2 ft from the generation point, the particle count should be less than 100 per cubic foot of the 0.5 μm size and larger.

K. Airborne Microbial Sampling

1. *Purpose*

To determine the airborne microbial contamination level.

2. *Equipment*

Solid surface impactor with a rotating collection surface and/or staged plates (Anderson-Slit).

3. Method

After proceeding with calibration and indications given in the operating manual, proceed as follows:

Aseptically prepared collection plates are placed in the sampling apparatus. Petri dishes used must be sterilized prior to filling. Verify the adequacy of Petri dish dimensions so that the operational characteristics are maintained according to the manufacturer's specifications. (Plastic Petri dishes are not recommended because static charges are likely to be present in plastic that will reduce the collection efficiency.)

Any general-purpose, solid bacteriological medium, such as trypticase soy agar or blood agar, can be used. Selective media are not recommended, since they inhibit the repair and growth of injured or stressed cells.

Verify the air sample rate, time, and location of the plate before starting the sampling. Sampling time should be 20 min at every location. After the sampling is completed, remove the collection plate(s), cover and identify them. Identification should include date, sampling instrument number, location, and plate number.

Plates then are taken to an incubator and maintained inverted, to prevent condensation drop, for a period of 18–24 hr at 35°C.

After incubation, the number of colonies on each plate is counted, using a standard bacterial colony counter.

4. Acceptance Criteria

The total number of colonies from sample plates in the same location divided by the time in minutes assuming a sample of a cubic foot per minute will give the number of viable particles per cubic foot of air sampled. This number should not exceed .1, assuming the accepted microbiological theory that each colony represents a single particle, and the correlation to the class 100 laminar-flow conditions in a controlled environment. This criterion has also been established by relating the number of colonies per cubic meter of air, limiting that amount to 3.5 colonies in class 100.

Note: Fallout sampling is not an acceptable criterion to determine the microbial environmental quality of laminar-flow devices. Because of the air-flow patterns over Petri dishes, a minimum percentage of the air gets in contact with the culture medium, rendering the test invalid. The only way to assure adequate contact is by drawing the air over the medium by mechanical force.

Filtration devices that employ membrane filters are also used, but with some drawbacks, because following filtration, the filter must be agitated to remove all particles. This could result in damage to the cells, causing loss of some organisms. Blending of the membrane with liquid media is a better technique for a more representative analysis.

Table 5 provides the NASA proposed limit of microorganisms in accordance with cleanliness-level classification.

L. Surface Sampling

1. Purpose

To determine the microbial contamination level on surfaces.

2. Equipment

Rodac plate (nutrient agar culture medium).

TABLE 5   Number of Live Organisms as Proposed by NASA
Stds. NH135430 and MSFC-STD-246

Class	Live organisms per	
	Cubic foot	Cubic meter
100	0.1	3.5
10,000	0.5	17.6
100,000	2.5	88.4

3. Method

Press the Rodac plate directly against the surface to be sampled. In-cubate until colonies develop. Use this technique for flat and smooth surfaces such as tables, floors, walls, etc.

This technique is to be used after decontamination procedures. Agar media left on surfaces could represent a problem. Therefore, immediate decontamination procedures should follow sampling.

Identify every plate, indicating the exact location where the sample was taken. Room landmarks should be noted for present and future reference.

4. Acceptance Criteria

The maximum number of colonies per square foot should not exceed 100. (Note: This is an arbitrary number set by NASA.)

V. AT-REST AND DYNAMIC TESTING

Performance tests executed under "at-rest" conditions serve as baseline information and are needed to determine the degree by which the environmental parameters are affected by the process after they are repeated at dynamic conditions (simulated fully operational conditions). It is after this analysis that certain procedures, equipment, methods, etc., are changed.

Performance tests executed at dynamic conditions are the only way to obtain a clean representation of the prevailing environmental conditions. The qualification and validation of an environmental control system can be made only if final performance tests are executed under "at rest" and "dynamic" conditions.

Protocols then should be set for each of the above conditions.

VI. STRESS TESTING

The protocols described in Section IV present the general concept in formatting an environmental control validation program related to the hardware portion. The fundamental concept is to determine the ability of the system to remain stable at all times during operation conditions defined as continuity. Stress conditions are created to determine the span of control for an individual system or rooms. Artificially created conditions representing possible but unlikely situations are predetermined based on the particular system design, and performance tests such as temperature, particle counting, etc., are executed. The results obtained are verified with adequate operational conditions and a determination is made if the system is acceptable; if it is not, then alert systems are set to report the unacceptable condition. Stress testing is also used to determine the ability of the system to recover after an unacceptable limit has been reached. Here is where the knowledge of hardware, software, and industrial pharmacy play a fundamental role. Stress testing and alert systems for hardware and software are an important part of the scope of work for the task force. Every system (hardware and software) is unique and demands specific knowledge to achieve necessary goals and not to under-/or overdo.

VII. REPORTING FORMS

The protocols define the procedures to be used to verify the performance of qualified equipment. As part of validation, the results obtained should be carefully recorded and compared with the design conditions. Deviations or diversions contrary to the specified levels determine the suitability of the controlled environment, so the reporting form represents the document for certification or acceptance of the system.

The reporting form should show the following information:

Date, start and finish time
Name of person performing the test
Location of the test
List of testing equipment with serial numbers
Calibration dates
Temperature (when applicable)
Humidity (when applicable)
Air velocity (when applicable)
Design conditions
Actual conditions
Signatures of those involved in the test
Diagrams showing test locations

The list of reporting information can be expanded as required.

VIII. MEASURING EQUIPMENT

The definitions of the various measuring apparatus are given in the definition section, and uses are indicated in the protocols for performance testing. Every measuring device is a comparison element. Comparison is made against a reference standard, in the process known as calibration. Calibration needs and procedures also vary, therefore every time a piece of equipment is used during the validation procedures, compliance with calibration requirements is to be verified before starting. Lack of adequate documentation could in many cases render the validation procedure invalid.

Adequate knowledge of the operational capabilities of the system is also fundamental. Inadequate location for sampling processes, such as badly placed particle counters, can render confusing and inaccurate results. A comprehensive training program should be in place for new operators and a minimum of qualifications should be demanded prior to acceptance of a candiate.

IX. CONCLUSION

Process validation is a documented program that provides a high degree of assurance that a specific process will consistently produce a product meeting predetermined specifications and quality attributes. This is the way the Food and Drug Administration defines validation.

This concept requires a precise definition of the suitability, performance, and reliability of materials as well as of systems, equipment, and facilities employed for the manufacturing process.

The correct perception of the environmental control concept should include all of those components, either hardware or software, that in one way or another create, control, monitor, modify, or change the components of this critical part of a parenteral drug manufacturing operation. Therefore, careful analysis should be made when selecting where and how to validate the air system so that all the critical components are tested and challenged appropriately, reflecting the level of performance, suitability, and reliability expected.

Every facility is designed and built with a specific scope. This creates a need for customized environmental control validation programs. The objective of this chapter is to address some of the prevailing concepts used for air systems validation. Nevertheless, because of the nature of the industry and the validation concept, this is a dynamic process, and those in charge of this aspect in a pharmaceutical operation should keep themselves informed on current techniques and the state of the art.

STANDARDS

Flooring
"Test for surface burning characteristics of building materials"
ASTM E 84, 182, C531, C-190

National Fire Protection Associations

Flooring specifications
Federal specification L-F-475a 8 SS-T-312

MIL-D-3134
Walls Refer to ASTM (D std.)

Air handling system
AMCA Standards 210-67 (Fans)

NFPA Standards 90A
NEMA for motor and electrical components
NEC for wiring

ASHRAE for ducting and controls
AABC for balancing

Federal Standard 20 gh.

AACC—CS-85

ASTM—Method F-50

MIL-F-51068C HEPA fire resistant

UL 586

ASHRAE 70—72

Electrical
OSHA S-1910, 309

American National Standards Institute

Duct Work and Piping

OSHA subpart C (1910.93)

ACGIH (American Conference of Governmental Industrial Hygienist)

ANST Standard VZ9

NFDA

Federal Standard 209b

Good Manufacturing Practices (Fed. register - Feb. 13, 19, 26)

Good Laboratory Practices (Fed. register - Dec. 1978)

BIBLIOGRAPHY

Agnew, B. 1965. *Laminar Flow Clean Room Handbook*. Agnew—Higgins, Los Angeles, Calif.

American Conference of Governmental Industrial Hygienists. 1980. *Industrial Ventilation*. Edwards Brothers, Ann Arbor, Mich.

ASHRAE. 1971. *Guide and Data Book*. American Society of Refrigerating and Air Conditioning Engineers, New York.

Clean Room and Workstation Requirements, Federal Standard 209-B, 1966. GSA, Washington, D.C.

DeVecchi, F. 1978. *Training Personnel to Work in Sterile Environments*. Pharmaceutical Technology, Los Angeles, Calif.

DeVecchi, F. 1981. *Clean room analysis*, in *Pharma. Tech. Conference Proc.*

DeVecchi, F. 1982. *Air systems validation*. Center for Professional Advancement, Course Notes.

Dimmick, R. L., and Wolochow, H. 1981. *Problems of measuring numbers of microbes in occupied spaces*, in *Institute of Environmental Sciences*, Proceedings.

Fuscaldo, A., Erlick, B. J., and Hindman. 1980. *Laboratory Safety*. Academic Press, New York.

McCrone, W., Draftz, R., and Delly, J. G. 1968. *The Particle Analyst*. Ann Arbor Science Publishers, Ann Arbor, Mich.

NASA. 1971. *Symposium on Clean Room Technology in Surgery Suites*. Midwest Research Institute, St. Louis, Mo.

NASA. *Handbook for Biological Engineers*. Technical Information Services, Washington, D. C.

U.S. Air Force. 1963. *Standard and Guidelines for Design and Operation of Clean Rooms and Clean Work Stations, Technical Order 00-25-203*. Technical Information Service, Washington, D.C.

U.S. Department of Defense. 1970. *Military Specification Filter, Particulate, High-Efficiency, Fire Resistance*. MIL-F-51068C. June 8.

U.S. Food and Drug Administration. 1976. *Current Good Manufacturing Practice in Manufacture, Processing, Packing or Holding*. *Federal Register*, February 13.

7

Monitoring of Nonviable Particles

ALVIN LIEBERMAN

HIAC/ROYCO Division, Pacific Scientific, Inc., Menlo Park, California

I. INTRODUCTION

Monitoring of nonviable airborne particles is required in pharmaceutical manufacturing areas even though terminal sterilization of products is frequently
used. The reasons for the airborne particle monitoring requirement include
several areas of concern. The most important is the need for product quality
control. The products that are manufactured must be assured to be free of
inert dust, even though that material may not be viable. Inert dust particles will affect the clarity and appearance of liquid products; they may be of
such a size as to interfere with passage of dry powders or may result in irregular compacts when powders are pressed. The possibility also exists that
capillary blockage can occur as a result of ingestion of badly contaminated
parenteral solutions. In addition, the inert dust may consist of chemically
reactive materials that will degrade the chemical purity of the product. In
most pharmaceutical organizations, there will be company standards and specifications that limit the quantities of inert particles in any product. In
order to assure product cleanliness, then, standards for air cleanliness levels are part of any good manufacturing process. These standards are proprietary and may vary from company to company, depending on product requirements and on experience in manufacturing pharmaceutical products.

The Food and Drug Administration's Good Manufacturing Practice Regulations, 21 CFR 210–219 [1] also incorporate airborne particle concentration
specifications. These are based on the airborne particle concentration levels
in Federal Standard 209 [2]. This standard is an example of one of the specifications imposed and administered by a government agency. For the most
part, government agency specifications were derived during the developmental times when the aerospace industry was involved in spacecraft design.
The needs for precision operations and for ensuring that any landing module
would not contaminate its target generated many of the specifications. The
requirements for precision in guidance systems were of great importance in
establishing the need for manufacturing and assembly area environmental
cleanliness.

A third source for airborne particle monitoring specifications is the voluntary standards organizations. These include groups such as the American

Society for Testing and Materials (ASTM), the Society of Automotive Engineers (SAE), the Institute of Environmental Sciences (IES), the Parenteral Drug Association (PDA), the Pharmaceutical Manufacturers Association (PMA), and the National Fluid Power Association. Source information for specifications and standards are shared by virtue of the fact that most of the personnel in the voluntary standards groups also participate in developing standards for government agencies and/or are employed by a concerned manufacturer. Further, most groups maintain liaison in following activities between agencies.

It can be emphasized that specifications are needed to ensure product quality control. Technology today requires that pharmaceutical products be pure. It is necessary to ensure that no airborne bacteria or other viable particles fall into open or otherwise exposed components, liquids or containers. In addition, normal cleanliness and appearance must be maintained. No obvious cloudiness or sediment should be present in containers of liquid; no excessive graininess should be noted in powdered or pressed solids; no detectable particulate contamination should be found on or in medical devices of any kind. Once these basic needs are satisfied, then the government imposed specifications must be satisfied as well. Note that the FDA can close down an operation if in-house specifications are not met. That requirement is based on particular operations and an associated air cleanliness level. For example, large volume parenteral (LVP) filling must be done in a Class 100 environment or better. This means that the number of particles larger than 0.5 μm cannot exceed 100 per cubic foot in the filling environment air.

II. OPERATING STANDARDS

During the course of this discussion, reference will be made frequently to Federal Standard 209. At this point, it is in order to discuss this important document in some detail. FS 209, as of 1983, was being revised from the "b" version. The pertinent parameters in FS 209 are establishment of several air cleanliness classes, in terms of number of particles per cubic foot of air (100, 1000, 10,000, and 100,000) 0.5 μm and larger and determination of environment temperature and pressure. In addition, a number of "nonmandatory" recommendations for establishment and control of air cleanliness are provided. These recommendations cover both facility design and operation. In addition, reference is made to other standards that discuss system operation. Of concern now are the standards that describe procedures for measurements in the clean room, such as ASTM F-25 [3] and ASTM F-50 [4], those that describe procedures for operation of particle counting and sizing instruments, such as ASTM F-328 [5] and ASTM F-649 [6], and those that describe methods of testing the filtration systems in the clean devices, such as MIL-F-51068 [7], ANSI N101.1 [8], and U.S. DOE Std NE-F3-41 [9]. Method F-25 describes the procedure for defining particle concentrations in a clean room by collecting particles on a filter medium and counting under a microscope to determine size and concentration data. F-50 describes procedures for operating a light-scattering single-particle counter in a clean room to define airborne particle concentration and size data. Method F-328 describes a method for calibration of an automatic particle counter for size and counting accuracy, while method F-649 defines a method for secondary calibration of a particle counter to allow correlation with a master system.

The last three specifications define both performance and operational testing of clean-room filter systems. In addition, the requirements always exist for adherence to good practice in instrument and system maintenance and operation. In most cases, adherence to manufacturer's recommendations for operation and calibration of instruments will be acceptable to the FDA.

III. PARTICLE SOURCES

In order to operate control and measurement systems that will permit adherence to the standards and other requirements for acceptable clean room operation, it is necessary to understand what is controlled and how controls are achieved. The design and construction of clean rooms and filtration systems are beyond the scope of this discussion and are covered elsewhere. However, the system that is being monitored is primarily processed air from the external environment. The nature of the airborne particles will affect the performance of the filtration system and of the end product of the filtration process. Therefore, the nature of the airborne particle system being treated is important.

Inert particles come from a number of natural sources as well as from various anthropogenic processes. The composition and particle size distribution of these particles will vary with the nature of the source. The concentration and the size distribution of the particles will vary both with location and time. Without going into too much detail, it is apparent that natural particles produced from a marine environment will differ in both composition and size distribution from those produced in a rural agricultural or from an urban industrial environment. Similarly, the particle descriptors will vary both with time of year, depending on fuel utilization for heat, power, and/or transportation, as well as diurnally and locally depending on industrial activity. All of the particles to be monitored and controlled are transported into the clean area from the environment. They may be airborne, entering through ducts and ventilation systems, or they may be brought into the area on the surfaces of devices used and processed in the clean area or on the surfaces of skin, clothing, shoes, etc., of plant personnel.

Particles from natural sources are derived primarily from soils, vegetation, or sea salt. Most soil particles are composed of silica, sand, granite or other rock particles, humus, or other organic or inorganic particles deposited on the soil and reentrained into the air. Vegetation fragments include such organics as terpenes and other complex molecules emitted from leaf surfaces. Animal emissions are primarily skin or hair fragments produced by abrasion, as well as dried waste product fragments entrained from the ground. For the most part, the natural aerosol particles are fairly large. Most are at least several micrometers in diameter, with specific gravities ranging from less than 1 up to 4 or 5.

Most airborne particles are produced by anthropogenic processes. Combustion product materials are generated by fuels use. They range in size from submicrometer to several micrometers in diameter. They are mainly metal or metal oxide, carbon or sulfur compounds. In addition, in many urban areas, gas-phase air pollution is present and retained for periods long enough that gas-phase reactions take place between such materials as hydrocarbon vapors and nitrogen oxides. The result is the familiar smog aerosol present in all urban areas and extending now to reduce visibility even in rural areas.

These reaction products or secondary aerosols are generally present as submicrometer particles, usually with specific gravities less than 1.

The major source of particle contamination in clean rooms of any sort derives from personnel activities in the areas. The important sources of particles include skin and hair fragments; droplet emission from skin surfaces or respiratory tract releases; material deposition as an effect of personnel activity, or transport of particles into an otherwise clean air stream by personnel movements at a rate faster than the air velocity in the clean stream. Figure 1 shows the significance of material that may be present in the external environment and its relationship to that present in the ventilation (HVAC) system in a plant. This illustration shows the changes in aerosol concentration over a period of time and the relationship between inside and outside air for a standard air conditioning filter system in operation. Figure 2 shows the particle size distribution of aerosols within an air conditioned building. The size distribution function that is shown in this figure is typical of particles that may be present in an area where some filtration is effective in reducing the number of larger particles more significantly than the smaller ones are removed. Unfortunately, the present FS 209b does not take into consideration the possibility that the size distribution of aerosol particles may be affected by filtration and that in any clean room, atypical large particles are generated by processes other than those that will produce a size distribution with a simple set of parameters. In other words, the large particle concentration is not defined correctly by the size distribution

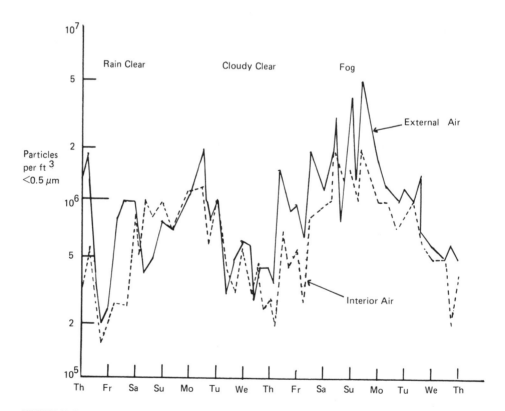

FIGURE 1   Interior/external particle concentrations.

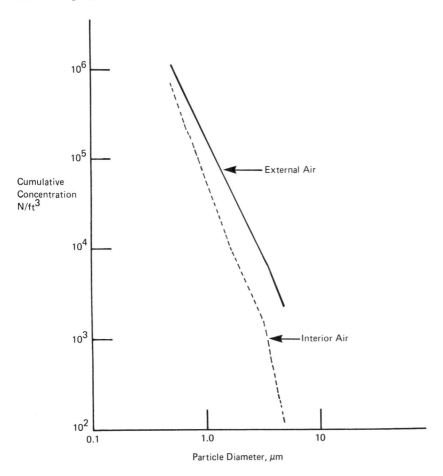

FIGURE 2   Interior/external particle size distribution.

curve assumed effective in FS 209. The relationships between the 0.5- and the 5.0-μm particle concentrations do not follow the idealized distribution form shown in FS 209b.

The filters present in the air cleaning system will modify the particle size distribution to a different range than that assumed by FS 209. This arises since the filter can be considered to be a probability device. That means that the probability of any particle being present in the effluent air from a filter will depend on the removal efficiency for that particle size and the number of particles of that size originally present in the air fed to the filter. For example, if one considers typical Los Angeles air, the number of particles of 0.3 μm may be in the range of 10 million per cubic foot, while the number of 1-μm particles may be less by a factor of 500 or so. A typical HEPA filter will be 99.997% efficient for 0.3 μm particles and probably will remove 1-μm particles more efficiently by a factor of 1000 or so. It can be seen that the number of 0.3 μm particles will be reduced to approximately 3000 per cubit foot, while the number of 1-μm particles will be smaller by a factor of 500,000. However, the number will *never* be zero. Figure 3

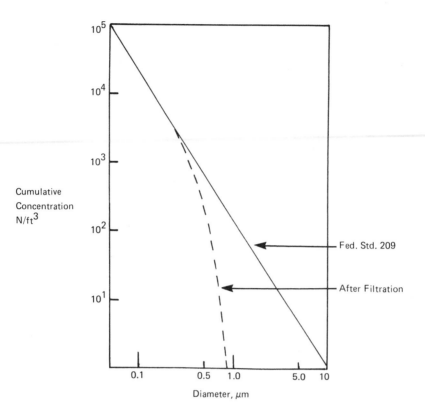

FIGURE 3   Filter-processed size distribution.

shows an example of the particle size distribution that one may expect from "filter-processed" air. Note the truncation effect on the larger particle size range. It must be remembered that the size distribution effects above are considered only for materials that are brought into the air through the HVAC system. Particles that are brought into the room on or by personnel or that are generated by operational activities within the clean room are not affected by the filter system. They are essentially atypical, stochastic events that do not fit into the statistically described airborne particle size distributions.

IV. MEASUREMENT SYSTEMS

In defining the operation of systems to typify clean room air levels, one may subdivide them into three general categories. These are collection and observation, particle array observation, and single-particle counters. The first system is used mainly if one is interested in identifying the material in the room. The second is used for measurements of gross system effectivity (such as filter testing). The third is used for general clean room testing and for detailed system performance definition. Since all three are used in clean room and device characterization, it is worthwhile discussing them here. Note that these systems are used to define particles in an air sample obtained from the clean room or device of concern. The problems and procedures for ensuring that the air samples are representative and acceptable will be discussed later. At this time, it is assumed that the air samples being examined have been obtained correctly and that they are satisfactory in all respects.

Filters used to define clean room particle levels require only that a section of suitable filter medium be sealed to a porous support that will allow air passage through the filter. Particle samples obtained in clean room characterization are almost always obtained on membrane filters. Porous membrane filters can be obtained with a wide range of pore-size distributions, with the pores being extremely tortuous in cross section through the membrane. Particle collection efficiency is quite high, with most of the particles trapped in the outer layer. Many membrane materials can be obtained that are quite soluble and have a low ash content. Thus, composition analysis for the collected particles is made easier. These comments also apply to Nuclepore filters. While conventional membranes are produced by formation of a gel which results in a porous structure, Nuclepore filters are made by placing thin polycarbonate sheets in a neutron flux that penetrates the plastic. Subsequent chemical etching penetrates and dissolves the neutron-damaged material in such a way that uniform holes with diameters ranging from approximately 0.1 to 10 μm can be produced. Because of their extremely smooth surface, Nuclepore filters are often used for collecting particles for measurement by visual or electron microscopy.

Membrane filters for clean room characterization are usually retained in a filter holder of 25 mm or 47 mm diameter. Gas flow rates from 0.1 to 50 liters/minute are used. A pressure drop of approximately 1/3 bar is usually maintained for ease of flow control. The filter holders are usually operated until sufficient particles (based on expected room concentration level) have been collected or until a preset volume of gas has been filtered. Following sample collection, the filters are removed from the holder, placed in a suitable container for storage and viewing, moved to the microscope area or to the analytical facility, and examined for particle content or composition. For particle size and concentration determination, the method is suitable for particles larger than approximately 5 μm in diameter. For composition analysis, the method is suitable for particles as small as 1 μm in diameter. The apparent discrepancy in size sensitivity exists because concentration determination requires collection of a sufficient number of particles for good statistical definition, while composition determination can be carried out on any individual particle, as required. The concentration determination requires collection of at least 1000 particles for room characterization values with standard deviation of less than 3% of the mean value.

Airborne particles present in clean rooms are usually within the size range from 0.1 to 25 μm in diameter. These dimensions are within approximately one order of magnitude of the wavelength of visible light. When particles are illuminated by a beam of light with wavelengths from roughly 450 to 800 nm, light is scattered by each particle, the amount varying roughly with the projected area of the particle. If a beam of light is used to illuminate an assemblage of particles, then the amount of light that is scattered will indicate the total projected area of all the particles within the illuminated volume. Photometers are used for this measurement in relatively clean air as may be found in clean rooms. Forward-scattering-angle photometers are optically similar to the dark-field microscope. A cone of light converges at a point in the aerosol cloud and dark stops are used to protect the photodetector from the direct beam. Only the light scattered by the particles in a near-forward direction is collected by the photodetector. The instruments

usually read out data in terms of either a mass or a number concentration
based on previous calibration with sets of submicron particles. One typical
design is shown in Fig. 4. This system is a near-forward-scattering instrument that draws air at 28.3 liters/min. The air sample passes through the
light cone, and light scattered from particles over a range of angles from 4°
to 36° in the forward direction falls on a photomultiplier, whose current output indicates the aerosol particle concentration. The design is essentially
that given by Knudson and White (1945) [10]. Note that this device is still
used for testing of high-efficiency air filters. It is incorporated as part of
the filter manufacturer's testing system that defines the stated penetration
efficiency for a specific filter.

A wide range of single-particle counters is available. They all have in
common a capability for transporting an air sample through an illuminated
volume that is sufficiently small that only individual particles are present at
any time within that volume. As the particle passes through the illuminated
volume, a pulse of light is scattered out and collected over a solid angle defined by the optical system. Figures 5—7 show some optical layouts for
several optical systems, including right-angle, near-forward, and wide-angle
optical systems. Illumination can be obtained from focused tungsten filament
lamps or from collimated laser light beams. The differences in response are
shown for a few specific scattering angles in Fig. 8 to indicate the change in
scattered signal level with size and with refractive index of the particulate
material being measured. In operation, pulse-amplitude data are referred to
the calibration material data on output pulse amplitude vs. known size for
transfer from measured amplitude to actual particle size data. Concentration
information is obtained by counting the number of pulses in each of a number
of size ranges and referring that number to the gas sample volume used to
collect the data.

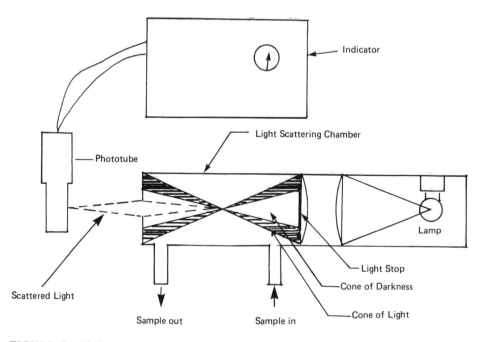

FIGURE 4   Light-scattering photometer.

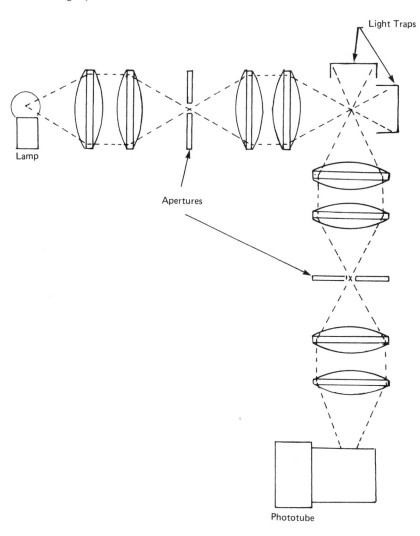

FIGURE 5   Right-angle-scattering optical system.

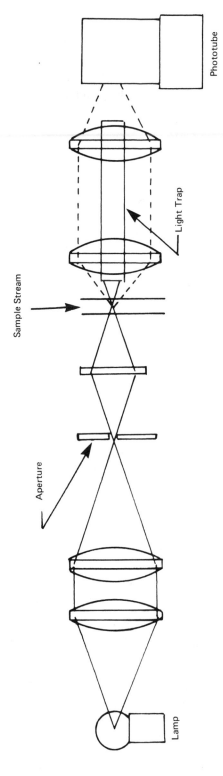

FIGURE 6   Near-forward-scattering-angle optical system.

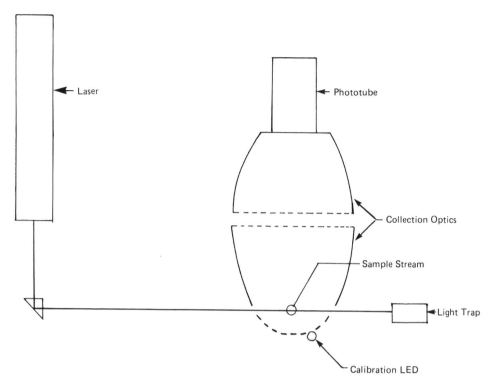

FIGURE 7   Wide-angle-scattering optical system.

Single-particle counters are generally used in defining clean-room particle concentration. They are capable of sizing and counting particles as small as 0.1 μm in diameter and in concentrations from essentially zero to several hundred thousand per cubic foot. Their advantages arise from their overall convenience in operation, their speed in determining aerosol concentration and size-distribution data, their portability, and their ability to be used over a wide range of operating regimes in terms of particle size, particle concentration, and sample size. Their disadvantages are due primarily to difficulties in correlating data from one optical-size measurement base to other size analyzers that may be based on other size parameters, such as aerodynamic or inertial size, or a longest dimension as is commonly used for microscope measurement. In addition, the difference is scattering angles from one instrument to another results in somewhat different sizing for the same materials. These difficulties have been discussed previously in more detail by Lieberman [11]. Even with the problems of correlation, the optical particle counters are still used generally throughout clean rooms for monitoring purposes; in addition, many are being used for in-place filter testing as well. It should be pointed out that the procedures of both FS 209 and ANSI N 101.1 still specify the use of photometers for leak testing of HEPA filters. Nevertheless, the much greater sensitivity of the single-particle counters has resulted in their use as test devices, with subsequent formal validated testing with a photometer.

In recent times, impetus has come from semiconductor manufacturers for measurement below 0.1 μm. For this purpose, it may be necessary to use

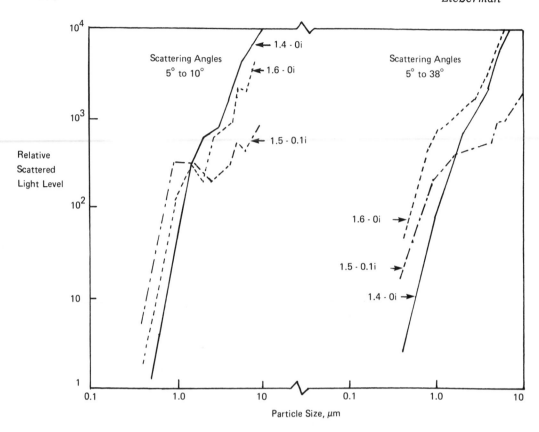

FIGURE 8   Relative scattered light levels vs. scattering angles.

other systems. Condensation nuclei counters have been used to define the concentration of particles smaller than 0.1 μm. These devices operate by exposing the sample gas stream to a supersaturated vapor; any particles larger than approximately 0.003 μm can act as condensation nuclei to cause vapor deposition and growth to particles as large as 5–10 μm—which can be seen easily by a standard optical system. No definitive size data can be obtained from a condensation nucleus counter beyond the total number of particles larger than the threshold size. Another instrument used for in situ definition of very small aerosol particles is the electrical aerosol analyzer. This device charges the particles in a gas stream, passes them through an electric field with stepwise changes in intensity gradient, and determines the mobility range of the particles in the sample. From these data, the particle size distribution can be determined. At this time, very little use is made of either device, primarily because the need for measurements below 0.1 μm has not been important and because of the need for rapid response along with definitive particle size data.

V. PARTICLE COUNTER CONTROLS AND FLOW

In the operation of any particle counter, one has a range of choices in terms of gas flow control. Where one is concerned with very clean environments, it is necessary to use as large a sample as possible in order to obtain sufficient data to be statistically significant. On the other hand, if one is concerned with the nature of the particles in the area, then one may wish to have very good data on the particle size distribution, so as to allow some aid in defining source type or nature. In this case, particle sizing resolution is aided if the sample stream through the sensing volume is controlled so that all the particles pass through a specific part of the illumination where intensity will be very well controlled. This can best be done by constricting the sample gas stream within a sheath of clean air. Considering the restriction of weight and volume, available gas pump sizes mean that a large air sample can not be easily obtained with sheath flow. Thus, good sizing resolution is seldom obtained if large flow rates are desired.

Some consideration should be given here to the type of data that are produced and what can be done with that data. The raw information is in the form of a series of pulses, usually of duration less than 1 msec, with amplitude ranges from microvolt to volt levels. The interpulse spacing may be in the microsecond range. The particle-counter electronic system must then separate the pulses into several amplitude (particle size) categories, as required by the clean-room monitoring specifications, count ,and define the number of particles from which the pulses arose, and either store the data, display it, record it, or transmit it to other storage or data processing devices. The nature of the data being handled may range from raw particle size and count data to processed information covering concentration as a function of time or sample volume, statements as to source of the data, definitions of whether or not the data is within preset limits, trend information, long-term or short-term averages, etc. In some cases, storage capacity may limit the data transmission only to information on unacceptable conditions; that is, if no "alarm" levels have occurred, then no data are retained.

For the most part, data considerations are made in terms of the operation of a single-particle counter. However, for practical use, multiplexing is often the only way to obtain useful information without excessive expenditure of time, funds, or personnel activities. Multiplexing can be done in terms of sequential sample line inputs to a single-particle counter or in terms of sequential or simultaneous input of data from several counters (with or without sample line multiplex) to a central computer station. As an example of some capabilities for this type of system, one may consider a fairly simple computer software system that will allow simultaneous collection of data from a combination of digital particle counters and analog environment monitors. The system will permit setting alarm levels for different areas at desired particle count levels. Data can be accumulated and averaged over any desired time interval, with means, standard deviations, and outlier values reported. During the measurement program, interactive viewing and control of any single-station operating parameters can be carried out. Off-line data processing can be carried out as part of the off-line operations. Data grouping can be handled so as to separate systems that perform similar processes in groups, even though they are not monitored by the same sensing system. Local and/or remote alarm indication can be handled easily. Note that this type of control and data recording can be accomplished easily with an off-the-shelf microcomputer.

VI. PARTICLE MONITORING PROCEDURES

Once the justification for particle monitoring has been established and the measurement system selected, then the exact monitoring procedures must be

defined, beginning with selection of a suitable protocol for measurement.
The first step is to select the standard or specification that defines operating
levels to be monitored in the clean area. If one is involved in filling large
volume parenteral solutions, there is no real choice; Class 100 conditions or
better *must* be maintained in the filling line area. If noncritical device manufacture is carried out, then the assembly or fabrication line may be operated
at Class 1000 or 10,000 levels. Once the operating level has been selected,
then the sampling location(s) on the line can be defined in terms of the work
and personnel flow paths, the working level, and the air flow in the area.
Next, the sampling flow rate is selected so as to obtain statistically significant
data at the contaminant levels to be expected. Consult with the company
statistician for the data required to define the expected particle levels with
acceptable confidence limits at the average values expected. In general,
when measuring data with a Gaussian distribution of values, the standard
deviation expected is equal to the square root of the average value. That is,
for a Class 100 room, the relative standard deviation for data from a 1-ft^3
sample will be 10%; for a 10-ft^3 sample, it will be 3.16%; for a 0.1-ft^3 sample,
it will be 32%. If the instrument available has a low flow rate, decide if the
required sample size does not require so long a sample acquisition time as to
result in variations in the sample air package being examined.

Next, decide on the sample acquisition frequency in terms of the work
pattern in the area. If continuous operations are to be monitored, then continuous data may be required. If clean device operations are to be defined,
then sample frequencies of once per month may be adequate. Finally, determine the quality of the data that is required. This refers to the range of
particle sizes and concentrations that must be determined. If only room
classes are needed, then measurements at 0.5 μm are adequate; if specific
activities must be followed, then a complete range of particle sizes may be
needed. If assurance of compliance with room classes is enough, then measurement of concentrations at the room class limits may be enough, with over-range
indicated only as excess. If details on problems that may arise from specific
operations are needed, then detailed particle size and concentration data
during those operations may be desired. At all times, consider the statistical
effects on data accuracy. Such considerations as the effects of atypical
particle size distributions on the concentrations measured due to particle
size outliers should be included. Measurement system performance limits
should not be exceeded. As an example, the manufacturers of particle counters usually define concentration limits as maximum values; these must be
understood to be coincidence error limits that are always present and are
typically stated at the 5—10% levels. Finally, determine the data format that
is required for the satisfaction of the specification being used for the area.
If the specification is a company limit, use the values defined therein. If
the specification is based on a GMP requirement, then define it as stated
there.

VII. AIR SAMPLING CONSIDERATIONS

Successful air sampling requires that a sample be acquired from the environment to be characterized, that the sample be transported to a suitable measurement or collection system, and that the sample not be affected by the sampling
process. The sample must be representative of the environment from which
it was obtained. It must be large enough to permit accurate and statistically

valid characterization of that environment, but not so large as to disturb it. In addition, the collection and transport process must consider the fact that the aerosol particles are not in a stable system and that the transport system must be designed so as to minimize modification of the aerosol during transport.

Two general types of aerosol sampling systems are of concern in clean room measurement. In the first, the aerosol exists in a relatively open environment—the clean area—with practically no net air flow in any specific direction, since the air velocity may be affected by a number of transient effects, ranging from personnel activities to parts movements. In the second situation, the air is transported in one direction at a relatively constant velocity. The latter situation is what exists in a "laminar-flow" clean room or in the air flowing from a filter. The air is normally moving at 90 ft/min in a single direction with very little turbulence.

Since most aerosols have a log-normal particle size distribution and are present in random spatial distribution, geometric mean values are often used in expressing sizes, concentrations, or composition distributions in aerosols. If the sample size is too small, then errors can be unacceptably high, as shown by Michels [12]. He points out that as the geometric standard deviation of the distribution increases, the sample size must be increased accordingly to ensure that the statistical error for any measurement that is made in the clean room or area (enclosure) by whichever instrument or method that is being used at the time is acceptably low. In other words, the sample size must be adequate to ensure acceptably small statistical error, as shown in Fig. 9. At the same time, as the concentration of particles is any single

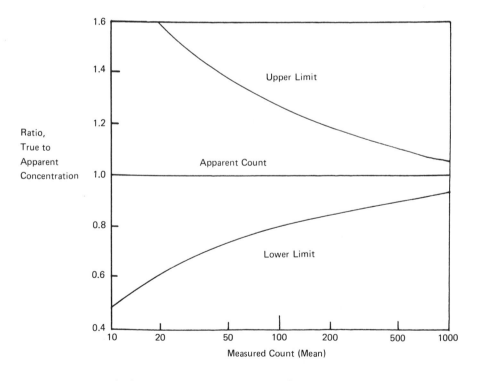

FIGURE 9 Statistical errors at low values of the mean count.

sample increases, it is necessary that the concentration capability of the particle counter being used for the measurement is not exceeded. Otherwise the errors due to coincidence of particles within the sensing volume at any time will result in serious undercounting of the actual particle concentration and oversizing of the particles being recorded [11]. Figure 10 shows loss effects that can arise from coincidence errors.

Aerosol sampling in relatively calm air requires that both the gas and the particles be sampled without changing the relative location of particles within the gas sample. During sample acquisition it is necessary to accelerate the gas and particle sample into the sampler inlet. The relaxation time for gas molecules is essentially zero; the relaxation time for aerosol particles increases with particle size. The net result is that the gas molecules adjust easily to the flow streamline change, while the particles do not follow the streamlines and may impact on the sample tube inlet. Since the gas approaching the sampler inlet will accelerate—or simply change direction—the particles will tend to fall behind, owing to their inertia. The efficiency of any sampler inlet can be expressed in terms of the particle size, the inlet dimensions, and the sampling flow rate. Agarwal [13] computed efficiencies for vertical thin-walled tubes facing upwards, considering the boundary trajectories of particles

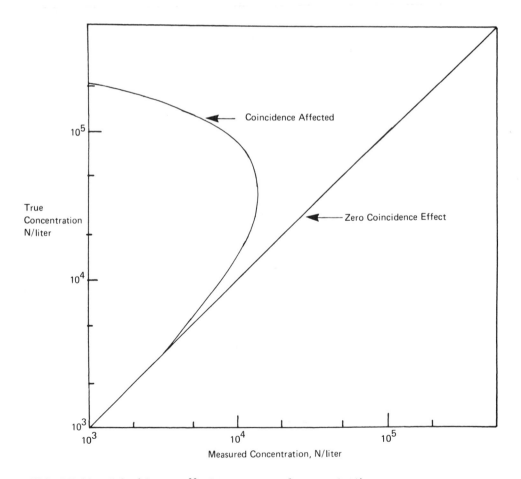

FIGURE 10   Coincidence effect on measured concentration.

falling through the flow fields. He prepared a graph showing the inlet efficiency as a function of the relative settling velocity (the ratio between the
settling velocity for the particle and the aspiration velocity for the probe in
question) and the Stokes number (the ratio between a particle dimension and
the inlet tube dimension). The relationship is shown in Fig. 11. Note that
efficiencies as shown here can be used for inlet systems in essentially calm
air. Even with these recommendations, it can be expected that occasions will
arise where the ideal sample inlet dimensions cannot be used. In those cases,
it is suggested that for sample flow rates of 20–30 liters/min, a tube with a
1-cm inside diameter be used. The inlet should be conical with a 60° flare
opening to about 3 cm and facing upwards. With this arrangement, particle
losses of less than 10% will occur for unit-density particles as large as 20 μm
in diameter.

   If one is sampling in air flowing at a definite velocity, then isokinetic
sampling is highly desirable. Isokinetic sampling is defined as the situation
where the inlet velocity is matched to the ambient air velocity. This situation
is usually recommended where filter emissions are being observed or where
particle concentrations in a laminar-flow clean room are being determined.
The requirement also exists when sampling in a duct. The axis of the sampling probe should be parallel to the flow lines in the gas stream, and the
sample probe inlet velocity should be equal to that of the flow in the air being

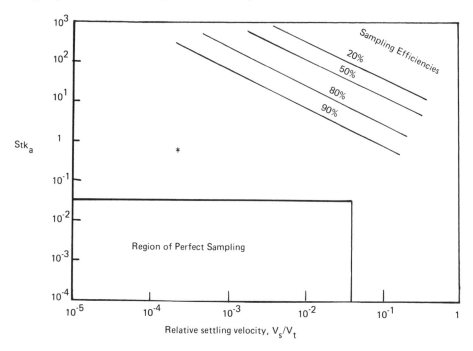

FIGURE 11   Sample tube inlet efficiency in calm air. Stk_a is the Stokes
number. It is a function of the relationship between the particle dimension
and the inlet sampler tube dimension. The Stokes number is the product of
the particle relaxation time (time for a particle to accommodate to a change in
air velocity) and the particle velocity, divided by the diameter of the sample
tube inlet. V_s is the particle settling velocity and V_t is the inlet sample
tube velocity. Inlet efficiency for a sample tube of 0.7-cm inside diameter,
drawing air at 28.3 liters/min as shown at ‡.

sampled. If the ambient air velocity is less than the sample inlet tube velocity, the gas flow lines diverge at the sample tube entry. The particles will then drift across the flow lines, owing to their inertia, and will continue on in a straight line, missing the sample tube inlet. If the ambient air velocity is greater than the sample tube inlet velocity, the larger particles will be drawn into the tube at a rate greater than they should be. These situations are illustrated in Fig. 12. It can be seen that the effects of anisokinetic sampling are significant for particles smaller than 1–2 µm in diameter. Thus, definition of clean room classes at the 0.5-µm level does not positively require isokinetic sampling for acceptable results. Nevertheless, good sampling will be done isokinetically, whether in a duct or in a clean room.

Once an aerosol sample has been acquired, some transport in a tube is normally required to reach an analytical device. In some cases, the analytical device is very close to the sample tube inlet; in other situations, it may be necessary to transport the sample over distances up to 25–30 m because of economic or convenience reasons. As an aerosol is transported through a tube, a number of changes can occur to the aerosol. These changes include accelerated agglomeration within the aerosol, or losses to the walls of the tube due to thermal, electrostatic, or mechanical forces. Particle losses can occur due to diffusive or gravitational deposition at low Reynolds number flow or from turbulent diffusion at higher Reynolds numbers; particle losses can occur in curved ducts due to the inertia of the particles and the effect of

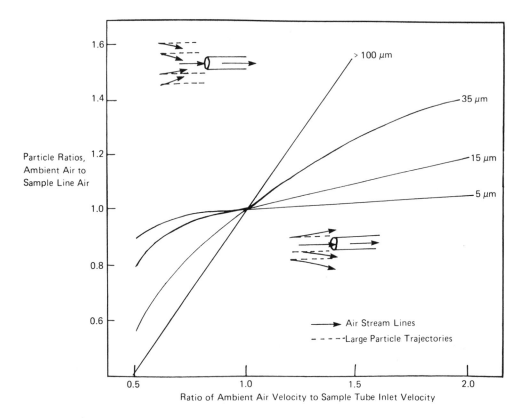

FIGURE 12   Anisokinetic sampling errors.

centrifugal force during transit through the curved section. Wall losses in a duct of uniform cross section will vary directly with the Reynolds number for fluid flow, the duct length, the particle size, the aerosol electrical charge, and inversely with the radius of curvature of the tube. It is strongly recommended that any tubing used for aerosol transport not be installed with any bend or curve in the line with radius of curvature less than 20 cm.

For solid particles being transmitted through a tube, the losses will increase with size until the particles are large enough so that they extend through the boundary layer in the tube at the wall. At that level, they can be reentrained into the air flow in the duct by either impact from other particles or by turbulent eddies in the air stream. This effect will not occur for liquid droplets, of course. Once these have impacted on a surface that can be wetted, they will spread on the surface and lose their identity.

Experience has shown that tubing composition is of great importance in minimizing particle losses during transport. In order of preference, tubing composition is stainless steel, flexible polyester or polyurethane, high-density polyethylene, copper, glass, or Teflon. Note that the desirability of material increases as the conductivity increases. This generality holds until oxidizable metals are included. These materials can form friable oxide coatings that can be emitted into an otherwise clean area after long service.

VIII. PROCEDURE

An example of monitoring procedure that will be discussed briefly is that of monitoring in a "conventional" clean room with ceiling diffusers, side wall exhausts, and localized Class 100 clean area operations. This is typical of a manufacturing area with filling operations in a cleaner portion of the area.

The first step is to determine the cleanliness of the area to be monitored and the monitoring frequency. Generally, one may assume that the overall area will be Class 1000 or Class 10,000 and that the filling line air will be specified at Class 100 or better. The next step in the process would be to verify that the filters in the air lines are free of leaks. The procedures to be used are described in Federal Standard 209b, section 50, and IES Procedure CS-1T [14]. The filters will be challenged with air-generated cold DOP smoke. Penetration of the smoke through the filter will be measured either with a photometer or with a single-particle counter. Any smoke penetration at a concentration greater than 0.01% of the upstream level will indicate a leak that must be repaired or the filter replaced. Note that the use of a single-particle counter is not general practice, since it is not specified in the standards. However, by reducing the upstream challenge by a factor of 10,000 or so from the normal 100 μg/liter, it is possible to define both the up- and downstream concentrations without overloading the counter. Even so, strict adherence to the standards requires the use of a photometer to define filter integrity. Next, the air velocity at the filter face will be measured and ensured to be 90 ft/min, plus or minus 20%.

The concentration of particles equal to or larger than 0.5 μm will be determined at "representative" locations within the overall clean area. This measurement will be made while either actual work or acceptable simulation activities are being carried out in the clean room. This procedure defines the general room class level. (Note that this measurement may be required to be repeated at intervals ranging from daily to monthly.) Following these tests, the airborne particle concentrations within the filling line or other critical areas will be determined. A particle counter probe will be inserted into the critical area with the probe inlet facing into the air flow streamlines as closely as possible and with dimensions so as to permit isokinetic sampling as closely as possible. Measurements of the airborne particle concentration at the 0.5 μm level will be made while actual operations are being simulated. Simulated operations are suggested, since many filling or other critical pharmaceutical operations can be contaminated by the presence of the extraneous elements represented by the counter probe. In some cases, the probe can be in place during actual filling if the probe elements are sanitized, but caution is recommended here. These measurements may have to be repeated not only at scheduled intervals, but if operational modifications occur that indicate different operating conditions. These may include process modifications, filter changes, room repair, etc.

In making any clean room measurements of particle levels, a number of operational guides should be considered. These include the necessity for making sure that all equipment brought into the clean room is also clean. This means the test equipment—such as the particle counter, cleaning materials and devices, tools and personnel effects, including clothing.

The need for an effective training program cannot be overemphasized. The program should cover any and all aspects of clean room activity, from gowning procedures through clean room decorum and processes. Emphasis should be placed particularly on personnel procedures. Proper record keeping is of great importance. The measurements should take into account the kind of records needed by the control agency, the frequency of recording, and the details to be maintained within the records. At the same time, the materials used to record data should be acceptable for clean room work; i.e., no pencil copies are allowed, and printer paper that produces lint should be avoided. Alternately, transmission of data to external recording points could be used.

One may consider the problem of cost control where many sample points are required and a sample sequence is specified. One may choose between using multiplexed particle sensors feeding data to a central data processing system or using multiplexed air handling devices that feed a series of samples to a single sensor system. If cost and convenience are of primary importance, the best approach is to multiplex the air lines. Although some particle losses will occur in the lines, as shown in Sec. VII, these will be relatively unimportant at the 0.5-μm level and the small error due to the losses may well be made up by the savings in time and cost and by the convenience of not needing more than one particle sensor calibration setting. The cautions mentioned in Sec. VII must be used in sample acquisition and in line layout and configuration. If several samples must be obtained simultaneously, then use of multiplexed sensor/counter systems will be required. In this case, it is necessary to ensure that the sensors are matched and that the matching is retained during normal sensor life, maintenance operations, and lamp replacements.

In any case, sooner or later, the requirement will arise to examine a series of data that have been obtained over a period of time or from several particle counters. Frequently the data will not correlate well. Measurements taken from the same location with several instruments may not agree. The question is always asked as to the reason. The answers may lie in the area of errors due to instrument operation or performance, sampling methodology, system operation, or interpretation. It can only be pointed out that some of the points raised in this discussion should aid in both tracing the problem and deciding if the magnitude of the problem deserves attention. A difference of 10% in particle counts, at the Class 100 level especially, is not worth spending any time to define; a difference of 50% at the Class 10 level is equally insignificant (consider the paucity of data at these levels). However, a difference of 50% at the Class 100 or greater level is indeed an important question that must be answered.

REFERENCES

1. Current Good Manufacturing Practice in manufacturing, processing, packing and holding of large volume parenterals. June 1, 1976. *Fed. Reg. 41* (106): 22202–22222.

2. *Clean Room and Work Station Requirements, Controlled Environments,* 1973, Federal Standard No. 209b, Washington, D.C., General Services Administration.

3. *Sizing and Counting Airborne Particulate Contamination in Clean Rooms and Other Dust-Controlled Areas Designed for Electronic and Similar Applications,* ASTM F 25-68, 1968, Philadelphia, American Society for Testing and Materials.

4. *Continuous Sizing and Counting or Airborne Particles in Dust-Controlled Areas Using Instruments Based upon Light-Scattering Principles,* ASTM F 50-83, 1981, Philadelphia, American Society for Testing and Materials.

5. *Determining Counting and Sizing Accuracy of an Airborne Particle Counter Using Near-Monodisperse Spherical Particles,* ASTM F 328-80, 1980, Philadelphia, American Society for Testing and Materials.

6. *Secondary Calibration of Airborne Particle Counter Using Comparison Procedures,* ASTM F 649-80, 1980, Philadelphia, American Society for Testing and Materials.

7. *Military Specification, Filter, Particulate, High Efficiency, Fire Resistant,* MIL-F-51068, 1961, Washington, D.C., U.S. Department of Energy, Division of Operational Safety.

8. *Efficiency Testing of Air-Cleaning Devices for Removal of Particles,* N101.1-1972, New York, American Institute of Chemical Engineers.

9. *In-Place Testing of HEPA Filter Systems by the Single-Particle, Particle-Size Spectrometer Method,* NE F-41, 1980, Oak Ridge, Tenn., U.S. Department of Energy, Oak Ridge National Laboratory.

10. Knudson, H. W., and White, L. 1945. *Development of Smoke Penetration Meters,* Naval Research Laboratory Report P-2642.

11. Lieberman, A. 1976. Variability sources in data from airborne particle counters. *Proc. 3rd Int. Symp. Contamination Control,* Copenhagen, pp. 144–162.

12. Michels, D. E. 1977. Sample size effect on geometric average concentration for log normally distributed contaminants. *Environ. Sci. Technol. 11:* 300.

13. Agarwal, J. K., and Liu, B. Y. H. 1980. A criterion for accurate aerosol sampling in calm air. *Am. Ind. Hyg. Assoc. J. 41:* 191.

14. *Standard for HEPA Filters,* CS-1T, 1968, Mt. Prospect, Ill., Institute for Environmental Sciences.

8

Validation of Utilities

BARRY D. GARFINKLE

Merck Sharp & Dohme, Inc., West Point, Pennsylvania

The modern aseptic pharmaceutical production facility requires various utilities in order to maintain an appropriate environment, as well as operate equipment within the building. Unless the utilities supplied are appropriate in quality and quantity, it is not possible for the equipment to operate according to validated parameters. Assuming that these statements are correct, it therefore becomes necessary to "certify" the utilities in order to ensure that the processes conducted within the building will perform routinely within validated parameters.

The certification of utilities usually consists of several parts:

1. Definition of the system by the process engineer
2. Construction or installation qualification
3. Operational qualification of the system
4. Validation or certification documentation of the system from a construction as well as an operational standpoint

Utilities must meet both qualitative and quantitative specifications in order to be satisfactory. The actual criteria that are applied vary from one utility to another, and may even be influenced by the particular equipment being serviced. Therefore, it is impossible to present any scheme for validation of utilities without prefacing it with the comment that all validation programs will vary and there is never only one correct way to validate.

I. GASES

The most commonly used gases in pharmaceutical manufacture are the following:

1. Nitrogen
2. Carbon dioxide
3. Compressed air (oil-containing and oil-free)

The steps involved in validation of these gases involve the following:

1. Supply of gas (adequate purity and quantity). Gas is tested for purity, and usage at maximum rate must be less than the system can generate.
2. The storage facility should be of adequate size and made of appropriate materials so that it is not reactive with the gas.
3. The distribution system must be of adequate size to provide the volumes of gas required, should be constructed of suitable materials so that the system does not detract from the quality of the gas supplied to it, and must not be interconnected to any other system that could contaminate the gas it was designed to transport.

A. Validation of a Nitrogen Gas System

1. Quality of Nitrogen Produced by Generation System

1. Test output of the gas generator to ensure that the gas produced meets specifications in USP XX. This requires sampling the gas using a gas bag or other suitable means and testing that the gas is 99% pure and that the content of carbon monoxide is 0.001% or less. A typical setup for sampling gas for purity is shown in Figs. 1 and 2. The generator must also be tested to show that under conditions of maximum demand, adequate quality and quantity can be supplied. This can be determined by doing quality testing while simulating maximum demand for gas. Maximum demand can exceed generation for short periods if a large reservoir is utilized.
2. Document specifications that the generator should meet. This includes the purchase order and all paperwork used to specify the generator that was ordered. This information then becomes the basis for the qualification protocol.
3. Installation qualification of the gas generator:
   a. Utilities required for operation
      (1) Electrical supply (voltage, amperage, frequency)
      (2) Chilled water (supply volume, temperature)
      (3) Compressed air (pressure, cubic feet per minute, oil-free)
   b. Pre-startup procedures
      (1) Clean out system to remove construction debris, lubricants, and residue from manufacture.
      (2) Fill all lubricant reservoirs.
      (3) Check all utility connections.
      (4) Test safety devices (automatic shutdown and general safety equipment) for proper operation.
   c. Calibration of all critical gauges and instrumentation
      (1) Write standard operating procedures for calibration.
      (2) Establish accurate standards for conducting calibration.
      (3) Define critical vs. convenience gauges and instruments.
4. Operational qualification of the generator:
   a. Write standard operating procedure for startup and operation.
   b. Determine and document normal operating parameters.
   c. Test and document all system instrumentation and alarms.

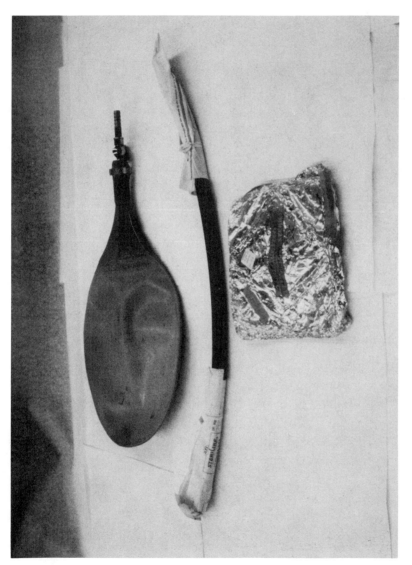

FIGURE 1   Equipment necessary for sampling gases for purity. All equipment is sterilized prior to use and consists of: (1) rubber bladder bag, (2) rubber tubing, and (3) aluminum foil squares.

FIGURE 2 Sampling technique for gas purity. Rubber bladder bag is attached to outlet being sampled with sterile tubing. The bag is inflated and deflated several times manually to displace residual air. The valve is closed on the bag and covered with sterile foil.

2. *Storage Tank*

1. Check the storage tank for adequate capacity for the process and conformance to purchase specifications.
2. Check that material and construction conforms to purchase specifications.
3. Conduct a pressure hold test to determine that the leak rate is within specifications. This can be conducted according to ASME specifications using hydrostatic and/or pneumatic tests.
4. Document cleaning procedures done on the tank after installation.
5. Check and document all pressure ratings for the tank and components against purchase specifications.
6. Calibrate and document all pressure gauges and sensors, both monitoring and controlling.

3. *Distribution System*

Installation Qualification

1. The materials of construction and design parameters specified by the process engineer must be confirmed and documented.
2. The design drawings of the system are used to trace the actual constructed system and an "as built" drawing made to show any necessary modifications during construction.
3. The system is pressure-tested and documented to confirm its integrity. The appropriate ASME reference hydrostatic and/or pneumatic tests are performed and the results documented.
4. The system is cleaned and the procedures used documented and all branches labeled as to contents.

Operation Qualification: The actual use points are then tested for the following parameters.

1. All use points are tested for gas identity, nonviable particle counts, and microbial counts (slit to agar or Anderson air sampler).
2. Several worst-case locations are tested for purity of the nitrogen gas and dew point. The worst-case locations are typically designated as the farthest locations on each branch of the distribution system. The dew-point testing is useful to ensure that the system is dry, since a wet system typically may create conditions whereby the system chemically degrades as well as creating a condition that will support microbial growth. A device and setup for measuring dew points is shown in Fig. 3.

Validation: Validation consists of completing the documentation from the various steps mentioned above along with repeating the operational testing specified in the validation protocol (adequate supply during maximum usage, purity testing at various points, dew-point testing, nonviable particle counts, and microbial counts).

Filters: If filters are used in the system (common at use points), they should be tested for integrity periodically and documentation provided to ensure that they are not particle-shedding. Use data and routine testing can be used to develop service life of the filters. When this is developed, a documentation system can be developed to control maintenance of the filters.

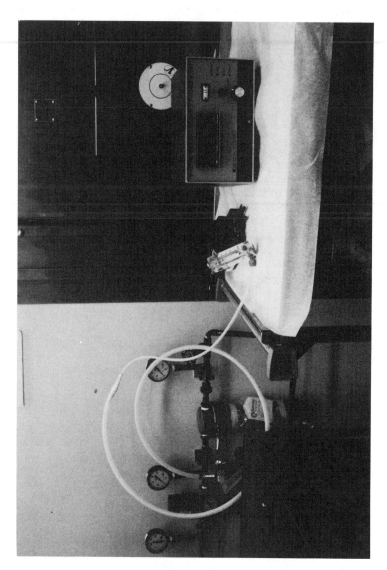

FIGURE 3 An automatic device for determining the dew point of gases. The dew point is used to determine the dryness of the source of gas. This can be extremely important with compressed air. This is one way of testing a compressed air dryer.

B. Validation of a Carbon Dioxide Gas System

A carbon dioxide gas system is validated in a similar manner to a nitrogen system except that the purity required is that specified by USP XX, "Carbon Dioxide," p. 119. An easy-to-use identity test consists of using a sampling device shown in Fig. 4, which utilizes a Bendix sampling pump and a special tube manufactured by National Draeger, Inc. This system contains a chemical indicator that changes color in the presence of the gas; by drawing a known volume of gas through the tube, its purity can also be determined. Other gas detection systems are also available and may be satisfactory.

C. Validation of Compressed Air Systems

Generally two types of compressed air systems are found in a modern aseptic manufacturing facility. An instrument air system normally consists of conventional oil-lubricated compressors and is used for operating instruments and machinery where no contact with the product or product environment exists. An oil-free compressed air system is normally used in aseptic areas and often may be involved with product contact. Because of the similarities of the two systems and the greater importance of the oil-free systems, only the validation of oil-free systems will be addressed.

The oil-free compressed air system generally consists of an oil-free compressor, dryer, storage tank, and distribution system.

The normal validation process consists of installation qualification, operational qualification, and actual validation testing of the operational system. A typical installation and operational qualification procedure for each component of the system will now be presented.

1. Oil-Free Compressor

For installation qualification:

1. Check and document specifications on purchase order against actual delivery specifications.
2. Verify and document that no oil or other lubricant is used in the compressor.
3. Determine and document that all required utility requirements have been met and connected properly.
4. Document that pre-startup procedures were performed.
5. Document that all critical instrumentation was calibrated.

The actual specifications used for purchase of the compressor are the basis for writing the qualification protocol.

2. Compressed Air Storage Tank

1. Confirm and document the materials of construction as specified by the process engineer.
2. Check and document the storage tank for adequate capacity against the purchase specifications.
3. Conduct and document pressure hold test to determine that the leak rate is within specification. This can be done according to ASME testing procedures using hydrostatic and/or pneumatic tests (ASME Boiler and Pressure Vessel Code, Section VII, Division 1).

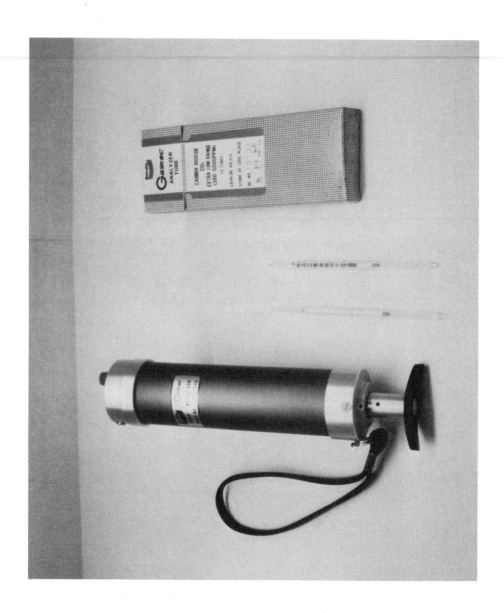

4. Check and document the cleaning procedures done on the tank after installation.
5. Check and document all pressure ratings for the tank against purchase specifications.
6. Calibrate all critical instrumentation on the storage tank and document the procedures. This includes pressure gauges and control sensors.

3. Distribution System

Installation Qualification:

1. Confirm and document the materials of construction and design parameters as specified by the process engineer.
2. Use the drawings of the system to trace the actual constructed system and make an "as built" drawing to show any necessary construction modifications.
3. Pressure test the system to confirm its integrity. The appropriate ASME hydrostatic and/or pneumatic tests should be performed and the results documented (ASME Boiler and Pressure Vessel Code, Section VIII, Division 1, or ANSI B31.3, Section 337, Pressure Tests).
4. Clean the system and document the procedures, labeling all piping and components as to contents. Actual cleaning procedures vary and may include washing with detergents or solvents.

Operational Qualification: With all components of the compressed air system functional, the following tests are conducted:

1. All use points are tested for identity, nonviable particle counts, and microbial counts (slit to agar or Anderson air sampler).
2. Several worst-case locations are tested for purity and dew points of the compressed air. The worst-case locations are typically defined as the farthest locations on each branch of the distribution system.
3. All instruments and alarms should be tested and documented as operational.
4. Test the compressor output for hydrocarbons with an appropriate assay. This can be accomplished using the Bendix pump and a special Drager tube.

Certification then consists of completing the documentation from the various steps mentioned above along with repeating the operational testing specified in the certification protocol (adequate supply during maximum usage, purity testing at various points, dew-point testing, nonviable particle counts,

---

FIGURE 4 Gas analyzer device. Pictured is equipment which can be used for direct analysis of gas purity. The apparatus consists of a calibrated pump which draws a known volume of gas through the analyzer tube. The tubes contain reagents that cause a color change to occur which is proportional to the amount of gas present. The height of the colored column increases as the amount of gas increases. The column at the left is unexposed while the column on the right shows the presence of carbon dioxide >5000 ppm. Columns are also available for other gases.

and microbial counts). These operational tests for purity, capacity, and instrumentation checks should then be repeated over several days.

II. STEAM SYSTEMS

Two types of steam systems are normally found in modern aseptic manufacturing facilities. One steam system is usually called "house steam" and consists of a steam generator and distribution system made of iron or steel, which are both subject to rusting. The system is normally treated with various amines, hydrazines, or other boiler additives in order to limit the rusting that occurs. This type of system is normally used in applications where contact with product or product contact surfaces does not occur. In fact, GMP regulations 200.11 and Proposed LVP GMP 212.227 go as far as to say that this must be so. The second type of steam system is referred to as "clean steam." "Clean steam" systems are normally constructed of nonrusting (stainless steel) materials and typically use either distilled or deionized water as feedwater. Another significant feature of "clean steam" is that no additives are allowed to be used. This is because this type of steam is normally used for product contact or product contact surfaces. Since our major concern in this case is normally clean steam, we will confine our discussion to validation of a "clean steam" system. However, many of the same documentation and testing can be done on "house steam" if desired.

Table 1 summarizes the differences between the two types of systems.

The validation of a "clean steam" system involves showing that it does what it was designed to do. This is a system constructed of nonrusting material that produces steam of adequate purity and quantity without the use of boiler additives. In order to certify the system, it is first necessary to make a process diagram in order to block out the major process steps. After this is done, the major equipment in each process is defined and then installation and operational qualifications are conducted. After all of this is completed, the actual certification studies can be conducted to show that the clean steam system produces the required amount of steam of acceptable quality.

TABLE 1 Two Types of Steam Systems

	Plant steam	Clean steam
Feedwater	Potable, softened, or deionized water	Water for injection (distilled, reverse osmosis) or purified water
Material of system Construction	Iron or steel or stainless steel	Stainless steel
Use of additives	Yes—hydrazines, amines, etc.	None
Condensate	Commonly reused	May or may not be reused

A. Process Outline

Municipal water
Water pretreatment (deionize)
Distillation equipment
Holding tank (alternative procedure*)
Steam generator
Distribution system

B. Major Pieces of Equipment

1. Deionizer
2. Distillation equipment (optional)
3. Holding tank
4. Steam Generator
5. Distribution system

Once the major components of the system have been defined, an installation and operational qualification scheme can be devised for each piece of equipment.

1. Deionizer

Installation Qualification:

1. Examine unit for conformance to purchase specifications and document.
2. Connect unit to required utilities and document that the utilities are correct.
3. Check and document that all plumbing connections have been connected as specified by the process engineer.
4. Calibrate and document that all instrumentation is operating correctly.

Operational Qualification:

1. Test and document that water of appropriate quality (conductivity) is produced by the system using written standard operating procedures. The necessary quality depends on whether this water is feeding a distillation apparatus or a steam generator directly.
2. Test and document that the regeneration system works satisfactorily. Frequency of regeneration will vary, but most new systems are designed to be regenerated at least once a week.

Discussion: Most modern deionization systems are regenerated with acid and/or alkali on a frequent basis. This provides benefits in that the water quality (chemically) stays very good and the acid and alkali help in sanitizing the resin bed. Sometimes, especially if the deionized water is used without being distilled, it may be necessary to sanitize the resin bed chemically in addition to the acid and alkali treatment. Some firms also use constant recirculation of water through the beds as a means of preventing microbial growth. Ultraviolet light devices are also used for maintaining deionized systems in a sanitary condition.

---

*Some firms may go right to a steam generator.

2. Distillation Equipment

Installation Qualification:

1. Check and document that the distillation equipment received conforms to the purchase specifications.
2. Connect the unit to required utilities and document that utilities are correct.
3. Complete and document all required pre-startup maintenance procedures (including cleaning).
4. Calibrate, check, and document all critical process instrumentation.

Operational Qualification:

1. Using the written standard operating procedure, start up and run the distillation equipment. Determine and document the normal operating parameters of the system.
2. Check and document that the water produced by the still conforms to specifications (quality and quantity).

3. Holding Tank

Installation Qualification:

1. Check and document that the tank conforms to purchase specifications.
2. Pressure test the vessel to determine that the leak rate conforms to specifications and document. This can be done using hydrostatic and/or pneumatic ASME specified tests. (See previous sections on compressed air.)
3. Check and document that the pressure rating of the vessel conforms to specifications.
4. Perform and document all required cleanout procedures for startup.
5. Calibrate, check, and document all instrumentation systems.

Operational Qualification:

1. Check all instrumentation systems during actual operation and document.
2. Check heating system (control) for correct operation and document.
3. Fill tank with distilled water and hold for typical production cycle to determine that the water quality does not change adversely during storage. Test water quality and document.

4. Clean Steam Generator

Installation Qualification:

1. Check and document that the steam generator conforms to purchase specifications.
2. Connect the generator to the required utilities, verify and document that they are correct.
3. Tighten flanges or other fittings, clean generator chemically, passivate generator after installation, and label pertinent utilities feeding the generator.

4. Perform and document pressure testing of the generator to confirm that it meets specifications.
5. Calibrate, check, and document all critical process instrumentation.

Operational Qualification:

1. Using the written standard operating procedures, start up and run the clean steam generator. Determine and document the normal operating parameters of the system.
2. Check and document that all instrumentation and alarms are working correctly.
3. Check and document that the steam produced meets quantitative and qualitative specifications. The steam output should be condensed and then tested against USP XX, "Water for Injection," p. 850–851. A device for condensing clean steam is shown in Fig. 5.

5. *Distribution System*

Installation Qualification:

1. Check and document that materials of construction conform to specifications of the process engineer.
2. Using design drawings, trace constructed distribution system to determine that specifications have been met. This should include dimensions and all design features (traps, sensors, etc.). An "as built" drawing should then be created to document the constructed system. All branches of the system should be labeled.
3. Complete and document the cleaning of the system prior to startup. This typically consists of chemical cleaning and passivation.
4. Pressure test the system under actual production conditions and document the results.

Operational Qualification:

1. Test and document all use points of the system for adequate supply of steam under maximum load or production conditions. If standard operating procedures allow only limited use of equipment simultaneously, then these conditions should be tested as "worst-case" production conditions.
2. Steam quality should be tested at use points by condensing steam and conducting USP XX, "Water for Injection," p. 850–851, on the condensate.
3. Use points should also be tested to determine that excess condensate is not present under operating conditions. If excess condensate is present, it should be removed through additional trapping or other means such as insulating the system and use of controlled bleeders.

C. Certification of the Total "Clean Steam" System

Once the operational qualification is complete, the validation protocol should be written. The actual production conditions for validation of the system should be specified (steam load) as well as the locations to be sampled and the specifications required to pass.

FIGURE 5 Device for sampling clean steam. Steam is condensed in a stainless steel condenser using water to cool the steam. The apparatus was built on a hand truck to make it portable.

The certification then consists of the required testing specified in the protocol. A typical protocol consists of several tests under defined load conditions. Testing consists of condensing of the steam at various use points followed by USP XX, "Water for Injection," pp. 850–851, on the condensate, determining that appropriate steam pressure can be maintained under "worst-case" conditions, and that control and alarm features of the system work as designed (i.e., low-pressure alarms, etc.).

III. VACUUM SYSTEMS

Three types of vacuum systems are commonly found in modern asceptic manufacturing facilities: (a) house vacuum systems; (b) vacuum systems dedicated to lyophilization equipment; (c) vacuum systems dedicated to autoclaves or other sterilization equipment. We will address the certification of the house vacuum system in this discussion, because the other two systems are normally validated as part of the specialized equipment they service.

A. House Vacuum Systems

The house vacuum system normally consists of the following:

1. Vacuum pumps
2. Reservoir tank
3. Distribution system

The normal scheme for certification of such a system involves installation qualification, operational qualification, and finally capacity testing under production "worst-case" loads.

1. Vacuum Pumps

Installation Qualification:

1. Check and document that the pumps conform to purchase specifications.
2. Connect the pumps to the required utilities and document that the utilities are correct.
3. Tighten flanges and mounts; fill pumps with oil (if required); checking shock mountings and removing shipping restraints; calibrating, checking, and documenting all critical process instrumentation.

Operational Qualification:

1. Using the written standard operating procedure, start up and run the vacuum pumps. Determine and document the normal operating parameters of the system.
2. Check and document that the pumps have the required capacity and pull down to the vacuum required in the purchase specifications. This means capacity and depth of vacuum.

2. Reservoir Tank

Installation Qualification:

1. Check and document that the reservoir conforms to purchase specifications.

2. Verify and document that the vessel meets or exceeds the pressure rating (vacuum) specified in the purchase specifications.
3. Perform vacuum hold tests on the tank and document. Testing may be done via ASME (reference ANSI-337) hydrostatic and/or pneumatic testing procedures. Another commonly used technique involves the use of Freon and detection of leaks via a halogen detector. Acceptance criteria for the vacuum hold test will vary with the size of the system. A positive pressure test is often done in order to find leaks.
4. Perform and document cleaning procedures used prior to placing the vessel in service.

This completes the normal testing done on the tank prior to joining it to the vacuum system.

3. Distribution System

Installation Qualification:

1. Check and document that materials of construction conform to specifications of the process engineer.
2. Using design drawings, trace the constructed distribution system to determine that specifications have been met. This should include dimensions and all design features such as filters, strainers, check valves, etc. An "as built" drawing should then be created to document the system. All branches of the system should be labeled.
3. Pressure test the system using positive and negative pressure testing (pressure and vacuum hold tests), and document all testing.
4. Complete and document cleaning procedures prior to system startup.
5. Calibrate, check, and document all instrumentation systems. This includes all critical gauges, alarms, and automatic controllers.

B. Operational Qualification of the Vacuum System

Once all components of the system have been checked and are satisfactory, the actual qualification can proceed.

1. Using the written standard operating procedure, start up and operate the system. While this is running, determine the normal ranges of operation. This includes maximum vacuum obtained; time to pump down system; maximum vacuum obtained under load; temperature of oil, pump heads, etc. These parameters will be used later for determining that the system is operating correctly.
2. Perform a vacuum hold test by pumping the system down to its maximum vacuum and then isolating the pump from the system via valving. The system should hold vacuum with no appreciable loss for an extended period of time. A tight system should not lose more than 1 or 2 in. of mercury over a 30-min period.

   The actual performance will vary depending on the length of the system and the number of valves in the system. Therefore, the acceptance requirements will have to be determined for the actual system under test. This parameter should be determined by the process engineer and become one of the specifications for validation.

If the system will be used to evacuate tanks, the tanks should be protected from exceeding their vacuum rating by appropriate rupture disks or other safety equipment.

3. Determine the time required to evacuate the process tanks (or other equipment) and document for future system performance evaluations. Testing should also be performed using maximum demands on the system to determine a "worst-case" load. Finally, the system should be tested to determine the effects of placing additional load on the system during the evacuation of a vessel. This is necessary only if more than one tank or device will be evacuated at a time. If additional load is placed on the system by simultaneous evacuation of a second tank, it tends to decrease the vacuum in the first tank. This may hinder air removal in the vessel. This may be a critical point if the vacuum system is being used to remove air prior to sterilization in a sterilize-in-place system. An easy way to avoid this problem is to evacuate only one vessel at a time and then isolate it from the system using valving.

C. Certification Testing of Vacuum System

The validation protocol can now be written for the performance specifications of the system. Now the system is run under production conditions to determine that it can reproducibly reach the vacuum required within the normal time constraints. These time constraints are determined from the operational qualification runs and will vary depending on the size of the vessel or equipment to be evacuated and the load on the system. The results of the testing should then be documented for future reference.

If the time required to evacuate the tanks or equipment increases greatly, this can indicate that a problem exists with the vacuum system. All alarm systems should also be tested and their performance documented.

IV. ELECTRICAL SYSTEMS

The certification of electrical systems follows the same scheme as other utility validation. The objective is to provide the qualitative (frequency, phase, voltage stability) properties needed and quantitative properties (load demand) required. Additionally, several additional features may come into play: (a) digital equipment requires protection from voltage changes; (b) backup systems must be tested to determine that they come "on line" when failure occurs; (c) monitoring systems must be tested, if present, to determine that they perform correctly under normal conditions as well as in "worst-case" situations. The actual hookup of electrical utilities to equipment becomes part of the installation qualification for each piece of equipment. Schematics for the electrical system should be created. These should show all relevant features of the system (sensors, location of wire, transformers, etc.). Documentation of all components should be done vs. specifications (wire gauges, capacitance of transformers, etc.). The actual validation testing involves primarily monitoring systems, adequacy of supply under maximum load, and automated backup systems. Additionally, it is important to test emergency procedures that will be used in case of failure to minimize load when bringing the system back "on line." It may also be necessary to test the operation of equipment on the emergency power system in order to determine that it operates within validated parameters. This is one utility that may also be influenced by seasonal demand. Therefore, the validation should try and mimic these conditions if possible.

It is impossible to give a very specific validation scheme, since systems vary so much. However, we will point out system parameters that should be monitored. The engineers responsible for the facility will have to determine what voltage variation the various equipment can tolerate.

Systems to be tested include the following:

1. Monitoring system (computer, gauges, and individual equipment operation). All sensors, gauges, and monitoring devices should be calibrated prior to testing.

2. Backup system (batteries, generators, automatic switching systems) should be tested for automatic fail-over. If manual procedures are used, they should also be tested to determine if the standard operation procedures are satisfactory.

3. Special protective systems (voltage stabilizer, suppressors, etc.) should be tested for operation under "worst-case" conditions.

4. Equipment known to be sensitive to voltage fluctuations should be identified and tested to see if operation is satisfactory under "worst-case" conditions. If operation is not satisfactory, alarm systems or procedures should be developed to stop processing in this equipment when conditions are not satisfactory.

5. A "worst-case" condition should be determined and used in all test procedures (maximum current draw). If procedures are present to prevent simultaneous startup of equipment, this "worst-case" situation may be modified to be maximum continuous load, which is less severe.

6. Procedures used to bring the system "back up" after failure should be tested. Procedures used to place in-process material in a safe state should also be tested. This becomes critical if process valves are electrically operated. Systems should be designed to fail to a safe position, which may be open or closed depending on the process system.

7. Actual testing consists of monitoring line voltage and determining that process equipment is operating within validated parameters. Another approach might be to keep lowering the line voltage until failure occurs. However, this might endanger the process equipment, and it is suggested that a straight monitoring test procedure be used instead of a challenge. Documentation of the procedures should also be performed. Based on the test results, it might be necessary to modify operating procedures or emergency procedures. Testing of alarm systems and backup systems should also be done. The results of these tests may also be used to modify alarm points, especially with respect to voltage sensitive equipment.

V. DRAINAGE SYSTEMS

When discussing an aseptic facility, it also becomes necessary to discuss drainage systems that carry away water used for washing tankage, equipment, coding, washing containers, and sanitary waste. Generally these waste streams can be grouped into process and sanitary waste. Open floor drains should be avoided in an aseptic area. This can be accomplished by either not placing drains in an aseptic area or by capping the drains when they are not being used. Additionally, it is a good idea to separate "process" and "sanitary" systems to avoid the possibility of introducing "sanitary" waste into process systems. All systems must be equipped with devices that will prevent backflow or back-siphonage (such as atmospheric breaks, check valves, etc.). Cross-connections between "process" and "sanitary" systems should be avoided. Placement of piping should also be considered in order to prevent back-siphonage (i.e., waterproof walls may serve as pools and submerge water system piping, thereby defeating back-siphonage features).

A. Installation Qualification

The format should be similar to other piping systems, and encompass specifications for materials of construction, valving, leak testing, features and documentation via "as built" drawings; slope of piping and "backflow" prevention are especially important. Hard connections between water systems and drainage systems must be avoided unless "atmospheric breaks" are present.

B. Operational Qualification

The important feature to test here is prevention of back-siphonage during maximum "worst-case" load to the system. Again, the "worst-case" load may be minimized via standard operating procedures.

VI. APPENDIX OF METHODS

A. Collection of Clean Steam Samples

1. Materials

1. Steam condensor such as Calgon model no. 3531062 (cooling coil).
2. Fittings required to tap into clean steam system port (will vary) depending on the system.
3. Stainless steel, braided, Teflon-lined high-pressure hose (Aeroquip AE 101/614-11-C1 or equivalent).
4. Source of cold tap water or chilled water source for cooling condensor.
5. Pyrogen-free 1-liter sample bottles.

2. Procedure

1. Attach inlet of condensor to steam sample port.
2. Attach coolant lines to condensor.
3. Turn on clean steam sample port and allow steam to flow through condensor with no coolant flowing through condensor for approximately 30 min. This will sterilize the condensor and allow it to be cleaned out.
4. After this purge, turn on coolant, place sample bottle under bottom outlet of condensor, and collect approximately 1 liter of condensate. Caution: This procedure is dangerous, and proper safety equipment and procedures should be observed.

B. Method for Dew-Point Measurement Determination

1. *Materials*

All materials are only suggested and may be substituted.

1. General Eastern System 1200 AP Dew Point Hygrometer and Series 1211 sensor
2. Flow meter (Dwyer Instruments) with tubing
3. Polyethylene tubing (Eastman Poly-Flow)

2. *Procedure*

1. Adjust regulator on line to be tested to 3 psi, open the sample port, and flush for 3–5 min.
2. Attach the tubing and flow meter as shown in Fig. 3 and flush for 3–5 min. Now attach the tubing to the sensor and check the system for leaks.
3. Adjust the flow meter so that it reads 1 SCFH in an upright position. Wait 3–5 min for the system to stabilize.
4. Turn the instrument on and turn the dial on the monitor to "balance."
5. Wait for the display to read 100 and center the needle at "0."
6. Turn the dial to the "operate" position and wait for the reading to stabilize. Record the reading (°F) obtained. It may be necessary to convert readings obtained at these pressures to equivalent temperature under pressure ranges. A chart is provided in this procedure if this is necessary.

C. Method for Use of the Bendix/Gastec Pump and Analyzer Tubes

1. *Materials*

All materials are only suggested and may be substituted.

1. Bendix/Gastec pump, model 400, part no. 2417535
2. Bendix/Gastec Analyzer Tubes, CO_2 catalog no. 2LL

Other tubes are also available from Drager, Inc., for other gases such as carbon monoxide and hydrocarbon testing.

2. *Procedure*

1. Break the pointed ends off a detector tube by inserting each end in the hole provided in the pump.
2. Insert the detector tube in the inlet of the pump with the arrow on the tube pointing toward the pump. With the pump handle all the way in, align the red dots at the base of the pump.
3. Insert the other end of the detector tube into the sample port. Pull the pump handle out until it locks on one pump stroke (100 cc). Hold the pump with the tube in place for the time required for the tube to develop. (Time needed is indicated on each box of indicator tubes.) Read the concentration at the interface of the colored/uncolored reagent tube. Unlock pump by turning handle one-quarter turn in either direction.

D. Method for Sampling Gases for Chemical Testing

1. Materials

1. Gas bag, 3.8 liter capacity, with stopcock
2. Rubber tubing—appropriate size
3. Aluminum foil squares, 4 in. × 4 in.

2. Preparation

Tubing and foil must be sterilized prior to use.

3. Sampling

Attach one piece of sterile tubing to the sample port. Open the port and set the regulator for approximately 3—5 psi. Allow the line to flush for several minutes. Connect the other end of the tubing to the sample gas bag and fill. Disconnect the bag from the tubing and deflate. Refill the bag three more times, close the stopcock, and deliver to the lab for testing. The bag is filled and emptied several times in order to flush any remaining air from the bag. This is necessary in order to obtain a representative sample. Use the foil squares to cover the stopcock during transport.

9
Water Systems Validation

DAVID H. ARTISS

Artiss and Associates, Medfield, Massachusetts

I. DEFINITIONS AND CLASSIFICATIONS

A. Definition of "Water"

There must be no doubt that water should be classified as a product ingredient. This is true whether the water is used in the actual formulation, in a processing operation and then completely removed, or as a final rinse of a product contact surface.

B. Classes and Quality Standards

There is a wide variety of terminology used for different classifications of water. Water is referred to by many different names depending on its source, treatment, quality, or use, and not every group involved uses the same terminology.

It is also necessary to define carefully the minimum quality requirements for each classification of water with regard to chemical and microbiological purity.

Table 1 shows water classes and quality standards. The names for the different waters in the left-hand column are taken from three sources, the *United States Pharmacopeia* (USP XXI/NF XVI); the Food and Drug Association (FDA), Part 211, Current Good Manufacturing Practices for Finished Pharmaceuticals, dated Sept. 29, 1978; and the FDA Proposed Good Manufacturing Practices for Large Volume Parenterals (GMPs for LVP), dated June 1, 1976, Part 212. It is important to note that none of these names refer to processes for manufacturing water, such as deionized water or distilled water. This is a more flexible type of nomenclature, i.e., to keep the process that the water undergoes out of the name and to classify the water according to its quality from a chemical and microbiological standpoint. In this manner the process methodology for any class of water is left open and flexible. To quote from the preamble to Section 212.5 of the FDA proposed GMPs for LVPs, "it is not the intent of the FDA to curtail technological advance in the form of new facilities, types of equipment, processes or controls where such advance accomplishes at least the results attainable by strict

TABLE 1   Different Water Classes and Quality Standards

	42 CFR PT. 72	Mineral removal	Microbiological control[b]	Total microbial removal[d]	Pass pyrogen test	Quality level
Well water	—	—	—	—	—	I
Potable (USP)	X	—	X	—	—	II
Potable (FDA CGMP)	X	—	X	—	—	II
Purified (USP)[a]	X	X	X	—	—	III
Water for initial rinse and cleaning (FDA LVP)	X	—	X	X	—	IV
Water for drug product cooling (FDA LVP)	X	—[e]	X	X	—	IV
Water for injection (USP)[c]	X	X	X	X	X	V
Water for mfg. (final rinse) (FDA LVP)[c]	X	X	X	X	X	V

[a]Methods of achievement not specified. Historically, resin bed deionization has been the most common method.

[b]Methods of achievement not specified. Filters have been discouraged by the FDA because of operational problems. Microbiological control is interpreted as the FDA CGMPs, Section 211.48: "Potable water shall be supplied under continuous positive pressure in a plumbing system free of defects that could contribute to contamination." In other words, no further or additional change in the level of microbes is allowed.

[c]Method specified as reverse osmosis or distillation. System to be hot recirculation or drainage every 24 hr.

[d]1, 10, and 50 viable particles (v.p.)/100 ml are the same as zero v.p./100 ml in a practical sense.

[e]Although the LVP GMPs do not specifically address themselves to the chemical content of the drug product cooling water, it is the author's opinion that the FDA may necessarily have to place a restriction on the chemical content of the water because improper chemical concentration could potentially be more detrimental than a high microbial count to the individual receiving the drug.

compliance with the regulations." The eight different names shown for water in Table 1 are the only names given to water in the governmental documents mentioned.

The quality standards shown in Table 1 come from government regulations combined with the author's interpretation of these regulations, in order, left to right.

1. *Federal Register*, Part 141, as amended July 1, 1982 (41 FR 28404, July 9, 1976) is the basic regulation in the Code of Federal Regulations applying to municipal drinking water. The standard applies mainly to bacteriological purity.

2. *Mineral removal* is a specification set in the USP for chloride, sulfate, ammonia, calcium, heavy metals, etc. These standards are very stringent. In effect, they mean that water meeting this standard contains no added chemical substance. Herein lies the major problem, because this type of water is a perfect breeding ground for bacteria. Potable drinking water is less of a problem, because it usually has been chlorinated.

3. *Microbiological control* is what has been interpreted as the first level of microbial control set by the FDA. It basically means that you can take drinking water and handle it in a manner that does not contribute to the microbe content; i.e., the microbial level is unaltered from the city water supply to the final use point. Provided that there is an effective level of residual chlorine, microbial control should be simplified.

4. *Total microbial removal*: The FDA calls for different numbers for allowed microbe content of water, such as 1 v.p./100 ml of sample in one case and 10 and 50 in two other cases [ref. 212.226(b), 212.225(b), and 212.224(c), respectively]. It is impossible, however, to distinguish between 10 v.p./ 100 ml and 50 v.p./100 ml. Once the microbes are there, they can multiply rapidly, and the goal or quality standard must be no v.p./100 ml., that is, zero, for total microbial removal. This interpretation of the proposed government standards has been supported by every microbiologist consulted.

5. *Pyrogen test* as specified in the USP XXI/NF XVI is the standard rabbit test.

C. Consolidation of Water Classifications

Close examination of Table 1 reveals basic similarities in the different names given to water. The following three key points should be noted:

1. Purified Water (USP) must contain no added substances, and therefore microbial control of this water is difficult unless it is handled in a manner similar to that of Water for Injection (USP). The use of this class of water should therefore be restricted to those operations that mandate the use of Purified Water (USP). Investigations indicate that many operations can be performed using the more easily controlled drinking water and do not need the high chemical quality of the more difficult to control Purified Water (USP).

Although there are no microbial limits on purified water beyond that of drinking water, the Quality Assurance group will set reasonable target and action limits for the microbial levels in the purified water system.

2. Water for Initial Rinse and Cleaning has no regulatory requirement for chemical purity beyond that of drinking water. Therefore, if the proposed microbial levels can be maintained, initial rinse and cleaning operations can be performed using drinking water, which is inexpensive and relatively easy to control. Microbial control can be achieved by additional chlorination if

needed, or by heating. Many cleaning and initial rinsing operations will also be improved by the use of hot water.

The final rinse operation must be validated to ensure that all traces of chemical impurities in the water used for initial rinse and cleaning are rinsed free of produce contact surfaces. The regulations do not preclude the treatment of water used for initial rinse and cleaning to improve the chemical quality, but any such treatment must not jeopardize the microbial quality of the water. The requirement for treatment to improve the chemical quality must be evaluated on a case-by-case basis depending on the drinking water quality and the efficiency of the final rinse operation.

In addition, potable drinking water may well be adequate for washing floors, walls, and other nonproduct surfaces where soap or other cleaning agents are to be added.

3. The proposed LVP GMPs do not specify any limit on the chemical purity of water used for drug product cooling and therefore permit the use of drinking water that is monitored for residual chlorine and microbial content. There is concern, however, that any contamination from chemical impurities in the water could be as undesirable as microbial contamination.

To satisfy this concern for chemical purity, additional treatment processes may be applied to drinking water, provided that the microbial quality is not compromised. If the required chemical quality is such that chlorides are not permitted, then this will preclude the use of chlorine as a microbial control agent, and any drug product cooling operation will have to be performed using water that is treated and handled in the same manner as Water for Injection. As an alternative, the water for drug product cooling may be sterilized before use.

The different water classifications listed in Table 1 can be reduced to four basic types as shown in Table 2.

1. Level I Water

Level I is called well water because this is simply descriptive. This is untreated water used for utilities and may be from a well or surface source. Figure 1 illustrates Level I water.

TABLE 2 Four Basic Types of Water Classification

Level	Name
I	Well water
II	Drinking water
III	Purified Water (USP) used for critical bulk batch applications
IV	FDA water for final rinse and formulation (Water for Injection, USP) in parenteral areas

Cleaning and initial rinse operations in parenteral areas can be performed using drinking water with suitable chemical and microbial qualities.

Drug product cooling can be performed by using drinking water of suitable chemical and microbial quality or by use of water for final rinse and formulation [WFI (USP)] *or* by water that has been presterilized.

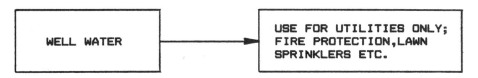

FIGURE 1   Level I, well water.

2. *Level II Water*

Level II is called drinking water because this is the name everyone is accustomed to and it doesn't appear to cause any interpretive problems in industry. It is simply potable water from a private or city supply that has a
variable degree of hardness and added chlorine for microbial control.
Figure 2 illustrates Level II water.

Use points should be monitored to ensure adequate residual chlorine and
lack of microbial contamination.

Chlorine levels should be maintained by adequate usage or by additional
flushing.

3. *Level III Water*

As previously discussed, Purified Water (USP) is the most difficult to control from a microbial standpoint and should be used for bulk batch application
where there is no reasonable alternative and for nonparenteral product
formulation.

The water shall contain no added substance and must be chloride-free,
which precludes the use of residual chlorine as a microbial control agent.
Figure 3 illustrates Level III water.

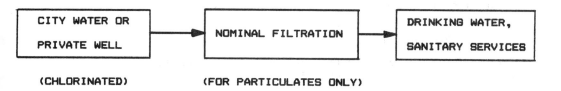

FIGURE 2   Level II, drinking water.

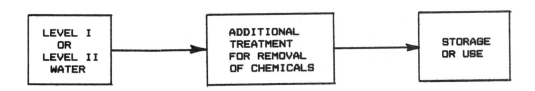

FIGURE 3   Level III, purified water U.S. Pharmacopeia.

WITH SUITABLE
PRETREATMENT

FIGURE 4   Level IV, water for manufacturing or final rinse (water for injection, U.S.P.).

4. Level IV Water

Level IV water is the most critical quality level. Due to the proposed regulation that this water satisfy the specifications for Water for Injection as defined by USPXXI, there are stringent chemical as well as microbiological and pyrogen requirements. This water must have a final treatment method that is either distillation or reverse osmosis as permitted by USPXXI/NFXVI. Figure 4 illustrates Level IV water.

II. DISCIPLINES, RESPONSIBILITIES AND DOCUMENTATION

A. Definition of Validation

Validation is defined as assuring that the particular system will consistently produce water of predictable quality when operated in the prescribed manner.
This means that not only the physical aspects of the system but also all related procedures and process monitors and controls must be subjected to the validation process.

B. Responsibility for Validation

The final responsibility for the water system rests with Quality Assurance, as it does with any product ingredient. Many other specialist disciplines will be involved in the actual performance of the validation project.

C. Disciplines Involved

Production, Engineering, Quality Control, Process Development, and Regulatory Affairs are all involved in the validation process.

D. Organization Structure

Quality Assurance
▼
Validation Project Manager
▼
Designated Personnel Responsible for Various Project Subparts

(These people will use whatever special disciplines
are indicated by the nature of the project subpart
to be validated)

E. Documentation

Documentation includes:

> Written validation procedures
> Approval of procedures
> Written validation protocols
> Approval of protocols
> Written validation reports
> Physical report forms

The approach to validating a water system can be the same as that employed for other critical systems with modifications as required to suit the specific design features and equipment used in the water system.

F. Degree of Validation

"How far is it necessary to go?" The type of equipment used, the mode of operation, and the system design will affect the validation requirements.

G. "Challenge" to the System

"Challenging" the system involves a critical challenge of all the operational, control, and supportive features of the system rather than a microbiological challenge. During this "challenge" the equipment and all procedures must be evaluated during normal and abnormal conditions to ensure that the system will either continue to produce water of suitable quality or will shut down in a suitable manner; i.e., fail-safe conditions must be adequately demonstrated.

A microbiological challenge to the system is not recommended. The danger of introducing thermophilic organisms into the system, which cannot be totally removed by the steaming or other sterilization/sanitization procedures, is of great concern. It is considered more suitable for the treatment program to be validated by demonstrating that the steam or chemical used for microbial control totally reaches all portions of the water system equipment and piping.

III. DESIGN CONSIDERATIONS THAT AFFECT VALIDATION

Quality assurance should be achieved by careful design of the system. This should ensure a minimum of reliance on procedural controls. This must be balanced against a system that is made overly complicated with too many alarms and controls that can cause maintenance and calibration problems.

The system should be as simple as possible, with no features that are not absolutely required for safe operation. The "belt-and-braces" concept, which provides backup or redundant equipment, should be avoided.

Frequently, several systems can be combined to provide fewer systems, thereby reducing overall system complexity and reducing the total amount of sampling and monitoring required.

Much of the water treatment equipment that is currently available for use in a pure water system was originally developed to improve the chemical quality of the water—the microbial quality was of little concern. Frequently the concern was for absolute economy, which resulted in the design of equipment where malfunction would be tolerated if it could be justified economically.

Some equipment, by virtue of construction and design features, is inherently more "predictable" in performance than other equipment. This type of equipment is easier to validate than equipment that is more variable in operation. Thus, the method and degree of validation will vary with the type of equipment selected and also with whether that equipment is used for pretreatment or final treatment of the water.

A. Revalidation

Revalidation should not be required on a routine basis. Revalidation should be performed only when there has been a significant change to the system or to the operational parameters. Routine monitoring and inspection will continue under the same conditions as those that existed during the original validation.

Routine maintenance or replacement of parts should have a specific written procedure, which must be validated at the time of the original validation. These procedures may require that certain tests be performed to ensure that the system will not be jeopardized when restarted.

The frequency of inspection will depend on the durability of the components selected, and the frequency of inspection may require adjustment depending on the actual service life observed. Until such inspection frequency has been established empirically, it seems that all, or a representative number, of components should be inspected at no longer than 1-year intervals, possibly much more frequently, depending on component durability.

B. Related Services

Related services can profoundly affect the performance of a high-purity water system. The areas of major concern include the following.

1. Clean steam is used to steam-sterilize the water system. In large pharmaceutical plants the main steam system provides steam for building heat and for process temperature control. The condensate from this system is returned to the boiler and is reevaporated to make more steam. Any impurities from leaks in the process heat exchangers could easily be returned to the boiler, evaporated, and then delivered to the critical pure water system. It is not sufficient, therefore, just to ensure that there are no volatile boiler additives; it is preferred that the clean steam system be a completely separate system that uses no returned condensate.

This type of system uses water of good chemical quality, which is evaporated and has the impurities separated out to form clean, pyrogen-free steam. The clean steam separation and distribution piping should be constructed of the same quality materials as those used for the pure water system to ensure that there will be no corrosion of the clean steam piping that could "carry over" and cause subsequent corrosion in the pure water piping.

2. Compressed air may be used to overpressure or cool down a pure water system after steaming, or may be used to remix the resins in a mixed-bed deionizer after regeneration. This air must be clean, dry, and oil-free.

Using an oil-free air compressor may not be sufficient, as this will not remove ambient hydrocarbons. The air must be "dry," with a low enough dew point to ensure that there will be no moisture condensation in the compressed air distribution piping system.

It may be necessary to install moisture, oil, and particulate removal equipment in the compressed air delivery system. This equipment must be subjected to the complete validation process.

3. Nitrogen may be used as an overpressure for the pure water storage tanks. The design and construction of the nitrogen delivery system must be validated, and there must be suitable sampling and testing to verify the quality of the nitrogen being supplied.

C. Instrumentation

Instrumentation should be kept to the minimum amount necessary and used:

1. For the proper operation of the system
2. As an aid to preventive maintenance
3. For quality assurance
4. To provide documentation that the proper conditions have been maintained

Instruments will either indicate, record, or control some vital function such as temperature, pressure, flow, pH, or conductivity.

Temperature instruments should be of the type that has a separate well so that the primary element can be removed from the piping system for calibration without risking the contamination that might result from draining the system.

Pressure-sensing instruments should be of the type that have a sanitary, stainless steel diaphragm to isolate the instrument internals from the process fluid.

Flow measurement and all instruments should be designed so that the primary element that is in contact with the pure water has no crevices and is easily cleaned by the circulation of pure water.

D. "Batch" or "Flow-Through" Methods of Operation

It is the policy of many pharmaceutical manufacturers to batch water for formulation of parenteral products. This gives a degree of security in that a certain volume of water can be isolated and held while testing is performed. This water can be held until results of the USP chemical tests are evaluated. Figure 5 illustrates this batch concept.

This style of operation is expensive from the point of view of capital outlay and presents design problems in the elimination of "dead legs" and assurance of batch integrity. This style of operation is practical only in manufacturing areas where there is a high product value and there is a need for water batch identity to protect that value.

With the requirement that final rinse water has to be treated in the same manner as product water, the volumes involved become much larger. In complex systems this can result in two or three very large storage tanks to provide the necessary batching facility. Under these conditions the "flow-through" or continuous-operation design has many advantages. In this concept the treatment equipment supplies water automatically to maintain a level in the storage tank. The capital outlay is lower, and the piping around storage tanks is less complex, making it easier to avoid dead legs. Figure 6

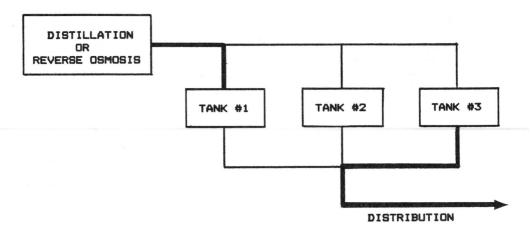

FIGURE 5 Tank #1, filling; tank #2, isolated while awaiting approval; tank #3, in use.

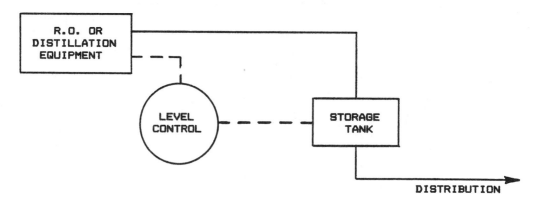

FIGURE 6 "Flow through" or continuous operation. Water treatment unit starts and stops automatically on signal from the level control. Additional features such as automatic timed flush to drain on start up should be considered.

illustrates this concept. This style of operation is more practical in areas where there is a lower product value and water batch identity is less critical.

Either of these methods of operation can be used with heated recirculation, and both must be designed to permit periodic sterilization.

Note that the equipment used and the system design are much more critical when using a "flow-through" concept. Therefore the validation requirements are much more stringent to ensure that the system is consistent and predictable in operation.

IV. EQUIPMENT AND SYSTEMS

There is no "perfect" system to suit all applications. Each system is designed to suit a wide variety of feedwater conditions, and process requirements such as flow, pressure, temperature, and water quality required.

Equipment selection is of major importance. The choice of a manufacturer, and of type and size of equipment, should be made only after the concerns of the Engineering, Production, and Quality Assurance groups have been carefully considered.

It should be remembered that much of the water treatment and pretreatment equipment that is available today was developed for industries where the chemical quality of the water was the major concern and the microbial quality was less important. This equipment, developed for boiler feedwater and related applications, must be carefully evaluated in the light of the different use to which it will be put in a pharmaceutical application. Other treatment equipment may have been designed originally for producing potable water from brackish or sea water. The mere substitution of stainless steel construction and the use of some sanitary components does not necessarily make this equipment suitable for the production of water for pharmaceutical purposes.

The suitability of the equipment is the responsibility of the user, and any claims of regulatory compliance made by an equipment manufacturer must be critically evaluated. The equipment design and construction should be carefully examined to ensure that there are no questionable features, not covered by present regulations, that may jeopardize the quality of the water. These features may well be subject to closer investigation in the future and could involve an expensive replacement at a later date if evidence of questionable equipment design is discovered.

The size and capacity of the equipment should be considered from the standpoint of the microbiologist as well as that of the engineer. The equipment selection that is ideal from the standpoint of capital investment, operational costs, and labor requirements is frequently of a size that is conducive to bacterial growth. Thus, some operations that improve the chemical quality of of the water unfortunately permit a decrease in microbial quality. This problem must be minimized by careful selection of the type and size of the equipment such that the operating characteristics are less likely to encourage microbial growth.

The objective of the design should be to build a system that satisfies the water requirements while controlling the quality throughout the treatment process from the feedwater to the final point of use. To permit a system to have uncontrolled microbial growth, while hoping to correct the problem in the final treatment process, is totally unacceptable.

Figure 7 shows a possible overall water block diagram. There are many with other possible arrangements.

The following is a brief discussion of the various methods of water treatment in common use, the mechanisms of the treatment process having been adequately described in other literature. The purpose of this review is to discuss the effect of these treatment processes on the microbial population of the water and to highlight some of the potential problems inherent in the use of certain equipment.

Following the discussions of microbial characteristics, the major features of the equipment are reviewed as they relate to validation.

A. Raw Water

Raw water fed to a pharmaceutical manufacturing facility is usually supplied by the local community water department. This water may be from a ground or surface source, and the type of treatment to which it is subjected will

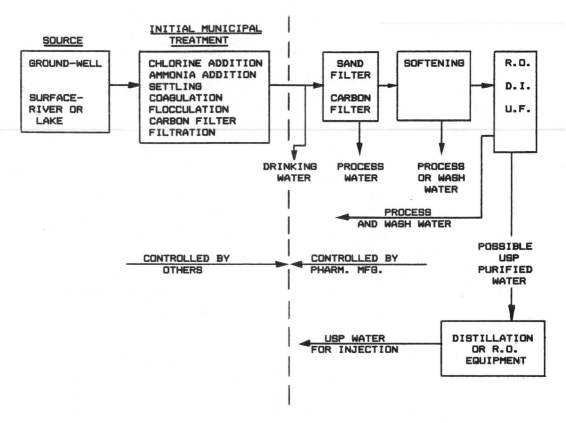

FIGURE 7   Overall water block diagram.   Note: Total water supply may be
under control of pharmaceutical manufacturer.

depend on the locality and the types of contaminants in the supply.   Most
municipalities add chlorine as a means of microbiological control.

Due to the variabilities of source, temperature, season, organic level, and
complex distribution network, it is impossible for the municipality to ensure
a consistent level of free residual chlorine to all of the customers being fed
by the distribution system.   Therefore, the bacteriocidal effect of the initial
chlorine addition may no longer be available by the time the water is fed into
the pharmaceutical processing facility.

This level of free available chlorine will further decrease during the distribution through the piping system within the manufacturing plant.   This
frequently results in potable water at the use point that contains significant
levels of microorganisms.   Any dead legs in the distribution system can contribute greatly to the problem and can recontaminate clean feed water.

A flushing program can be initiated to bring a supply of water into the
plant that has residual chlorine on a regular basis, especially after a period
of low usage.   Additional chlorine can be added to city water to maintain the
residual chlorine at acceptable levels or to permit periodic "hyperchlorination."
This, combined with a flushing program, will effectively clean the city water
distribution system.

B. Water Softening

Softening is a mechanism whereby the hardness ions of calcium and magnesium are exchanged for sodium ions in a resin column. If the infeed water does not contain a high level of residual chlorine, microbial growth may occur in this equipment. The high surface area and frequently low flows that are often encountered are extremely conducive to the growth of bacteria. The high flow rate of the back-washing operation will displace some of these organisms, but the use of sodium chloride as a regenerant chemical has little bacteriocidal effect.

The quality of the water should be monitored periodically for residual chlorine level and for microbial content. The results of this sampling program may well indicate that a periodic sanitizing treatment of the softener resin bed by chlorine solution is required to control the level of microorganisms in the soft water effluent.

Softening equipment considerations include:

1. Regeneration frequency
2. Requirement to sanitize bed
3. Replacement of resin
4. Monitoring pressure drop and hardness

C. Activated Carbon

Activated carbon filtration is frequently employed to remove chlorine and organics from the water to protect ion exchange resins and certain types of reverse osmosis equipment from premature degradation. Once the chlorine has been removed, there is no residual bacteriocidal agent in the water and the microbial population can multiply rapidly. The carbon beds themselves can become breeding areas for reasons of high surface area and low flow. As with softening equipment, the bacteria levels in the carbon filter must be monitored, and sanitizing treatments will be required.

Sand and carbon filtration considerations include:

1. Backwash frequency and time to clarify
2. Continuous recirculation
3. Requirements to sanitize beds
4. Replacement of carbon
5. Monitoring pressure drop

D. Filtration

Filtration can be divided into three main classifications.

1. Prefiltration to remove large particulates. These may be the cleanable type or those employing replaceable cartridges. The usual purpose is to prevent particulate contamination from other water treatment equipment or to prolong the service life of final filtration equipment.
2. Microfilters or "bacteria-retentive" filters. It is normally accepted that 0.22 μm absolute filters are needed to remove most bacteria.
3. Ultrafiltration (UF) is a loosely defined (0.001–0.01 μm) porosity range between microfiltration and reverse osmosis. This equipment will remove particulates and bacteria but may not remove pyrogens,

depending on the pore size of the UF membrane and the nature of the pyrogenic contaminant. They will not remove dissolved salts.

Filters constitute an enlarged section of a piping system and are subject to low or intermittent flow conditions. If there is no residual bacteriocidal agent in the water, any microorganisms on the downstream side of evan a bacteria-retentive filter or UF will have ample opportunity to multiply. It is essential in any system employing filters for the control of bacteria that the filters and all of the downstream piping be effectively sterilized on a regular basis.

In systems where current regulations permit the use of filters, the following concerns must be evaluated:

1. Microfilters should be installed only where there is a demonstrated need to reduce the bacteria levels. They should not be applied indiscriminately as a policy of insurance.
2. The use of a filter should not be to correct a microbiological defect in the operation of another component in the system; i.e., it should not be used to treat the symptom while the disease goes untreated.
3. Filters must be carefully selected to suit the particular application.
4. The installation must be suitable to permit the best utilization of the filter capabilities.
5. The filter selection should be validated to ensure that there will be no migration, particle release, or leaching of extractables under the anticipated actual use conditions of varied flow, temperature, and hydraulic shock.
6. There must be a written procedure for filter inspection, replacement, integrity testing, and monitoring.
7. Filters used for microbial control and all downstream piping must be sanitized periodically to protect the filter from becoming a bacterial growth medium.
8. If the filter is found to be ineffective when used properly, it should be removed.

Many of the preceding concerns are also applicable for ultrafiltration and reverse osmosis.

Filtration equipment considerations include:

1. Porosity of membrane
2. Integrity testing of membrane (cartridge)
3. Integrity testing of membrane to housing seal
4. Pressure drop across membrane (differential pressure)
5. Microbial buildup in filter assembly
6. Method of sanitizing assembly
7. Removal of sanitizing chemical residues
8. Particulate shedding of filter membrane

E. Ion Exchange

Demineralization by ion exchange (DI) will remove dissolved ionic impurities. DI units themselves are usually excellent breeding areas for bacteria. The regeneration process tends to remove some bacteria from the resin beds because of the high flow rate of the backwashing operation and the sanitizing action of the chemical treatment used to regenerate the resins. The bacterial population tends to increase as the service period progresses, but temperature and flow rate will also affect the rate of growth.

DI does nothing to improve the microbiological quality and usually contributes significantly to the bacteriological degradation of the water. The high bacteria loads can also produce pyrogenic problems.

There may be impurities in the feedwater that cannot be effectively removed by methods other than some form of ion exchange. While the use of ion exchange is less desirable than other methods of water treatment from the standpoint of microbial control, there are several design considerations that can help restrict bacterial growth in a DI unit. Equipment should be sized to ensure frequent regeneration, though this may not be the most economical selection from the standpoint of capital expenditure and operating costs. The use of "polishing" units should be avoided, as these may be in service for extended periods. The chemical quality of the water is used to determine when these units need to be regenerated; if one waits this long, one will be encouraging the growth of bacteria and possibly shedding pyrogenic material. Intermittent and low-flow conditions can be minimized by installing a recirculation system on the DI equipment. The flow rate through this system should approach the rated service flow of the DI unit.

Ion exchange is performed either by means of portable "exchange" units or by use of fixed equipment.

The portable exchange equipment involves using small tanks of 1 or 2 ft^3 of resin capacity that are replaced when they become "exhausted"—i.e., all of the resin capacity has been used in removing impurities.

These tanks are then collected and transported to a central service area, sometimes many miles away, for regeneration. The resins of many tanks are usually mixed together and regenerated in mass. The resins are then returned to the small tanks and made ready for service again. The resin tanks may be subjected to sanitization while empty.

Portable dionization (DI) equipment considerations include:

1. Presanitizing before use—by supplier
2. Contaminants from resins
3. Contaminants from rinse water
4. Microbial control in intermittent usage

Fixed ion exchange equipment (see Fig. 8) is designed to be regenerated in place. The chemicals that are required are supplied by means of small drums or from large bulk containers.

Fixed deionization equipment considerations include:

1. Measuring quality and conditions at various stages through the DI train, e.g., influent, postcation, postanion, post-mixed bed, etc.
2. Varying conditions during the service cycle
3. Condition of beds—microbial
4. Possible continuous recycling of water through the resin bed
5. Quality of regenerant chemicals—H_2SO_4, HCl, NaOH
6. Condition and quality of air used for air blow—on mixed-bed units only
7. Dissolved and colloidal silica—not detected by conductivity
8. Amines from resin—new and old
9. Sanitization and regeneration
10. Frequency of regeneration and bed size

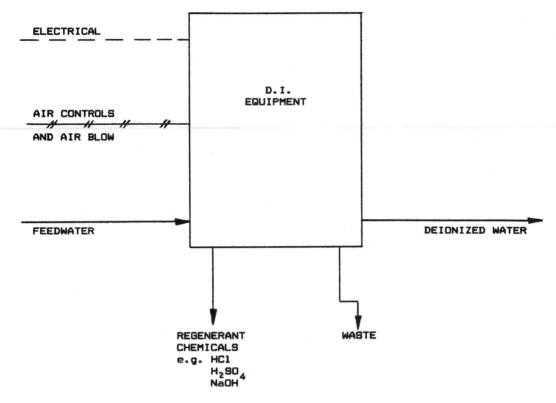

FIGURE 8   Fixed deionization equipment considerations: Monitor flow, pressure, and throughput.

    11. pH adjustment to meet USP requirements
    12. pH measurement problems

F. Reverse Osmosis

Reverse osmosis (RO) treatment will remove a large portion of dissolved salts and also particulates, bacteria, and pyrogenic materials. While the proposed GMPs for LVPs permit the use of RO for preparation of product water for parenteral applications, there is limited operations history to support this contention. In the theoretical sense the RO membrane should prevent the passage of all bacteria and pyrogens. Studies, however, reflect conflicting results, and there are many questions in the design and construction of RO units that have yet to be resolved.

    There is no meaningful test as to the integrity of the RO unit, either to determine a small hole in a membrane, a broken fiber, or a defective seal. The membrane itself can be subjected to chemical or microbial degradation that may be extremely difficult to detect by statistical sampling. The units must be routinely sanitized to prevent excessive bacterial growth, and even under ideal test conditions microorganisms have been detected in the permeate stream. Procedures must be carefully written to ensure that the equipment is properly operated, monitored, maintained, and sanitized on a regular basis.

The economic considerations of using RO over another treatment mechanism are very attractive, but the operational requirements of preventive maintenance and periodic sanitization must not be ignored. The microbial quality desired in the effluent must be carefully considered, and the potential limitations of the equipment must be realistically evaluated and procedures implemented to prevent damage to the equipment and to ensure the continued production of water of acceptable quality.

Due to the large number of operational concerns related to the use of reverse osmosis, there is a much greater degree of effort required in the validation of this type of equipment as opposed to more predictable types of water treatment equipment (see Fig. 9).

Reverse osmosis considerations include:

1. Integrity test—chemical and bacteriological rejection (feed poor-quality water to unit and perform dye test)
2. Multiple modules—composite permeate
3. Temperature-dependent flow rate
4. Chlorine effect—cellulose—Cl_2 preferred polyamid—Cl_2 intolerable
5. pH-dependent—cellulose—3-7.5 approx. polyamid 3-13 approx.
6. Sanitization and flushing residuals—time to flush
7. Replacement program for modules
8. Monitoring flow, pressures, temperature, Cl_2, pH, reject rates, and conductivity

G. Ultrafiltration

Some ultrafiltration (UF) equipment is very similar to some reverse osmosis equipment except that the membrane porosity is greatly different. Thus many of the considerations stated above may also apply to ultrafiltration equipment.

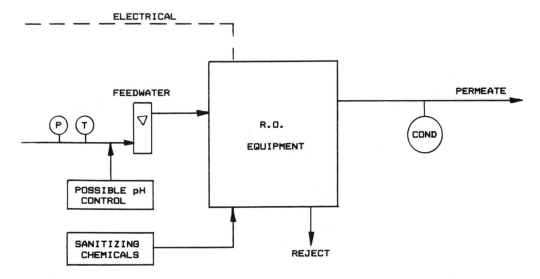

FIGURE 9   Reverse osmosis considerations. Ultrafiltration similar to R/O, except U/F will not remove dissolved chemical impurities.

Some UF membranes are manufactured from polysulphone materials which exhibit better pH stability and tolerance to certain chemical sanitizers and cleaners.

H. Distillation

Distillation is the most widely accepted method of producing water for critical pharmaceutical purposes. If the distillation unit is properly designed, constructed, and operated, it should give consistent and reproducible quality of sterile pyrogen-free water.

Recent government proposals have caused a reevaluation of the long-accepted designs, and every distillation manufacturer should be critically evaluating his own equipment. Apart from the areas of heat exchanger design and vent filter installation, there are many other questionable features in the design of most distillation units that must be modified and improved.

Distillation is the safest but the most expensive method of treating water. Because of the capital and operational costs involved, this may not be the best method of producing water for purposes other than those most critical applications.

The three most common methods of distillation in current usage are single-effect and multiple-effect thermal distillation and vapor compression distillation.

1. *Thermal Drive—Single Effect* (see Fig. 10)

1. Heat exchangers—Evaporators—no control—feed side only (steam to feedwater)
    —Preheater—tube within a tube*
    —Condenser—double tube sheet design or tube within a tube*
2. Vent filter—design by user—controlled flow directions or vent feed side only (with single backflow preventor); may need overflow shut-off valve
3. Blowdown—continuous overflow
4. Overflow protection—not needed
5. Cooling water flow—manual or thermostatic valve
6. steam flow—on/off
7. Condensate—trap supplied
8. Instrument air—may not be required
9. Electrical controls
10. Auto dump valve—conductivity control with delay timer available
11. Pressures and temperatures monitored

2. *Multiple-Effect Still* (see Fig. 11)

1. Heat exchangers—Condenser—tube within a tube (no internal connections) or double tube sheet
    —Evaporators—relay on proper differentual pressure—distillate or pure vapor is at higher pressure than feedwater

---

*Joints inside heat exchanger body are *not* recommended due to the possibility of leakage at these joints causing contamination of the distillate.

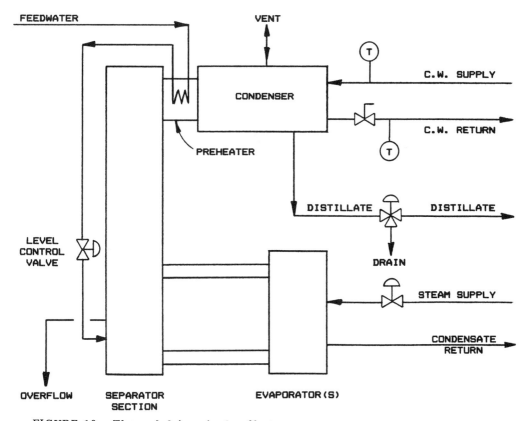

FIGURE 10   Thermal drive single effect.

—Preheaters (inside evaporator body)—tube within-
   tube concept
—Preheaters (outside evaporator body)—double-tube-
   sheet concept, or use feedwater-to-feedwater design
2. Vent filter—double-check-valve concept or controlled flow direction
   to keep filter dry. Need blowdown shutoff
3. Blowdown—controlled by fixed orifice and manual flow adjustment on
   feedwater
4. Overflow protection—controlled by level switch in first column, which
   interrupts feedwater supply—highly recommend overflow protection
   in each column for total protection
5. Cooling water flow—thermostatic flow control valve with on-off control
6. Steam flow—on continually, with low-pressure switch recommended
7. Condensate—trap supplied
8. Instrument—control air for auto dump valve
9. Electrical—controls
10. Conductivity control with delay timer to operate dump valve

3. *Vapor Compressor Distillation* (see Fig. 12)

1. Heat exchangers—Evaporators—differential pressure in proper
                     direction

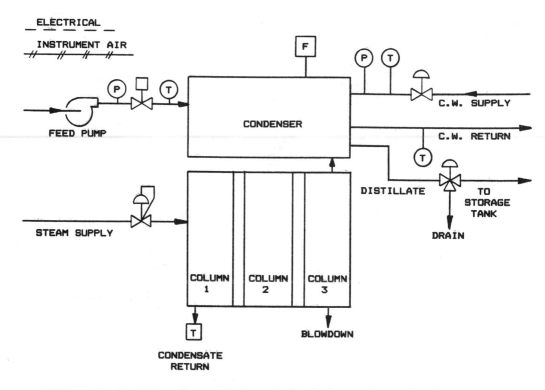

FIGURE 11 Multiple effect still (3 to 8 effects is usual range): features monitored, pressures, temperatures, flows, conductivity, and vapor compression distillation.

       —Vent condenser—must be double tube sheet or use
        distillate as coolant
       —distillate cooler should be double-tube-sheet style
 2. Vent filter—must admit filtered, compressed air into equipment; note that this equipment is designed to operate at or just above atmospheric pressure
 3. Blowdown—float valve control or foam pipe
 4. Overflow protection—none if float valve fails, or rely on foam pipe, depending on specific design
 5. Cooling water flow—none required
 6. Steam or electric—makeup heat only
 7. Condensate trap supplied
 8. Control air as required
 9. Electrical controls
10. Conductivity controls—timer can be supplied
11. Lubricating oil system required with controls
12. Compressor steam traps must have shutoffs
13. Dead legs were inherent in the design of early units; the user must confirm that these have been eliminated on the specific equipment under evaluation

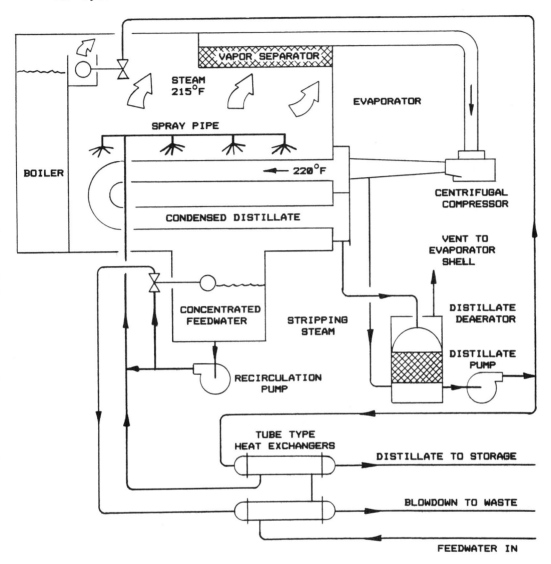

FIGURE 12 Horizontal evaporator type shown—vertical evaporator type is also available.

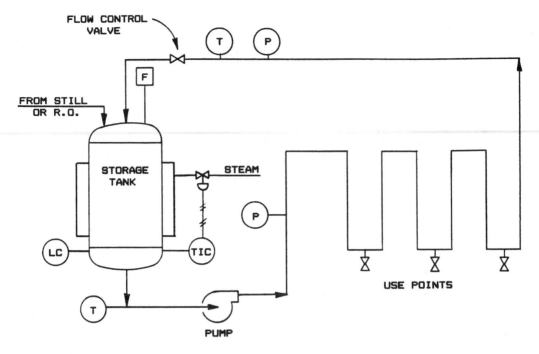

FIGURE 13   Basic hot recirculation system.

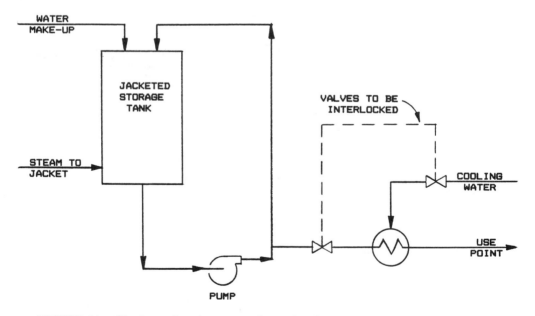

FIGURE 14   Single cool water use point. Cooling water valve is open only
when the header valve is open. Heat exchanger design must comply with the
proposed LVP GMP. Note: System temperature can be maintained by means
of a jacketed water storage tank or by use of a heat exchanger in the recirculation loop.

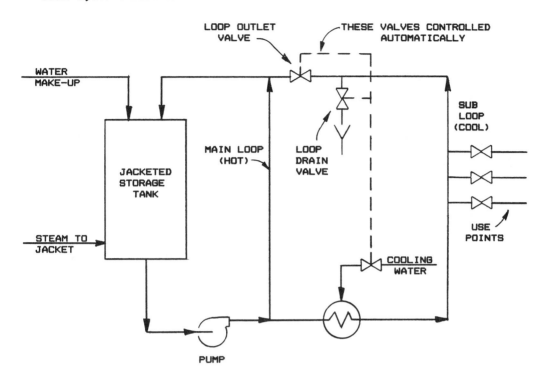

FIGURE 15   Multiple cool water use points. When cold water is not needed,
water will circulate through the main loop and the sub loop at 80°C. During
use, the cooling water valve is open and the loop outlet valve is closed.
After use, the cooling water valve is kept closed and the loop drain valve
opened to flush all the cooled water to drain. This will prevent any water
that has been cooled from being returned to the storage tank. Heat exchanger design must comply with the proposed LVP GMP. Note: System
temperature can be maintained by means of a jacketed water storage tank or
by use of a heat exchanger in the recirculation loop.

I. Ultraviolet

Ultraviolet radiation has limited application due to the many factors that can
reduce its effectiveness. In too many cases it has been installed with no
verification that more than a minimal bacterial reduction has been achieved.
Bacteria can grow so rapidly that even a 90% reduction in bacteria can soon
have little effect. Once again, unless a particular treatment mechanism has
a demonstrated benefit, it should not be used in a pharmaceutical water
system.

J. Heat

The heating and storing of water at 80°C has been shown effectively to control the microbial quality. This has the advantage that, as no chemicals are
added, there will be no problems of objectionable residuals. This concept is
expensive, energy consuming, and requires that the storage tank and distribution system be insulated for heat conservation. Water at this temperature
is difficult to handle and hazardous to operating personnel, and certain drug

components cannot be formulated at this temperature. If the water has to be cooled before use, there is a potential for microbial growth and pyrogen development in the portion of the system that is operating at lower temperatures. Some users have validated systems operating at temperatures as low as 65°C.

Figure 13 shows a simple hot water recirculation system with basic instrumentation. It is impossible to show all the possible system designs that may satisfy all of the operation performance and regulatory compliance requirements.

Figure 14 shows one method of installation of a single-use-point heat exchanger.

Figure 15 shows one method of installation of a single heat exchanger for multiple cool use requirements.

V. VALIDATION OF EXISTING SYSTEMS

Many existing systems, which for years may have satisfied all of the in-process quality control test requirements, may fail a rigorous scientific validation challenge. The concept of retroactive validation was established whereby a preexisting system may be exempt from certain validation requirements due to its past history of meeting all test parameters.

A retroactive validation does not, and should not, permit the continued use of a system that has serious defects or is out of control, whatever the testing history shows.

The areas of greatest concern appear to be the following:

1. The concept of total systems design with all components compatible with the system function
2. Quality assurance by design
3. Definition of specific quality levels to be achieved and established alert and action levels
4. Detailed and specific written procedures for system operation, cleaning, sanitization, maintenance, and preventive maintenance
5. A comprehensive sampling program to ensure detection of out-of-specification quality levels and to provide continuous control over the system.
6. Proper training of operating and maintenance personnel
7. Proper documentation and record keeping
8. Quality control unit to bear the final responsibility of the acceptability of any system—not Engineering, Production, or any other discipline
9. Validation to assure that the design, construction, and operational procedures are suitable for the intended purpose

There are also key areas of concern regarding equipment. Most of these concerns are based on actual experience of defective equipment design, operation, or maintenance that could jeopardize the quality of the water being processed.

1. Heat exchangers—the single-tube-sheet type with rolled-in tubes can develop leaks, especially when subjected to varying temperature cycles.
2. Pumps—concerns about the materials used for seal packing make a mechanical seal the preferred method of construction. If an external source of seal lubricant is required, there are concerns regarding the potential contamination from this external source. A properly designed

mechanical seal should not require external lubrication but should rely on the internal water being pumped to serve this purpose.

3. Filters—although filters can be extremely useful, their application may pose problems if they are not selected, installed, used, and maintained properly. This concern for the misuse of filters was one of the reasons why the FDA prohibited their use in water systems in the proposed LVP GMPs.

4. Concerns with volatile extractables from plastic piping and the preference for steam as a sanitizing agent has led the FDA to propose the use of stainless steel piping systems. Great concerns exist over the construction quality employed when welding stainless steel.

5. Other concerns, such as sloping lines to drains, and eliminating dead legs, have fairly obvious reasons.

An extremely valuable quality control tool is the system audit and a careful evaluation of the audit report.

Audits should *not* be conducted by the personnel responsible for the operation or maintenance of that particular system, for obvious reasons.

The personnel conducting the audit need not be experts in water systems design or in water treatment equipment, provided that they ask the proper questions; however, the services of an expert may be required to answer searching questions. The format for the water system audit can follow the format used for other systems, with minor modifications to suit the particular characteristics of the system. Many companies employ a standard approach to systems audits, as they do toward validation.

One approach to an audit is to try and be more critical than you can possibly imagine an FDA inspector will be.

You should issue your own Form 483, but with one major difference to the official report of findings: You should grade your list of deficiencies as to your interpretation of their severity; e.g.:

Class 1 indicates probable citation by a critical FDA inspector—such as violations cited in the proposed LVP GMPs (if applicable) or based on what the FDA has been known to object to in the past.

Class 2 indicates possible citation by a critical FDA inspector. These are less severe, but are still deficiencies that the FDA inspector would certainly discover if he searched thoroughly.

Class 3 is not likely to result in a citation, but in the author's opinion violates the intent of the Good Manufacturing Practices. Many of these Class 3 deficiencies would be apparent only to someone thoroughly conversant with treatment equipment and the specific design and operating characteristics of various controls and components.

This grading system allows immediate attention to be focused on the critical items so that corrective steps can be taken swiftly. Quite often procedures can be modified in the interim until physical changes to the plant or system can be implemented.

Some of the more common problems likely to be discovered include:

1. Total lack of definition of quality requirements at various stages in the treatment and delivery system. This is a primary requirement for establishing operating parameters.

2. Lack of a comprehensive sampling and monitoring program to ensure that required quality levels are being consistently satisfied and that each piece of equipment is performing according to design specifications. This sampling program is absolutely necessary to identify

problem areas. On many occasions there are intermittent but recurring problems that cannot be traced with the inadequate sampling program in use at the time. The only recourse when such a problem occurs is a "shotgun" approach of sanitizing everything in the hope that this will solve the problem.

3. Lack of written procedures for operating, cleaning, sanitization, maintenance, etc. Frequently all that is used is the equipment manufacturer's checklist, which may be totally inadequate for GMP requirements. Also, a lack of written procedures may result in inconsistent operation of the equipment such that no meaningful baseline data can be generated.

4. Lack of definition of the system—no schematic or "as built" layout drawings. Frequently no one knows why it was built this way, or that way, or when, or by whom, or why modifications have been made. Tracing the system through physically to identify dead legs frequently results in "losing" the lines. They go above a ceiling or through a wall and do not come out the other side. The person who installed the system may have retired or left the company years ago, and no one else in the plant really knows all of the routing of the lines or even the location of all the use points.

5. Inadequately trained operating personnel. Often the people responsible for the equipment are from the Production department and their only understanding of the equipment has been obtained by listening to the supplier's sales pitch and by reading the limited operating manuals furnished with the equipment. Although Production personnel are familiar with GMP concepts, their lack of engineering background may hamper their total understanding of the capabilities and limitations of the system. Sometimes the equipment operation is the responsibility of the Plant Engineering or Maintenance group. With their numerous other responsibilities for production equipment, facilities equipment, and other critical systems, it is not surprising that the only attention paid to the water system is frequently just enough to keep it functioning.

   The Utilities personnel usually have a pretty good understanding of the chemical processes employed in the water treatment system and frequently have the responsibility for this equipment.

   The last two groups, Plant Engineering and Utilities, frequently have little time to try to understand the complexities of GMPs and usually have more urgent concerns keeping up with the numerous regulatory requirements of OSHA, the EPA, and local and state codes.

6. Equipment not suited to pharmaceutical applications. The majority of the equipment in use was designed primarily for the efficient removal of chemical impurities from the water. To achieve the most effective capital investment and operating costs, this equipment usually is oversized and designed with no regard for controlling microbial quality. Hence, the equipment becomes breeding areas for microorganisms, and the operating procedures employed do nothing to correct this situation.
   Typical examples of this type of equipment are oversized sand and carbon filters and ion exchange equipment such as water softeners and DI systems.

7. Use of "add-on" equipment for added security. Frequently there are cases where filtration equipment, ultraviolet units, and other equipment

are used as "insurance." But there may be no data to support their use and no adequate procedures for their proper operation. Without proper procedures these pieces of equipment can easily magnify rather than alleviate microbial problems.

8. Inadequate maintenance or preventive maintenance programs. This lack is frequently evident from deficiencies that would be simple and fairly inexpensive to correct except that personnel are not available and there are always better ways to use the money.

   These obvious deficiencies are evident from water leaks around the equipment, gaskets that have deteriorated and are visually crumbling, gauges and instruments that are broken or obviously out of calibration, dirt in the sight ports of flowmeters, hoses that have been in place so long that they are cracked or brittle and show gross discoloration.

9. Lack of good housekeeping—equipment that is covered with dust or dirt, and work areas that are littered with an assortment of nonrelated components. Frequently, the equipment is in a noncontrolled Utilities area or jammed into a small room or corner where it is impossible to keep the area clean. This may seem acceptable for a closed system, but there are such things as tank vents, and equipment does have to be opened up for service or inspection from time to time.

10. Specific areas of compliance such as heat exchanger design, pump design, unfiltered vents, air gaps at drains, hoses left full of water for long periods, dead legs, threaded fittings, etc.

11. Other areas of concern, such as compatibility of all materials for construction, including gasket material, piping construction, lining materials used for chemical treatment equipment such as DI units, and materials used for filters, such as reverse osmosis and ultrafiltration equipment.

VI. VALIDATION OF NEW SYSTEMS

The pharmaceutical manufacturer, when faced with the problem of designing a new water system, is somewhat at a loss for useful reference guidelines. Unfortunately, there are no meaningful design or construction standards presently used throughout the drug industry.

The manufacturer often has to rely on information and recommendations made by equipment suppliers. These suppliers are seldom qualified to make recommendations outside their own field of expertise and may not be conversant with the particular problems of an individual pharmaceutical operation. Even when the equipment supplier is qualified, it must be remembered that their assessment of the customer's needs may be less than objective. While general engineering consultants may be experienced in process design using accepted engineering practices, they are usually unfamiliar with the special concerns of pharmaceutical production and quality assurance. The application of long-established design concepts that may have been developed for process and potable water applications, even if updated by the use of sanitary components, can be counterproductive when used for pharmaceutical applications. A different design approach is frequently needed to satisfy critical operating and quality assurance requirements.

Some benefits can be derived from studying the standards and practices that have been developed for the food and dairy industries, and many of the components available are quite suitable. It should be remembered that these standards were formulated for use with different products in a different operational environment, and their applications must be carefully evaluated by the pharmaceutical manufacturer. There are components and construction procedures that have been developed for other industries concerned with contamination, such as the electronics and aerospace industries, that may offer solutions to some of the problems facing the pharmaceutical industry.

In the absence of any widely accepted standards, the individual pharmaceutical manufacturer must consider all reference sources for design information and make his own judgment as to the suitability of any particular design concept.

The system requirements must be carefully defined. Desired operating and performance characteristics must be established in terms of quality levels and physical capabilities. Acceptance specifications must be established to satisfy predefined requirements.

The system should be designed so that it can be easily cleaned both after construction and following any routine maintenance. Preventive maintenance must be an integral part of the system design. Provision should be made for equipment shut down for inspection, testing, calibration, repair or service, cleaning, and sterilization. Each type of equipment will have its own maintenance characteristics and must be considered on an individual basis. The procedures must ensure that spare equipment while on standby does not constitute a threat to the integrity of the system by permitting microbial growth.

Provision must be made for periodic sterilization by an appropriate means. The frequency of sterilization will be determined by field experience and the actual microbial history developed.

The needs of the future must be considered, and the design should provide sufficient flexibility to permit later modification. Numerous redundant connections, installed for future use points, should be avoided if at all possible. These are sites for potential contamination and must be included in the preventive maintenance schedule for gasket replacement and valve repair. The system should be kept as simple as possible. Any component or valve that cannot be shown to have a critical function should be eliminated from the design. Instruments and controls should be used only when it is necessary to monitor and control vital functions, and the selection of these instruments should be made with due consideration to their sanitary construction as well as their reliability and sensitivity.

Careful consideration should be given to the consolidation of several classifications of water. All too often operating cost considerations are based on utilities and chemical costs. When the costs involved in maintenance, calibration, sampling, laboratory assay, system cleaning, sterilization, and documentation are considered, there is a compelling incentive to consider seriously the consolidation of several classifications of water into a smaller total number of systems.

The reliance on statistical sampling as a means of monitoring the quality of the water is practical only if the sample is truly representative of the condition. It is imperative, therefore, that the system be designed and operated in such a manner as to ensure the production of water of a consistent and predictable quality, both chemically and microbiologically.

The validation project should be comprised of five major sections:

1. Prevalidation of the total system design
2. Construction validation

3. Startup validation:
   a. Functional operation
   b. Procedures verification
   c. Quality limits
4. System qualification
5. Approval of the system for use

A. Prevalidation of the Total System Design

The historical concept that design is the sole realm of the Engineering department needs to be reevaluated. While any system must be functional from an engineering standpoint and satisfy all code and safety requirements, there are many considerations far more important than delivering a certain volume of water at a certain pressure for the lowest capital cost. The critical concerns of operational suitability, microbial control, and regulatory compliance must be carefully specified first, and then the engineering design should be formulated to satisfy these requirements. The actual system design should be a group effort, with participation from Production, Quality Assurance, Engineering, and Product Development to ensure that the system will meet present needs and accommodate future requirements. The purpose of the system and its operational, sanitization, and maintenance aspects should be "designed in" and not "added on," as is the case in many instances where only one discipline has the responsibility for system selection. The considerations of equipment suitability, material selection, operational controls, component compatibility, construction techniques, cleaning procedures, sanitary practices, sampling procedures, preventive maintenance programs, sterilization regimens, and compliance with regulatory requirements that must be considered as part of the overall system design are so complex that in general no single group is qualified to make a determination as to the system suitability.

With the participation of all disciplines the design should proceed in a logical manner. The objectives and quality requirements of the water system should be carefully defined. This will set the design parameters and frequently will determine the selection of the type of water treatment equipment to be used. The next important step is to develop the basic system design package, which should include the following information:

1. Flow schematics for the proposed water system showing all of the instrumentation, controls and valves necessary to operate, monitor, and sterilize the system. All major valves and components should be numbered for reference.
2. A complete description of the features and function of the system. This is of critical importance to enable Production and Quality Assurance personnel, who may be unfamiliar with engineering terminology, to understand fully the manner in which the system is to be designed, built, operated, monitored, and sterilized.
3. Detailed specifications for the equipment to be used for water treatment and pretreatment. The final equipment selections should be reviewed by all disciplines to ensure compliance with overall system objectives.
4. Detailed specifications for all other system components, such as storage tanks, heat exchangers, pumps, valves and piping components.
5. Detailed specifications for sanitary system controls, and a description of their operation.

6. Specifications for construction techniques to be employed where quality is of critical importance. These techniques should be suitable for exacting sanitary applications.
7. Procedures for cleaning the system, both after construction and on a routine basis.
8. Preliminary standard operating procedures (SOPs) for operating, sampling, and sterilization. These procedures will be cross-referenced to the valve and component numbers on the system schematics.
9. Preliminary SOPs for filter replacement, integrity testing, and maintenance.
10. Preliminary sampling procedures to monitor both water quality and the operation of the equipment.
11. Preliminary system certification procedures.
12. Preliminary preventive maintenance procedures.

The design package should be as complete as possible to enable all disciplines involved to understand what the final system will entail. This package is of extreme importance because it will spell out before capital commitments are made exactly what the system will be, how it will be designed, built, operated, monitored, and sterilized, in a manner that all groups can readily understand and evaluate. This package should be reviewed, modified as necessary to rectify any deficiencies, and adopted as the basis of the project design by all disciplines involved. The project, once approved, should proceed with strict adherence to the specifications adopted. Any deviation should be reviewed by the total group involved in the original system approval. Only after approval of the basic system concept should the system layout design be completed.

1. System Layout Design

Equipment Area: Ideally the water treatment equipment should be located in an area of controlled access to minimize tampering or adjustment by untrained personnel.

The environment should be reasonably controlled so that operators are not discouraged from attending to routine operational, monitoring, and maintenance functions.

There must be reasonable access to all components for sampling, monitoring, and maintenance.

Distribution System: The physical configuration of the distribution system must be reviewed to ensure the proper slope and drainage and access to components for operation and maintenance.

At this point the total system design will be subjected to a critical review to determine:

1. Does the system satisfy all of the requirements?
2. Can the system be validated?
3. Can the system be monitored?
4. Does the system have the required "fail-safe" features?

B. Construction Validation

Construction Validation will ensure the implementation of the predetermined design specifications. This phase of the project is of extreme importance, because normal construction techniques are totally unsuited to the pharmaceutical industry and irreparable damage can be done if proper procedures are not enforced. The concepts of documentation and accountability are particularly difficult to communicate.

1. System Components and Construction Materials

For major equipment, such as distillation and other water treatment equipment and WFI storage tanks, consideration should be given to conducting an inspection of the equipment before it is shipped from the supplier. Features of operational function and compliance with specifications can be verified and any deviations can be corrected without incurring the cost and time delay of reshipment. The accountability of the major water treatment equipment should not be left to the supplier or unqualified contractor to determine. Note also that once the equipment is shipped "FOB shipping point," the customer legally owns the equipment, and claims of noncompliance may be more difficult to resolve.

The equipment should be examined immediately upon arrival to determine any damage or losses incurred during transit.

The equipment should be examined once more after final placement to ensure that the installation is proper and that no damage was caused during handling.

Other components and materials, such as pumps, valves, and piping components, may not warrant preshipment inspection, but all such material should be examined upon receipt to ensure compliance with purchase specifications and absence of damage during transit. This material should be placed in quarantine until approved, and all documentation such as material certification has been reviewed and accepted.

These materials must be stored, handled, and installed in such a way as to prevent any damage to the components that could affect their suitability.

2. Verification of Construction Procedures

Construction and inspection procedures must be carefully monitored throughout the project to ensure compliance with the written specifications.

3. Construction Completion

The physical installation of the system must be carefully reviewed for compliance with design specifications. Any "dead legs" must be identified and eliminated. The piping must be physically measured to ensure the proper slope for drainage. "As built" drawings must be prepared that accurately depict the completed system.

4. Pressure Testing of the System

During construction it is impossible to avoid contamination of the piping with airborne ferrous particles from installation of structural steel and carbon steel piping components. If the stainless steel is kept dry, this may not be a problem. If the stainless steel piping is allowed to become wet, such as when a hydrostatic pressure test is performed, corrosion of the stainless steel by the ferrous particles can occur rapidly. Therefore, it is recommended that the system be tested with dry, oil-free air; if water is used, then provision must be made to thoroughly clean the system immediately after the hydrostatic pressure test.

5. Postconstruction Cleaning

The cleaning usually is accomplished by recirculation of cleaning fluids through the system (clean in place or CIP) or by disassembly and cleaning by hand (clean out of place or COP)—either way the cleaning agents are the same.

First flush system to remove dust and major debris. Then recirculate detergent or alkali cleaner at elevated temperatures to remove grease or oil. Then flush and recirculate an acid at elevated temperatures to dissolve any ferrous particles in the system. This acid will help to passivate the stainless steel. Then flush with water of the same quality as will be used in service.

The cleaning procedure can be validated by removing suitable "take-down" section of piping and performing chemical analysis of surface residues.

6. System Functional Checkout

The instrumentation and controls should be adjusted and calibrated to ensure that they will properly monitor and control the functioning of the system.

At this point the system has received an "engineering validation" that the system does function as designed and that the construction project requirements have been satisfied.

C. Startup Validation

1. Functional Operation

1. Consistency of operation of equipment and controls must be established by:
   a. Repeated cycles of startup and shutdown of all equipment and controls.
   b. Manual, automatic and emergency conditions must be simulated to ensure suitability of design under all conditions.
   c. Assurance of consistent, stable, and predictable operation is essential to the concept of validation.
2. System "failure" checkout to demonstrate that the loss of any required service:
   a. Does not jeopardize water quality
   b. Results in a "safe" system shutdown
   c. Will not compromise water quality when service is restored
   d. Repeatability can be established
   e. Identify "weak points" that may require additional procedural protection
3. The preliminary monitoring program must be examined to ensure that:
   a. It is adequate to ensure that "validation" conditions actually exist
   b. Sampling procedures are so specific that they are invariable in implementation
   c. Instrumentation calibration is suitable and maintained throughout the varied operational cycles.
4. The maintenance program must be shown to be:
   a. Comprehensive to cover the total system
   b. Specific—all components subject to wear are included
   c. Regular—inspect all components to establish frequencies of maintenance
   d. Short-term validation of previously selected procedures
   e. Long-term validation to refine procedures as long-term history is developed.

5. Equipment logs, filter logs and monitoring records must be:
   a. Comprehensive, to cover all components in the system
   b. Specific, with regard to the items included
   c. Adequate—this will be verified by actual service
   d. Properly documented, to be of value in predicting serviceability of equipment

2. Procedures Verification

Procedures verification includes:

Validation of the previously written operating procedure for the system.
These procedures may need revision based on actual system operation.
Assurance that the procedures are so specific as to eliminate human variability.

3. Quality Limits

1. Verify that the water produced and handled by the system meets all the predefined chemical specifications.
2. Verify that the water produced and handled by the system meets all the predetermined microbial and pyrogenicity specifications.
3. Verify that the sterilization programs are in fact capable of sterilizing the system. This is usually accomplished by verification that all parts of the system are contacted by steam, at the prescribed temperature and pressure.
4. Establishment of the following limits for chemical and microbial quality:
   a. Target limit—based on the anticipated quality level of the water to be produced
   b. Alert limit—deviation from normal (target) that cannot be attributed to sampling variation or otherwise identified
   c. Action limit—when deviation shows that the water quality may become compromised.
   d. Acceptance limit—when quality fails to meet the predefined acceptable limits.

Any deviation from normal should have a prescribed written course of action and a specific reporting procedure.

The final limits may not be set until sufficient operational history determines what the normal operational characteristics of the system are. Continual comparison should be made between actual and expected values to establish realistic baseline data.

D. System Qualification

Once the validation report for Part 3 is completed and approved, a qualification run should be made with the system to verify that validation conditions will be duplicated in normal operation.

E. Approval for Use

If all the requirements have been satisfied and all of the validation documents have been approved, the Quality Assurance group may release the water system for production use.

F. Master File

A master file should be compiled to contain all relevant information on the water system. This file will contain all of the basic information plus drawings, specifications, procedures, basis for equipment selection, basis for cleaning and sterilization frequencies, equipment and filter logs, record of modifications to the system or procedures, and the recertification data and operational information on the system. This file will form the major reference material for the system, both for internal purposes and for review by a regulatory agency.

VII. SAMPLING PROGRAM

The purpose of a sampling program is to be able to demonstrate that a system is operating under the same conditions as existed during the validation. If a system design is such that the system does not operate consistently, then the reliance on a small sample as an assurance of quality is totally unacceptable.

The sampling procedure must be concisely written and then adhered to absolutely to ensure that there is no variability caused by different personnel or procedures.

The method of obtaining the sample must be consistent throughout the system. It is recommended that the sample valve be of small inside dimensions that will allow full opening and a fast, high-velocity flush. This will ensure the removal of microorganisms on the downstream side of the valve, before the actual sample is taken. The same type of valve should be used throughout the system to ensure uniformity. The key is the fact that the sample taken should be representative of the actual system conditions and not be modified in any way by the method of sampling.

Samples should be taken both upstream and downstream of any piece of treatment equipment to ensure that any problem areas are correctly identified.

A water system can be segregated into several areas for sampling:

1. Pretreatment and treatment equipment
2. Storage and recirculation
3. Point of use
4. Related services such as clean steam and compressed air

The point-of-use sample should be taken through the same hose or pipe as the water is delivered for manufacturing or rinsing. This will give the most meaningful results in terms of the water quality as used and can frequently show deficiencies in the method of water usage. The storage and distribution loop sample should accurately reflect the quality of the water in the loop.

Thus, if a high microbial count is determined by a use-point sample and a low microbial count is obtained by the loop sample, then probably the method of water usage is to blame. Therefore, there is no point in draining and steaming the whole loop, as the problem arises in the method of obtaining the sample, e.g., a dirty hose.

The tables (Figs. 16—21) show probable sample points throughout a water system, from incoming city water to final point of use. The frequency of sample is given during the validation period and during normal operation.

LOCATION SAMPLE POINT	COMPONENT	FREQUENCY		COMMENTS
		VALIDATION	OPERATION	
RAW WATER (POTABLE)	MICROBIAL	DAILY	DAILY	REVIEW TOGETHER TO DETERMINE CONTACT TIME
	CL$_2$ RESIDUAL	DAILY	DAILY	
(1)	CHEMICAL TDS	DAILY	WEEKLY	FAST, LOW COST TEST
(2)	FULL CHEMICAL	WEEKLY	6 MONTHS	
	pH	*	*	DEPENDS ON EQUIP. USE
SAND FILTER	MICROBIAL	DAILY	DAILY	
	CL$_2$ RESIDUAL	DAILY	WEEKLY	

FIGURE 16   (1) TDS, total dissolved solids (by conductivity); (2) may vary considerably depending on source and season.

LOCATION SAMPLE POINT	COMPONENT	FREQUENCY		COMMENTS
		VALIDATION	OPERATION	
CARBON FILTER	MICROBIAL	DAILY	DAILY	
	CL$_2$ RESIDUAL	DAILY	WEEKLY	
D.I. EQUIPMENT (3)	CONDUCTIVITY	CONTINUOUS	CONTINUOUS	
	TOTAL SOLIDS USP	DAILY	DAILY	DEPENDS ON USE OF THIS WATER
	pH	DAILY	DAILY	DEPENDS ON USE OF THIS WATER
	MICROBIAL	DAILY	DAILY	
	PYROGEN	DAILY	WEEKLY	DEPENDS ON USE OF THIS WATER
	SILICAL – COLLOIDAL & DISSOLVED	DAILY	WEEKLY	DEPENDS ON USE OF THIS WATER
	RESIN ANALYSIS	INITIAL	6 MONTHS	

FIGURE 17   Will vary depending on service cycle.

LOCATION SAMPLE POINT	COMPONENT	FREQUENCY		COMMENTS
		VALIDATION	OPERATION	
REVERSE OSMOSIS EQUIPMENT	MICROBIAL	DAILY	DAILY	
	pH	CONTINUOUS	CONTINUOUS	CRITICAL ON SOME EQUIPMENT
	CL₂ RESIDUAL	CONTINUOUS	CONTINUOUS	
	PYROGEN	DAILY	DAILY	DEPENDS ON USE
	CONDUCTIVITY	CONTINUOUS	CONTINUOUS	
	CHEMICAL USP	DAILY	DAILY	DEPENDS ON USE
	FEEDWATER HARDNESS	DAILY	DAILY	CRITICAL ON SOME EQUIPMENT

FIGURE 18   Sampling program.   Check individual modules during validation period and weekly thereafter.

LOCATION SAMPLE POINT	COMPONENT	FREQUENCY		COMMENTS
		VALIDATION	OPERATION	
DISTILLATION EQUIPMENT (ASSUME USP-WATER FOR INJECTION)	MICROBIAL	MULTIPLE TIMES IN CYCLE	DAILY	
	pH		DAILY	
	PYROGEN		DAILY	
	CONDUCTIVITY	CONTINUOUS	CONTINUOUS	INLET AND OUTLET
	CHEMICAL – USP	MULTIPLE TIMES IN CYCLE	DAILY	
	BLOWDOWN –TDS		WEEKLY	
	PARTICULATES		WEEKLY	

FIGURE 19   Sampling program.   For R.D. and distillation equipment, establish repeatability and time for system stabilization.

LOCATION SAMPLE POINT	COMPONENT	FREQUENCY		COMMENTS
		VALIDATION	OPERATION	
STORAGE	MICROBIAL	MULTIPLE TIMES IN CYCLE	DAILY	
	pH		DAILY	
	PYROGEN		DAILY	IF REQ'D FOR WFI
	CHEMICAL USP		DAILY	

FIGURE 20   Sampling programs. Sample period to be daily or to coincide with batch of water.

LOCATION SAMPLE POINT	COMPONENT	FREQUENCY		COMMENTS
		VALIDATION	OPERATION	
DISTRIBUTION USE POINTS	MICROBIAL	DAILY	WEEKLY	ON ROTATION
	PYROGEN	DAILY	(6)	
(4)	CHEMICAL TDS	DAILY	MONTHLY	FAST-LOW COST TEST
(5)	CHEMICAL USP	WEEKLY	(6)	
	PARTICULATES	DAILY	MONTHLY	
	pH	WEEKLY	(6)	
CLEAN STEAM GENERATOR	BLOWDOWN CHEMICAL TDS	DAILY	WEEKLY	TO PREVENT SCALE BUILD-UP

FIGURE 21   (4) TDS, total dissolved solids (by conductivity); (5) TDS, total dissolved solids (by evaporation); (6) sample only when indicated by failure to satisfy other tests.

VIII. REGULATIONS INVOLVED

The *Federal Register*, part 141 (41 FR 28404, July 9, 1976), establishes standards for potable water, which is frequently the feedwater to a pharmaceutical plant.

USP XX1/NF XVI specifies the limits and method of testing for chemical and pyrogenic contaminants for various compendial classifications of water, such as Purified Water and Water for Injection.

The U.S. Food and Drug Association has established various Good Manufacturing Practices for pharmaceutical products. Selected excerpts of these, which have impact on water quality, are reproduced on the following pages. The underlining has been added by the author for emphasis.

§210.3 Definitions.

(a) The following definitions of terms apply to Parts 210 through 229 of this chapter.

(b) The terms are as follows:

* * *

(3) "Component" means any ingredient intended for use in the manufacture of a drug product, including those that may not appear in such drug product.

* * *

(5) "Fiber" means any particle with a length of at least three times greater than its width.

(6) "Non-fiber-releasing filter" means any filter, which after any appropriate pretreatment such as washing or flushing, will not release fibers into the component or drug product that is being filtered. All filters composed of asbestos or glass fibers are deemed to be fiber-releasing filters.

* * *

(2) "Batch" means a specific quantity of a drug that has uniform character and quality, within specified limits, and is produced according to a single manufacturing order during the same cycle of manufacture.

* * *

(10) "Lot" means a batch, or a specific identified portion of a batch, having uniform character and quality within specified limits; or, in the case of a drug product produced by continuous process, it is a specific identified amount produced in a unit of time or quantity in a manner that assures its having uniform character and quality within specified limits.

§211.48 Plumbing.

(a) Potable water shall be supplied under continuous positive pressure in a plumbing system free of defects that could contribute contamination to any drug product. Potable water shall meet the standards prescribed in the Public Health Service Drinking Water Standards set forth in Subpart J of 42 CFR Part 72. Water not meeting such standards shall not be permitted in the plumbing system.

§211.72 Filters.

(a) Filters used in the manufacture, processing, or packing of injectable drug products intended for human use shall not release fibers into such products. Fiber-releasing filters may not be used in the manufacture, processing, or packing of these drug products unless it is not possible to manufacture such drug products without the use of such a filter.

(b) If use of a fiber-releasing filter is necessary, an additional non-fiber-releasing filter of 0.22 micron maximum mean porosity (0.45 micron if the manufacturing conditions so dictate) shall subsequently be used to reduce the content of particles in the drug product. Use of an asbestos-containing filter, with or without subsequent use of a specific non-fiber-releasing filter, is permissible only upon submission of proof to the appropriate bureau of the Food and Drug Administration that use of a non-fiber-releasing filter will, or is likely to, compromise the safety or effectiveness of the drug product.

§212.3 Definitions.

* * *

(11) "Static line" means any pipe containing liquid that is not emptied or circulated at least once every 24 hours.

* * *

Subpart B—Organization and Personnel

* * *

§212.22 Responsibilities of quality control unit.

(a) The quality control unit shall have the responsibility and authority to test and accept or reject the design, engineering, and physical facilities of the plant, the equipment, and the manufacturing process and control procedures to be used in the manufacture, processing, packing, and holding of each large volume parenteral drug product. The quality control unit shall reject any such plant, equipment, process, or procedure if it does not comply with the provisions of this part or if, in the opinion of the quality control unit, it is not suitable or adequate to assure that the drug product has the characteristics it purports or is represented to possess.

* * *

(c) The quality control unit shall have the responsibility and authority to test and approve or reject any changes in previously approved plant, equipment, processes, procedures, and container-closures and delivery systems before utilization in the manufacture, processing, packing and holding of a large volume parenteral drug product.

Subpart C—Buildings and Facilities

§212.42 Design and construction features.

* * *

(c) There shall not be horizontal fixed pipes or conduits over exposed components, in-process materials, drug products, and drug product contact surfaces, including drug product containers and closures after the final rinse.

(d) In each physically separated area, pipes or conduits for air or liquids shall be identified as to their contents. Such identification shall be by name, color code, or other suitable means.

§212.49 Water and other liquid-handling systems.

(a) Filters may not be used at any point in the water for manufacturing or final rinse piping system.

(b) Backflow of liquids shall be prevented at points of interconnection of different systems.

(c) Pipelines for the transmission of water for manufacturing or final rinse and other liquid components shall:

(1) Be constructed of welded stainless steel (nonrusting grade) equipped for sterilization with steam, except that sanitary stainless steel lines with fittings capable of disassembly may be immediately adjacent to the equipment or valves that must be removed from the lines for servicing and replacement.

(2) Be sloped to provide for complete drainage.

(3) Not have an unused portion greater in length than six diameters of the unused pipe measured from the axis of the pipe in use.

§212.67 Equipment cleaning and maintenance.

The following requirements shall be included in written procedures and cleaning schedules:

(a) All equipment and surfaces that contact components, in-process materials, drug products or drug product contact surfaces such as containers and closures shall be cleaned and rinsed with water meeting the quality requirements stated in §212.224.

(b) Immediately prior to such contact, equipment and surfaces specified in paragraph (a) of this section shall be given a final rinse with water meeting the quality requirements stated in §212.225.

(c) Steam used to sterilize liquid-handling systems or equipment shall be free of additives used for boiler control.

§212.68 Equipment calibration.

(a) Procedures shall be written and followed designating schedules and assigning responsibility for testing or monitoring the performances or accuracy of automatic or continuously operating equipment, devices, apparatus, or mechanisms, such as, but not limited to, the following:

(1) Alarms and controls on sterilizing equipment.

(2) Temperature-recording devices on sterilizers.

(3) Pressure gauges.

(4) Mechanisms for maintaining sterilizing medium uniformity.

(5) Chain speed recorder.

(6) Heat exchanger pressure differential monitor.

(7) Mercury-in-glass thermometer.

(b) Written records of such calibrations, checks, examinations, or inspections shall be maintained, as specified in §212.183.

§212.72 Filters.

(a) The integrity of all air filters shall be verified upon installation and maintained throughout use. A written testing program adequate to monitor integrity of filters shall be established and followed. Results shall be recorded and maintained as specified in §212.183.

§212.76 Heat exchangers.

Heat exchangers, other than the welded double-concentric-tube type or double-tube sheet type, must employ a pressure differential and a means for monitoring the differential. The pressure differential shall be such that the fluid requiring a higher microbial quality shall be that with the greater pressure. Written records of the pressure differential monitoring shall be maintained as required in §212.183.

§212.78 Air vents.

All stills and tanks holding liquid requiring microbial control shall have air vents with non-fiber-releasing sterilizable filters capable of preventing microbial contamination of the contents. *Such filters shall be designed and installed so that they do not become wet.* Filters shall be sterilized and installed aseptically. Tanks requiring air vents with filters include those holding water for manufacturing or final rinsing, water for cooling the drug product after sterilization, liquid components, and in-process solutions.

§212.79 Pumps.

Pumps moving water for manufacturing or final rinsing, water for cooling the drug product after sterilization, and in-process or drug product solutions shall be designed to utilize water for injection as a lubricant for the seals.

§212.100 Written procedures, deviations.

* * *

(b) Written procedures shall be established, and shall be followed. Such procedures shall:

(1) Ensure that all static lines are flushed prior to use. Such procedures shall require that flushing produce a turbulent flow for 5 minutes and that all valves on the line are opened and closed repeatedly to flush the valve interior.

§212.182 Equipment cleaning and use log.

(a) Written records of the corrective action taken pursuant to §212.24 (a) and (c), and §212.225 (a) and (b), including validation of the effectiveness of the action, shall be maintained.

(b) <u>Written records</u> of <u>equipment usage</u> shall include documentation of the length of time the equipment was in use as indicated in §212.111.

(c) <u>Written records</u> demonstrating a <u>positive pressure differential</u>, as described in and required by §212.76, shall be maintained.

* * *

(e) For <u>filtration equipment</u>, or devices, <u>written records documenting the installation, replacement, and sterilization</u> (where appropriate) of filters such as those indicated in §§212.72, 212.77(b) and (c), 212.78, and 212.222(a) shall be maintained.

§212.183 Equipment calibration and monitoring records.

<u>Written records of calibration and monitoring tests</u> and readings performed shall be maintained *for at least 2 years* after the expiration date of each batch of drug product produced by the equipment.

(a) Calibration records shall include:

(1) A description of the equipment.

(2) The date the equipment was purchased.

(3) The operating limits of the equipment.

(4) The date, time, and type of each test.

(5) The results of each test.

(6) The signature of each person performing a test.

(7) The date the equipment was installed.

(b) Monitoring records shall include:

(1) A description of the equipment.

(2) The date the equipment was installed.

(3) The date the equipment was last calibrated, if appropriate.

(4) The operating limits of the equipment.

(5) The date and time of the recording.

(6) The reading.

(7) The signature of each person performing the monitoring.

(c) Corrective measures employed to bring the equipment into compliance with its operating specifications shall be:

(1) Recorded in the appropriate equipment log.

(2) Noted in the calibration and/or monitoring record.

(3) Immediately followed by testing to assure that the corrective measures were adequate to restore the required operating characteristics.

§212.188 <u>Batch production and control records</u>.

These records shall include the following information where appropriate:

(1) <u>Verification that static lines were flushed prior to use</u> according to established written procedures in §212.100(b).

§212.192 Production record review.

The <u>review and approval of production and control records</u> by the <u>quality control unit</u> shall extend to those records not directly related to the manufacture, processing, packing, or holding of a specific batch of large volume parenteral drug product but which have a bearing on the quality of batches being produced. Such indirectly related records shall include:

(a) <u>Those dealing with equipment calibration or standardization</u>.

* * *

(c) Those demonstrating the quality of water produced by various processing systems.

(d) Those demonstrating the quality of air produced by various systems.

§212.190 Air and water monitoring records.

Written records of the air and water monitoring test results, readings, and corrective measures taken shall be maintained for at least 2 years after the expiration date of each batch of drug product produced in the area being monitored or containing the water as a component.

The record shall include, at a minimum, the following information:

(a) Identity of the material being monitored.

(b) Each characteristic being monitored.

(c) Each specification limit.

(d) Each testing method used.

(e) Site sampled or monitored.

(f) The date and time of each monitoring or testing.

(g) The result of each test or monitoring reading.

(h) Batch number and expiration date of the drug product being processed in the area or equipment, or to which the component is being added at the time of monitoring or sampling.

(i) Corrective measures employed to bring the area, component or product into compliance with specifications.

(j) Retesting results to verify the adequacy of the corrective measures.

Subpart L—Air and Water Quality

§212.220 General requirements.

(a) Air or water as described in this part may not be used until the plant, processes, and procedures used in producing and distributing it have been tested and approved by the quality control unit as capable of consistently producing air or water meeting the requirements set forth in this subpart.

(b) In addition to the requirements of this subpart, air and water quality shall be monitored as specified in Subpart J.

(c) The results of all testing and data generated shall be recorded and maintained as required by §212.180.

(d) Procedures designating schedules, assigning responsibility, and describing in detail the action to be taken to assure that the systems produce and deliver air and water that conform to the requirements set forth in this subpart shall be written. Such procedures shall also specify the corrective action to be taken when testing reveals that the established standards are not being met. Records of corrective actions shall be maintained, as specified in §212.190.

§212.223 Compressed air.

Compressed air used in manufacturing and processing operations, including the sterilization process, shall be:

* * *

(b) Supplied by an oil-free compressor and be free of oil and oil vapor unless vented directly to a noncontrolled environment area.

(c) Dehumidified to prevent condensation of water vapor in the pipes.

§212.224 Water for cleaning or initial rinsing.

Water used to cleanse or initially rinse drug product contact surfaces such as containers, closures, and equipment shall:

(a) Meet the standards prescribed in the Public Health Service Drinking Water Standards set forth in Subpart J of 42 CFR Part 72;

(b) Be subjected to a process such as chlorination for control of microbial population;

(c) Contain not more than 50 microorganisms per 100 millimeters in three consecutive samples from the sampling site when tested by the method specified in §212.225(b) after neutralizing bacteriocidal agents, if present.

§212.225 Water for manufacturing or final rinsing.

Water used as a component or as a final rinse for equipment or product contact surfaces shall:

(a) Conform to the specifications in the U.S.P. for "Water for Injection":

(b) Contain not more than 10 microorganisms per 100 millimeters in three consecutive samples from the same site when samples of 250 millimeters or more are tested for total aerobic count by the plate method set forth in Microbial Limit Tests in the current revision of the U.S.P. Alternate methodology may be used provided that data are available to demonstrate that the alternate method is equivalent to the official method. When the microbial quality falls below that specified in this section, use of such water shall cease, and corrective action shall be taken to clean and sterilize the system so that the water conforms to the limit.

(c) Be stored in a suitable vessel or system including a piping network for distribution to points of use:

(1) At a temperature of at least 80°C under continuous circulation, or

(2) At ambient or lower temperatures for not longer than 24 hours, after which time such water shall be discarded to drain.

§212.226 Water for drug product cooling.

Water used in the sterilizer as a drug product cooling medium shall:

(a) Be treated to eliminate microorganisms:

(b) Contain not more than one microorganism per 100 millimeters in three consecutive samples from the same sampling site when one liter or more are tested for total aerobic count by a membrane filtration method and placing each membrane filter on appropriate nutrient media after neutralizing any bacteriocidal agents present in the water samples.

§212.227 Boiler feed water.

Feedwater for boilers supplying steam that contacts components, in-process materials, drug products, and drug product contact surfaces shall not contain volatile additives such as amines or hydrazines.

§212.233 Water quality program design.

(a) Water quality monitoring shall include:

(1) <u>Sampling and testing</u> of water for manufacturing or final rinsing at least once a day. All sampling ports or points of use in the distribution system shall be sampled at least weekly.

(2) Sampling water for drug product cooling at a point just before entry into the sterilizer at least once each sterilizer cycle and testing by the method described in §212.226.

(3) Sampling and testing water for cleaning or initial rinsing at least once a week. All sampling ports or points of use in the distribution system shall be sampled at least monthly.

(b) Boiler feed water shall be sampled and tested periodically for the presence of volatile additives.

(c) <u>If three consecutive samples</u> of drug product cooling water <u>exceed microbial limits</u>, the sterilizer loads shall be rejected and shall not be reprocessed.

§212.231 <u>Monitoring</u> of air and <u>water quality</u>.

(a) <u>After the plant, equipment, manufacturing processes</u>, and control procedures have been <u>tested and approved</u> by the <u>quality control unit</u>, there shall be performed in accordance with <u>written procedures</u> and schedules a <u>sampling and testing program</u> that is designed to monitor the microbial flora of the plant and its environment. The design of the sampling and testing program shall include monitoring of air and water quality in accordance with requirements set forth in this subpart and taking corrective action when such requirements are not met.

(b) If the results of any <u>one sample</u> of air or water <u>exceed the quality limits</u> specified in this subpart, <u>more frequent</u> sampling and testing shall be required to determine the need for corrective action.

(c) Representative colonies of microorganisms found by the monitoring required in this section shall be identified by genus. The colonies shall be quantified.

(d) <u>Written records of all test findings</u> and <u>any resultant corrective measures taken</u> shall be <u>maintained</u>, as specified in §212.190.

10

Microbiology of Sterilization Processes

TIMOTHY J. LEAHY

Millipore Corporation, Bedford, Massachusetts

I. INTRODUCTION

Clearly, the key element in the manufacture of parenterals is the production of a sterile product. Nothing highlights the importance of sterilization more that the lengths to which manufacturers of sterile products go when validating sterilization. The emphasis of sterilization for parenterals is well placed; injectable drugs contaminated with viable organisms or their by-products (e.g., pyrogens) violate the requirement for drug safety and provide ample opportunity for doing more harm than good during therapy. Thus, drug manufacturers strive to provide safe, sterile products by well-controlled manufacturing operations.

Validation is the result of a multidisciplinary team effort. Typically, personnel with backgrounds in engineering, pharmacology, biochemistry, and microbiology work together to demonstrate that a process does what it is designed to do. The success of this effort relies on each discipline understanding the fundamentals of another science and applying those fundamentals in terms of his or her own technical background. In this way, there will be synergy in problem solving and a successful end result.

The goal of this chapter is to introduce the basic concepts of microbiology, with special emphasis on sterilization microbiology, to those who are involved in validating the various methods of sterilization (e.g., steam, radiation, ethylene oxide, and filtration). This chapter will address sterilization in general terms and highlight its microbiological aspects. The proper starting point for this review is defining *what sterility is* and *how it can be achieved.*

II. STERILITY AND STERILIZATION—AN OVERVIEW

The definition of sterility, most simply (and correctly) stated, is the complete absence of life. It is an absolute term; a product cannot be almost sterile. Defining the term is disarmingly simple and straightforward. The problem comes when one must prove the sterility of an item. Realizing that we live in an imperfect world, sterilization microbiologists define sterility in practical (and practicable) terms. Conventional practice is to define sterility as the absence of living material as demonstrated by growth and reproduction. Thus, the most common way of proving sterility is by tests that promote growth. A material is sterile when tests show that nothing grows in or on it. The absence of growth means no living material and, therefore, signifies sterility. This seems reasonable until one realizes the range of environmental conditions that can support growth and the variety of living things that make something nonsterile.

Putting aside for the moment the issue of proving sterility, there are a variety of methods for obtaining a sterile condition. In fact, the control of microorganisms has been central to the field of microbiology since its founding as a science. Microbial growth, although primarily beneficial, is responsible for both economic losses and diseases that profoundly affect people. It is not surprising, therefore, that the various means of preventing growth and destroying microorganisms have been extensively studied.

There are many approaches to the inhibition, destruction, or removal of microbial growth. It is convenient to categorize these approaches into either physical or chemical. Physical methods include heat, radiation, and filtration. Examples of chemical methods are ethylene oxide, disinfectants, and antibiotics. These broad-based examples are not intended to be all-inclusive, but rather to illustrate the variety of methods available for controlling the microbial content of a substance.

The extent to which microbial control is applied, from preventing the growth of microorganisms to achieving sterility, also varies widely. In many instances, the mere inhibition of microbial growth is sufficient. An example of this approach is found in food preservation. Other situations (particularly those associated with formulation) require the selective destruction or removal of offensive microorganisms while leaving other organisms unaffected. Disinfectants—for example, phenolics—are designed to kill pathogens while often allowing other microorganisms to survive. It is clear, however, that the complete destruction or removal of microorganisms, commonly termed sterilization, represents the most effective control method available.

Sterilization is achieved by any one of several methods. These include thermal (Chap. 11, 12, 13), gaseous (Chap. 14), radiation (Chap. 15), and filtration (Chaps. 18 and 19) processes. The most widely used and most extensively studied method is based on heat. Thermal sterilization is a well-characterized approach to complete microbial removal and is often regarded as the method of choice.

Characterization of thermal sterilization and, for that matter, any sterilization method, includes the following major elements. First, a biological indicator of performance is chosen that is resistant to the chosen sterilization method. *Bacillus stearothermophilus* spores fill this role for thermal sterilization. A second consideration is the influence of other variables on the destruction of indicator spores. Examples of such variables in heat studies include spore propagation, interactions between the biological indicator and the medium being sterilized, and the physical characteristics of the sterilized material in response to heat. Third, a quantitation of organism removal efficiency is established for the sterilization method under defined conditions. For example, the exposure time at a given temperature during thermal sterilization predicts the rate of spore kill. Finally, the concept of assigning a probability of sterility to materials undergoing sterilization represents a natural extension of the orderly and progressive removal of the biological indicator under defined conditions. More succinctly put, characterization of sterilization implies a collection of studies that prove the reliability and predictability of the chosen method.

Before outlining details of sterilization microbiology, a review of the major groups of microorganisms encountered in pharmaceutical products will be presented. This will be followed by a more detailed discussion of sterility testing and sterilization.

III. THE MICROBIAL WORLD AND ITS DIVERSITY

All things living are classified into groups based on certain characteristics. For example, the broadest classification of living things is whether they are plant or animal. This process of classification in biology is called taxonomy, and there are several major taxonomic groups of microorganisms that are important to consider in sterilization microbiology. The taxonomic groups addressed in this chapter are based on the complexity of the organism in terms of growth and reproduction.

A. Viruses

The simplest taxonomic group are viruses. In fact, there is considerable debate among biologists whether viruses are living at all. This stems from the classic definition of life, which is the ability to reproduce independently. Viruses are unique among the major groups of microorganisms in that they require another living thing in order to multiply. Yet viruses contain the essential component of all living things, nucleic acids, which make up the genetic material that determines their structure and function.

Most viruses are composed of two major components: a shell or container, which is commonly made of protein; and a core, which contains the nucleic acids, ribonucleic acid (RNA) or deoxyribonucleic acid (DNA). The shell protects the nucleic acids, which provide the blueprints for making more viruses. Viruses reproduce by entering a living cell (the type of cell classifies the type of virus) and redirecting the activities of the cell to make more virus. This means that the virus itself does not need all the complex cellular machinery required for reproduction. Viruses are usually very small (a fraction of a micrometer) and not very difficult to kill, or, more properly, inactivate. They can, however, show great survival ability in certain environments. This is, in part, due to their simple structure.

B. Bacteria

Next in ascending order of microbial complexity are bacteria. Free-living entities, they commonly occur in a single-cell form. Bacteria possess two traits that merit remembering. First, they exist virtually everywhere in one form or another. There are bacteria capable of growing from just above the freezing point of water to well above 90°C. Also, bacteria are capable of using diverse food sources, ranging from complex organic compounds to simple inorganic matter. Second, bacteria can reproduce extremely rapidly. Their principal method of reproduction is by simple binary fission, a process whereby one cell yields two cells, which then yields four cells, then eight, and so forth. The doubling in cell number can occur as rapidly as every 20 min. To illustrate this prodigious growing ability, consider a single cell that weighs

1 pg (10^{-12}g) and reproduces every 30 min. If this cell were to grow un-
bridled for a year, the mass of all the daughter cells would be greater than
the mass of the sun.

Fortunately, given their ubiquitous nature and rapid ability to grow, most
bacteria are either harmless or beneficial to people. Those that are dangerous, termed pathogens, are few in number and, in most instances, readily
controlled. However, any bacteria that get past a person's normal defenses
can be dangerous. This is certainly the case when a microorganism enters a
normally sterile body site. Thus, the only good bacterium is a dead bacterium when discussing sterilization.

Bacteria range in size from a fraction of a micrometer to several micrometers. Bacteria exist in one of three basic shapes: a sphere (coccus), a
rod (bacillus), or a corkscrew (spirillum). Although each cell is an independent living thing, some types are found in multiple-cell clusters. The
arrangement of these cells, whether an irregular mass or an orderly chain of
cells, helps to classify them. In addition to the different cell shapes and
cluster arrangements, the basic chemistry of the cell wall helps to classify
bacteria. There are two major groups of bacteria that can be differentiated
by the interaction of colored dyes with the cell wall. Discovered by a Dan-
ish microbiologist, Christian Gram, bacteria demonstrate either a positive or
negative staining reaction to crystal violet, depending on how their cell wall
is constructed. For example, Gram-positive bacteria will retain crystal violet,
giving them a purple color when viewed in a microscope. Gram-negative bacteria will not complex the crystal violet firmly when treated with a decoloring
agent. They can then take up a contrasting color stain (e.g., safranin, which
gives a red color), and can be readily distinguished from Gram-positive cells.
Besides giving a convenient binary classification to bacteria, Gram stain reactions can give useful information about where the bacteria come from and how
difficult to sterilize they will be. In fact, by combining the simple information
of cell arrangement, cell shape, and Gram reaction, much can be deduced about
the source and, thereby, the control of a specific organism. To illustrate this
principle, consider a nonsterile pharmaceutical product that contains both a Gram-
negative bacillus that occurs singly, and a Gram-positive coccus that occurs
in a random cluster of multiple cells. The most probable source of the Gram-
negative organism is water, since such organisms typically live in aqueous
environments. On the other hand, a Gram-positive coccus occurring in
clusters suggests a human source of origin, since Gram-positive cocci are
normally found on the skin. Although these relationships are not hard and
fast, they aid the microbiologist in tracing sources of bacterial contamination.
Table 1 lists some examples of Gram-positive and Gram-negative bacteria and

TABLE 1   Examples of Gram Positive and Gram Negative Bacteria and Their
Typical Habitats

Organism	Habitat	Gram reaction
Escherichia coli	Human and animal colon	Gram negative
Pseudomonas aeruginosa	Water	Gram negative
Bacillus subtilis	Soil	Gram positive
Staphylococcus aureus	Human skin	Gram positive

their typical habitats. When one understands the sources of contamination, it is easier to minimize the microbial content of a product from these sources.

One characteristic of bacteria with special application to sterilization microbiology is the ability to produce a dormant form. Normally, bacteria exist in a vegetative state. Vegetative bacteria are actively metabolizing cells with all biochemical pathways functioning. Certain bacteria can produce a state of suspended animation in response to environmental conditions. This differentiated form of the bacteria is called a spore and represents an enhanced survival characteristic for those organisms capable of forming spores. When an environment containing spore-forming organisms becomes hostile to the vegetative state (e.g., lack of nutrients, accumulation of toxic materials, dessication, adverse temperatures), the organism responds by initiating spore formation. A complex series of unique biosynthetic pathways, the sporulation process results in a condensed, stable, and resistant life stage (dormant form) capable of survival until better environmental conditions prevail.

C. Fungi

Fungi represent the next major group of microorganisms. Fungi occur in one of two forms, either as single cells or in long, branching chains. Single-cell forms are called yeasts and are either spherical or oval in shape. They are much larger than bacteria and reproduce differently. The most common type of reproduction is by budding, whereby a small swelling appears on a yeast cell. This swelling continues to increase in size until it separates from the original cell and lives independently. Some types of yeast form resistant spores similar to those formed by bacteria. These spores, which sometimes play a role in reproduction, are not as resistant to sterilization processes as their bacterial cousins.

The multicelled fungi that form long, branching chains are called filamentous fungi. The most notable examples of filamentous fungi are those that produce antibiotics. The branched chains of growth, called mycelia, are larger in diameter than bacteria, on the order of several micrometers. Filamentous

TABLE 2 Representative Genera that Contain Species from the Three Major Growth Temperature Groups

Growth temperature group	Representative genera
Psychrophiles	*Achromobacter*
	Flavobacterium
	Alcaligenes
Mesophiles	*Escherichia*
	Salmonella
	Streptococcus
	Staphylococcus
Thermophiles	*Bacillus*
	Clostridium
	Lactobacillus

fungi show more complex forms of reproduction, which differ depending on the type of fungus. In fact, the method of reproduction is one of the principal characterists that classify the fungi into taxonomic groups. They, too, are capable of producing spores that serve as dormant forms. Fungal spores, like yeast spores, are less resistant to sterilization than bacterial spores.

So far, this discussion of microbial diversity has highlighted the major groups that are germane to sterilization microbiology. These groups are commonly encountered during studies of sterilization and sterility testing. There are several other groups of microorganisms, such as *Rickettsia*, *Mycoplasma*, and *Actinomyces*, which are included in the major taxonomy of microorganisms. The reader is referred to any standard text on microbiology for a description of their properties.

IV. CLASSIFICATION BASED ON ENVIRONMENT

In order to understand better how sterilization methods are validated and how sterility is tested, it is useful to look at the classification of microorganisms in a way different from the taxonomic approach described in the previous section. Microorganisms can also be described by their ability to grow under various environmental conditions. Some of the conditions typically analyzed in this classification system include:

1. Temperature
2. pH
3. Food source
4. Oxygen requirement

A. Temperature

All of the microorganisms discussed earlier have an optimum temperature at which they will grow and reproduce. Traditionally, there are three major groupings: psychrophiles, mesophiles, and thermophiles. Psychrophiles, or cold-loving microorganisms, prefer temperatures ranging from 0 to 10°C for growth and reproduction, and include several types of Gram-negative bacteria such as *Achromobacter* and *Flavobacterium* (Table 2). From a practical viewpoint, they comprise the major group of organisms associated with refrigerated food spoilage. Mesophiles, or middle-loving microorganisms, prefer more moderate growth temperatures. They thrive at temperatures ranging from 10 to 45°C. Examples of the mesopholic group of bacteria are human pathogens (Table 2). Their optimum growth temperature is 37°C, or normal body temperature. Many, if not most, of the organisms found contaminating pharmaceutical preparations are mesopholic organisms. This is because the operations, materials, and personnel involved during drug manufacture are usually performed near the optimum growth temperature range for mesophiles. The last group classified by growth temperature includes the thermophiles, or heat-loving organisms. Their optimum growth temperature ranges from 50 to 90°C. Thermophiles include bacteria that live in hot springs and, of special interest in sterilization microbiology, an organism called *Bacillus stearothermophilus*, which is used to validate steam sterilization (Table 2).

Two aspects of temperature classifications are important in microbial control. First, there is considerable overlap in the permissible growth temperatures of microorganisms. The optimum temperature may be in the mesophilic range, but that does not mean that the organism will not still grow (although more slowly) at psychrophilic or thermophilic growth temperatures. Second, organisms may not grow at a particular temperature, but that does not imply that they will not be able to survive. For example, refrigeration, or for that matter freezing, may stop the growth of mesophiles, but once brought back to the growth temperature range, the organisms will resume growth. In other words, most organisms can survive, if not grow, at a wide variety of temperatures. This is best illustrated by their bacterial spores, which can survive in temperatures in excess of 100°C.

B. pH

There are also three major growth groups of organisms with respect to pH. Acidophiles, as their name implies, prefer low-pH growth conditions, where growth occurs at a pH of from 1 to 5. For example, some of the organisms associated with milk fermentations (e.g., yogurt) prefer low-pH conditions for efficient conversion of sugar to organic (principally, lactic) acids (Table 3). Neutrophiles, on the other hand, require growth conditions around pH 7 (pH 6–8). Most of the common organisms contaminating pharmaceutical preparations fall into this group (Table 3). At the other extreme of pH, alkaliphiles thrive at pH 8–10. Organisms that digest proteins and some soil organisms often grow well at an alkaline pH (Table 3).

The points made about overlap and survival with respect to temperature also apply to pH. Many organisms are capable of growth over a wide range of pH, albeit not at the fastest rate possible. An example of a group of microorganisms that grow at a wide range of pH are the fungi.

C. Food Source

A review of the care and feeding of microorganisms will be detailed later in this chapter. It is useful at this point, however, to briefly introduce food sources as a classification criteria. There are essentially two groups of microorganisms with respect to food source: autotrophs and heterotrophs. Autotrophs possess the ability to synthesize all of the components required for growth and reproduction from simple inorganic compounds. In everyday life, plants are the best examples of autotrophs. There are also autotrophic

TABLE 3 Representative Genera that Contain Species from the Three Major Growth pH Groups

Growth pH group	Representative genera
Acidophiles	*Streptococcus*
	Lactobacillus
Neutrophiles	*Escherichia*
	Bacillus
Alkaliphiles	*Vibrio*

TABLE 4   Representative Genera Containing Species
of Different Oxygen Requirements

Oxygen requirement	Representative genera
Strict anaerobe	*Clostridium*
	Bacteroides
Strict aerobe	*Bacillus*
	Micrococcus
Facultative	*Streptococcus*
	Staphylococcus
Microaerophils	*Leptospira*
	Lactobacillus

microorganisms, many of which are found in the soil. In contrast, heterotrophs use preformed organic compounds in their metabolism. The type and
complexity of the required organic compounds varies widely depending on the
microorganism. The vast majority of microorganisms isolated during pharmaceutical manufacturing operations are heterotrophs.

D. Oxygen Requirement

Microorganisms are also described in terms of their need for molecular oxygen
to sustain growth. In the broadest of terms, there are two groups, aerobes
and anaerobes. Aerobes require oxygen, while anaerobes do not. This sim-
plistic classification belies reality, however. There are shades of gray between the extremes. At one extreme, a strict anaerobe not only does not
need oxygen to grow, but is poisoned by the presence of oxygen. The level
of oxygen that inhibits growth varies among strict anaerobes, but they share
the characteristic of oxygen sensitivity. At the other extreme, strict aerobes
have an oxygen requirement for growth. If the concentration of oxygen falls
below some critical level, growth ceases. In the gray area, there is a group
of microorganisms that can grow in either the presence or absence of oxygen.
Called facultative organisms, they generally grow out in the presence of oxygen, but will continue to grow under anaerobic conditions. To confuse this
classification even further, there is a group of aerobes that require oxygen
for growth, but only at low concentrations. Called microaerophiles, they
stop growing when too much oxygen is present.

V.   PROFILE OF A TYPICAL CONTAMINANT

It is sometimes difficult to tie together all of the terms to describe a contaminant that might be found in manufacturing operations; it might be a mesophilic,
neutrophilic, heterotrophic, facultative organism. The range of possible organisms is quite large, and it is possible to find any of the organism types

described earlier. Nonetheless, a given manufacturing process usually has a characteristic profile of organisms that populate an environment (e.g., aseptic processing area), called the microflora, and its composition is a function of several factors. The raw materials used in compounding, for example, have an inherent microflora. Similarly, the air within a facility and the people involved in manufacturing also have their unique microflora. Thus, there are many inputs to the microbial makeup of a pharmaceutical product.

Knowing the microflora (or, more specifically, the bioburden, which is the combination of both the type and number of organisms) is important for several reasons. From an economic standpoint, a heavily contaminated raw material may be degraded by the organisms present. Health and safety reasons also dictate the need to control the microflora. Clearly, no pathogens should be present. Many microorganisms produce by-products that could contaminate a product even if the organisms are eventually removed. The most notable example of such by-products are pyrogens. Produced by Gram-negative bacteria, pyrogens cause a febrile response when injected into the body. Although there are several methods for removal of pyrogens, one logical approach to their control is to minimize the opportunity for Gram-negative bacterial growth. The final reason for monitoring the microflora is related to sterilization. Knowing how many of what kind of organism must be destroyed during sterilization helps define the exact conditions of sterilization. Further elaboration of this aspect will be addressed in the general approaches to validating sterilization systems.

VI. CULTIVATION OF MICROORGANISMS

It should be clear from the earlier discussion that a wide range of conditions is needed to grow all the possible types of microorganisms. In fact, it is impossible to define one set of conditions that will guarantee the cultivation of all groups. Nevertheless, there are some basic requirements that are universal for the growth of all living things. Once these requirements are satisfied, the specific needs of a particular group of organisms can be introduced to optimize the environment for its growth. This basic and specific formulation process results in what is termed a culture medium (pl., media).

A. Basic Growth Requirements

All microorganisms need certain essential elements for growth and reproduction. The two major elements that must be supplied by all culture media are carbon and nitrogen. Carbon, of course, is the backbone element needed for the synthesis of all complex organic compounds characteristic of living systems. Nitrogen is essential for the synthesis of amino acids, the building blocks of proteins. Nitrogen is also an important component of the nucleic acids, RNA and DNA. Depending on the organism, the forms of carbon and nitrogen required may be as simple as CO_2 and NH_3 or as complex as carbohydrates and proteins. Some of the other major elements required are hydrogen, oxygen, phosphorous, sulfur, potassium, sodium, and calcium. Oxygen and hydrogen are typically provided along with the carbon and nitrogen sources, as in the case of $C_6H_{12}O_6$, NH_3, and NO_2. Additional oxygen for aerobes is supplied from the atmosphere. Sulfur, also important for protein synthesis, can be supplied in inorganic (sulfates) or organic (sulfhydryl groups in proteins) form. Phosphorous (usually provided as the phosphate salt) is an essential element for nucleic acid synthesis. Potassium, sodium, and calcium are provided as inorganic salts (potassium phosphate, sodium chloride, and calcium chloride or carbonate). There are other elements that are required in low concentrations for growth (e.g., magnesium, iron, cobalt, copper, zinc). Their primary function along with potassium and calcium is as parts, or cofactors, for the biological catalysis of living systems as performed by enzymes.

B. Culture Media

Historically, the first culture media developed to grow microorganisms were made from natural products. For example, many media contained extracts of plants, meats, milk products, and other materials available from the kitchens of the pioneering microbiologists. Many of the media routinely used for cultivation still contain natural products to provide all the essential elements for growth. Examples of such media include brain heart infusion, soybean casein digest, and potato dextrose broths. All these are termed complex media, and because of their source materials, are ill-defined chemically. In sharp contrast to complex media, synthetic media are, by definition, chemically defined. Concentrations of chemically pure compounds, whether inorganic or organic, are added to fulfill the requirements of growth. In general, complex media are more commonly used. This is largely due to the empirical data base developed over the years on the efficacy of complex media for growing microorganisms. Also, microbiologists have not determined the exact requirements for organism growth for all microorganisms.

Once the essential requirements for cultivation are satisfied, culture media may be tailored to encourage the growth of specific groups of microorganisms. For example, the pH may be adjusted to grow acidophiles. Usually, a medium that is modified to grow a specific group of microorganisms is called selective. This selective property may be accomplished by adding substances that inhibit organisms other than the desired ones. For example, dyes and antibiotics are often used for this purpose in selective media. In reality, any one culture medium is selective by its very nature. This is because no single medium is able to grow all possible organisms.

VII. STERILITY TESTING

The question of sterility testing may now be readdressed, having established the diversity of potentially contaminating microorganisms and their requirements for growth. It should be evident that a single set of cultivation conditions cannot satisfy the absolute definition of sterility. On the other hand, it is impractical (and unnecessary) to test for every possible organism. Thus a compromise must be accepted based on a logical review of the objectives of sterility testing. The primary reason for sterilization of a parenteral product is to avoid introducing infective material into the patient. Thus, the ultimate environment that a harmful contaminating microorganism will find is the human body. In terms developed earlier, this suggests that mesophilic, neutrophilic heterotrophs would find the human body a satisfactory environment for growth and reproduction. With respect to oxygen utilization, both strict anaerobes and strict aerobes can find some place in the body to grow. Thus, one approach to sterility testing is to select test conditions that optimize the growth of organisms that find the body a suitable environment. Another approach to sterility testing is to use conditions that are favorable to organism commonly found as contaminants in pharmaceutical preparations. As discussed earlier, many contaminants are of the mesophilic, neutrophilic, heterotrophic, facultative, or aerobic organism groups. A reasonable sterility test method would promote the growth of this group.

The approaches to sterility testing outlined may be pursued by concurrently using various media and incubating at mesophilic growth temperatures. The formulations for sterility test media specified in the *U.S. Pharmaceopeia* (USP XX) will support the growth of the organisms described earlier. An examination of the components of the various media and their purpose follows.

A. Fluid Thioglycollate Medium

Fluid thioglycollate medium (FTM) is a complex medium designed to support the growth of anaerobes.

Ingredient	Function
L-cystine	Reducing agent to maintain anaerobic environment
Sodium chloride	Source of ions and osmotic (isotonic) maintenance
Dextrose	Carbon source
Agar	Growth-promoting, especially anaerobes
Yeast extract	Carbon, nitrogen, and vitamin source
Pancreatic digest of casein	Carbon, nitrogen, and essential amino acid source (weak buffer)
Sodium thioglycollate	Reducing agent to maintain anaerobic environment and mercurial preservative inactivator
Resazurin	Redox potential indicator

The appropriate concentrations of ingredients are mixed with water and the pH is adjusted so that it will be 7.1 ± 0.2 after sterilization. The medium is dispensed into individual culture tubes. These tubes are usually long in comparison to their diameter. This is to minimize the air/liquid interface, where oxygen will dissolve into the medium. After dispensing, the medium is then sterilized in an autoclave. The process of sterilization will drive off much of the dissolved oxygen (since the solubility of oxygen is inversely related to temperature). The reducing agents, cystine and thioglycollate, will "scavenge" and tie up both residual oxygen and any oxygen that enters the medium during incubation. The efficiency of oxygen depletion is monitored by the indicator dye, which will give a visible (pink = oxygen present) check on anaerobic growth conditions. Generally, FTM is incubated at 30–35°C for 7 to 14 days depending on the specific sterility test method (membrane filtration or direct inoculation).

To summarize, FTM is a complex medium that, when incubated at 30—35°C, will support the growth of mesophilic, neutrophilic, heterotrophic, faculative or anaerobic microorganisms.

B. Soybean-Casein Digest Medium

Soybean-casein digest (SCD) medium is a complex medium designed to support the growth of aerobes.

Ingredient	Function
Pancreatic digest of casein	Carbon, nitrogen, and essential amino acid source
Papaic digest of soybean meal	Carbon, nitrogen, and essential amino acid source
Sodium chloride	Source of ions and osmotic (isotonic) maintenance
Potassium phosphate	Source of ions and buffer
Dextrose	Carbon source

Each ingredient is added at a specified concentration to water and the pH is adjusted to 7.3 ± 0.2. After dispensing into culture tubes, it is sterilized in an autoclave. SCD medium is incubated for 7 to 14 days (depending on the test method) at 20—25°C. Oxygen required for aerobes is supplied by diffusion at the air/liquid interface. SCD is a complex medium supporting the growth of mesophilic, heterotrophic facultative and aerobic organisms when incubated at 20—25°C.

It was mentioned earlier that organisms require a variety of metal ions for growth, yet none are listed in the medium formulations above. These metal ions are provided as "contaminants" of the other media components. The reader is referred to the *U.S. Pharmaceopeia* for more information on the sterilization, and quality control of media in sterility testing.

C. Incubation

Considering that microorganisms are capable of rapid reproduction, it seems curious that incubation times of several days are utilized for sterility testing. In fact, healthy cells of even slow-growing organisms require, at most, just a few days to yield dense growth. The majority of bacterial isolates often need as little as 24 hr to produce visibly turbid cultures. There are two main reasons for the 7—14 day incubation times. First, the growth conditions provided by the culture media may not be optimal for a contaminant, and the additional growing time will compensate for a suboptimal growth rate. Second, rapid growth is dependent on healthy cells; a weakened cell will not reproduce until the damage that has weakened it is repaired. The term to describe this weakened condition is a stressed or injured cell. For example, cells exposed to sublethal concentrations of disinfectants or, for that matter, incomplete sterilization conditions are often damaged in the process. Also, cells exposed to environments that are hostile to growth can become injured. On the molecular level, many biochemical pathways responsible for such things as nucleic acid or protein synthesis essentially become nonfunctional when stressed. Fortunately, from the organisms' viewpoint (and unfortunately from the sterilization microbiologist's viewpoint), it can repair cellular damage. This, however, takes time (whether in a sterility test or in a "sterilized" product). Also, there are some potentially contaminating organisms that are inherently slow growers. Thus, extended incubation of sterility test media is warranted.

A second question with regard to sterility test incubation times arises when comparing inoculation vs. membrane filtration (MF) techniques. The former requires 14 days, while the latter calls for 7 days. Given that the media and potential contaminants are identical, why is there a twofold difference? Shorter incubation times for MF are due to two factors. First, because cells are concentrated on the membrane and washed with sterile buffers after concentration, any inhibitory agent in the product (e.g., an antibiotic or a preservative) is removed prior to immersion into the culture medium. Second, cells exposed to a culture medium often must "condition" that medium before efficient utilization of the nutrients. This conditioning occurs in the microenvironment immediately around the cell. An example of conditioning includes production and secretion of extracellular enzymes that break down complex nutrients into simpler compounds for transport into the cell. Cells concentrated by membranes tend to stay in the vicinity of the filter. Thus, they can condition their environment more easily than a free-floating cell.

This discussion of sterility testing has been limited to the why of the procedure, as opposed to the when, where, or how. There are several sources of information, the most definitive of which is the *U.S. Pharmacopeia*, that provide details of tests and sampling plans for individual classes of sterile pharmaceuticals.

D. Sterilization

There are five principle sterilization methods from which manufacturers of sterile products may choose. These include steam, dry heat, gas, ionizing radiation, and filtration. Each differs in the mechanisms of microbial removal, parameters of operation, and applicability to any given product. They do, however, share two common characteristics:

1. Providing sterility, as defined by compendial tests
2. Requiring validation and monitoring to prove their effectiveness

This section will discuss sterilization in terms of the following aspects:

1. How to select a method
2. How the methods remove or destroy microorganisms
3. How to prove microbiologically that the methods remove microorganisms

E. Method Selection

The question of which sterilization method is most appropriate for a given product is a function of the product itself. Each product will have a preferred method. For example, thermolabile liquids are typically sterilized by filtration. Selection is then based on such items as the impact of the method on product quality or esthetics, the economics of the sterilization process, and the logistics of sterilization compared to those of the overall manufacturing process.

The guiding phrase in the regulated manufacture of drugs and medical devices is "safe and effective." These simple words form the basis of complex network of statutes and regulations that dictate many of the practices and procedures employed in the pharmaceutical industry. Therefore, any sterilization method that compromises the safety and effectiveness of the product is precluded from use. There are situations, however, when a property of the product unrelated to either safety or effectiveness may be altered by a given sterilization method. To illustrate this, consider plastics, which are commonly used in the production of medical devices. The sterilization methods typically applied to these devices are either ethylene oxide or ionizing radiation. Some plastics, when exposed to high doses of ionizing radiation, will discolor. While this may not affect the performance of a device, it results in a cosmetic change that is unacceptable. Ethylene oxide may then become the method of choice.

Clearly, an important consideration in manufacturing processes is the economic impact of each process step on the cost of the final product. Thus, Process Development people strive to choose steps, or unit operations, that are cost-effective. When the option of more than one sterilization method is open to the process engineer, he or she will usually select the least expensive method. Moreover, any one sterilization method's economics can be optimized (minimized) by proper design of the sterilization process. For example, in sterile filtration, different combinations of prefilters with the final sterilizing filter can change the economics of the process. Generally, prefilters are cheaper than sterilizing filters, so the most economical system uses sufficient prefiltration to prevent plugging of the final filter.

F. Mechanisms of Removal

In the broadest sense, all sterilization methods perform identically: They all render products sterile. Close examination of the individual methods demonstrates that each operates in a different way. This section describes the biological basis of microbial removal for each of the five major methods of sterilization (moist heat, dry heat, ethylene oxide, ionizing radiation, and filtration).

1. Moist Heat

Moist heat, or steam under pressure, is the most studied method of sterilization. First developed by Pasteur and Chamberlain in the late 1800s, it has been characterized in terms of its operational parameters, predictability, and mode of action. As with all sterilization methods, the cellular function that is of primary interest is reproduction (no reproduction means no growth, which means sterility). The reproductive process of microorganisms is directed by nucleic acids (DNA) and mediated by enzymes, protein biocatalysts, which among other things direct nucleic acid synthesis and the construction of cellular components. Generally speaking, the three-dimensional structure of proteins, especially enzymes, determines their function. This structure is the result of the linear arrangement of amino acids, each of which has different chemical properties. When proteins are formed, the sequence of amino acids dictates the shape of the protein. This is because the individual amino acids interact with each other and their aqueous environment to yield the most stable shape. If the shape of the protein is changed after its formation (e.g., through protein denaturation), then its function changes. Often this change is irreversible and results in nonfunctionality. Cooked egg whites are an example of irreversible protein denaturation. (When was the last time you saw a chicken hatch out of a frying pan?) During moist heat sterilization, it is the irreversible denaturation of vital enzymes that results in cell death. It is important to note that both water vapor and elevated temperature are required to effectively denature proteins (kill cells). If water vapor is present, much lower temperatures are required in heat sterilization. Generally, moist heat sterilization is performed with water-saturated steam under pressure (15 psig, 121°C). The water vapor contributes to the available heat at any temperature (e.g., saturated steam at 121°C provides at least seven times as much available heat as air at the same temperature). This alone, however, does not explain the efficiency of kill for moist heat. The water vapor also interacts directly with the protein at the elevated temperature to denature it. The exact protein or proteins that are rendered nonfunctional by moist heat sterilization are largely unknown, but from a practical standpoint this is unimportant. The process of cell destruction is predictable and reproducible under defined conditions of operation.

2. Dry Heat

Dry heat is also used to sterilize materials. In this case, higher temperatures, on the order of 160—170°C (and longer time periods) are required for sterilization as compared to moist heat. Sterilization by dry heat actually represents an incineration process. Cells are destroyed principally by non-specific oxidation of cellular components through elevated temperatures (although the inherent water content of the cells plays a contributing role). Again, the exact site of action is unknown, but the process is predictable and reliable.

3. Ethylene Oxide

Ethylene oxide [$(CH_2)_2O$, ETO], the most commonly used gaseous sterilant, works through a chemical reaction with macromolecules contained within the cell. Its chemical activity is as an alkylating agent, and it is through this mechanism that it is thought to kill cells. ETO replaces labile hydrogen atoms with hydroxy ethyl ($-CH_2CH_2OH$) groups. Macromolecules, like proteins, contain functional groups such as $-COOH$, $-OH$, $-SH$, and $-NH_2$ whose hydrogens are labile to alkylation. Since many of these groups play an important role in protein structure and function, their modification by ETO will disrupt or destroy the protein's activity. If the protein is vital to cell replication, then death occurs after activity is lost. An interesting feature of ETO's sterilization ability is that it is almost as effective against spores as it is against vegetative cells. Although not clearly understood, this may be due to ETO's spectrum of reactivity with a variety of hydrogen-containing functional groups in macromolecules contained in both spores and vegetative cells. Apparently, evolution has not prepared the protective (dormant) stage of bacteria, the spore, from chemical attack by ETO.

4. Radiation

Ionizing radiation, in contrast to heat and gaseous sterilization, is thought to get its lethal effect by interaction with nucleic acids, primarily DNA. The lethality of ionizing radiation is due to both direct and indirect effects, but direct effects seem to predominate. Direct effects imply interaction of radiation with the target molecule, DNA. The energy released during this interaction disrupts DNA's structure. Since DNA is the essential blueprint of living systems, any major changes in the blueprint result in an improperly built structure, and in the cell's case, nonviability. Indirect effects are those attributed to reaction products produced by ionizing radiation and water (e.g., free radicals and peroxides). These highly reactive compounds can interact with macromolecules and disrupt their activity. It appears, however, that the direct interactions with DNA are more important. It has been shown that the sensitivity of an organism to radiation is a function of the volume of DNA within the organism (more DNA means more sensitivity).

5. Filtration

Sterilization by filtration represents a special case with respect to mechanism of action. In contrast to the other methods described thus far, filtration relies on the physical removal of microorganisms rather than their destruction. Filtration, obviously limited to fluids, restrains organisms as the fluid passes through a filter. The mechanism of removal is a function of filter type. Depth filters, composed of fibers randomly pressed together, remove by a combination of adsorption and entrapment in their internal structure. Screen filters, typified by membrane filters formed by a controlled polymer precipitation process, use a sieving mechanism. Currently, membrane filters are more commonly used in sterile filtration because of their greater reliability and predictability in sterilizing solutions.

VIII. VALIDATION OF STERILIZATION—BIOLOGICAL INDICATORS

All sterilization methods are routinely validated through a common approach. First, a biological indicator of performance is chosen that is resistant to the sterilization method. A second consideration is the influence of different variables on the resistance of the biological indicator to the sterilization method (e.g., indicator propagation and interactions between the indicator and the product being sterilized). Third, the quantitative nature of indicator destruction by the sterilization process is established. Finally, the concept of assigning sterility probabilities to materials undergoing sterilization is determined for a specific process. More succinctly, the validation of sterilization methods implies a collection of studies that prove the reliability and predictability of the method.

A. Characteristics of Indicators

The principal function of any sterilization method is to remove or destroy microorganisms. This function is usually validated by studies that use a particular microorganism as a biological indicator of performance. Although each sterilization method uses a specific organism, all indicators share certain common characteristics. These include the following.

1. An Inherent Resistance to the Sterilization Method

An inherent resistance to the sterilization method is clearly the primary characteristic to consider when choosing an indicator. It makes little sense to characterize a sterilization method if the indicator is easily removed or destroyed by the method when compared to other microorganisms.

2. *A Stable and Reproducible Resistance to the Sterilization Method When Used Under Defined Conditions*

The effectiveness of a sterilization method is expressed in terms of its ability to remove an indicator organism. If the indicator shows wide variability with respect to resistance, then it is of limited utility for characterizing either new sterilization processes or monitoring existing ones. It must demonstrate the same resistance time and again. Thus, the results obtained during validation will accurately predict the effectiveness of the sterilization method in routine operation.

3. *Efficient Recovery After Exposure to Sterilization Method*

Typically, sterilization studies expose an indicator to a variety of sterilizing conditions, and the effectiveness of these conditions is expressed in terms of indicator survival. If a test organism is not capable of reproducing, for reasons other than the effect of sterilization conditions, then the impact of these conditions will be overestimated. In other words, any indicator that survives sterilization should be amenable to cultivation after exposure.

4. *Nonpathogenicity*

Biological indicators are often handled by individuals with limited training in microbiology. The use of an indicator should pose minimal hazard of infection to those exposed to it.

5. *Characteristic of the Organisms Commonly Occurring in the Product to Be Sterilized*

Although the bioburden of products to be sterilized varies widely, there are some commonly occurring microbial species that require removal. The type of biological indicator used in sterilization validation should reflect (and be more resistant than) those that must be removed during the actual operation of the sterilization process. To quote USP XX: "The effective use of biological indicators for the monitoring of a sterilization process requires a thorough knowledge of the product being sterilized and its component parts (materials and packaging) and of the probable types and numbers of microorganisms constituting the microbial bioburden in the product immediately prior to sterilization."

Historically, each sterilization method has been validated employing a bacterium that possessed the above characteristics. With the exception of one or perhaps two sterilization methods, the biological indicator conventionally used has been a spore—the dormant form of some Gram-positive bacteria. This stands to reason, since the spore confers survival ability (high resistance) to the microorganism under a variety of adverse environments. The spore state is essentially a form of suspended animation.

B. Spore Formation

Spore formation is the result of complex metabolic or morphologic changes that certain bacteria are capable of undergoing. Given the unique suitability of spores as biological indicators, it is useful to examine closely the process of spore formation. The process of differentiation from a vegetative cell to a spore is initiated in a cell population as it passes out of exponential growth (a time of most rapid cell replication) and approaches the stationary phase (a time of essentially no replication). Most microorganisms will, after a time in the stationary phase, enter a death phase, where cells decrease in numbers. Spore-forming bacteria thwart this otherwise inevitable consequence by triggering biosynthetic pathways to produce an endospore. (Bacterial spores are called endospores because the spore is formed and often contained *within* the bacterial cell.)

Briefly, the steps during spore formation are as follows.

1. Forespore Formation

When conditions are appropriate for spore formation, the genetic material of the cell reorganizes and is segregated from the rest of the cell by a membrane. This membrane-bound container of DNA is then surrounded by an outgrowth of the normal cell membrane. Thus, the genetic material is surrounded by a double membrane layer resulting in the forespore. At this point, the cell is on a nonreversible path to spore formation.

2. Cortex and Spore Coat Formation

After forespore formation, there is a rapid synthesis of new structures that enclose it. The cortex, composed of material unique from, but similar to, normal cell wall material (peptidoglycan), is formed between the two layers of membrane surrounding the forespore. Shortly after cortex formation, another layer of material, largely protein, is formed around the outermost membrane. This layer is called the spore coat. The spore coat contains amino acids that confer a high resistance to treatments that solubilize proteins.

3. Dipicolinic Acid Formation

Even with the formation of two layers of material, the newly formed spore has little resistance to heat. The development of heat resistance closely follows two major chemical changes: a massive uptake of Ca^{+2} ions and the synthesis in large amounts of dipicolinic acid, a compound absent from vegetative cells. This material is contained within the spore, and its formation is highly correlated with heat resistance. As an interesting aside, it is during spore formation that the peptide antibiotics such as edeines (inhibiting DNA synthesis), bacitracins (inhibiting cell wall synthesis), and polymyxins (disrupting membrane structure or function) are formed.

4. Spore Liberation

Once fully formed, the endospore is commonly liberated by autolysis of the mother cell. At this point, the endospore is highly dehydrated, shows no detectable metabolic activity, and is effectively protected from heat and radiation damage and from attack by either enzymatic or chemical agents. Figure 1 illustrates the major steps in spore formation.

Understanding spore formation is only one side of the coin when spores are used in sterilization studies. The process when the cell returns to an actively metabolizing, vegetative form is also important. This process begins when the state of dormancy is broken. Called activation, the return to "life" by the spore can be initiated by a variety of stimuli. A typical example of

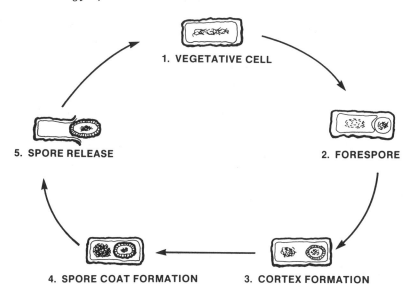

FIGURE 1

activation is heat shock, where the spore is exposed to sublethal temperatures for several minutes or hours. After activation, the spores undergo germination, but only if placed in conditions that favor growth. Germination requires a chemical trigger, for example, the presence of certain amino acids, ribosides (e.g., adenosine, inosine), glucose, and various inorganic ions. Germination is characterized by a loss of heat and chemical resistance, release of spore components, and restoration of metabolic activity. If the proper nutrients for vegetative growth and reproduction are present, the germinated spore will grow out into a vegetative cell, form a new cell wall, and begin cellular division. The requirements for germination and vegetative growth are provided by such growth media as are used in sterility testing (SCD broth).

Sterilization by moist heat (steam), dry heat, ethylene oxide, and ionizing radiation are all validated with spores of Gram-positive bacteria. Sterilization by filtration is characterized by a small Gram-negative rod. The methods of sterilization and their corresponding indicators are as follows:

Sterilization method	Biological indicator
Steam	*Bacillus stearothermophilus*
Dry heat	*Bacillus subtilis* var. *niger*
Ethylene oxide	*Bacillus subtilis* var. *globigii*
Ionizing radiation	*Bacillus pumilus*
Filtration	*Pseudomonas diminuta*

As seen in the above table, all the indicators except *P. diminuta* are members of the genus *Bacillus*. *Bacilli* are commonly found in the soil and,

because their spores are resistant to desiccation, are often airborne contaminants. These indicators are mesophilic (except *B. stearothermophilus*,
which is thermophilic), neutrophilic, heterotrophic aerobes. The particular
species or subspecies is selected based on the resistance of that species to
the sterilization method to which it has been assigned. Thus, it is inappropriate to substitute one spore species with another when characterizing a
particular sterilization method. The indicator of filtration, *P. diminuta*, is
distinct from the other indicators. This reflects the mechanism of sterilization by which filters work. As mentioned previously, filters sterilize by
physically excluding microorganisms. Thus, the size of the indicator becomes the critical resistance factor. *P. diminuta* is a small bacterium which,
in addition to meeting the resistance criteria, also satisfies the other characteristics of a biological indicator. It, too, is a mesophilic, neutrophilic,
heterotrophic aerobe.

IX. VALIDATION OF STERILIZATION—QUANTITATION
OF INDICATOR REMOVAL

The underlying rationale for sterilization validation by biological indicators
is that removal or destruction of high numbers of the indicator organisms will
confirm the removal or destruction of the organisms that make up the product
bioburden. Typically, large numbers of biological indicators are exposed to
a set of sterilization conditions, and the effectiveness of the sterilization
method is expressed in terms of the removal of the indicator. Since sterilization methods are broken down into two basic categories, those that destroy
microorganisms (heat, gaseous, and radiation) and those that remove them
(filtration), the discussion of indicator removal quantitation will be presented
in two parts.

A. Indicator Destruction

The basic tool in sterilization studies involving the destruction of indicator
organisms is the survival curve, an exponential relationship derived by plotting the number of surviving biological indicators as a function of some parameter of the sterilization method (Fig. 2). For sterilization by heat and
ethylene oxide, survivor numbers are plotted as a function of exposure time
under fixed conditions of sterilization (i.e., temperature for heat and the
combination of gas concentration, temperature, and relative humidity for
ethylene oxide). Ionizing radiation survival curves are plotted as a function
of total radiation dose expressed in rads or megarads. Generally speaking,
such a plot, when done on semilog graph paper (with number of survivors
on the logarithmic, Y axis), results in a straight line with a negative slope.
It is from such survival curves that D values, a measure of sterilization resistance, are calculated. The D value is defined as the amount of time (for
heat and ethylene oxide) or dose (for radiation) to reduce the population of
the organism by one order of magnitude. Put in terms of the survival curve,
the D value is the slope of the line. Typical determinations of the D value
start with a spore population of 10^5–10^6 and expose that population to an
abbreviated sterilization process. The number of surviving viable cells are
quantitated by standard microbiological techniques (plate counts) at various
time intervals during the sterilization process. The resulting data are plotted
as a survival curve and the D value obtained from the curve. Typical

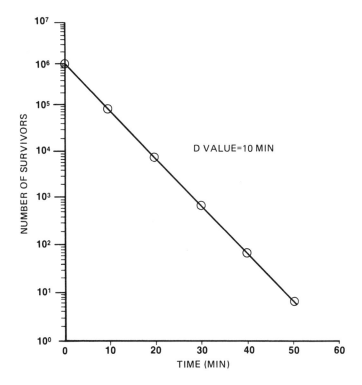

FIGURE 2

performance characteristics (D values) for spore-forming biological indicators as spore strips are shown in the following table (*source*: USP XX).

Biological indicator	Sterilization process	D value
B. stearothermophilus	Saturated steam—121°C	1.5 min
B. subtilis var. *niger*	Dry heat at 170°C	1 min
B. subtilis var. *globigii*	Ethylene oxide (600 mg/liter), 50% RH and 54°C	3 min
B. pumilus	Gamma radiation—wet	0.2 mrad
	—dry	0.15 mrad

Thus, if one wanted to reduce a population of cells by six orders of magnitude and the cell had a D value of 2 min (for heat), then the total exposure time required to kill the population would be 12 min. Usually, sterilization methods are validated by an overkill approach. By this, it is meant that a sterilization procedure is extended beyond a 6-log kill to, say, a 10^{-6}

probability of a survivor (12-log reduction or 24-min exposure time). There are various experimental approaches to D value determinations as well as anomalies in their determination, and the reader is referred to texts on sterilization for additional information.

Another term commonly applied in thermal sterilization validation is the F_0 value. The F_0 value is defined as the time in minutes required to kill all the spores in a suspension at a temperature of 121°C. For example, if the spore population is 10^6 and the $D_{121°C}$ value is 2 min, the F_0 is 12.

A third quantitative expression used in thermal sterilization studies is the Z value of a particular organism. The Z value measures the rate of change in the D value as a function of temperature. Mathematically, it is defined as follows:

$$Z = \frac{T_2 - T_1}{\text{Log}(D_2/D_1)}$$

Z of 10°C = 18°F

where T is in degrees Fahrenheit and D is the D value corresponding to the specified temperature in the numerator. Z values are obtained experimentally by plotting the logarithm of the D values as a function of the temperature at which they are derived. Such a relationship is known as a thermal resistance curve. The Z value is the slope of the thermal resistance curve and is expressed in degrees of temperature (Fig. 3).

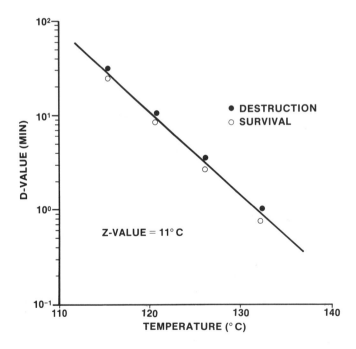

FIGURE 3

The combined usage of D and Z values is necessary from a practical stand-point. In reality, thermal sterilization processes do not reach a fixed sterilization temperature (121°C) instantaneously. More likely, a product undergoing thermal sterilization will gradually heat up to and cool down from the sterilization temperature. The heat destruction of microorganisms is not a discrete phenomenon where all the cells die at, and only at, the sterilization temperature. Rather, microbial destruction is a continuous process during product heat-up and cool-down where the rate of kill (the D value) at any one temperature changes as the temperature changes (reflected in the Z value). Thus, it is possible to integrate the individual kills for each temperature during product heat-up and cool-down by knowing the thermal profile of the product (temperature change as a function of time) and the Z values.

The term used to account for spore destruction throughout a sterilization cycle is the F_0 value. F_0 is a lethality factor equating the equivalent time, in minutes, at the various temperatures during the cycle required to produce a given sterilization effect at 121°C, where the Z value is 10°C. In other words, F_0 values account for the real world of process heat-up and cool-down where microbial destruction is occurring throughout the process cycle. Mathematically, it is defined as

$$F_0 = \int 10^{\frac{T - 121°C}{10}} dt$$

For situations where the Z value is different from 10°C, the lethality factor of a process can be generalized as follows:

$$F_T^Z = \int 10^{\frac{T - 121°C}{Z}} dt$$

There are several approaches to determining the F_0 value experimentally for a sterilization process. The reader is referred to detailed descriptions found in Chapters 11 and 12.

B. Indicator Removal

Sterilization by filtration is a process of microbial removal rather than destruction. Sterilization terms such as D values and Z values, therefore, do not apply. Nonetheless, quantitations of sterile filtration performance have been developed and used to validate filtration processes. The quantitative term widely used to express the efficiency of microbial removal by filters is the log reduction value (LRV). The LRV is defined as the $\log_{10}$ of the ratio of the number of organisms challenging a filter to the number of organisms passing through the filter. The LRV is determined under standard conditions of biological indicator numbers (10^7 organisms/cm^2 of filter area) and filtration conditions. Most manufacturers of filters provide sterilizing filters that exhibit no passage of indicator organisms (LRVs greater than the total bacterial challenge).

As implied in the D value concept of indicator organism destruction, there is a predictable relationship between microbial death and some sterilization parameter (e.g., time and temperature for thermal sterilization). This is important, since the measure of such physical parameters during sterilization helps validate and routinely monitor the effectiveness of the sterilization process. This is especially important for sterile filtration.

Routine use of biological indicators during filtration is precluded, as microbial retention testing is a destructive test. The indicator organism, *P.
diminuta*, is also a Gram-negative bacteria, the primary source of pyrogens.
If *P. diminuta* was used during product manufacture, it would compromise
the nonpyrogenic requirement of parenterals. Also, such artificial contamination of the product would alter the economics of a filtration process,
since the filter would plug prematurely. Thus, there is a requirement for
a relationship between microbial removal and some measure of filtration performance. Such a relationship exists between the LRV of a filter and integrity test values measured during routine filter usage (bubble point and
diffusive air flow). Empirically derived under standard conditions and
commonly provided by filter manufacturers, these relationships provide
useful information to users of filters when validating their filtration process.
(See Chaps. 18 and 19.)

X. SUMMARY

This chapter serves as a microbiology primer, with particular attention paid
to the microbiology of sterilization. Sterilization methods are designed to
yield the total absence of living entities in a product, and the success or
failure of any method is defined in terms of standard tests for sterility.
Sterility tests focus on the ability to exhibit microbial growth under defined
conditions of cultivation. The world of microorganisms is highly diverse,
with few environments without microbial inhabitants. Nonetheless, there are
certain organisms typically found in products requiring sterilization. Knowledge of these organisms helps define both sterilization procedures and sterility test methods. Each sterilization method differs in its mechanism of action,
but all share the common characteristic of producing sterile products in a
predictable and reliable manner. Chapters 11 through 18 translate the principles outlined here to actual practice when describing the validation of the
sterilization methods used in pharmaceutical processes.

XI. GLOSSARY

Bioburden	A term used to describe the microbial content of a material, including both the types and numbers of microorganisms present.
Biological indicator	A specific species of microorganism used to test the effectiveness of a sterilization process, chosen for a specific sterilization method based on resistance to that method.
Dormant	Resting or inactive state of a microorganism, i.e., not reproducing or metabolizing.
Enzyme	Biological catalyst, often a target of a sterilization process (e.g., thermal sterilization), which results in microbial death.
Febrile response	Reaction of the human body to such stimuli as microbial by-products (i.e., pyrogens), which results in an elevated body temperature.

Gram reaction	A binary differential staining procedure for bacteria based on the chemistry of the cell wall. Results in either Gram-negative or Gram-positive classification.
Medium	A solution of chemical components designed to supply the nutritional needs of microorganisms for their growth and production.
Microflora	The inherent population of microorganisms contained in or on a material.
Nucleic acids	The macromolecular components comprising the genetic information of living systems. Principally of two types, deoxyribonucleic acid (DNA) and ribonucleic acid (RNA), and the primary target of sterilization by radiation.
Pyrogen	A substance that causes a febrile response when introduced parenterally to the body. The most common source of pyrogens are Gram-negative bacteria (the lipopolysaccharide portion of their cell wall).
Spore	A dormant form of a microorganism that confers resistance to adverse environments. In the context of sterilization, when they are most resistant to destruction by a sterilization method.
Sterility	The complete absence of living material defined in practice by the absence of growing microorganisms when tested with growth media.
Sterilization	The process of achieving sterility.
Validation	The collection of studies applied to a pharmaceutical manufacturing operation that substantiate the production of a safe and effective drug.
Vegetative	A physiologic state of microorganisms where they are capable of growth and reproduction. In the context of sterilization, when they are most susceptable to destruction by a sterilization method.

Quantitative Terms in Sterilization

D value	Time required to reduce a microbial population by 90%, i.e., a one-logarithm reduction.
F value	Time required to destroy all spores of a suspension when using a temperature of 121°C.
F_0 value	Time required at any given temperature that is equivalent to the sterilization effect at 121°C.
Z value	The number of degrees Celsius required to change the D value by a factor of 10.
LRV	The log reduction value, which describes the microbial ability of a filter in terms of the logarithmic reduction of a microbial population.

11

Validation of Steam Sterilization in Autoclaves

PHIL De SANTIS* and VINCENT S. RUDO

E. R. Squibb & Sons, Inc., New Brunswick, New Jersey

Validation has been called "proof that a process does what it purports to do." Validation of sterilization must be viewed as a continuing process, though, beginning in the R&D and Engineering stages, and proceeding through to manufacturing and maintenance.

Validation develops in stages, like a new product or plant. It starts with ideas, takes shape in the form of equipment, goes through a testing phase, and is perpetuated in a continuing operation. The experimental phase that has come to be called "validation" is only a part of the program. The authors will examine those major attributes encompassing the development of a validation program. One must:

1. Understand the principles of microbial death and the meaning of sterilization
2. Design and build equipment capable of consistently and reliably providing the conditions needed to sterilize
3. Understand the particular characteristics of the loads to be sterilized and design appropriate processes
4. Validate the cycles in the equipment to prove that they will do the job expected of them
5. Maintain a state of control to ensure the quality of all materials and product sterilized by the cycle

In this chapter we will develop a method to be employed in steam autoclave validation.

I. STEAM STERILIZATION IN AUTOCLAVES

Steam sterilization under pressure is the most efficient sterilant [1]. It is the method of choice except for sterilizing products and equipment where heat and moisture damage are a problem.

Current affiliation: PACO Pharmaceutical Services, Lakewood, New Jersey.

The temperature range for the development of living organisms is $-5°C$ to $80°C$ [1]. Exposure to temperatures above this range usually result in the death of the organism, except in the case of some heat-resistant spore formers. The mechanism responsible for the death of microorganisms is not clearly understood. Indeed, to date, the most commonly utilized criterion for describing microbial death has been the loss of the cell's ability to reproduce. This is a simplified view that has not been totally effective in predicting the sterility of sterilized medical products. Traditionally, the sterility of a batch or lot of products has been certified by tests such as that described in USP XX. These tests utilize a small statistical sampling of the sterilizer load to determine the presence of viable (reproducing) organisms in the entire lot. Frequently in the past this has been done without consideration for the mechanism of microbial death or the conditions required to facilitate that mechanism. Such a test as the finished product test in USP XX, which requires 20 samples, can only detect a contamination level of 15% with 95% confidence. This corresponds to an approximate probability of survivors of 10^{-1} (10%) [2].

It is obvious that increasing sample sizes to the point where the probability of surviving organisms is decreased significantly can be costly and wasteful. Therefore, an understanding of microbial death, or at least the conditions required for microbial death, is essential.

Probability of survival is an alternative approach in describing sterilization. The most prevalent description of sterility used today is the reduction of anticipated levels of contamination in a load to the point where the probability of survival is less than 10^{-6} (one in a million) [2].

This swing in thought regarding sterilization as a probability function is closely linked to the concept of validation. Once the levels of microbial contamination and resistance to the sterilizing process are known, probability of survival can be calculated. Validation involves the gathering of data which ensures that the sterilizing process is experienced throughout the load.

The sterilization process described in this chapter is the use of steam under pressure. Discussion will be limited to batch-wise sterilization in autoclaves.

II. MECHANISM OF MICROBIAL DEATH

It is generally believed that microbial death can be linked to the denaturation of critical proteins and nucleic acids within the cell. This denaturation is a result of the disruption of intramolecular hydrogen bonds. These are partially responsible for the spatial orientation of the molecule. Proteins are specifically ordered chains of amino acids, linked by polypeptide bonds. Nucleic acids are polycondensations of ribose sugars joined by phosphate linkages. Each is dependent on a specific spatial orientation to perform its function. As the hydrogen bonds are broken, the structure, and thus the function, is lost. It must be noted, though, that the denaturation may be reversible or irreversible. The functional structure of the molecule is lost in stages. If halted before a critical number of hydrogen bonds are cleaved, it is possible for the molecule to return to its original state. For example, DNA (deoxyribonucleic acid) gradually changes from helix to a random coil.

Significant research data support the theory that microbial death may be described as a first-order chemical reaction. This leads to the conclusion that death is essentially a single-molecule reaction. We are probably dealing with the denaturation of a critical molecule within each cell [1].

Bacterial spores have been shown to be the forms most resistant to thermal death. The spore is the normal resting state in the life of certain groups of organisms, namely, *Bacilli* and *Clostridia*. During this stage the processes of the cell are carried out at a minimal, though not a stagnant level. Spores are the most resistant of all organisms in their ability to withstand hostile environments. Their thermal resistance has been linked to the relative absence of water in their dense central core. There is considerable disagreement on the subject. Some investigators attribute this heat resistance to the existence of the spore core as an insoluble gel or the presence of lipid material. The dry-heat resistance of spores is greatly influenced by the history of the spore with regard to water as well as the water content of the spore during the heat treatment. All of the foregoing highlight the importance of moisture in thermal death. It is well known that bacterial spores are much more rapidly destroyed in the presence of saturated steam than by dry heat. It is possible that the water causes the hydration of a stabilizing polymer (calcium dipicolinate) within the spore. Furthermore, water is linked directly to the denaturation of proteins and nucleic acids by hydration [1].

III. ORDER OF DEATH AND MATHEMATICAL MODELING

The consideration of microbial death, and more specifically spore inactivation, as a monomolecular reaction with water is consistent with first-order reaction kinetics. That is, the rate of reaction is governed by the concentration of the reactant (spores). Mathematically this is expressed as

$$\frac{dN_a}{dt} = kC_a$$

where t is time, C_a is the spore concentration, and k is a reaction-rate constant at constant temperature. In integral form,

$$\log \left(\frac{C_a 0}{C_a} \right) = k(t - t^0)$$

where the superscript 0 indicates initial conditions. Also, $(t - t^0)$ is usually simplified by arbitrarily setting $t^0 = 0$. Thus, a semilog plot of concentration vs. time will yield a straight line of slope k, as shown in Fig. 1. The rate constant k is expressed as reciprocal minutes (min^{-1}). In turn, the negative reciprocal of the rate constant is equivalent to the number of minutes required at a given temperature to destroy 90% of the organisms present (a one-log reduction). The reciprocal of the rate constant is referred to as the D value and is expressed in minutes. D is the measure of the relative heat resistance of an organism at a constant temperature.

As shown in Fig. 1, the simple logarithmic model yields a straight-line survivor curve. Although it does not fit all experimental data, its use is recommended because of its wide applicability and simplicity.

In general, sterilization takes place over a range of temperatures, including heat-up and cool-down. Therefore, the sterilizing effect must be integrated over a range of temperatures. This requires a temperature-dependent model.

A common measure of the temperature-dependence of a chemical reaction is the Q value. Q is defined as the change in the reaction-rate constant k for a change of 10°C. This can be written as

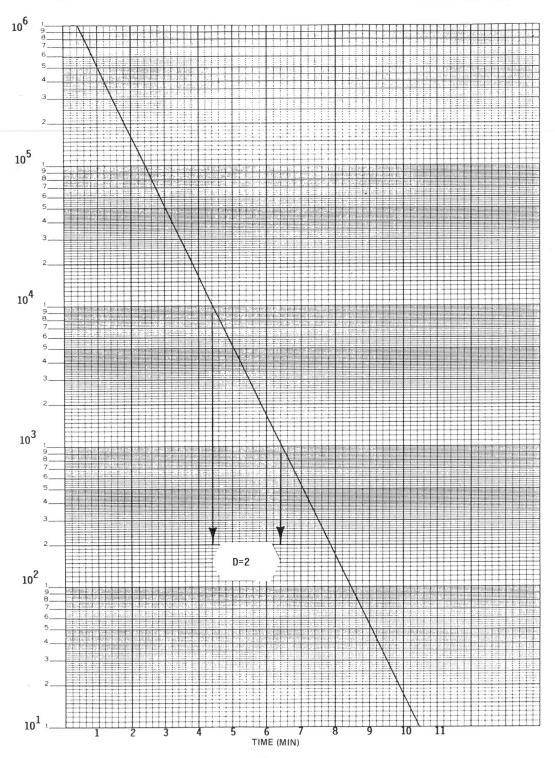

FIGURE 1   Typical curve of microbial population vs. time; D value.

$$Q = \frac{k_{(T + 10°C)}}{k_T}$$

The Q value for many chemical reactions is around 2. For spore destruction with standard steam it is much higher, from 10 to 18.

Another common temperature coefficient model for chemical reactions is the Arrhenius equation. This is written as

$$k = A \exp\left(\frac{E_A}{RT}\right)$$

where

k = the rate constant

A = a constant

E_A = activation energy

R = universal gas constant

T = absolute temperature

A plot of ln k (determined experimentally) vs. $1/T$ will give a straight line of slope E_A/R.

This model is consistent with empirical data gathered on the temperature dependence of spore D values. A typical plot of the effect of temperature on D, the thermal resistance, is shown in Fig. 2. The negative slope of this thermal resistance curve is called the Z value. Z is defined as the temperature change required to cause a one-log decrease in the D value and is expressed in degrees Celsius. Remembering that D is the reciprocal of the rate constant k, Z can be related to Q as follows:

$$Z = \log \frac{Q}{10}$$

Similarly, it can be related to E_A in the Arrhenius model:

$$Z = 2.303RT^2 E_A^{-1}$$

The use of the D and Z values to predict microbial death over time and temperature should be approached with caution. The straight-line relationships predicted by these models will hold over a limited temperature span and then only for a homogeneous culture of a single species of microorganism. Mixed populations of several levels of heat resistance will produce a curve determined by the relative populations and D values of the organisms. The usefulness of D and Z, though, is that in nature one subpopulation, by virtue of its high thermal resistance (D) and initial concentration, is usually controlling with regard to reaching sterility. This subpopulation will follow the model [3].

IV. THE THERMAL DEATH TIME CURVE

As previously mentioned, the usefulness of the temperature-dependent model in the steam autoclave is to calculate the lethality of the cycle over a range of

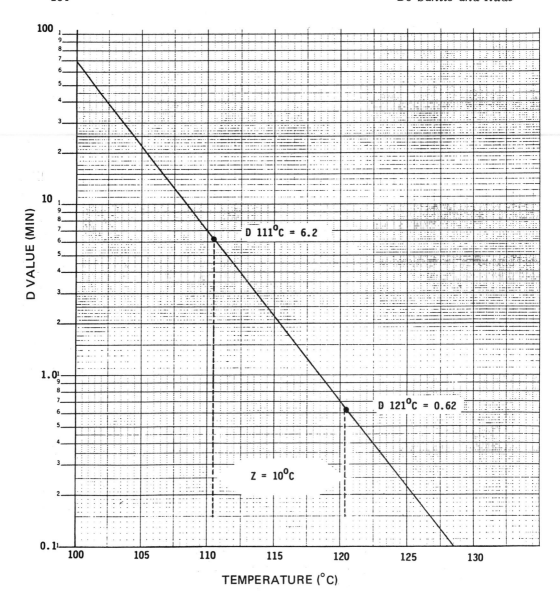

FIGURE 2   Effect of temperature on D value; Z value.

temperatures (including heat-up and cool-down). To do this a new variable, closely related to D, is introduced. This is called F, the thermal death time. F is defined as the time in minutes to produce the equivalent sterilization effect at 121°C (250°F). This temperature is chosen as a base because it is an economical and effective one for saturated steam sterilization. It may be considered a benchmark, like a .300 batting average in baseball.

Both the thermal resistance curve in Fig. 2 (log D vs. T) and the thermal death time curve (log F vs. T) are dependent on Z as follows:

$$\frac{D_T}{D_{121°C}} = \frac{F_T}{F_{121°C}} = 10^{(T-121)/Z}$$

The curves are parallel, both with a slope of Z. The most commonly used value of Z for the destruction of microbial spores is 10°C (18°F). This is based on experimental observations for *B. stearothermophilus*, a highly heat-resistant organism. When the assumption of Z = 10°C is made, F is written as F_0. This is the most commonly used measure of the lethality of a sterilization process spanning a range of temperatures.

As can be seen, F_0 is a summation over time of the lethal rates at a series of temperatures. In integral form this is

$$F_0 = \int 10^{(T-121)/10} \, dt$$

This can be solved in many ways, manually or by computer. These generally reduce to the simple form

$$F_0 = \Sigma \, 10^{(121-T)/Z} \, \Delta t$$

where t is the chosen time interval and T is the average temperature over that interval. The smaller the interval chosen, the more accurate the calculation.

Using this important value, F_0, enables one to simply measure the effectiveness of any steam sterilization process.

V. STERILIZER DESIGN

The validation of a steam sterilization cycle is dependent on the equipment chosen. The autoclave and its support systems must be qualified to deliver the cycle repeatedly and consistently. Equipment qualification is made up of proper design, installation according to design, and operational testing to ensure that design criteria and specifications are met.

Autoclave design is geared largely to the type of cycle chosen. All steam sterilization cycles are based on direct contact with saturated steam. Saturated steam is water vapor in equilibrium with liquid water. The values of temperature and pressure at which pure saturated steam can exist are shown by the phase diagram in Fig. 3. Saturated steam can exist only along the phase boundary; that is, the relationship between its temperature and pressure is fixed. An increase or reduction in temperature results in a corresponding increase or decrease in pressure and vice versa.

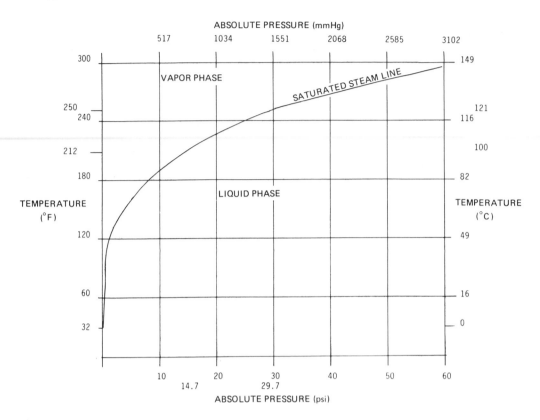

FIGURE 3   Water-steam phase diagram; saturation line.

The utility of saturated steam in sterilization cycles has been well documented [1,4]. The sterilizing effect is accomplished by the heat transfer
from the steam to the load and by the hydrating effect of the resultant condensate. Condensate is formed because of the return of the steam to the
lower-energy liquid state. This phase change requires the transfer of the
latent heat of the steam (that which was required to change it from liquid to
vapor—970 BTU/lb) to the surroundings, thus heating the autoclave and its
load. The heat transferred by the condensation of saturated steam is many
times greater than that which would be transferred from steam above its
boiling point, called superheated steam. This heat amounts to only 1 BTU/
lb–°F. Also, superheated steam is sometimes known as "dry steam," as it
does not form condensate as it cools. The important hydrating effect is not
present.

Sterilization with superheated steam is a dry-heat phenomenon, less efficient than a saturated steam process. Superheat may be avoided by maintaining the steam in equilibrium with water at the boiler or steam generator.
Also, supplementary heat sources, such as jacket heat, must be controlled so
as not to drive the system above the vapor-liquid equilibrium line.

Condensation to water causes a volume decrease in excess of 99%. This
would result in a pressure decrease if the condensed steam were not immediately replenished, as is the case in the autoclave. It is the condensation-
replenishment cycle that allows the steam to penetrate to all the surfaces to

be heated until they reach an effective sterilization temperature. Autoclaves and cycles are designed to ensure that saturated steam reaches these surfaces.

There are several criteria common to all modern steam sterilizers in use in the pharmaceutical industry. These include:

1. A pressure vessel constructed according to the Americal Society of Mechanical Engineers (ASME) code. This will withstand the required internal steam pressures. It may be rectangular or cylindrical in cross section.
2. A steam jacket and insulation. These are energy-conserving devices designed primarily to heat the metal mass of the vessel and to limit heat loss from within the vessel. Some laboratory and small special-use sterilizers are unjacketed.
3. A safety door mechanism to prevent opening while the unit is under pressure. (It is interesting to note that the term "autoclave" means self-closing). The locking device may be actuated directly by internal pressure or indirectly through an automatic switch. The door itself may be of the swing-out or sliding type.
4. A thermostatic steam trap to efficiently remove all and/or condensate from the chamber. This is open when cool and closed when in contact with steam. As condensate collects, the trap opens due to the slight temperature reduction and the condensate is discharged. There is also a trap to remove condensate from the steam jacket.
5. A temperature control system. Although operating under pressure, temperature is the controlling factor in steam sterilization. The modern temperature controller is made up of several key elements to sense, record, and react. These are discussed in a later section.
6. A cycle timer and (usually) a sequencing controller.
7. A microbial retentive vent filter (optional).
8. A chamber pressure indicator.

VI. STERILIZER CONTROL SYSTEMS

A key to improved design of modern steam sterilizers lies in the overall trend toward increased automation. Automatic temperature and sequence control provide the needed assurance that the "validated" sterilization cycle is consistently and repeatedly delivered.

A typical control scheme is shown in Fig. 4. The temperature sensor, or element (TE), is located in the autoclave and is indicative of the temperature throughout the chamber. It is usually in the coldest part of the chamber, the condensate drain line. The sensor may be of several designs, among which are liquid-filled bulbs, thermocouples, and resistance temperature devices (RTDs). RTDs are most often used for this purpose because of their accuracy over a wide temperature range, durability, and utility in a fixed position. They operate on the principle of varying resistance in a wire as a function of temperature. The wire is usually platinum, wound around a ceramic or glass core, and sheathed in stainless steel (see Fig. 5).

The temperature transmitter (TT) modifies and sends the signal generated by the sensor. It may not be necessary if the controller (TC) is equipped to receive the signal without modification. The controller then acts on the signal according to some predetermined set point (desired value) and set of control parameters. The set point may be a pointer position on a scale or chart

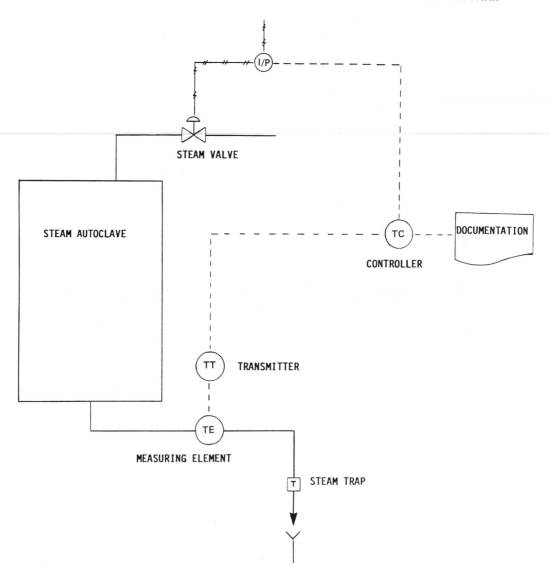

FIGURE 4   Typical temperature control schematic.

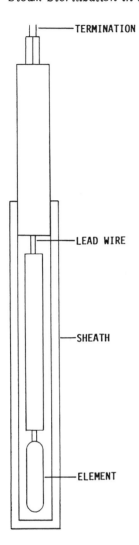

FIGURE 5   Schematic of an RTD.

(analog), or a series of digits set by pushbutton or thumbwheel (digital). The latter is more precise and is being increasingly specified. The controller also usually displays the measured variable. It may also record or send the signal to the recorder.

The control parameters may be simple or complex, depending on the mode of control chosen. The simplest mode is "on-off." In this mode, the steam valve is fully opened or closed depending on whether the measured temperature is below or above the set point. The only parameter to set is the sensitivity of the controller or "dead band." This determines the range of temperature experienced. "On-off" control is common in older sterilizers and is still used today. Good control can be maintained if the controller is sensitive enough and the steam valve and line are properly sized.

The LVP-GMP (Large Volume Parenteral—Good Manufacturing Practices) regulations proposed in 1976 (but never promulgated) require precise temperature control, within ±0.5°C of the set point [5]. In order better to meet these proposed requirements, manufacturers have offered more complex control modes. These require the use of an algorithm that acts on the difference between the set point and the measured variable (error signal). This algorithm may be multiplication by a constant (proportional control), integration over time (integral control), or rate of change (derivative control). These functions are often combined in a single controller called a PID controller. The PID controller uses the error signal to calculate a precise correctional signal to send to the steam valve. This signal may vary continuously over a given range (analog control) or be a series of small increments (digital control).

The signal from the controller is usually an electrical one (amperes or volts). Electronic controllers have become less expensive, more reliable, and are compatible with computer control systems. Valves, though, are generally still pneumatic (air-operated). Thus, a transducer (I/P) is used to change the electronic signal (I) to a pneumatic (P) one. In the case of "on-off" control, the transducer is replaced by a simple solenoid valve, which allows air to pass to open or close the valve. In the case of PID control, the air signal is variable and its magnitude determines the degree of opening of a special proportioning valve. This gives smoother, faster response and more precise control at the set point.

Automatic sequence control works with the temperature control system to determine the overall sterilization cycle. The earlier sequence controls are a system of timers and switches set to open or close valves, or to turn motors on and off. This is done in an exact sequence and can be interfaced with key process variables, such as temperature or pressure. (For example, reaching some predetermined temperature may start a timer.) This system is called an electromechanical one, or sometimes "relay logic," as its major components are electromagnetically actuated switches called relays.

Newer systems are entirely electronic and are based on microprocessors, small computer circuits. The simplest of these are "programmable controllers" (PCs), which do essentially the same things as a relay logic network. The timers and relays are contained within the PC circuitry. They are highly reliable and, because access to set points and controlling variables is more limited, very repeatable. They are long-lived because they have no mechanical wear. Programmable controllers can be quickly and simply reprogrammed, eliminating the need for costly and time-consuming wiring changes. They are versatile and can be controlled by a single unit.

More complex PCs have built-in PID capability, eliminating the independent temperature controller. They can also interface with higher-level computers.

This is done for data storage, trend analysis, and storage and retrieval of a wide range of programs.

Computers, usually minicomputers, can be programmed for process control and combine all of the functions discussed. Because of expense considerations, process control is most often left to microprocessor-based units, such as PCs or similar instruments. The computers are used to perform the peripheral functions the microprocessors are incapable of, such as long-term storage and trend analysis.

Another critical function of all control systems is documentation. The LVP-GMPs require a precise record of the sterilization cycle in the form of a temperature chart. The temperature recorder is shown as TR in the schematic. This recorder may accept input from one or several temperature sensors. When sensors other than the control RTD are recorded, these are most often thermocouples strategically placed within the load. Thermocouples are more flexible than RTDs, reach into difficult spots, and are easier to fix in place. The recorder itself may be of the chart variety (either round or strip chart), where a series of pens scribe continuous lines on a scaled chart. They may also be of the data-logging type, which periodically print out times and temperatures. The temperature record is required to demonstrate that the state of control is within the limits of the validated process. The records also allow analysis of batch-to-batch variations and trends. This is invaluable for anticipating and avoiding problems.

The third function of the control system is to alarm. It recognizes situations beyond the norm and notifies the operator by means of visual or audible alarms. The alarm function may also include contingency control patterns to interrupt, hold, or abort cycles that are out of control.

The emphasis on the control system for a steam sterilizer should be noted. It is the key to establishing, maintaining, and assuring the control necessary to validate a sterilization process. Without a well-designed and maintained control system, assurance of sterility cannot be attained.

VII. STERILIZER CYCLES

Removal of air is a common problem in autoclave design. Air entrained within the load depresses temperature and prevents the penetration of steam to all the required surfaces. The efficiency of heat transfer (heat transfer coefficient) from steam to the load is reduced. The most well-known sterilization processes, or cycles, have been designed to remove air from the autoclave chamber.

A. Gravity Displacement

The classic steam sterilizer cycle is the downward or gravity-displacement cycle. This is based on the principle that the cold air within the chamber is heavier than the steam entering. The density of air at 20°C is about 1.2 g/liter; that of steam at 100°C is 0.6 g/liter. As the steam enters the chamber, air is pushed out the bottom drain and exits (with the condensate) through the thermostatic trap. The trap of a steam sterilizer is specially designed to permit the passage of large volumes of air. The success of the cycle in removing air depends on the proper operation of the trap and the proper distribution of steam. The steam is injected through a baffle or spreader bar (e.g., a perforated pipe). The steam must be added slowly enough so that its natural buoyancy will carry it upward, forcing the colder air down. If steam is added too rapidly, or not distributed properly, air pockets may be trapped near the top of the load. If steam is added too slowly, the air can be heated, diffuse into the steam, and be more difficult to remove.

The effectiveness of air elimination from the chamber is observed by measuring the drain line temperature. Air will gravitate to the lower area of the chamber, depressing the temperature measured in the drain line. As air is eliminated, it will be replaced by pure saturated steam. The change in temperature, from that of the cooler air to that of the hotter steam, causes the steam trap to close. In this manner the autoclave chamber will reach the pressure coinciding with the desired temperature set point. A sketch of a gravity displacement sterilizer is shown in Fig. 6 along with a typical time/temperature chart of its cycle.

The gravity displacement cycle is more applicable to smaller sterilizers and those that are not loaded to capacity.

B. Prevacuum Cycle

A more effective method is to remove the entrapped air mechanically before the actual sterilization begins. This is done by means of a mechanical vacuum pump or a steam eductor. This cycle is particularly suited to porous materials, such as surgical packs. A great deal of study has taken place on the effect of various levels of prevacuum on subsequent steam penetration. Vacuum as low as 15–20 mmHg (less than 0.4 psia), applied for 8–10 min, is required to remove air from some porous loads [1]. A sketch of a typical prevacuum cycle is shown in Fig. 7.

C. Pulsing Cycles

Because of the difficulty in obtaining the high vacuum conditions needed for air removal, manufacturers developed pulsing systems. These employ a series of alternating steam pulses followed by vacuum excursions. The maximum and minimum pressures are variable. In general, the pulsing system removes air effectively without achieving the level of vacuum required in the prevacuum cycles. Figure 8 is an example of a multiple, or pulsed, prevacuum cycle.

D. Air-Steam Mixtures—Large Volume Parenterals

Although air is generally considered a culprit in reducing the efficiency of steam sterilization, there are times when its presence is required.

Aqueous solutions of parenteral drugs are often terminally sterilized in steam autoclaves. In this case the major function of the condensing steam is to provide rapid heat transfer to the wall of the product container. (The hydrating moisture is contained within.) These products may be filled into rigid or flexible containers. In either case there is air or nitrogen in the head space above the liquid. As the solution is heated, this gas expands at a greater rate than the equivalent volume of water vapor. Thus, the pressure within the container will exceed the chamber pressure.

Glass vials can be sealed with special closures to withstand this pressure. As long as the pressure differential does not become too great during the steam exhaust portion of the cycle, the vials will not burst or blow their tops.

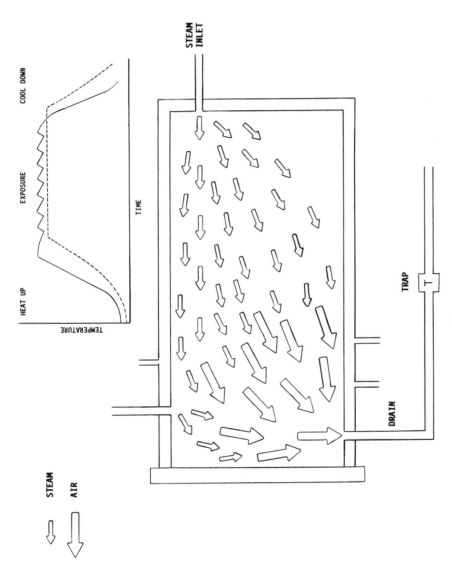

FIGURE 6 Gravity displacement sterilizer.

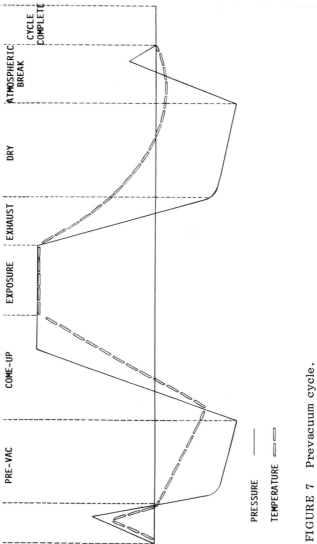

FIGURE 7 Prevacuum cycle.

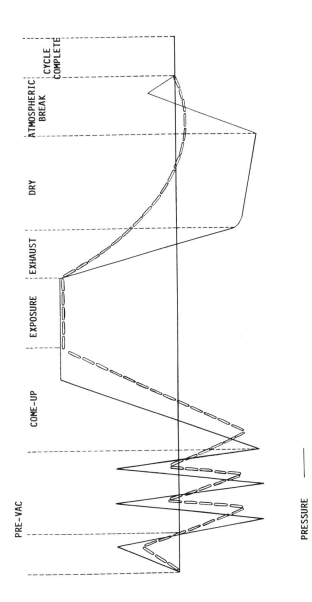

FIGURE 8 Pulsing cycle.

Plastic bags and semirigid containers present a greater problem. Because they do not have the inherent strength of glass, they may burst as the pressure differential increases. To prevent this, air must be injected into the chamber to raise the pressure above the saturation pressure of the steam. The steam is still saturated, because it is still in equilibrium with condensate. It is important to understand the physical principle involved in a mixture of air and steam. The relationship between temperature and pressure seen in Fig. 3 no longer applies.

Dalton's law states that the pressure of an ideal mixture of gasses is equal to the sum of the partial pressures of the gasses, or

$$P = p_A + p_B + p_C \cdot \cdot \cdot$$

Raoult's law further states that for ideal mixtures the partial pressure of the gas is equal to its vapor pressure multiplied by the mole fraction in the liquid. For steam in equilibrium with pure condensate, this reduces to

$$p_A = p_A^*$$

where p_A is the partial pressure of steam and p_A^* is the vapor pressure of the condensate. The difference between the observed chamber pressure, P, and p_A is the partial pressure of air.

The presence of air, although necessary, does reduce the heat transfer efficiency. The objective of the design in the "air overpressure" cycle is to maintain a well-mixed chamber. This assures that the heat transfer to the load will be uniform.

Mixing may be accomplished in several ways. The air may be injected directly into the incoming steam. Usually, though, some mechanical means is selected.

Some sterilizers utilize a fan built into the top of the chamber, which circulates and mixes the air and the steam (see Fig. 9). A second method employs an external pump to circulate condensate from the floor of the chamber through a series of distribution nozzles (see Fig. 10). This "raining" effect serves to mix the air and steam.

Both of these designs have an additional use in the cooling of terminally sterilized products. The circulating air or water (through a heat exchanger, as shown) serves to cool the containers more rapidly, increasing throughput. This rapid cooling may also be necessary to product stability.

VIII. QUALIFICATION

Qualification centers on the equipment rather than on the sterilization process. It is the procedure by which the sterilizer is proven to be designed properly and to perform according to its design criteria. Qualification takes place before any load is introduced for sterilization. It may be divided into installation qualification and operational qualification.

Qualification of the sterilizer and its ancillary equipment is an often underemphasized prerequisite to validation of the sterilizer cycle. The equipment must not only be designed to perform its function, it must do so in practice, and be maintained to do so.

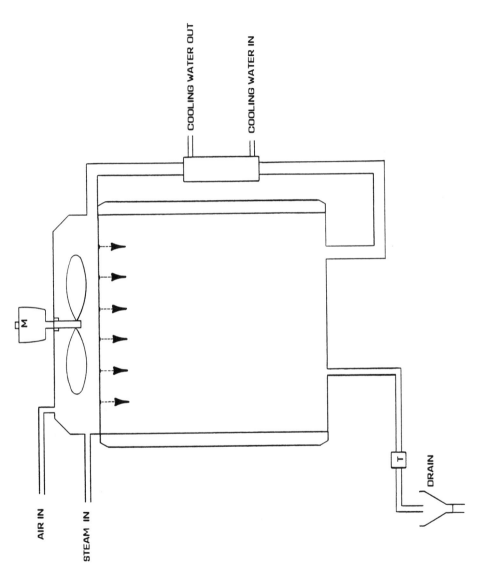

FIGURE 9   Fan-mixed air overpressure autoclave (rototherm design).

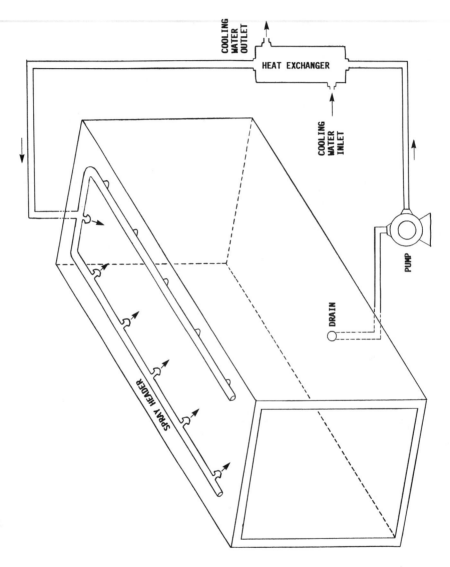

FIGURE 10 Water cascade ("raining") autoclave.

A. Installation Qualification

A "qualified sterilizer" begins on the drawing board. Modern sterilizer design is the result of years of experience by manufacturers and users. Sterilizers can be made to meet the varied needs of many users. They can be flexible or highly specialized.

The process engineer, in conjunction with the sterilization scientist and the manufacturing expert, must prepare a specification to meet their needs. The process engineer may also be assisted by the sterilizer manufacturer. This specification is a highly detailed and formal document, covering all aspects of design, construction, and even financial terms. It serves as a control on the manufacturer as well as a future reference.

The next documents to be generated are drawings for approval. These are issued by the manufacturer to the user before construction has reached a critical stage. The drawings are studied by all the concerned parties. They are checked to be in conformance to the specification and to agree with each reviewer's understanding of the sterilizer's use. Comments, if any, are compiled, disagreements are resolved, and the manufacturer is notified of needed adjustments. The process continues until drawings are approved. At this point the manufacturer proceeds toward completion of the unit. Even then, changes in design can be made. It is important that these be recorded, usually in the form of revised drawings. A complete historical set of drawings should be kept, with the latest revision clearly indicated.

Upon completion of installation the sterilizer must be thoroughly inspected by the new owners. This may be done by a team composed of Engineering, Manufacturing, Maintenance, and Validation personnel. They should look for adherence to the drawings and specifications, and quality of workmanship. Even more important, they should obtain an understanding of the system as it exists at the time of installation and as it will be validated. Some record of the installation must be maintained.

An important tool for the startup or qualification team is the prevalidation protocol or documentation. This should consist of the following:

1. A brief description or "scope." This is a basic but complete explanation of the sterilizer and its ancillary equipment, including physical characteristics and function.
2. A list of detailed specifications. These must be on file and available for review.
3. A list of pertinent drawings. These, too, must be available for review.
4. Sign-off sheets to attest that the system has been properly installed. This is usually done by the Engineering Department.
5. Reference to the calibration of all instrumentation. Calibration records must be maintained and available for review.
6. A listing of key devices and a brief description of each. An example is shown in Fig. 11. This is critical, as it gathers key information into a single future reference. This can be used as a comparison for proposed or actual changes.
7. An operational record that compares actual operating parameters to specifications. An example is shown in Fig. 12 and will be discussed in the next section.

The prevalidation protocol is an index to pertinent documentation as well as a record in itself. All of the drawings and specifications listed therein

Instrumentation

  a) Critical Process Instruments

    viii)   Type: _____ Function _____

               Manufacturer: _____ Model: _____

               Serial No. _____ Range _____

               Calibration No. _____ Frequency _____

               Proper ID _____

               Original Equipment _____

    ix)   Type: _____ Function _____

               Manufacturer: _____ Model: _____

               Serial No. _____ Range _____

               Calibration No. _____ Frequency _____

               Proper ID _____

               Original Equipment _____

    x)   Type: _____ Function _____

               Manufacturer: _____ Model: _____

               Serial No. _____ Range _____

               Calibration No. _____ Frequency _____

               Proper ID _____

               Original Equipment _____

    xi)   Type: _____ Function _____

               Manufacturer: _____ Model: _____

               Serial No. _____ Range _____

               Calibration No. _____ Frequency _____

               Proper ID _____

               Original Equipment _____

    xii)   Type: _____ Function _____

               Manufacturer: _____ Model: _____

               Serial No. _____ Range _____

               Calibration No. _____ Frequency _____

               Proper ID _____

               Original Equipment _____

Qualified By: _____ Date: _____

FIGURE 11   Installation qualification checklist (partial).

DATA SHEET
PREVALIDATION STEAM AUTOCLAVE CHECKOUT
(Step numbers Reference the SOP)

Date _____ Investigators _____

Autoclave ID _____ Building # _____ Room # _____ Autoclave Size _____

Calibration Dates: RTD Monitor _____ Sensotec _____

  Pressure Recorder _____ Drainline Temp Recorder _____

           Load temp Recorder: T1 _____ T2 _____

Cycle Designation: Type of cycle _____

(Step 6):
  Door Open: Sensotec Reading _____

(Step 9):
  Set Points: Drainline Temp _____ Load Temp ____ Number of Prevacs _____

(Step 10):
  Sensotec: Relay Setting Expected Value   Relay Setting Expected Value

            #1   _____ _____   #5   _____ _____
            #2   _____ _____   #6   _____ _____
            #3   _____ _____   #7   _____ _____
            #4   _____ _____   #8   _____ _____

(Step 13):
  Sensotec Reading _____ Pressure Recorder Reading _____

           Test Pressure Gauge Reading _____

(Step 14):
  Start of cycle: Time _____ Vacuum On: Time _____

(Step 15):
  Prevac Data

Vacuum #1   _____   Vacuum # 2   _____   Vacuum #3   _____
End Time   _____   End Time   _____   End Time   _____
Pressurize # 1   _____   Pressurize # 2 _____   Pressurize # 3 _____
End Time   _____   End Time   _____   End Time   _____

FIGURE 12   Operational qualification checklist (partial).

must be current and on file. They are an integral part of the qualification. The protocol itself satisfies an important record-keeping requirement.

B. Operational Qualification

The validation of the sterilization process is an integrated, continuing program that begins with conceptualization of the equipment. It continues with application of the equipment to the process. Then it moves on to maintenance of the equipment in a state that has been proven to yield a successful, or valid, process. A key phase in validation follows installation. This is the startup and operational qualification.

This task revolves around the operational qualification record referred to previously. This is generally a listing of critical sterilizer variables and their specifications. These variables are measured under operating conditions and recorded. When a minimum or range is specified, it is not adequate to note that the variable "meets spec." The actual values should be recorded. In the case of a range of values, both the minimum and the maximum should be checked.

Operational qualification should not be underemphasized. An understanding of how the autoclave and its support systems work is important to process development and validation, as well as future troubleshooting. Knowledge of actual operating parameters allows trend analysis, which can avoid potential problems.

The qualification of a new sterilizer is the most complete and complex. An existing system being applied to a new process should also be qualified. This can be an abbreviated "check-up" of key variables. It should be done prior to the validation runs.

Several mentions have been made of sterilizer ancillary and support systems. It is important that these be checked under operating conditions, as well as certified to be in conformance to design specifications. These systems include vacuum and steam. The latter is generally a clean or filtered system and may be the subject of an independent qualification or validation.

IX. CYCLE DEVELOPMENT

A great deal has been said about the mechanism of microbial death, its mathematical description, and the cycles used to bring it about. It is well to touch briefly on how these cycles are developed.

The sterilization cycle must take several factors into account. Among these are the nature of the load (porous materials, heat-labile products, etc.), the type of sterilizer available, and the containers and closures employed. These factors all influence the air removal methodology, whether an air-stream mixture is employed, the rate of steam exhaust and cooling, and the F_0 range desired.

When sterilizing heat-stabile materials, an overkill approach may be adopted. Remember that the accepted criterion for sterility is the probality of survival of no greater than 10^{-6}. The objective of the overkill cycle is to assure that level regardless of the number and heat resistance of the organisms in the load. Extremely high F_0 values are generally used. Because the load is heat-stable, thermal degradation is of no concern and only the minimum F_0 in the load is considered. This is usually chosen to provide at least a 12-log reduction of microorganisms having a D value of 1 min at 121°C [7]. Only the most heat-resistant organisms typically found in production environments have D_{121} values ranging from 0.5 to 1.0 min. Thus, a population of 10^6 spores/unit of even these heat-resistant strains will be reduced to 10^{-6} by the minimum overkill cycle. Less resistant organisms will be reduced to a much greater extent.

Bioburden studies are not required, nor are they usually carried out when an overkill cycle is planned. An assumption of $D_{121} = 1$ min and a minimum target of a 12-log reduction are adopted. These are used to calculate the F_0 to be delivered to the cold spot in the load. Cycle parameters of time and temperature, as well as the location of the cold spot, are determined during the validation studies.

An overkill approach cannot be used when sterilizing heat-labile loads. This situation is particularly prevalent in the terminal sterilization of drug products. A cycle must be developed that will adequately destroy the microbial load and yet not result in production degradation. The cycle is then dependent on bioburden studies to determine the number of microorganisms associated with the product. These are isolated and can be tested for heat resistance. Generally only the highly resistant spore formers need be subject to the D value determination. The less resistant cells can be screened out by heat-shocking the solution (10—15 min at 80—100°C). This also fosters spore germination.

D-value studies are best performed in a square-wave retort, or BIER (Biological Indicator Evaluator Resistometer) [6]. This is a small steam autoclave, designed to heat up to a desired control temperature and cool down very rapidly. Time and temperature control are very precise. (A typical temperature chart for a BIER steam vessel is shown in Fig. 13.) In this manner, the spore population is subjected to a uniform temperature. The Parenteral Drug Association, in its Technical Monograph No. 1, *Validation of Steam Sterilization Cycles*, outlines a general methodology for performing D-value experiments [7]. In brief, the carrier used for the spores is important, as it may affect heat resistance. It is recommended to inoculate the spores into the actual solutions to be sterilized. For comparison purposes, D values can also be determined in standard solutions (e.g., Sorensen's buffer, distilled water). For solid materials, the spores can be inoculated onto precut strips of the same material.

The spore suspension should contain a known number of spores, on the order of 10^4–10^7 per sample. At least five samples should be exposed at a specified temperature for at least three different time intervals. The D value is determined by plotting the number of survivors vs. time on a semilog plot. D is the negative reciprocal of the slope.

The BIER steam vessel can also be used to determine Z values. By determining D values as above, at three different temperatures, and constructing the thermal death curve, Z is obtained from the slope. It is common to adopt a Z value of 10°C. This is from experimental values for *B. stearothermophilus* (F_0 is based on this). Such an assumption is valid, as this organism is the most common biological indicator for steam sterilization. Nevertheless, it is valuable to understand the Z values of the indigenous bioburden. This allows a correlation with the biological indicator results.

Several factors are common to validation of both overkill-/and bioburden-related cycles. These include:

1. Precaution in material and production preparation to prevent microbial contamination. The use of controlled environments and good manufacturing practices is important.

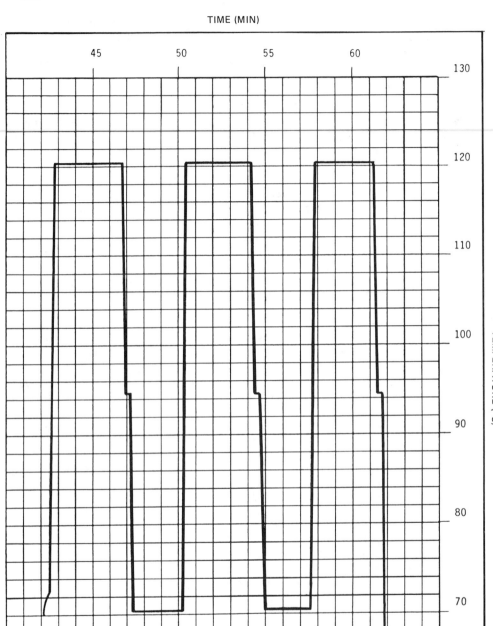

TIME (MIN)

FIGURE 13   Temperature chart for a BIER/steam vessel.

2. Equipment qualification.
3. Temperature distribution and penetration studies.
4. The use of bioindicators (suspensions of heat-resistant spores). It is important to characterize these with regard to D and Z values so that they can be compared to the naturally occurring bioburden (i.e., be a worst case). The main use of bioindicators is to prove that the cycle (desired F_0) is delivered.
5. Maintenance of control, both by continued microbiological monitoring and equipment maintenance.

X. PREPARING FOR VALIDATION

Once the validation protocol has been prepared, the equipment and materials for validation must be readied. A critical part of the validation study is the temperature measurement. Several items will be required to measure and record temperature effectively.

The most versatile sensing devices for validation are thermocouples. These are constructed from two wires of dissimilar metals. They can be encased in flexible sheaths, Teflon being widely used. Type T (copper-constantan) thermocouples are most applicable in steam sterilizer validation work. Their working temperature range is wide and they are resistant to corrosion in moist environments. A high grade of thermocouple wire should be chosen. Standard grades have an inherent error as high as 1°C. This is very significant when calculating the experimental F_0. Premium grades of wire, accurate to as close as 0.1°C at 121°C, are recommended. These must then be calibrated against a temperature standard traceable to the National Bureau of Standards (NBS).

The temperature standard may be a mercury-in-glass thermometer or a platinum RTD. The RTD is recommended because of its greater durability and accuracy. The thermocouples to be calibrated are then placed in a highly stable temperature source (ice-point or hot-point reference) along with the reference device. The differences in the readings between thermocouple and reference device are recorded. The acceptable error should be no greater than the sum of the thermocouple wire accuracy (e.g., +0.1°C to −0.3°C) and the degree of traceability of the NBS reference instrument (e.g., ±0.2°C). Thermocouples that do not meet this criterion should be replaced.

Calibration of thermocouples should be carried out at two temperatures. One of these is an ice-point reference at 0.0°C. The other should be a hot point slightly higher than the expected sterilization temperature (130°C is commonly chosen). Correction factors are applied at both temperatures and the response of the thermocouple over the temperature range can be linearized. The corrected temperature measurements are used to calculate F_0. An example of how calibration and linearization are used to correct thermocouple readings is shown in Fig. 14. Calibration should be repeated after a series of validation runs.

Thermocouple access into the sterilizer should be considered during the design phase. Most sterilizer manufacturers routinely include one or more unused ports in their pressure vessels. These can be tailored to the specific needs of the validation team. All penetrations must be made before the vessel's ASME code is stamped. To make modifications at a latter date is troublesome. These must be made by a board-certified welder. They are also subject to reinspection and test by a code inspector.

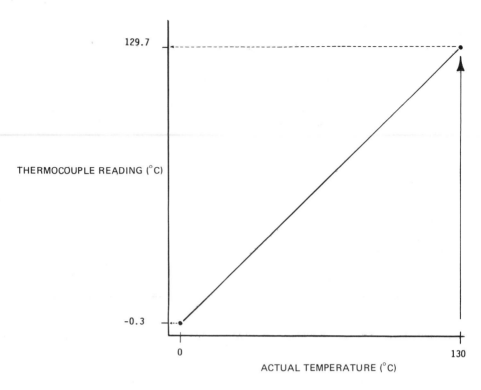

FIGURE 14   Calibration and linearization curve for thermocouples.

Special adaptors are joined to the access ports that allow the thermocouples to pass into the chamber without developing pressure leaks. The adaptor can be a pressure gland made of two mated flanges separated by two flexible gaskets. The thermocouples pass between the gaskets and the flanges and are bolted together tightly to prevent leaks. Another method is to use special-purpose fittings made for the express purpose of thermocouple access (e.g., Conax). This is a specially drilled rubber gland within a compression-type housing.

Validation runs involve a large number of temperature measurements. These can be recorded in a number of ways. Because of the frequency and number of recordings, a data logger is usually employed. This is a digital-output, multichannel device capable of frequent printouts of a large number of temperature points. These can be very sophisticated and can be preprogrammed to make thermocouple calibration corrections, store data, and even calculate and print out cumulative F_0 values. The best data loggers have large capacity (32–48 channels), precision to 0.1°C or better, fast scan rate of all thermocouples (20 sec to 1 min), and ability to interface with a computer either by way of stored data (paper tape, magnetic tape) or directly through an RS-232 output connector.

A necessary adjunct to temperature studies is the biological challenge. Temperature studies determine the level of heat applied. Biological challenges, or bioindicators, reveal whether the proper conditions of temperature and moisture required to deactivate the microorganisms are met. These should be prepared for use upon completion of the temperature distribution studies. Details will appear in a later section.

These preliminary steps in the validation program are important. Calibration of thermocouples and bioindicator D- /and Z-value determinations become part of the validation record. They should be carried out and documented carefully.

XI. VALIDATION PROTOCOL

The documentation (installation qualification, operational qualification, etc.) established prior to initiating validation studies provides the preliminary foundation for the subsequent validation. The validation protocol is an experimental design thoroughly delineating the validation program. This document outlines the precise methods for obtaining and analyzing process data. The focus of the protocol surrounds the monitoring of critical process parameters associated with the steam sterilization cycle (temperature, F_0, etc.). The scope of the validation protocol is not limited to defining the experimental design, and may incorporate additional information. A comprehensive steam sterilization protocol should include the following items:

1. An introduction defining the objectives of the validation study
2. Responsibilities of validation personnel and operating department personnel
3. Identification and description of the sterilizer and its process controls
4. Identification of standard operating procedures for the process equipment
5. Description of and /or SOP for instrument calibration procedures
6. Identification of calibration procedures for temperature-monitoring equipment (thermocouples, data loggers, etc.)
7. A description of the following studies to be conducted:
    Bioburden determination studies
    Microbiological challenge studies
    Empty-chamber heat distribution studies
    Loaded-chamber heat penetration studies
    Container mapping studies
    Evaluation of drug product cooling water (where applicable)
    Integrity testing of vent filter membranes associated with the sterilizer
8. Process parameter acceptance criteria

The completed validation protocol should be subjected to a thorough review and approval process. The review process may initiate supportive changes in the experimental design resulting in protocol revision. Once the protocol is approved, the validation study may begin.

XII. HEAT DISTRIBUTION STUDIES

The intent of this study is to demonstrate the temperature uniformity and stability of the sterilizing medium throughout the sterilizer. Temperature distribution studies should be conducted on both the empty and loaded chambers with maximum and minimum load configurations. Temperature uniformity may be influenced by the type, size, design, and installation of the sterilizer. A satisfactory empty-chamber temperature uniformity should be determined by the manufacturer of the vessel based on the variables mentioned. A narrow range is required and is generally acceptable if the variation is less than ±1°C (±2.0°F) of the mean chamber temperature. Significant temperature deviations greater than ±2.5°C (±4.5°F) of the mean chamber temperature may indicate equipment malfunction [7]. Stratified or entrapped air may also cause significant temperature variations within the sterilizer chamber.

Initially, a temperature distribution profile should be established from studies conducted on the empty chamber. Confidence may be gained through repetition, and therefore empty-chamber studies should be conducted in triplicate in order to obtain satisfactory assurance of consistent results. Subsequent to the empty-chamber studies, maximum-load temperature distribution studies should be conducted to determine if the load configuration influences the temperature distribution profile obtained from the empty-chamber studies.

The thermocouples utilized in the heat distribution studies are distributed geometrically in representative horizontal and vertical planes throughout the sterilizer as shown in Fig. 15. The geometric center and corners of the sterilizer should also be represented. An additional thermocouple should be placed in the exhaust drain adjacent to the sensor that controls vessel temperature, if possible. The number of thermocouples utilized in the heat distribution study will be dependent on sterilizer size. In a production-size sterilizer, 15–20 thermocouples should be adequate. The thermocouples

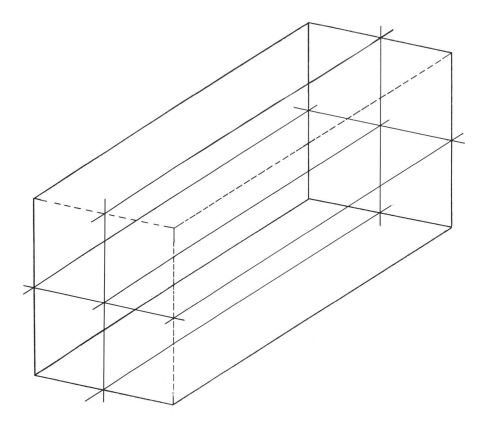

FIGURE 15   Representative horizontal and vertical planes.

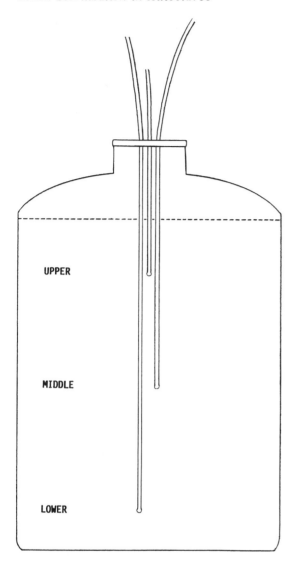

FIGURE 16   Container mapping configuration.

utilized for loaded-chamber heat distribution studies should be positioned in the same locations used for empty-chamber heat distribution studies. It is the uniformity and stability of the sterilizing medium that is monitored in the distribution studies, consequently, the temperature probes should be suspended to avoid contacting solid surfaces and should not be placed within any containers. Temperatures must be obtained at regular intervals (e.g., each minute) throughout the time duration specified for a normal production cycle.

XIII. CONTAINER MAPPING—CONTAINER COOL POINT

Prior to initiating loaded-chamber heat penetration studies, container mapping studies should be conducted. The intent of this study is to determine the coolest point within a liquid-filled container. In general, the smaller the container volume, the less likely the detection of a discernable cold spot. Nevertheless, temperature mapping should be conducted on all the different container types, sizes, and fill volumes that will be subject to validation.

The number of thermocouples positioned within the container will be dependent on the container volume. A sufficient number of thermocouples should be positioned in areas representing the upper, middle, and lower portions of the container (as shown in Fig. 16). Error in cold spot determinations may be introduced by employing an excessive number of thermocouples within the container. The error may be attributed to thermocouple mass and the resulting baffling effects that may influence the normal convection currents of the liquid. It is also possible to use a single thermocouple at different positions in multiple runs. This requires careful control of autoclave temperature to reduce error caused by run-to-run variation.

Repeat studies are required to establish reproducible cold points and temperature profiles of the liquid in the container. The profile point having the lowest temperature or lowest F_0 is designated as the cold spot. In subsequent loaded-chamber heat penetration studies, penetration thermocouples should be positioned within the container at the previously determined cold spot.

Container mapping studies can be conducted in a small autoclave or retort. The temperature profile of the container should remain constant among different sterilizing chambers, utilizing steam heat as the sterilizing medium [7].

XIV. LOADED-CHAMBER HEAT PENETRATION STUDIES—"LOAD COOL POINT"

The intent of this study is to determine the coolest point(s) within a specified load and configuration. Cool points originate because of the varied rate of heat transfer throughout the load. It is therefore imperative that heat penetration studies be conducted to determine cool points within a loading pattern and assure that those points be consistently exposed to sufficient heat lethality [7].

Load cool points are dependent on load configurations and the types of items that comprise the load (liquid-filled containers, process equipment, etc.). Prior to conducting heat penetration studies, maximum and minimum load configurations must be established.

The penetration thermocouples are positioned within liquid-filled containers at the cool point previously determined by the container mapping studies. The probed containers should be distributed uniformly throughout the load.

When the load consists of multiple layers or pallets, a sufficient number of thermocouple-probed containers should be employed to provide an equal representation among layers [7]. Heat penetration studies conducted on maximum and minimum loads should be repeated until temperature data are obtained for all representative areas of the load. It may be necessary to reposition thermocouples in order to study different areas. Several runs, usually three, of each thermocouple configuration will provide confidence in the repeatability of the temperature profile.

A heat penetration study defining load cool points is not limited to load configurations composed of liquid-filled vials. The same principles can be applied to process equipment loads (filters, hoses, etc.) subject to steam sterilization. Penetration thermocouples are positioned at points within the process equipment suspected to be the most difficult for steam heat penetration. Temperature data are obtained from representative maximum and minimum loads in order to establish temperature profiles depicting load cool points. Equipment load configurations may be designed to allow reasonable flexibility for the operating department by permitting the use of partial loads. In this case, partial loads would be defined as a portion of the established maximum validated load.

Heat penetration studies are also employed to determine points within a load configuration that achieve higher temperatures and consequently greater F_0 values. The temperature data obtained may be significant when heat-labile products are involved in the sterilization process and the potential for product degradation exists [7].

The cool points established for a specified load and configuration will eventually be utilized to control the exposure time in subsequent routine production runs. The temperature sensor(s) that control sterilization-cycle exposure time at process temperature may be positioned within the load at the previously detected cool point. This procedure will assure that the cool point and consequently the entire load is exposed to sufficient heat lethality and achieves the desired F_0. It may not always be possible or convenient to position a temperature sensor at the cool point. In this case it is necessary to know, through the validation study, the relationship between the cool point and the control point. Then the cycle can be adjusted to provide adequate time for the cool point to reach the desired F_0 value.

Lethal rates can be determined from the temperature data obtained from the heat penetration studies. The temperature data are converted by the following formula:

$$L = \log^{-1} \frac{T_0 - T_b}{Z} = 10 \, (T_0 - T_b)/Z$$

where

T_0 = temperature within the container

T_b = process temperature (121°C)

Z = temperature required to change the D value by a factor of 10

L = lethality

F_0 is then determined by integrating the lethal rates throughout the heating process:

$$F_0 = \int 10^{(T - 121)/10} dt$$

or

$$F_0 = \Sigma \, 10^{(T - 121)/10} \Delta t$$

where

Δt = time interval between temperature measurements

T = product temperature at time t in °C

When the sterilization process temperature deviates from 121°C, the amount of time providing equivalent lethality can be determined by the following formula:

$$F_t^Z = \frac{F_{121}^Z}{L}$$

where

F_t^Z = the equivalent time at temperature T delivered to a container for the purpose of sterilization with a specific value of Z

F_{121}^Z = the equivalent time at 121°C delivered to a container for the purpose of sterilization with a specific value of Z (if Z = 10°C, then $F_{121}^Z = F_0$)

XV. MICROBIOLOGICAL CHALLENGE STUDIES

Biological challenges are employed during heat penetration studies in order to demonstrate the degree of process lethality provided by the sterilization cycle. Calibrated biological indicators utilized for this purpose function as bioburden models providing data that can be utilized to calculate F_0 or substantiate and supplement physical temperature measurements obtained from thermocouples [7].

The microorganisms most frequently utilized to challenge moist heat sterilization cycles are *Bacillus stearothermophilus* and *Clostridium sporogenes*. These spore-forming bacteria are selected because of their relatively high heat resistance. In addition to the selection of an appropriate organism for use as a biological indicator, the concentration and resistance of the indigenous microbial population is established. The biological indicator can be prepared to adequately challenge a sterilization cycle designed to provide a 10^{-6} probability of microbial survival with respect to indigenous bioburden. The concentration of spores utilized as the biological indicator can be determined from the following formula:

$$D_s(\log N_i + 6) = D_{bi}(\log N_0 + 1)$$

where

N_i = the load of microorganisms on the product to be sterilized

D_s = D value of the most resistant isolate

N_0 = number of organisms on the biological indicator

D_{bi} = D value of biological indicator

Designated liquid-filled containers are inoculated with the microorganism selected as the biological indicator (*Bacillus stearothermophilus* or a more resistant isolate detected in previously conducted bioburden studies). This is accomplished by injecting an aliquot of a calibrated spore suspension into the suspending medium to provide the calculated concentration of spores. The suspending medium should be the specific liquid product. A product substitute or placebo may be used as the suspending medium if the liquid product contains preservatives or other antimicrobial agents demonstrating growth inhibition. The decision to use the product as the suspending medium should be supported by suitable studies to prove that microbial growth is not inhibited. A product substitute should possess physical characteristics similar to the specific parenteral solution. Considerations in selection and preparation include heat capacity, density, viscosity, etc.

Inoculation of the liquid-filled containers (product or placebo) should be conducted under aseptic conditions, exercising caution to prevent external contamination. Parenteral products usually have a low bioburden due to the process conditions associated with their manufacture. In this case direct inoculation of the spore suspension into the suspending medium would provide a conservative approach by including the addition of the challenge organisms to the indigenous organisms present. In products and placebo that demonstrate excessive bioburden, sterilization of designated filled containers prior to inoculation may be considered. The importance of sterilization prior to inoculation is emphasized for product substitutes that are used as the suspending medium and held for a substantial length of time prior to use.

In the case of inoculating solid materials, the spores can be introduced onto the surface of the item. Subsequent to inoculation, the spore suspension is allowed to dry on the surface. Commercially available spore strips may also be used when the validation loads are composed of devices and solid materials. Recovery counts should be conducted on selected inoculated containers, or components, in order to verify the delivered concentration of spores.

Microbiological challenge studies are conducted concurrently with the heat penetration studies. Dedicated containers previously inoculated with the biological indicator are positioned throughout the load adjacent to the probed containers. Both the inoculated containers and the probed containers should be positioned in the detected cool points of the load configuration. In order to expedite recovery and eliminate possible confusion, the inoculated containers should be identified by markings or other suitable means. After the sterilization cycle is complete, the inoculated containers are recovered and subjected to microbiological test procedures.

XVI. THE VALIDATION REPORT

Record keeping is a prime requirement of Current Good Manufacturing Practices. The records required for a validated steam sterilization cycle are listed below. They need not be stored in a common central file, but they must be readily accessible. It is wise to assign the task of organization and retrieval of records to a single group. These records are as follows:

1. Qualification reference documents (specifications, drawings, and calibration records)
2. Operational qualification protocol and record
3. Approved validation protocol
4. Raw calibration and validation data
5. Approved validation report

The validation report is the guideline to maintenance of a validated sterilization process. It describes the cycle and the operating conditions that have been proven to give adequate assurance of sterility. It explains in detail how the manufacturing group can obtain results consistent with the validation study.

Several formats and degrees of complexity are used in report writing. However, all reports should contain some common elements, as follows:

1. Identification of the task report by number.
2. Reference to the protocol under which it was carried out.
3. A brief summary of the range of operational conditions experienced and how they were controlled.
4. A procedure for maintaining control within the approved range. This may be in the form of a standard operating procedure.
5. A summary and analysis of the experimental results. This will include the range of lethality (F_0 range) and degree of sterility assurance.
6. A brief description of any deviation from expected results.

The F_0 range is calculated directly from the temperature data. It is important that a range be reported in the case of heat-labile products. The upper range of temperature exposure is critical with regard to product stability. A sterilization cycle can also be the product processing step. Its effect on the product, as well as on the microbial population, must be considered. The description of such effect need not be included in the validation report itself. It should be the subject of adjunct analytical or stability studies. A discussion of the importance of this consideration is included later in this chapter.

Cycle development reports are not usually a part of the validation report. Some reference to how the cycle was chosen may be included, though. This can be the title of the cycle development report or a brief summary of the results of that report. This should include the type of mechanical cycle recommended (high prevacuum, air-steam mixture, etc.), heat resistance and bioburden data or assumptions thereof, and level of lethality (F_0) required.

Bioindicator data is the ultimate proof that the sterilization cycle has taken place. As such, it should be highlighted in the validation report. The microbiology section of the report should include the methods used, a summary of results, and conclusions.

Upon completion, the final report is circulated for approval. This is generally given by the same people who approved the protocol.

XVII. STABILITY AND LETHALITY

Previously, we have emphasized the importance of determining a range of F_0 cycle lethality, in validation studies. This is particularly critical when sterilizing heat-sensitive drug products. The investigator must be concerned that the microbial load is not destroyed at the expense of product stability.

Assuming that both the microbial kill rate and thermal degradation of product follow first-order kinetics, both rate constants may be described by the Arrhenius equation (see section on order of death):

$$k = A \exp \left(\frac{-E_A}{RT} \right)$$

In expanded form this is

$$\ln \left(\frac{k}{k_0} \right) = \left(\frac{E}{R} \right) \left(\frac{1}{T_0} - \frac{1}{T} \right)$$

This means that the greater the activation energy E, the greater effect temperature has on reaction rate.

In describing the effect of temperature on the microbial death rate, the quantity Z is used:

$$\ln \left(\frac{D}{D_0} \right) = Z(T_0 - T)$$

By assuming that Z is a constant for a given temperature range and remembering that $D = 1/k$, we can calculate E_A for the microbial death curve. The degradation reaction that affects product stability has a different temperature dependence. This can be determined experimentally.

For any given temperature, microbial death and chemical degradation take place at different rates. It is accepted practice to validate the sterilization process at a fixed range of F_0, where

$$F_0 = \Sigma \ 10^{(121-T)/10} \Delta t$$

This is acceptable because we know the temperature dependence of the thermal death curve, as described by $Z = 10$. This cannot be extrapolated to the degradation reaction. Raising or lowering T requires a corresponding change in t to maintain F_0. This change in t affects the accumulated degradation of the product. Simply, if the degradation reaction is not altered significantly by the change in temperature, it will increase when time is extended. On the other hand, if degradation is highly temperature-dependent (high activation energy), the decrease in temperature may compensate for the increase in time, resulting in less degradation.

The key property is the activation energy, E_A. If the activation energy for the chemical degradation reaction is lower than that of the microbial death curve (i.e., it is less temperature-dependent), then it can be assumed that a decrease in sterilization temperature will result in greater product instability. Therefore, it is unwise to assume that sterilization cycles of equivalent lethality, but different with regard to time and temperature, will yield equally stable product. Experience has shown that a decrease in sterilization temperature can have a marked deleterious effect on product stability. Sterilization of sugar solutions in heat-sensitive plastic containers may require a sterilization temperature of 116–118°C to protect the container. The increased time required for sterilization often results in noticeable carmelization. Indeed, the activation energy of the death-curve reaction with Z = 10 is high (approx. 60 kcal/mole) compared to most first-order liquid-phase decompositions. This means that most products that degrade with heat are more affected by an increase in time than by an increase in temperature.

Several important points must not be overlooked. First, the above discussion assumes that chemical degradation follows first-order kinetics. This is probably a good approximation in many cases where a single active drug product is contained in the solution. Second, it assumes that product stability over the desired dating period can be extrapolated from the degradation measured just after sterilization. Chemical reaction kinetics indicate this, too, is reasonable. There is a chance, though, that some complex is formed during sterilization that triggers subsequent degradation. In this case, the complex would have to be isolated and its rate of formation studied. Obviously, this is a more difficult task.

In discussing F_0 and degradation, it must be remembered that both are cumulative over time and temperature. This means that come-up and cooldown variations will affect stability as well as lethality. Therefore, stability studies should consider the entire cycle, not just the dwell time at the control temperature. Again, these effects are more pronounced for a chemical reaction with a lower activation energy.

Perhaps the most critical point to consider is that F_0 is generally calculated at the cold spot in the load. For stability purposes the hot spot is more consequential. Therefore, the entire range of temperature and time must be recorded in order to substantiate stability claims.

As can be seen, stability claims for a sterilized product must be approached cautiously. It is best to compile stability data on the product in the production autoclave or an identical one. If this is not possible, all the variables discussed should be considered. These include determining the relative activation energies of the product degradation reaction and the thermal death curve. At the least, stability should be studied at the worst conditions of both time and temperature that might be encountered in the production autoclave.

XVIII. MAINTENANCE OF VALIDATION

The last, and often overlooked, step in validating any process is the establishment of a program to ensure that the operational conditions recorded during the validation experiments are maintained. If this is done, and no major changes in equipment or process are made, revalidation is not necessary. What is required is a periodic review of the system for adherence to the validation criteria. This may be very simple if a good program of "validation maintenance" is established. This term is used rather than "revalidation" to emphasize the continuity of the program. A validation maintenance review report may be issued to commit to record the attention being paid to this critical aspect of validation.

Some key points of a good validation maintenance program are as follows:

1. A routine calibration program for all instruments critical to the operation of the sterilizer and its support systems.
2. A preventative maintenance program for other system components. This should include periodic operational rechecks and comparison to the Operational Qualification Record.
3. Routine monitoring of bioburden and (optionally) periodic bioindicator challenges.
4. Well-maintained and accessible operating records and equipment logs.
5. Process and equipment change control procedures. These subject proposed changes to prior review to establish whether additional validation experiments are required.

The basis of continued validation maintenance is communication among the various operating groups (Manufacturing, Quality Assurance, Validation, etc.). Sterilization processes were the first for which validation was emphasized. They continue to be the most heavily reviewed. It is important that the state of control of these processes be strongly maintained and the subject of concern to all groups.

XIX. CONCLUSION

The authors have attempted to outline a systematic program of steam autoclave validation. It begins with an understanding of the microbiological principles involved, continues through autoclave design and installation, and proceeds through validation of the sterilization process. The program does not end there, though, being carried on in the validation maintenance system.

Steam sterilization is probably the most validated of pharmaceutical processes. The principles outlined in this chapter may serve as a guide for other process validation programs.

REFERENCES

1. Perkins, John J. 1973. *Principles and Methods of Sterilization in Health Sciences.* Charles C. Thomas, Springfield, Ill.
2. Phillips, G. Briggs, and Miller, William S., eds. 1973. *Industrial Sterilization*, International Symposium, Amsterdam, 1972. Duke University Press, Durham, N.C.
3. Pflug, Irving J., ed. 1979. *Microbiology and Engineering of Sterilization Processes*, 3rd ed., Environmental Sterilization Services, St. Paul, Minn.
4. Ball, C. O., and Olson, F. C. W. 1957. *Sterilization in Food Technology.* McGraw-Hill Book Company, New York.
5. Current Good Manufacturing Practices—Large Volume Parenterals (proposed). *Fed. Reg.*, June 1, 1976.
6. *BIER/Steam Vessels*, AAMI Standard BSV-3/81, Arlington, Va., 1981, Association for the Advancement of Medical Instrumentation.

7. *Validation of Steam Sterilization Cycles*, Technical Monograph No. 1, 1978, Philadelphia, Parenteral Drug Association.

8. Pflug, Irving J. 1980. *Syllabus for an Introductory Course in the Microbiology and Engineering of Sterilization Processes*, 4th ed. Environmental Sterilization Services, St. Paul, Minn.

9. Stumbo, C. R. 1973. *Thermobacteriology in Food Processing*, 2nd ed. Academic Press, New York.

10. Hougan, O. A., Watson, K. M., and Ragatz, R. A. 1968. *Chemical Process Principles, Part Two—Thermodynamics*. John Wiley and Sons, New York.

12

Dry Heat Sterilization and Depyrogenation Validation and Monitoring

LAURIE A. BURNS* and GAYLE D. HEFFERNAN

E. R. Squibb & Sons, Inc., New Brunswick, New Jersey

I. INTRODUCTION

Dry heat is one of the most commonly used methods to sterilize and/or depyrogenate pharmaceutical components and products. The equipment utilized to provide the dry heat medium must be validated to ensure that the system is able to provide sterile and/or depyrogenated components, on a reproducible basis. This chapter will detail the steps of a validation program that may be employed to properly validate a dry heat process. The topics discussed will include:

1. The types of dry heat sterilizers commonly utilized in the pharmaceutical industry
2. A discussion of the mechanics of dry heat processes; convective, conductive, and radiation forces; and the importance of air circulation within the unit
3. Qualification of the sterilizer's installation and operation, and implementation of the qualification report
4. The preparation of the validation protocol outlining the intended testing process, and calibration procedures for test equipment
5. Cycle development studies to determine adequate time/heat set points for proper sterilization and/or depyrogenation
6. The validation program sequence, including empty-chamber, loaded-chamber, and biochallenge studies
7. Certification of the validation program, required documentation, and revalidation

II. DRY HEAT STERILIZERS

The types of dry heat sterilizers commonly employed in the pharmaceutical industry are forced-convection batch sterilizers, infrared tunnel sterilizers, forced-convection tunnel sterilizers, and continuous flame sterilizers (see Figs. 1–6).

Current affiliation: Stearns Catalytic Corporation, Philadelphia, Pennsylvania.

FIGURE 1   Batch sterilizer photo. (Courtesy of the Gehnrich Company.)

Forced-convection batch sterilizers (Figs. 1 and 2) are the most commonly used type of dry heat sterilizers in the industry. The unit utilizes the principles of convective heat transfer to heat the components. The sterilizers can employ a range of cycles (by varying time and temperature settings) for utensils, glassware, stainless steel equipment, and product. The items are prepared in a controlled, nonsterile area (employing such control as limited access, reduced particulate levels, known air quality, hair covering, etc.). The items are loaded on racks or carts and placed into the sterilizer chamber. According to USP XX, a typical sterilization cycle should provide a minimum of 170°C for not less than 2 hr, while depyrogenation cycles must be at a minimum of 250°C for not less than 30 min [1]. Most batch sterilizer cycles are designed to exceed the minimum USP temperature and time requirements to provide additional assurance in achieving sterilization and depyrogenation. A typical cycle might employ temperatures ranging from 180 to 300°C. The temperatures at the lower end of this range will sterilize, while the higher temperatures in the range are suitable for depyrogenation. Conventionally, there is a cooling phase at the completion of the heating cycle, which serves to minimize component thermal shock and increase handling safety (see Fig. 7). In most installations a double-door oven is employed and the load is removed from the oven into the aseptic processing area.

Tunnel sterilizers may utilize convective heat transfer similar to the batch sterilizers, or infrared radiation to produce sterilization and/or depyrogenation. Tunnel sterilizers operate continuously and have the capability to process a larger quantity of glass vials and ampules than batch sterilizers (see Figs. 3 and 4). Bottles, vials, or ampules are usually washed and loaded on the nonaseptic end of the tunnel and are conveyed the length of the tunnel (10−25 ft) while encountering various air temperatures [2]. The glassware

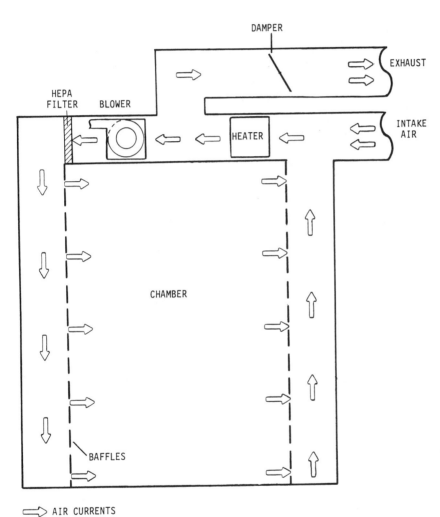

FIGURE 2   Batch sterilizer schematic.

FIGURE 3   Tunnel sterilizer photo.   (Courtesy of Bosch Company.)

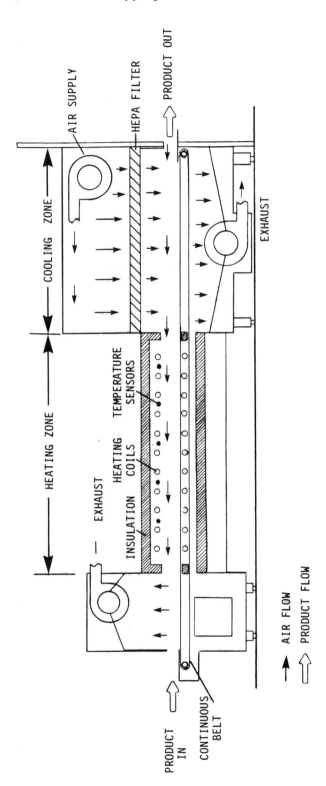

FIGURE 4   Tunnel sterilizer schematic.

FIGURE 5   Flame sterilizer. (Courtesy of the West Company.)

is heated in the initial and center portions of the tunnel to 250–450°C, and
gradually cooled by high-efficiency particulate air (HEPA) filtered air prior
to leaving the tunnel at the sterile end (see Fig. 8). The forced-convection
tunnel is usually heated by electric coils and employs the same principles as
forced-convection ovens. The infrared tunnel sterilizer is equipped with a
source of infrared radiation provided by either a resistance wire or quartz
tube. Temperature sensors to control heating are located within the sterilizing zone. Heat-up and exposure time can be affected by the geometry, color,
surface, and composition of the item being treated, as well as the air temperature and air velocity [3].

The flame sterilizer utilizes conduction and convection heat transfer in the
continuous processing of ampules (see Fig. 6). It can process up to 10,000
ampules per hour. Ampules are placed on a conveyor belt, washed with water-
for-injection, and channeled onto spokes of a rotating wheel. As the wheel
rotates, the ampules are heated to 800°F by natural gas heat for approximately
1 min. The ampules then pass from the heating chamber into a cooling chamber, where they are gradually cooled by HEPA-filtered air. The cooled ampules are then filled and flame-sealed. The flame sterilizer has a series of
baffles in the sterilizing chamber to increase the uniformity of heating.

III. PRINCIPLES OF HEAT TRANSFER AND CIRCULATION

Dry heat sterilizers generally use convective heat methods to increase the temperature of the product. Convection is a form of heat transfer whereby heat
flows from one body to another due to the temperature difference between
them. In the sterilizer air is heated by convective methods by passing it
across heating elements. Energy is transferred to the air from the heating
coils. The heated air transfers energy to the items being treated, because

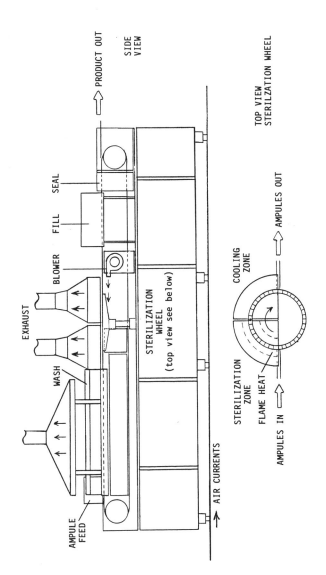

FIGURE 6   Flame sterilizer schematic.

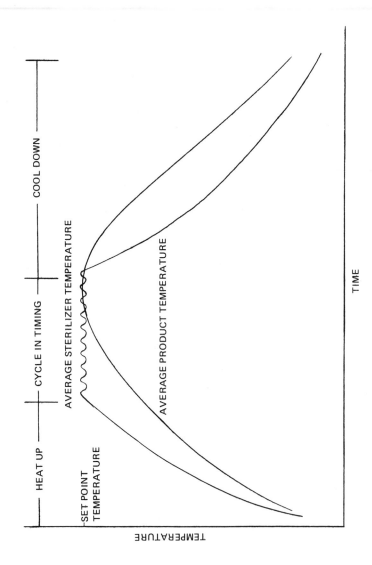

FIGURE 7 Batch process sterilizer come-up graph of chamber and product temperatures vs. time.

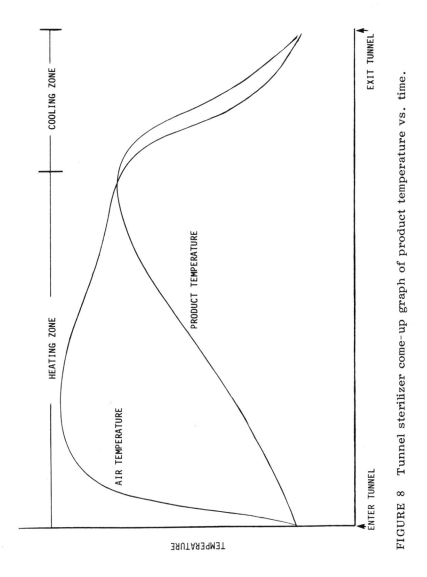

FIGURE 8   Tunnel sterilizer come-up graph of product temperature vs. time.

those items are at a lower temperature than the air. The rate of heat transfer (how fast the items will heat up) is related to the specific heat of the
various materials. Air has the disadvantage of having a relatively low specific heat; therefore it transfers energy at a slow rate. Saturated steam is an
excellent material to use for heat transfer, as it has a relatively high specific
heat ($c_v = 1.0$ Btu/lb$_m$ °F) as compared to air ($c_v = 0.1715$ Btu/lb$_m$ °F) [4].
But as detailed later, in certain cases steam may not be used and dry heat is
chosen as the heat transfer material.

Conduction is another means of transferring energy, achieved by molecular
interaction where atoms at high temperatures vibrate at high energy levels,
and impart energy (as heat) to adjacent atoms at lower energy levels. Adjacent materials (such as air surrounding the product) will transfer energy
from the higher-temperature material to the colder material because electrons
in an excited state bombard and collide with electrons of the lower-energy
(colder-temperature) material. The excitation of the molecules of the object
increases the level of molecular energy, which increases its temperature.
Again the rate at which heat conduction occurs is dependent on the materials
involved. A substance with a high thermal conductivity is a good heat conductor, while one with a lower thermal conductivity is a poor heat conductor.
While air is not considered a good heat conductor, the contact of hot air with
good heat conductors, such as metal objects, will provide a fairly rapid heat
transfer rate. Metal items, such as stainless steel equipment, will heat up
faster than other materials (such as glass), because of their greater thermal
conductivity.

Radiation is the third method commonly used for dry-heat sterilization
processes. Photons, which are concentrated bundles of energy, may occupy
different energy levels. Photons travel as an electromagnetic wave from the
emitting material to the object material. This photon propagation will transfer
thermal energy to the object and increase the surface temperature. Radiation
may be used as the sole source of heating an item, or it may be employed in
combination with the convective and/or conductive methods.

Because hot air has both a low specific heat and poor thermal conductivity
properties, there is a necessity for long sterilization periods at higher temperatures than those required in steam sterilization. The sterilization load is
typically slow in heating and cooling, and has a tendency toward temperature
stratification (causing wide temperature variations during the cycle) [5].
Despite these limitations, dry heat is chosen as the preferred method to induce sterilization and/or depyrogenation over moist heat or other methods in
certain specific instances. Some items are ideally sterilized by dry heat
methods: glassware, which should be maintained dry for filling; stainless
steel equipment having surfaces difficult to penetrate with steam; and items
that may corrode with moisture. Some products are damaged or contaminated
by the presence of water (e.g., petrolatum, oils, nonaqueous vehicles, fats,
and powders) [6].

To aid the heating process, a system to increase the circulation of the
heated air is often employed. During the heat-up cycle, air circulation will
transfer cool air from the chamber or heating zone and prevent temperature
stratification. Higher-temperature air replaces the cool air, and the load may
be heated more rapidly. The circulation of air is similarly useful at the end
of the heating cycle to cool the load.

Blowers or fans are used to circulate the air, used in the supply throughout the chamber (see Figs. 2, 4, and 6). The blowers may be either of the
propeller or squirrel-cage types, and may be either belt-driven or

direct-driven. Determining the flow rates of the air within all types of sterilizers is essential, since it is an important factor in the rate of heat transfer. An air velometer (or hot-wire anemometer) may be used to determine the flow rate of the intake, exhaust, and circulating air. If the sterilizer is utilized to supply to an aseptic environment, balancing of the air systems is necessary. A slight positive pressure should exist from the aseptic area to the open sterilizer to prevent contamination of the aseptic area. The sterilizer should also be slightly positive in pressure with respect to the nonaseptic area to prevent flow of dirty air into the sterilizer.

The air is usually supplied by the HVAC system or directly from the aseptic area. A filtered HVAC air supply is preferred because it has a lower particulate load and is both temperature and relative humidity controlled. Room air may be used, but it usually has a higher particulate count and variable temperature and humidity levels.

HEPA filters may be used for both cleansing the air supply and circulating air, but the filters in the air circulation path must be designed to withstand the operating temperatures and should be monitored for integrity. The air being introduced into the sterilizer and circulating within the unit should be tested for particulates at several locations while the fan is operating. If desired, these tests can be run at operating temperatures. High particulate counts may be caused by missing or dirty filters, vibrating and/or shedding materials, or inadequate sanitization practices. The use of a particle analyzer, such as those produced by HIAC-Royco or Climet Instruments, is suggested. Ideally, only Class 100 air should enter the oven. Class 100,000 air has been cited as the maximum condition for air circulating in the sterilizer [7]. Air cleanliness classes are defined as the maximum number of particles per cubic foot of air 0.5 μm and larger [8].

IV. INSTALLATION QUALIFICATION

The Installation Qualification (IQ) is designed to compare the system against the manufacturer's specifications for proper installation. To confirm that the sterilizer is properly installed, all devices, utilities, and connections must be checked against the manufacturer's recommendations and against the records of modifications made on the unit. Pertinent information about the sterilizer, including purchase orders, quotations, specifications, equipment changes, etc., should be part of the documentation file. These records must be compared against the equipment to verify that all documentation is correct. A schematic for all utilities supplying the sterilizer should be available to confirm that all connections are as specified and meet design limits, local and state codes, and Current Good Manufacturing Practices. The Installation Qualification documents should be reviewed and approved by those designated responsible individuals. The following information should be part of the Installation Qualification.

A. Records

Copies of or references to the following information: manufacturer's quotations and specifications, purchase orders, unit model number and serial number, corporate and/or department identification numbers, standard operating procedures (SOPs), preventative maintenance program, sanitization procedures, calibration procedures, and the identification and location of all drawings pertinent to the unit.

B. Structural Information

Check dimensions, identification plates, leveling, insulation, seals, and inspect for damaged parts.

C. Utilities

Check the workmanship and record the following information for each of the utilities, where applicable:

1. Electrical—Conformance to National Electrical Code standards, proper identification, safety cutoff, specifics on the service including volts, amperes, phase, wire size, and type.
2. HVAC—Conformance to corporate standards and codes.
3. Air supply to sterilizer—Identify source (HVAC or room air), duct size and material of construction, and air classification (as per Federal Standard 209B) [8].
4. Ventilation—Check that the ventilation duct exhausts to an appropriate area (not to a sterile environment): identify method used to prevent back-flow.
5. Cooling water—Identify source, pipe size and material of construction, and type and size of cooling coil tubes.
6. Gas or nitrogen supply—Check that the source and type of supply is consistent with the manufacturer's recommendations.

D. Door Gaskets

Check integrity of gaskets, and materials of construction.

E. Critical Instruments

Identify all controllers and recorders critical to the operation of the unit, including those for temperature, timing of cycle, pressure, belt speed, and air flow. Note serial numbers, corporate identification numbers, instrument output ranges, and calibration schedule.

F. Noncritical Instruments

Check all convenience instruments (those not critical to the operation of the unit). These may include instruments such as dial pressure gauges, indicator lights, and alarms. Where available, note serial numbers, corporate identification numbers, instrument output ranges, and calibration schedule.

G. Baffles

The integrity of all baffles or louvers must be checked. Ensure that the baffles are not damaged, misaligned, or missing entirely.

H. Heaters

Record the following information on the heaters: the manufacturer's model number, the number of heating elements, and the voltage, amperage, and wattage of the elements.

I. Lubricants

Make certain that all lubricants used are without potential for contamination.

J. Blowers

The blower must be mechanically sound, and the volute must be in place, correctly balanced, have the proper distance between the blades and the volute, and have the correct fan belt.

K. Filters

All filters used within the system must be recorded, such as those in the compressed air, steam, water, and nitrogen systems. Records on the filters should include the proper identification, type, size, change frequency, air capacity, flow rate, temperature limits, and laboratory testing required (include the SOP reference). Filters should be checked periodically for integrity, by performing a bubble-point or similar test. The air or liquid downstream of the filter should be tested for particulates to make certain the filters are within specifications, are not shedding, and are correctly installed (without leaks).

V. OPERATIONAL QUALIFICATION

After the equipment has been checked for proper installation, as detailed in the Installation Qualification, it is necessary to determine that the sterilizer performs as designed. The components of the system must satisfy the operating ranges as determined by the specifications set by the pharmaceutical manufacturer. The sterilizer must be operated to confirm that it functions correctly on a repeated basis. The Operational Qualification document should be reviewed and signed by the individuals. Each of the following process components must be identified, and the operating performance and ranges determined.

A. Temperature Monitors

The temperature controllers, recorders, and sensors on the process equipment to be validated must be calibrated before the unit can be operated reliably. The units are generally calibrated at the time of installation by the manufacturer or user, and should be recalibrated at periodic intervals. The calibrations should be performed by measuring actual temperatures in addition to electronic calibration methods. Often, electronically controlled units are calibrated only by electronic methods, such as checking voltage or resistance readings at various set points. Although this approval is useful, it is also essential that actual temperatures be checked at the set points, as described in Sec. VII. The recorder must accurately document the temperature sensor readings on a chart having a readability level consistent with the operating ranges. The controller must prove reliable in maintaining the temperature within the specified set points.

B. Cycle Timer

The accuracy of the timer must be determined, so that assurance is provided for cycle length.

C. Door Interlocks

If a unit is equipped with double doors, the interlocks must operate such that the door leading to the aseptic area cannot be opened if the door to the non-aseptic area is open, nor can it be opened unless the cycle is successfully completed.

D. Heaters

All of the heating elements must be functional. It is preferable to have them monitored continuously with ammeters in order that burned-out elements can be immediately detected. A failed element could cause a severe change in the operating performance of the oven.

E. Blowers

Properly adjusted blowers are very important to the effectiveness of the circulation in the sterilizer. The blower should deliver an air velocity consistent with manufacturer's specifications, which may be accomplished by adjusting the speed of the fan. It is essential that the blades are rotating in the proper direction.

F. Cooling Coils

To enable a faster cool-down cycle, the air is often circulated across coolant coils. If coils are present, the type and size of the coils and the temperature of the cooling water at the inlet and outlet of the coils should be recorded. The effectiveness of the cooling coils can be checked by determining the temperature change in the water entering and exiting the coils.

G. Belts

The belt speed is a critical operating parameter in both continuous hot-air tunnels and flame sterilizers. Recorders for charting the belt speed are recommended for units with adjustable speed settings, for proper qualification of the system. The belt speed and operating temperature are interrelated in these units, so a slower belt speed at a lower temperature will produce the same effect as a faster belt speed at a higher temperature.

VI. TEMPERATURE MEASUREMENT EQUIPMENT AND MATERIALS

Equipment employed to perform the validation studies must be traceable to the National Bureau of Standards. All testing equipment must be properly calibrated, and the correct use of the instrument fully documented in an SOP. The equipment used for validation testing of dry heat processes may include the following.

A. Thermocouples

Thermocouples are the most widely used devices for temperature measurements. The choice of thermocouple type and insulation surrounding the wires is dependent on the operating temperature and required temperature accuracy.

For dry heat sterilization or depyrogenation processes, both type T (copper and constantan) and type J (iron and constantan) thermocouples are used. The insulation most commonly chosen for high-temperature work is Du Pont's Kapton-H. This insulation is rated to 350°C, sufficient for depyrogenation use.

B. Resistance Temperature Detectors

The resistance temperature detector (RTD) probe is conventionally utilized for calibrating temperature measurement equipment used during validation testing. The RTD may be used with assurance to a hundredth of a degree celsius, compared to thermocouples, which have a level of sensitivity to a tenth of a degree celsius. The RTD is more stable than the thermocouple and must be traceable to the National Bureau of Standards for proper operation.

C. Data Loggers

Multipoint recorders are commonly used during validation studies to record the temperatures sensed by the thermocouples. The data logger takes the thermocouple voltage output and converts it to a numerical value. The thermocouples must be checked against the more sensitive and NBS-traceable RTD to make certain the thermocouples read correct temperatures. This is done by manually correcting the zero and span adjustments on the data logger, or by the use of an automatic calibration feature available on some models. Calibrations must be performed on the data logger/thermocouple system before and after the validation runs, as detailed in Sec. VII.

VII. CALIBRATION OF VALIDATION EQUIPMENT

All equipment used for validating production equipment must be calibrated. All critical instrumentation should be traceable to the National Bureau of Standards, which may be achieved by sending the unit to the NBS laboratory or to a contract calibration laboratory certified by them. The length of time between calibrations is determined by the stability of the instrument and the accuracy required. All calibrated instruments must be numbered, logged, and referenced. The use of a calibration decal on the unit, which includes the calibration date, by whom calibrated, and the date of the next calibration, is suggested. A calibration file must be maintained for each instrument, including the information cited for the calibration decal, a history file updated with any repairs made on the unit, and a list of the instruments used to calibrate it (such as resistance standards, voltage standards, etc.), identified with serial numbers. Standard operating procedures should be written and approved for the calibration of all instruments and included in the calibration file. A master file of all calibration due dates should be maintained for easy reference.

As mentioned previously, calibration of the temperature measurement system against an RTD is a critical step to be performed before and after the validation runs. Precalibration makes certain that all thermocouples are in working order, and compares each temperature reading against a known standard. The thermocouples are checked against the RTD after the runs in a postcalibration to ensure that the thermocouples are still operating properly and therefore that the recorded temperature data are valid.

To perform the calibration, the thermocouples, RTD probe and monitor, data logger, and two or three constant-temperature baths are required. The RTD and thermocouples are simultaneously placed in one of the baths. The data logger readings are compared against the RTD monitor, and zero and span corrections are made on the multipoint recorder until all thermocouple readings are within ±0.5°C of the RTD temperature readings. The thermocouples must stay within the range for at least 3 min to demonstrate stability of the thermocouples. The data logger is used to record these temperature readings, and the RTD temperature should be noted on the actual printout. The thermocouples are then transferred to the other bath, and without adjustment to the data logger, the temperature readings for the thermocouples must again be within the designated temperature range. If the temperature readings are not within the range, adjustments must be made, and the first bath sequence repeated. The printouts are designated as the "precalibration." The same sequence must be executed after the validation runs are completed, prior to any adjustment of the data logger. Any thermocouple that is out of range on "postcalibration" may not be used as a source of valid data. This postcalibration may be made after any number of validation runs. All of these validation tests may have to be repeated if the thermocouples fail to post-calibrate. An approved SOP for calibrating the thermocouples must be kept available for easy reference. The pre- and postcalibration records should be kept in the validation run file.

VIII. CYCLE DEVELOPMENT

An appropriate sterilization or depyrogenation cycle must be developed before validation testing commences. Cycle development is generally considered part of the prevalidation program. In cases where the validation program is separate from cycle development, complete records and documentation of the cycle development must be available or included within the validation documentation. All operating parameters must be defined during cycle development, including bioburden, pyroburden, biochallenges, temperature settings, cycle time, required F_H value, penetration temperature profiles, and belt speed (for tunnel or flame sterilizers).

The prevalidation laboratory studies should imitate actual manufacturing processes. The laboratory studies can identify manufacturing equipment design specifications required to deliver an effective sterilization or depyrogenation cycle [9].

Cycle development should include bioburden studies to determine the presterilization microbial load. Laboratory studies will define the D value, which is the time required to reduce the microbial population by 90% (one logarithm). The microorganism used as a biological indicator must have resistance characteristics (D and Z values) that are documented and appropriate for the sterilization or depyrogenation cycle. The relationship of lethality to temperature is expressed in the Z value. The Z-value studies will define the number of degrees that are required for a change in the D value by a factor of 10.

The bioburden data, Z and D values, can be used to calculate the minimum F_H value required. The F_H value is the integration of lethality when at a reference temperature of 170°C. A conservative approach to determining a minimum sterilization F_H would utilize the heat-resistance spores of *Bacillus subtilis* (v. *niger*) and assume a D value of 1.0 min (at a reference temperature of 170°C) and a Z value of 20°C. The lethality rate determines the increment of lethal heat effect obtained over various temperatures (as compared to a reference temperature) using the Z value. The F_H value is derived by integration of the lethal rate with respect to time. The F_H value (equivalent time at the reference temperature) accumulates the total lethality. When sterilization temperatures other than 170°C are used, the F value is reported as process equivalent time at the reference temperature of 170°C [10].

The equations used for equivalent time are as follows:

$$F_t^Z = \frac{F_{170}^Z}{L}$$

where F_t^Z = the equivalent time at temperature t delivered to a container for the purpose of sterilization with a specific Z value, F_{170}^Z = the equivalent time at 170°C delivered to a container for the purpose of sterilization with a specific Z value (when Z = 20°C, then $F_{170}^Z = F_H$) where L = lethal rate;

$$L = \log^{-1} \frac{T_0 - T_b}{Z}$$

or

$$L = 10^{\frac{T_0 - T_b}{Z}}$$

where T_0 = temperature within the container or item, and T_b = base temperature of 170°C.

As a supplement to temperature data, spores of *Bacillus subtilis* are often used to monitor the lethality of dry heat sterilization during the validation runs.

Some dry heat processes are intended to provide only sterilization; in other cases, both sterilization and depyrogenation are required. When the objective of the cycle is to depyrogenate (endotoxin inactivation), calibrated *Escherichia coli* endotoxin challenges are placed in the load including the coldest location in the loading pattern. The endotoxin challenge should be based on the pyroburden of the components, taking into consideration the desired safety factor. The presence of residual endotoxin can be detected by either the USP pyrogen rabbit test or the limulus amebocyte lysate test.

The rate of endotoxin (lipopolysaccharide) destruction at 250°C can be expressed using a Z value of 46.4°C and a D_{250} value of 4.99 min [11]. The cycle should be designed utilizing a worst-case situation where the required minimum time and temperature parameters are defined. If only sterilization is desired, this can be attained by either a probability of survival approach based on the bioburden for heat-labile products, or by the overkill method for heat-stable materials.

Heat-labile products require strictly controlled sterilization cycles, since underprocessing will result in nonsterile product while overprocessing will cause degradation of the product. The cycle development will determine the minimum amount of dry heat required to ensure that the probability of survival of the bioburden is less than 10^{-6}. The equivalent sterilization time and temperature can be described by the F value with a reference temperature of 170°C and assuming a Z value of 20°C [12].

Heat-stable materials, such as glassware and stainless steel equipment, can withstand excessive heat. Operating temperatures can be very high, and loading configuration is less restrictive than with heat-labile products. The F_H requirement will ensure a probability of survival of the bioburden of much less than 10^{-6}. The overkill method relieves the requirement for bioburden and resistance studies during cycle development. Component preparation is still very important, since cleaning and handling procedures can serve to minimize the level of contamination of both viable and nonviable particulates (including endotoxins).

Heat-stable items can tolerate depyrogenation cycles with temperatures far in excess of 250°C. In this case, the cycle lethality should be defined on the basis of endotoxin inactivation based on the pyroburden and not the bioburden [7]. The F_H can be calculated for a depyrogenation cycle using the general F-value equation with a reference temperature of 250°C.

Examples of F_H values (time = 1 min) at various temperatures are as follows:

Temperature (°C)	$F_H{}^{20}{}_{170}$	$F_H{}^{46.4}{}_{170}$	$F_H{}^{46.4}{}_{250}$
170	1.0	1.0	0.02
210	100.0	7.3	0.14
250	10,000.0	53.0	1.0
270	100,000.0	142.0	2.7

Assuming a cycle of 250°C for 30 min, the minimum F_H values for the total cycle would be:

Temperature (°C)	$F_H{}^{20}{}_{170}$	$F_H{}^{46.4}{}_{170}$	$F_H{}^{46.4}{}_{250}$
250	300,000.0	1590.0	30.0

The $F_{H(250)}$ that is determined can be used to calculate the number of logarithmic cycles an amount of endotoxin will be reduced per unit (L_{Dec}). L_{Dec} values are calculated by integrating the heat penetration-lethality curves. This model was experimentally determined for achieving a desired level of endotoxin destruction as follows [5]:

$$L_{Dec} = 6.065(10^{-0.201} \times F_H - 1)$$

where 6.065 is the linearization parameter (constant at a reference temperature of 250°C) for the dry heat destruction curve of *E. coli* endotoxin, and F_H is the lethal rate at 250°C for hot air.

IX. VALIDATION PROTOCOL

A Validation Protocol must be written and approved prior to the start of the actual validation work. The protocol is designed to outline the program to be employed, the specific tests that will be made, and the acceptance criteria for those tests. The protocol may be written to overview the process, or the specific piece of equipment. Once the protocol has been written, it must be approved by the designated responsible individuals.

Changes in the scope of the work after the protocol has been finalized may be addressed in Protocol Supplements or Addenda. These supplements must be approved by all parties. The validation report must refer to the issued Protocol in its entirety (see Appendix 3 for example of a validation protocol).

The following format may be utilized in a validation protocol:

1. Objective statement: A concise statement that defines the objective of the validation protocol.
2. Responsibility: Identification of specific departments, and their responsibilities in the validation project. This will assure that each group understands the specific information or materials that it is required to provide.
3. Test program: The test program should include a description of the tests that will be performed during the empty- and loaded-chamber studies, as detailed in the validation section, and the equipment to be used to perform those tests (see later sections for details of the specific tests to be employed in this phase). All standard operating procedures for each piece of equipment or testing process must be referenced. The type and form of biological challenges to be used must be stated. The general location of where the individual tests are to be taken, and where the bioindicators shall be placed, should be described.
4. Acceptance criteria: Acceptance criteria must be listed for each test in the test program section, with limits or ranges specifically identified. The limits or ranges chosen should be those commonly used by the firm, determined during cycle development or referenced from cited literature.

X. VALIDATION TESTING

Upon completion of qualification efforts and approval of the Protocol, validation testing may begin. The testing will include empty-chamber testing with heat distribution studies, and loaded-chamber testing consisting of heat distribution and heat penetration studies (see Appendix 4 for examples of diagrams and data sheets). Loaded-chamber testing requires the determination of bioburden and pyroburden on the various loads employing appropriate biological indicators and endotoxins during the biovalidation studies.

A. Empty-Chamber Testing

The initial testing is performed on an empty chamber to measure temperature distribution. The thermodynamic characteristics of the empty sterilizer are depicted in a temperature distribution profile. The temperature profile will serve to locate hot or cold areas in the sterilizer by mapping the temperatures at various points in the chamber. The temperature profile is obtained by placing at least 10 thermocouples distributed in the empty tunnel or batch sterilizer in such a way as to determine heat profiles. In the flame sterilizer the thermocouples should be placed at the level of the ampules. The thermocouple tips should be suspended to avoid contacting any solid surfaces (wall, ceiling, support rods, etc.). A good profile should demonstrate uniform temperatures across the sterilizer. The temperature range must conform to the protocol requirements. All environmental factors should closely represent actual manufacturing conditions (e.g., relative humidity, room temperatures, static air pressure, and balance). All control settings are recorded, including any variables that will affect the cycle (key process variables such as temperature set points, heating elements settings, cycle-timer set point, belt speed, etc.). The cycle timer (batch), belt speed (tunnel or flame), controller operating temperature span, and production charts can be verified by a multipoint temperature recorder with an integral timer. A thermocouple should be placed adjacent to the heat-controlling temperature sensor, which will confirm that the operational controls are maintaining the desired heating specifications. It is important to document the come-up time (the time to reach the temperature set point) and the cool-down time, since data variances may indicate electrical or mechanical malfunctions in the batch sterilizer. It is important that the tunnel and flame sterilizer be closely monitored within the sterilizing zone, since temperature variation is most critical at this location. The empty-chamber cycle can be one of maximum time with production operating temperatures or a shorter time period at a predetermined temperature, such as 250°C.

If the empty-chamber temperature distribution profile is not acceptable, sterilizer adjustments, modifications, or repairs must be performed and the profile studies repeated. If the empty-chamber temperature profile is acceptable, three consecutive replicate runs are performed to demonstrate cycle and sterilizer reproducibility.

A detailed diagram of thermocouple placement should be included in the empty-chamber data file. This file will be extremely valuable when revalidation of the sterilizer is necessary after adjustments, repairs, or modifications.

The empty-chamber data file must include originals (or copies) of all charts, temperature printouts, data calculations, and observations pertaining to the runs.

B. Loaded-Chamber Studies

As in the empty-chamber testing, validation studies during a partially or fully loaded chamber must include heat distribution testing with one thermocouple placed near the heat-controlling temperature sensor. Thermocouples used for loaded-chamber heat distribution studies should be positioned in some of the locations used for empty-chamber heat distribution testing. The distribution thermocouple tips should be suspended to avoid contacting any solid surfaces. Heat distribution studies must be performed to determine the effect of the load on the chamber temperature distribution.

Heat penetration studies should be monitored simultaneously with the heat distribution studies. Penetration information is critical in a partially or fully loaded chamber, since materials will heat at a rate different from that of the surrounding air. The rate of heat penetration will depend on the type of material in the load, how it is packed (loading configuration) and the distribution temperature uniformity. Heat penetration data are obtained by placing thermocouples inside the container, component, or item in such a way as to ensure contact with the surface (the thermocouple should not be reading air temperature; it should read surface temperature).

It is important in the loaded chamber to document both come-up and cool-down rates of the air and product. The come-up time of the distribution thermocouples will describe the time required for the air to reach the temperature-controller set point from ambient temperature. The come-up time of the penetration thermocouples will describe the time required for the load to reach the desired temperature. There is a heating lag as the components in the load reach the minimum required temperature after the air reaches that temperature (as measured by the distribution thermocouples). The heating lag is defined as the difference between the time required for the product to reach the minimum required temperature and the time required for the sterilizer air to reach the minimum required temperature. A heating lag will be magnified during the maximum load of product (i.e., maximum density or mass). The product temperature, as detected by penetration thermocouples, will heat at a slower rate, since convection and conduction is slower in a solid mass (product) than in a gas (air). It is not uncommon for temperature controller settings to be set well above the desired minimum sterilizing/depyrogenating temperature to make certain that the product will attain that temperature for the required length of time. The total time the product is at or above the required temperature is documented, as well as the final F_H value.

The tunnel or flame sterilizer temperature data may have large variations between runs because the product is heated to high temperatures for a short period of time, as compared to batch sterilizers with long sterilization periods. As a consequence, correlation between different types of sterilizers is difficult to achieve.

Care must be maintained to observe temperature ranges and fluctuations with awareness of any maximum temperature restrictions. Distribution temperatures (empty and load studies), penetration temperatures, come-up time, and F_H data can be evaluated for reproducibility between replicate runs using statistical methods.

For validation purposes, representative loads must be selected for testing. Ideally, each size and type of material should be tested by penetration studies. A careful decision must be made in choosing items to test, the size and material of each item, the quantity, and the geometry of the load, since it is often impossible to test all permutations of loads. Representative loads should include items of size extremes (i.e., smallest and largest) and items that are the most difficult for heat to penetrate (i.e., due to dense mass or tight packing).

An exact, detailed diagram of thermocouple locations must accompany all temperature data. The diagram is necessary to identify where the hot and cold areas are within each specific load. Hot areas in the load are more important for heat-labile items. Cold areas are important to monitor for sterility or depyrogenation assurance.

Load factors will predominate because air has poor conductive and convective properties. As a result, the hot and cold areas may vary for each type of load. This is most likely to occur if each material heats at a different rate (due to size, mass, and packing configuration). In the batch sterilizer it is recommended that the penetration thermocouple locations be changed after each run to obtain an overall view of heat penetration.

Container mapping will determine if some areas of a bottle or vial are heating at a different rate than other areas. In subsequent testing the vial or bottle should be monitored in the cold area.

Tunnel and flame sterilizers are particularly sensitive to changes in load configuration. Continuous runs (where bottles, vials, or ampules are flush side to side) are generally the worst-case loads due to the rapid come-up time, short length of sterilization period, and variations in component packing and movement.

If the temperature profile is acceptable, three consecutive replicate runs are utilized to demonstrate loaded sterilizer and cycle reproducibility. The replicate runs must verify that the minimum required F_H value is being achieved within the coldest portion of the load.

C. Biochallenge Studies

Biochallenge studies can be performed separately or concurrently with temperature penetration studies. If studies are performed concurrently, place the challenge items adjacent to items containing thermocouples.

Studies can be performed by placing the bioindicators in the coldest areas (minimum F_H values) of each load. An alternative to adding the biochallenge to each load would involve determining the load with the absolute coldest area and minimum F_H value. This load is then considered to be the worst-case load. Successful biochallenge of the worst-case load would eliminate the need to challenge all other previously tested loads (with higher F_H values).

For dry heat sterilization/depyrogenation to occur, there is a required minimum time and temperature. The biochallenge will demonstrate the lethality delivered by challenging the cycle with either microorganisms or endotoxin. The challenges can be accomplished using commercial strips or suspensions of *Bacillus subtilis* spores (for sterilization) or *Escherichia coli* endotoxin (for depyrogenation). A suitable challenge must represent the pyroburden or bioburden for heat-labile materials or exceed it for overkill processes. The concentration of the challenge for overkill processes must demonstrate adequate sterility assurance.

The biochallenge work is usually achieved by inoculating components with a known concentration of the challenge microorganism or endotoxin (i.e., *B. subtilis* suspension or *E. coli* endotoxin. In sterilization cycles, a challenge of 10^6 concentration of *B. subtilis* is common. In depyrogenation cycles, there appears to be no general consensus on the challenge level used; concentrations cited in the literature have ranged from 100 to 10,000 ng (500 to 50,000 endotoxin units) [7]. The required number of challenged units should be predetermined in the validation protocol. After the sterilization or depyrogenation cycle, the inoculated products are recovered along with unchallenged items (for negative controls), and tested for spore viability or endotoxin inactivation along with positive controls. If the challenge has spore survivors or residual endotoxin, the amount must be quantitated and analyzed with respect to the achieved F_H value and L_{Dec}. The results of this study confirm that the sterilization or depyrogenation process is effective.

XI. VALIDATION REPORT

After the empty- and loaded-chamber studies and biochallenge studies have been completed, the data must be analyzed to ascertain that all testing requirements have been achieved. The results of the biochallenge studies and F-value computation must demonstrate the required degree of lethality (sterilization or depyrogenation) according to the Validation Protocol.

The following information should be provided in the validation report (see Appendix 5 for a sample validation report):

1. Protocol achievement: A statement reflecting that the acceptance criteria of the identified validation protocol was met.
2. Summary of data: A summary of the data collected during the validation runs, including come-up times, minimum and maximum F values, and the locations of the slowest heating zone(s). Raw data are generally not included in the report, but remain in a central file (as described later).
3. Deviations: Exceptions to the validation report should be explained, including justifications if certain tests were not performed, or are to be performed in the future under an addendum. Any deviations from expected results should be analyzed and discussed.
4. Diagrams: Diagrams depicting the load, and placement of bioindicators and thermocouples, should be included. Detailed diagrams of unusual items, or of inoculated parts, should be shown. Other data may be included in the report, as desired, due to differences in protocol and equipment specifics.

XII. ROUTINE MONITORING AFTER VALIDATION

Once the equipment has been validated for the sterilization or depyrogenation process, the unit must be monitored so that it remains in a state of control. This is achieved by the use of various programs, including Sanitization, Preventative Maintenance, Engineering Change Control, and Revalidation.

The Sanitization Program should detail the cleaning methods used for the equipment, the SOPs covering each method, and the cleaning materials utilized. Proper sanitization should demonstrate that the level of organisms is controlled, so that the basis for the validation program does not change. Cleaning materials should be nontoxic and leave no residues.

The Preventative Maintenance (PM) Program provides a schedule by which the equipment is maintained. This includes physical checking of the system, changing of filters, testing of heater elements, calibration of controllers and recorders, etc. The schedule may be that suggested by the sterilizer manufacturer or one developed by the user based on the operating history of the unit. A proper PM program will help to prevent breakdowns during production. The specific adjustments that are made to the unit, scheduled or unscheduled, must be recorded in the PM log book.

Changes to the equipment that might possibly compromise the validation must be brought to the attention of the group or individual in charge of the Engineering Change Control Program. A change control form may be completed by the person requesting the change, outlining the modification or repair required, the reason for the change, and the expected results. The request form may be reviewed by a committee comprised of delegated representatives from the Validation department, Quality Assurance, Engineering, and Manufacturing. The committee would evaluate the modification to be made (or made earlier on an emergency basis), and determine if it would change the validated status of the equipment. The committee would then recommend specific revalidation checks to be made. A list should be compiled of common repairs made to the sterilizer that do not disturb the validation, to expedite the review. Subsequently, these types of repairs may be made to the unit without prior approval of the committee. The modification should still be noted on a change control form to ensure that good records are kept.

Revalidation studies may be required after changes or repairs are made on the unit, or at a predetermined periodic interval. Revalidation usually does not include all the original validation studies, but should include duplicates of some of the validated loads, including the worst-case load and the largest load. Addenda to the validated report may be written to include additional loads that differ from the previously validated loads.

XIII. DOCUMENTATION FILES

All validation information should be easily identified and kept in a permanent central file, where it can be readily retrived. The validation file should include the following:

1. Qualifications: All information recorded for installational and operational qualifications for the equipment and/or process. This includes all steps performed in the certification of the equipment. All original data, results, and conclusions must be contained in this file. Information may include blueprints, airborne particulate counts, velocity readings, HEPA DOP testing, etc. All reports should be dated, signed, and approved by a responsible individual.
2. Protocol: The experimental protocol is also located in this file.
3. Chamber studies: All original data, results, calculations, and conclusions must be retained for empty- /and loaded-chamber and biochallenge studies. One of the most important records from these studies is the run sheet, a form that is filled out with the appropriate information at the time of the run. Load diagrams (depicting the actual placement of components, thermocouples, and bioindicators) are kept with the run sheets to which the diagrams refer. The run sheets and diagrams assist in making certain that all required information has been recorded, and that the placement of any testing equipment or materials was correct. The diagrams should include the empty-chamber load, and all the different loads used in the loaded-chamber and biochallenge studies. Other data to be identified with chamber studies would include calibrations, original temperature printouts, equipment temperature charts, bioindicator calibrations and test results, and calculation sheets (such as F_H values and temperature ranges).
4. Validation report: The validation report is the formal document available for regulatory review. The validation report will contain data from the various studies (empty and loaded chambers and biochallenge).
5. Routine monitoring: All change control information and postvalidation mechanical changes are recorded along with any revalidation work. This will prevent voiding all previous validation studies.

It is important to consider the validation effort as being protected by proper documentation and permanent files. The initial validation data is necessary for comparison with subsequent validations, and the overall validation program is only as reliable as the traceability of its documentation.

XIV. CONCLUSION

Dry heat is a commonly used method to sterilize and depyrogenate. The necessity for this process to be validated has been demonstrated. Following the

outlined methodology of validation will result in a complete program documenting a reproducible dry heat process. This chapter has detailed the steps of
a validation program that may be employed to properly validate a dry heat
process.

XV. APPENDIXES

Appendix 1. Installation Qualification Sample Form

INSTALLATION QUALIFICATION

Equipment Description:

    a)   Type _____

    b)   Fixed Asset # _____

    c)   Department Equipment ID # _____

    d)   User Department _____

    e)   Location _____

    f)   Equipment Manufacturer _____

    g)   Model # _____

    h)   Serial # _____

Purchase Information:

    a)   Project # _____

    b)   C.A.R. # _____

    c)   Purchase Order # _____

    d)   Location _____ _____

    e)   Project Description _____

          _____

          _____

          _____

Manufacturer's Specifications:

    a)   Copy Available _____

    b)   Location _____

    c)   Correspondence on Specification Changes _____

          _____

          _____

    d)   Location

Instrumentation

   a)   Critical Process Instruments

        i)   Type: _____   Function _____

             Manufacturer _____   Model # _____

             Serial # _____   Proper ID ? _____

             Calibration # _____   Frequency _____

             Original Equip ? _____

        ii) Type: _____   Function _____

             Manufacturer _____   Model # _____

             Serial # _____   Proper ID ? _____

             Calibration # _____   Frequency _____

             Original Equip ? _____

Performed by: _____   Date: _____

Appendix 2.   Operational Qualification Sample Form

OPERATIONAL QUALIFICATION

The RPM of the fans on each oven were measured with an optical tachometer, the results are listed below for information:

	OVEN 1	OVEN 2	OVEN 3	OVEN 4	OVEN 5	OVEN 6	OVEN 7
Motor #1	1755	1740	1740	1740	1725	1745	1740
Cage 1 Shaft	1733	1753	1747	1738	1742	1720	1736
Motor #2	1740	1745	1740	1740	1745	1745	1735
Cage 2 Shaft	1740	1750	1738	1742	1755	1742	1753

Motor 1 is located closest to the prep side

Motor 2 is located closest to the sterile side

OVENS 1–7 LOCATED IN BUILDING 100 - VIAL PREP AREA

Appendix 3. Sample Validation Protocol

Validation Protocol 1.0

Hot Air Depyrogenation and Sterilization in Ovens

1.0 INTRODUCTION

This protocol provides a standard procedure for the validation of hot air depyrogenation and sterilization in dry heat ovens.

2.0 RESPONSIBILITIES

2.1 The Validation Group is responsible for overall adherence to this protocol. Their specific duties include the following:

2.1.1 Monitoring of protocol completeness, accuracy, technical excellence and applicability.

2.1.2 Maintenance and calibration of validation equipment.

2.1.3 Scheduling of the validation runs (in conjunction with appropriate department).

2.1.4 Conducting of the validation runs (with operating personnel provided by the department, whose ovens are being validated) including recording of all data, etc.

2.1.5 Data review and validation run acceptance.

2.1.6 Validation report preparation.

2.1.7 Schedule re-validation.

2.2 The Engineering and Maintenance Departments are responsible for the following:

2.2.1 Calibration of process equipment instrumentation on a regularly scheduled basis and after repairs.

2.2.2 Completion of major repairs/renovations prior to validation runs.

2.3 The responsibilities of Quality Control and/or Assurance are as follows:

2.3.1 Preparation/qualification of biological indicators, spore strips, and endotoxins.

2.3.2 Testing of biological indicators and reporting of results.

2.4 The Department whose oven is to be validated is responsible for the following:

2.4.1 Identifying the oven to be validated.

2.4.2 Providing the oven when agreed upon with the Validation Group representative.

2.4.3 Providing an oven operator.

2.4.4 Indicating responsible supervisory personnel.

2.4.5 Provide samples for bioburden and/or pyroburden.

2.4.6 Provide load type and descriptions to the Validation Group.

3.0 VALIDATION TEST PROGRAM

3.1 Air supply inspection

3.2 Heat distribution studies with empty and loaded oven.

3.3 Heat penetration studies in loaded oven.

3.4 Use of appropriate biological indicators and endotoxins during heat penetration studies.

3.5 Determination of bioburden and pyroburden for the various loads.

3.6 Determination of the number of airborne particulates.

4.0 LOADING PATTERNS

4.1 Three runs of each configuration shall be done for heat penetration, distribution and sterilization of biological challenges. Endotoxin challenges shall be run once on the load configuration maximum load which exhibited the minimum F_H during the cycle.

5.0 EMPTY CHAMBER HEAT DISTRIBUTION

5.1 The oven shall be qualified by the measurement of the temperature across the chamber by at least ten (10) thermocouples during a minimum 30 minute cycle.

6.0 LOADED CHAMBER HEAT DISTRIBUTION AND PENETRATION

6.1 In order to perform loaded chamber heat distribution, and penetration studies, an exact load configuration must be established (see Section 2.0) including the number and size of components to be depyrogenated or sterilized, a description of wrapping materials, containers, etc., such that the load can be standardized. The penetration thermocouples are to be placed at locations within each component type within the load at those locations deemed to be most difficult for heat to penetrate. Distribution thermocouples are to be placed in several of the locations for which empty chamber data was obtained. These studies are to be repeated three times for each load in an oven.

6.2 Upon completion of the experimental work, the slowest heating zone in the load and the location of the lowest F_H will be determined.

6.3 The F_H calculated will then be used to calculate the number of log cycles the concentration of endotoxin was reduced per unit.

7.0 EVALUATION OF RESULTS

7.1 The heat penetration information will be used to establish run reproducibility. If a consistent, uniformly lethal process, reproducible over three runs is indicated upon analysis of the accumulated data, the load configuration and oven parameters are satisfactory.

7.2 Determination of bioburden and its heat resistance relative to *Bacillus subtilis* in order to verify the process lethality for the indigenous organisms and/or log reduction of *E. coli* endotoxin for depyrogenation.

7.3 The data obtained in the course of the studies will be utilized to define sterilization and/or depyrogenation process parameters for each load configuration and will include the following information as a minimum:

7.3.1 A minimum F_H (250°C) of 30 minutes at the "slowest heating zone" part of each load for depyrogenation.

7.3.2 A probability of less than one non-sterile unit in 10^6 units for sterilization.

7.3.3 A definitive loading configuration, including identification of all wrapping materials.

7.3.4 A table outlining all the oven cycle set points.

Appendix 4A. Validation Data Sheet Sample Form

VALIDATION OF A HOT AIR OVEN

OVEN # _____ DATE _____

DEPARTMENT _____ PERSONNEL _____

RUN # _____ SUPERVISOR _____

LOAD DESCRIPTION _____

NO. PENETRATION THERMOCOUPLES _____

NO. DISTRIBUTION THERMOCOUPLES _____

KAYE # _____ SERIAL # _____

CALIBRATION   DATE PERFORMED _____

    HOT BATH SERIAL # _____ TEMPERATURE (RTD) _____

    COLD BATH SERIAL # _____ TEMPERATURE (RTD) _____

    RTD TYPE _____ SERIAL # _____

SETTINGS: TEMPERATURE SET POINT _____

              TIMER SET POINT _____

              OTHER SETTINGS _____

OVEN CYCLE

STARTING TIME _____

TIMER INITIATION _____

LAST THERMOCOUPLE TO REACH 250°C T/C # _____ TIME _____

TIMER ENDING _____

RESULTS

DISTRIBUTION TEMPERATURE   MAXIMUM _____ T/C _____

DISTRIBUTION TEMPERATURE   MINIMUM _____ T/C _____

TEMPERATURE DIFFERENCE _____

RANGE ± _____

MINIMUM PENETRATION F_H (250°C to 250°C IN CYCLE) _____

                   THERMOCOUPLE NO. _____

COMMENTS:

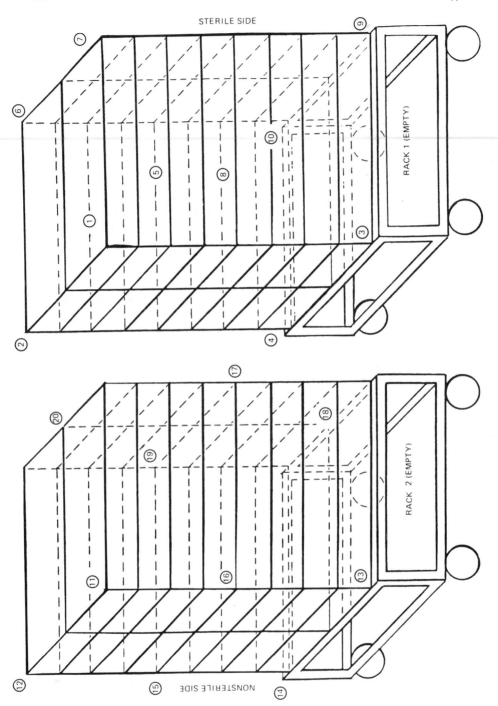

FIGURE 11 Empty chamber validation diagram. Side view of two racks in a hot air oven.

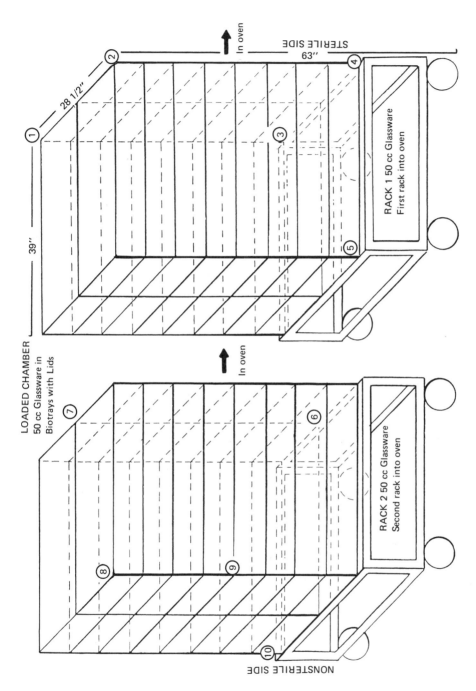

FIGURE 12 Loaded chamber validation diagram. Overall side view of two racks in an oven. Distribution thermocouples #1–10, penetration thermocouple #11–20.

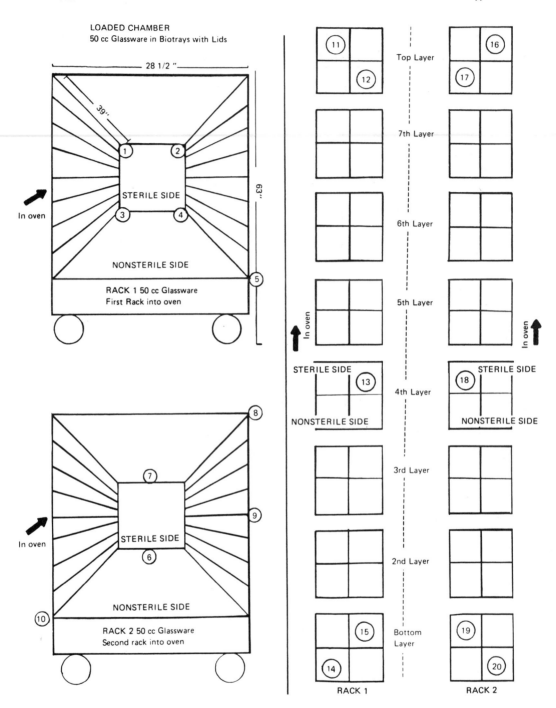

FIGURE 13   Loaded chamber validation diagram.   (A) Overall back to front view of two racks in an oven.   (B) Top view of each layer.

7.3.5 A minimum L_{Dec} of 6 for depyrogenation

7.3.6 Air velocities in the oven shall be adjusted to meet the empty chamber heat distribution.

7.3.7 Airborne particulate data shall meet the specifications of the air on the sterile side of the oven.

7.4 A report will be issued describing the validation/qualification program including the results of each phase of the studies conducted and stating load parameters and configurations which are validated. The report will be prepared by the Validation Group.

Appendix 5. Sample Validation Report

Validation Report #1—Hot Air Ovens Sterile Manufacturing

The hot air ovens #1–6 in Sterile Manufacturing Support have been validated. Experiments have been completed demonstrating effective sterilization and depyrogenation of glassware. The completed experiments include heat penetration studies, heat distribution studies and endotoxin challenge studies.

Plan of Study

A minimum of three empty chamber heat distribution runs were performed to determine the temperature distribution profile for each oven. Sterile Manufacturing Support departmental load configurations were used in all experiments.

Selected glassware loads were then placed within each oven. A maximum configuration was validated consisting of two full racks. The slowest heating zone and minimum Fh were identified for each load.

Ovens #1–6 are located in Sterile Manufacturing Support. They are identical models.

The standard production oven cycles used in the validation study are as follows:

Oven	No.	Components	Time/temperature
	1–6	SVP (< 100 cc)	XX min/XXX°F
		LVP (≥ 100 cc)	XX min/XXX°F
		Trays	XX min/XXX°F

Sterile Manufacturing processes many sizes of glassware ranging from 3 cc to 500 cc. The glassware chosen for this validation study was 3 cc, 50 cc, 125 cc, 300 cc, and 500 cc. The validation study included a load consisting of two racks of empty stainless steel trays used for the transport of lyophilized products.

Each of the five sizes of glassware and empty trays was tested a minimum of three times.

The time vs. temperature data generated by the heat penetration thermocouples was used to calculate an F_h value (250°C) and L_{Dec} for each selected type of glassware in each oven.

Two *E. coli* endotoxin challenges of 500 ng were placed at the slowest heating zone of the load most difficult to depyrogenate. The endotoxin challenge, in its original glass container, replaced a piece of glassware in a corresponding orientation and the standard oven cycle was run. The exposed challenges were tested for pyrogens using the LAL test.

The data obtained was compared against the following acceptance criteria: A minimum F_h (250°C) of 45 min for any part of the load and a 3 log reduction of the actual pyrogen challenge. The empty chamber study required holding 250°C ± 20°C for 30 min.

The results are listed in the summary tables. The load descriptions, thermocouple configurations and data calculations are described in the run summary sheets.

Pyroburden information was determined by studying Incoming Vial Endotoxicity of glassware as received from approved vendors. The results indicated incoming vials are essentially free of endotoxin contamination. The subject hot air ovens are utilized for depyrogenation only. The depyrogenation process is performed at temperatures higher than those required for sterilization, therefore, bioburden testing was deemed unnecessary.

Experimental

Either a Doric Digitrend 240 or a Kaye Digistrip were used to record all temperature data. Twenty type "T" (copper + constantan −) Kapton coated thermocouples were calibrated in high and low temperature baths with an NBS traceable probe (Doric platinum resistance thermometer). The thermocouples were inserted between the door and wall seal of the oven using a silicone and stainless steel plate. Distribution thermocouples were attached to the track frame with metal spring clips. Penetration thermocouples were inserted into the selected glassware or trays.

All data was obtained from either a Doric Digitrend 240 or Kaye Digistrip (II or III) printout. Temperature and Fh calculations were automatically or manually calculated, additional calculations were performed manually.

Two Pyrogen challenges (500 ng each) of *E. coli* endotoxin were placed in the slowest heating zone of the worst case load. A penetration thermocouple was placed adjacent to the two Endotoxin vials. After the run the challenge vials were removed and tested for pyrogens by LAL.

The ovens were validated with two racks. The racks were empty during empty chamber studies and filled for load studies.

Load Description

The penetration thermocouples were placed inside the inverted glassware. Penetration thermocouples were also placed inside the empty stainless steel trays.

Penetration thermocouple placement was changed three times for 50 cc glassware to record a temperature profile of a larger number of trays and levels. The penetration thermocouples remained in the same place for other sizes of glassware to observe reproducible temperature profiles.

Glassware smaller than 100 cc is placed in stainless steel biotrays with lids. Glassware larger than 99 cc is placed in perforated stainless steel baskets with lids.

All validation experiments were performed on glassware in containers (trays or baskets) with solid stainless steel lids. Presently, production uses lids only 300 cc glassware in baskets. The solid stainless steel trays used to transport lyophilized products also had lids.

It was decided to do all loads with lids on all containers since this was experimentally determined to be a more difficult situation for heat penetration.

The validation data for loads with lids (most difficult situation), provides assurance that the identical loads without lids is also acceptable. Therefore, it is permissable to process all sizes of glassware for the validated cycle in ovens #1−6 either with or without lids.

Validation oven loads			
Code	Glassware	No. bottles/container	Packing
ABBB	* 3 cc	468/tray	18 × 26
ACCC	50 cc	66/tray	6 × 11
ADDD	*125 cc	32/basket	4 × 8
AEEE	*300 cc	18/basket	3 × 6
AFFF	500 cc	15/basket (clear glass)	3 × 5
AGGG	500 cc	18/basket (amber glass)	3 × 6

*Stainless steel bottle support inserts were used.

Results

The F_h (250°C) calculations for each penetration experiment are indicated on the Kaye Digistrip printout or hand calculated. The F_h (250°C) in the summary tables is calculated between the time each penetration thermocouple reaches 250°C and drops below 250°C.

Distribution temperature ranges are calculated one minute after timer initiation (to allow for chamber equilibration) to the end of the timing cycle. These distribution temperature calculations were performed on both empty chamber and glassware load studies.

The minimum F_h and distribution temperature calculations are noted in the summary table. The minimum F_h value calculated for the ovens was observed in oven #4 (50 cc glassware) and was F_h = XXX.

All ovens validated exceeded the minimum depyrogenation requirement in Remington of 45 min at 250°C and USP-XX of 30 min at 250°C.

The slowest heating zone is defined as the last penetration thermocouple to reach 250°C. The slowest heating zone had sufficient heat to yield an L_{Dec} of 6. This indicates adequate heating of the load within each respective oven. The temperature distribution during chamber equilibration was within ±XX°C for the empty ovens #1−6 and within ±XX°C for the loaded ovens.

The *E. coli* endotoxin challenges were negative, according to the LAL testing.

The F_h (250°C) values calculated from the heat penetration data for the slowest heating zone of each load was used to calculate the number of log reductions (L_{Dec}) of *E. coli* endotoxin by the following method 1 (See reference below) for 250°C:

$$L_{Dec} = -B \ (10^{cx} -1)$$

$$250°C \begin{cases} B = 6.065 \\ C = 0.201 \\ X = F_h \ (250°C) \end{cases}$$

The L_{Dec} values calculated for the slowest heating zone of each load are listed in the summary table. The minimum value calculated was 6. By the above method the maximum achievable destruction of endotoxin (L_{Dec}) at 250°C is 6.07 and the F_h (250°C) required to achieve 90% of this value is 4.5 min.

Conclusion

Data from the experiments, as summarized in the following appendices, demonstrate sufficient sterilization and depyrogenation of glassware and trays in ovens #1—6 of Sterile Manufacturing. Certificates of validation will be jointly issued with Quality Assurance.

Reference

1. K. Tsuji, *Applied and Environmental Microbiology*, Nov. 1978, pp 705—719.

REFERENCES

1. *United States Pharmacopeia*, 20th ref. 1980. Mack Pub. Co., Easton, Pa. p 888.
2. Perkins, J. 1973. *Principles and Methods of Sterilization in Health Sciences*. Charles C. Thomas, Springfield, Ill. p 292.
3. *Validation of Dry Heat Processes Used for Sterilization and Depyrogenation*, Parenteral Drug Association Technical Report No. 3, 1981. p 19.
4. Halliday, D., and Resnick, R. 1967. *Physics* Parts I and II. John Wiley & Sons, New York. p 549.
5. Tsuji, K., and Lewis, A. 1978. Dry heat destruction of lipopolysaccharide: Mathematical approach to process evaluation. *Appl. Environ. Microbiol.* 36 (5):715—719.
6. Perkins, J. 1973. *Principles and Methods of Sterilization in Health Sciences*. Charles C Thomas, Springfield, Ill. p 286.
7. P. L. Simmons. 1978. Hot air and continuous sterilization, in Parenteral Manufacturers Association, *Proceedings, Validation of Sterile Manufacturing Process*, Reston, Virginia, March 15. p 44.
8. *Federal Standard Clean Room and Work Station Requirements, Controlled Environment*, Federal Standard 209B, April 24, 1973. p 4.
9. Wood, R. T. 1982. Parenteral Drug Association Short Course on Dry Heat Sterilization Validation and Monitoring, 6-17-82. pp 12—19.
10. *Validation of Dry Heat Processes Used for Sterilization and Depyrogenation*, Parenteral Drug Association Technical Report No. 3, 1981. p 24.

11. Tsuji, K., and Harrison, S. 1978. Dry heat destruction of lipopoly-
     saccharide: Dry heat destruction kinetics. *Appl. Environ. Microbiol.*
     36 (5):710–714.
12. *Validation of Dry Heat Processes Used for Sterilization and Depyrogena-
     tion*, Parenteral Drug Association Technical Report No. 3, 1981.
     pp 25–26.

BIBLIOGRAPHY

Akers, M. J., Avis, K. E., and Thompson, B. 1980. *Validation Studies of
    Parenteral Science and Technology*, 34: 330–347.
Ernst, R. R. 1977. *Sterilization by Heat in Disinfection, Sterilization, and
    Preservation*. Lea & Febiger, Philadelphia. pp 481–521.
Halliday, D., and Resnick, R. 1967. *Physics*. John Wiley & Sons, New York.
Holman, J. P. 1969. *Thermodynamics*. McGraw–Hill Book Company,
    New York.
Kochansky, D. Personal communication, Qualification of Dry Heat Ovens.
Lindboe, W. Personal communication, Validation Protocol—Hot Air De-
    pyrogenation and Sterilization in Ovens.
Parenteral Drug Association. 1981. *Validation of Dry Heat Processes Used
    for Sterilization and Depyrogenation*, Technical Report No. 3. pp 5–26.
Perkins, J. 1973. *Principles and Methods of Sterilization in Health Sciences*.
    Charles C. Thomas, Springfield, Ill. pp 286–310.
Pflug, I. J. 1971. *Sterilization of Space Hardware, Environmental Biology
    and Medicine*, Vol. 1. Gordon & Breach, Minneapolis. pp 63–81.
Remingtons Pharmaceutical Sciences. 1979. Mack Publishing Co., Easton,
    Pa. pp 1393, 1467.
Reynolds, W. C., and Perkins, H. 1977. *Engineering Thermodynamics*.
    McGraw–Hill Book Company, New York. pp 536–581.
Simmons, P. L. 1978. Hot air and continuous sterilization, in Parenteral
    Manufacturers Association, *Proceedings, Validation of Sterile Manufactur-
    ing Processes*, Reston, Virginia, March 15.
Simmons, P. L. 1981. The secret of successful sterilizer validation. *Phar-
    maceut. Eng.*, May/July, pp 38–46.
Tsuji, K., and Harrison, S. 1978. Dry heat destruction of lipopolysaccha-
    ride: Dry heat destruction kinetics. *Appl. Environ. Microbiol. 36*:
    710–714.
Tsuji, K., and Lewis, A. 1978. Dry heat destruction of lipopolysaccharide:
    Mathematical approach to process evaluation. *Appl. Environ. Microbiol.*
    36: 715–719.
United States Federal Standard 209B, *Federal Standard Clean Room and Work
    Station Requirements, Controlled Environment*, April 24, 1973, p 4.
United States Pharmacopeia, 20th rev. Mack Publishing Co., Easton, Pa.
    p 881.
Whitiker, G. 1978. Sterilization, validation, theory and principles, in Paren-
    teral Manufacturers Association, *Proceedings, Validation of Sterile Manu-
    facturing Processes*, Reston, Virginia, March 15.
Wood, R. T. 1982. Parenteral Drug Association Short Course on Dry Heat
    Sterilization Validation and Monitoring. pp 12–19.

13

Ethylene Oxide Sterilization and Validation for Practical Pharmaceutical Aseptic Production

JOHN R. GILLIS

Skyland Scientific Services, Inc., Belgrade, Montana

I. INTRODUCTION

The validation of the ethylene oxide gas (EO) sterilization process is one of the most complex and comprehensive programs facing the pharmaceutical process engineer. Ethylene oxide gaseous sterilization is an extremely effective process which can be performed with an infinite number of combinations of parameters. Key parameters that affect sterilization efficacy are (a) concentration of EO gas, (b) humidity, (c) temperature of the process, (d) accessibility to the product by these parameters, and (e) time.

The pharmaceutical process engineer must demonstrate that the selected combination of parameters is an effective sterilization process. The effectiveness of this process is measured by a calibrated microbial challenge and related to a calculated sterility assurance level, which is the probability of the occurrence of a nonsterile result. This level may vary depending on the product itself or the end use of the product. The pharmaceutical process engineer is also challenged with the task of assuring that the EO gas used does not create a health hazard for the employees in the working area or trace residuals to the consumer of the product. Adsorbed EO gas is removed fairly rapidly from the materials, while absorbed EO gas is released much more slowly. This absorption rate is highly dependent on the specific material being processed, as well as on the geometry of the product, which affects the surface-to-volume ratio. Appropriate measures must be taken to assure that EO gas used in the sterilizing environment is controlled and contained so that environmental insult and contamination is within acceptable limits.

During the EO gas sterilization process, the gas reacts with the materials processed by either absorption or adsorption. The EO gas is also trapped in the air spaces of the material being sterilized. This EO gas is rapidly removed through air exchanges. The product that is removed from the sterilizer must be controlled to prevent environmental insult to the workers. The best procedure is to place the sterilized materials in an environment that aids in the desorption of the gas, is environmentally controlled to minimize workplace contamination, and protects the sterility of the product or component.

II. PROPERTIES OF ETHYLENE OXIDE

Ethylene oxide is also referred to as EO, ETO, 1,2-epoxyethane, and dimethylene oxide. It has a formula of C_2H_4O: The following structure is illustrated:

$$H_2C\overset{}{\underset{O}{\diagdown\diagup}}CH_2$$

It is a colorless gas, with a molecular weight of 44.05. It has a characteristic etherlike odor. EO has a boiling point of 10.4°C (50.5°F) at 760 mmHg pressure, a melting point of −112.6°C (−170.7°F), a specific gravity of 0.8711 apparent at 20°C (60°F), or a specific gravity of 0.897 at 4°C. EO has a vapor density of 1.5, with air being equal to 1.0, and a vapor pressure at 20°C of 1095 mmHg. It is completely miscible in water, alcohol, acetone, benzene, ether, carbon tetrachloride, and most organic solvents, and is a powerful solvent for fats, oils, greases, waxes, some rubber formulations, and paints. It is highly exothermic and potentially explosive when heated or mixed with (a) alkali metal hydroxides, (b) highly active catalytic surfaces such as anhydrochlorides of iron, tin, or aluminum, and (c) the oxides of iron and aluminum. The explosive limits are 3−100% by volume in air. It has a flash point of −6°C (20°F). It is relatively noncorrosive for materials. EO is relatively stable in neutral aqueous solution and when diluted with carbon dioxide or gaseous halocarbons such as Freons.

Biologically, EO is an alkylating agent that reacts directly and nearly irreversibly with carboxyl groups (—COOH), amino groups (—NH2), sulfydral groups (—SH) and hydroxyl groups (—OH). It also reacts with ring nitrogen compounds such as purine and pyrimidine bases and with amino acids and proteins.

III. ETHYLENE OXIDE USE

The use of EO in the pharmaceutical and medical products industry is primarily for sterilization of those heat-sensitive products or components that cannot be sterilized conveniently by any other method. In the pharmaceutical industry these manufacturing components are used primarily in the aseptic fill of various types of pharmaceuticals. Ethylene oxide is also commonly used for terminal sterilization of medical devices.

The most commonly used form of EO gas for sterilization in the pharmaceutical industry is that which has been diluted with halocarbon products, primarily refrigerant 12, sold under trade names such as Freon 12. This product is normally composed of 12% EO with diluted 88% halocarbon. It may also be mixed with carbon dioxide in concentrations of 10% ethylene oxide, 90% carbon dioxide, or a 20% EO/80% carbon dioxide. In certain instances pure EO (100%) is used with no diluent. Since 20% EO/80% carbon dioxide and 100% EO are explosive, these substances must be used only in specially designed sterilizers and buildings that are designed to be intrinsically safe electrically.

A. Multiple Sterilization Charges from Single Mixed Gas Cylinders

1. Mixtures with Freon

Cylinders charged with ethylene oxide/Freon 12 mixtures contain a liquid that is a homogenous mixture of both the EO and the Freon 12. The pressure in these cylinders is low because of the vapor pressure of the liquid at the temperature at which the cylinders are stored. When the sterilizer is charged, homogeneous liquid is drawn off the bottom of the cylinder. The pressure in the cylinder remains virtually constant until the liquid level falls below the level of the educator tube. Multiple sterilizer charges can be performed with this mixture yielding consistant EO concentrations.

2. *Mixtures with Carbon Dioxide*

Cylinders charged with EO/carbon dioxide (CO_2) contain liquid EO and CO_2 in the vapor phase. The pressure of these cylinders is much higher than the EO/Freon mixtures. Because of the liquid phase/gas phase mixture, it is far more difficult to achieve multiple charges that are homogenous for EO/CO_2 ratio. Specially designed educator tubes draw the liquid EO from the bottom of the cylinder through a specially designed fixed orifice. Simultaneously, the gaseous CO_2 is bled off through these fixed orifices. These two phases are mixed before they are released from the cylinder. In theory, it works, provided the orifice openings are free-flowing. In practice, it is difficult to get consistent multiple charges from a single cylinder with this type of system. The approach most users take is to select a cylinder size that is equal to a single charge in the sterilizer. Therefore, inconsistencies that occur during the emptying process do not affect the final concentration of EO in the sterilizer.

IV. PRODUCT STERILIZATION

Ethylene oxide gaseous sterilization is frequently used for sterilizing aseptic manufacturing components and supplies. It is also used to terminally sterilize drug administration devices.

1. EO sterilization is used during the aseptic manufacturing process for items such as plastic bottles or tubes, rubber stoppers, plastic stoppers and caps.
2. EO sterilization is used for finished product in its final packaging. These products are primarily plastic or rubber drug administration devices.
3. EO sterilization is also used for process equipment such as freeze-driers used within the manufacturing area.

There are several major considerations that the pharmaceutical process engineer must be aware of in order to structure a validation program that will assure that the sterilization process does what it is intended to do. These considerations include: (a) the parameters that must be controlled during the process; (b) the physical control systems used to maintain these parameters; (c) the selection of appropriate process conditions; (d) the product design; (e) how the product is pretreated prior to exposure; (f) how the process is handled following sterilization; (g) how the process is monitored, including both cehmical and biological means of monitoring; and (h) the effect of residual EO and its reaction products on the material being sterilized.

V. PROCESS CONTROL PARAMETERS

There are four major parameters that must be controlled for the process: (a) temperature; (b) EO gas concentration; (c) moisture; and (d) time.

A. Temperature

The conventional limits on temperature are generally between 27°C (80°F) and 63°C (145°F). Most processes are run between 38°C (100°F) and 54°C (129.2°F). EO gas acts as a first-order kinetic reaction. First-order reactions are those that proceed at a rate exactly proportional to the concentration of one reactant. Temperature affects the rate of this reaction. An increase in temperature by 10°C (18°F) will approximately double the reaction rate, thus affecting the sterilization time. A basic doubling of the lethality of the process will occur with this rise in temperature. The lowest temperature limit is the temperature at which EO is converted from a liquid to a gas, which is 10.4°C (50.5°F). The upper limit is primarily affected by the temperature at which ethylene oxide polymerizes rapidly rendering it biologically inactive. Since this polymerization is not solely dependent on temperature, no specific temperature limit can be referenced.

B. EO Concentration

EO gas concentration below 300 mg/liter and above 1200 mg/liter are not commonly used in the industry. EO gas concentrations less than 300 mg/liter simply do not yield enough molecules of EO to be reliably effective in practical process times. Concentrations above 1200 mg/liter do not shorten the process times sufficiently to warrant the additional amount of gas required for the process. Sterilization effectiveness is dependent on the molecular collision of the EO molecule and the biological entity that is being sterilized. Therefore, more molecules lead to more efficient processing. A sterilizing process using 600 mg/liter of EO is approximately twice as fast as a process using 300 mg/liter, and a process using 1200 mg/liter is approximately twice as fast as a process using 600 mg/liter. However, considering the cost of EO, processes are generally designed toward the lower concentrations of EO. Concentrations of 400–600 mg/liter appear today to be the popular conditions.

C. Moisture

Moisture is the most important parameter in the EO sterilization process. Without adequate moisture, the process is greatly inhibited. With adequate moisture, the process will be dependent on the molecular activity of the EO and its interaction with the biological entity being sterilized. Ethylene oxide sterilization processes can be run between 30 and 90% RH. Generally 50–60% RH is selected for the process. Product and package compatibility generally determine this limit.

Moisture is extremely important in making the active sites on the microbial cell surface available to the alkylation action of ethylene oxide. The proteineous material of the cell surface contracts as it dries and the active sites are physically withdrawn, making it difficult for the ethylene oxide molecules to react. However, as the proteineous material is hydrated, it swells and expands. This exposes more active sites and allows the alkylation of ethylene oxide to occur more readily and rapidly. Without proper humidification, these active sites on the cell surfaces are protected and impede the lethality of the ethylene oxide sterilization process.

Moisturization of the microorganisms plays an extremely critical role in the sterilization of freeze-driers used in the pharmaceutical industry. Freeze-drying processes can stabilize organisms in a dessicated state, making them extemely resistant to the EO sterilization process. Freeze-dryers are also not designed as ethylene oxide sterilizers, and adequate mechanical means for moisturization are not generally supplied. Engineering modifications must be made to these machines in order to sterilize effectively with EO.

The most commonly used ethylene oxide sterilization cycles are (a) the static atmosphere cycle and (b) the dynamic environmental conditioning cycle.

The static atmosphere cycle (SAC) employs a prevacuum phase at the beginning of the cycle. This prevacuum is held static for a specified period of time. During this vacuum hold, moisture is admitted into the sterilizer in the form of either water or steam. This static hold has been commonly referred to as a dwell time. The water vapor moisturizes or humidifies the product to be sterilized during this dwell period. This dwell process is quite inefficient and takes many hours to moisturize the product enough for sterilization. If the goods have been preconditioned at high relative humidities, the SAC cycle will effectively replace the moisture removed by the evacuation process.

The dynamic environmental conditioning (DEC) cycle is an extremely effective cycle in moisturizing product to be sterilized. The DEC cycle also employs a preevacuation phase at the beginning of the sterilization cycle. However, when the vacuum level is reached, steam is pulsed to a preselected higher pressure. This pressure is usually about 10–20 mm higher than the vacuum level. During this introduction of steam the vacuum pump continues to run, therefore requiring large amounts of steam to create only a small rise in pressure. This pulsing action with the subatmospheric steam continues for approximately 15–30 min. The effect of this large quantity of steam is twofold. First, it heats the goods to be sterilized. This heating is caused by the condensation of steam vapor on the cooler goods. The condensation subsequently moisturizes the goods. Humidification and heating, therefore, occur simultaneously.

D. Time

The sterilization process time is related to: (a) moisturization level; (b) ethylene oxide gas concentration; and (c) temperature and packaging barriers around the product. The selection of the best process parameters will result in adequate EO sterilization process times of less than 2 hr. Process times for manufacturing components that are relatively easy to sterilize may even be less than 1 hr.

VI. PROCESS CONTROLLERS

This section deals with the physical considerations of control necessary to achieve an effective sterilization process.

A. Temperature Controllers

Process controllers are the thermocouple-type (TC) controllers or resistance temperature detector (RTD) controllers. They are compatible with temperature ranges within the sterilization process and give accurate and reliable information. Temperature is controlled primarily by using a jacket around the sterilizer. This jacket may be heated with a hot water/ethylene glycol mixture, or it may be steam-heated. The water/glycol mixture operates within a narrower temperature range than steam-heated jackets. Steam heating may be either an atmospheric condition or a subatmospheric condition. The atmospheric steam jackets give the widest spread of temperature, while subatmospheric jackets give the narrowest spread.

The location of the temperature control system is much less critical in a glycol-jacketed system. A few degrees of temperature range is generally noted in the glycol system. The temperature controller is located outside the sterilization chamber in a glycol recirculating line that heats the jacket. Steam-heated jackets, however, are usually monitored within the sterilizing chamber. Placement of the control bulb is extremely critical to overall temperature control within the chamber because of the hysteresis effect of the controller. There can also be temperature excursions because the controller calls for a signal and puts in excess steam into the jacket due to the thermal lag of the chamber mass.

B. Ethylene Oxide Gas Concentration Controllers

The ethylene oxide gas concentration is controlled in one of two ways. The most common method of control is through a pressure control system. The alternative control system is through analytical instruments that actually sense the ethylene oxide gas in the environment inside the sterilizer and control on direct analytical output.

The pressure controller is either a simple pressure switch or a pressure transducer. The ethylene oxide gas concentration desired is calculated as to the corresponding increase in pressure. The desired pressure settings are then maintained by conventional pressure controllers.

The analytical systems are either gas chromatographic or infrared detectors. These instruments are installed directly at the sterilizer. Periodic gas samples are withdrawn from the sterilizer and passed through the analytical detector. Electronic signals are sent to control valves in the supply lines to maintain a minimum gas concentration.

C. Relative Humidity Controllers

Relative humidity (RH) is controlled in the SAC-type cycles only, and is controlled during the sterilization process through the introduction of either water or steam vapor. Water is not commonly used, since it must be vaporized in order for it to be effective in humidifying the goods to be sterilized. The quantities of water can be measured very accurately using volumetric devices. This is usually accomplished as a one-time introduction with no ability to control after the initial introduction. It is very difficult to predict how much moisture the goods in a sterilizer load will absorb, so it is very difficult to predetermine the amount of water to add. This process is used more routinely on experimental sterilizers where loads are small and carefully controlled. Production loads are generally large and quite variable in the amount of moisture required to humidfy them.

The introduction of steam vapor is the most common method of controlling humidity inside the sterilizer. This system usually employs an electronic hygrometer that senses the moisture level inside the sterilizer environment.

When low levels are sensed, a steam valve is opened and more steam is emitted into the sterilizer. The hygrometer has a minimum and maximum set point. When the high-level reading is indicated, the steam valve is turned off. The humidity can then be controlled as the drop in environmental moisture reflects moisture absorption in the load. If this type of control is selected, it is always used in the cycle phases prior to the introduction of ethylene oxide gas. Since some hygrometers are sensitive to ethylene oxide gas, the control can only be used prior to the introduction of gas. Those systems that are compatible with the gas can be used throughout the cycle.

When the DEC cycle is used, no humidity control system is used. The amount of steam used and the thermal shock to the hygrometer render them incompatible. If a hygrometer is compatible it will undoubtedly read saturated or 100% RH after the initial steam pulse because of the condensation of steam on the cool hygrometer. As the hygrometer heats up during the cycle, it will begin to give readings less than saturation. The accuracy of hygrometer readings following this saturated condition should be checked by subsequent calibration.

Humidity control in the DEC cycle is built into the physics of the cycle design. The steam pulses purge all the air from the chamber and goods to be sterilized. A temperature control system measures the temperature of the steam condensate. This condensate is indicative of the temperature of the product being sterilized. Therefore, when the product has been heated to the steam vapor temperature, it has been moisturized by the steam condensate. At this phase of the cycle the goods are at temperature and more moist than may be desired. The next phase of the cycle takes care of the excess moisture, if any. When the ethylene oxide gas is charged into the sterilizer following this steam pulsing phase, a resultant rise in temperature occurs as a result of the increased pressure. This rise in temperature due to the compression of the steam vapor causes some of the moisture to flash off, thus drying out the product slightly.

VII. ETHYLENE OXIDE GAS CONCENTRATION

Ethylene oxide gas concentrations can be monitored in one of two general methods: the indirect method, or the direct method.

A. Indirect Method

The indirect method of monitoring ethylene oxide gas concentration is determined through pressurization of the ethylene oxide chamber using gas cylinders containing certified mixtures of ethylene oxide. If the chamber is pressurized at a specific delta of pressure, it is assumed that the certified mixture contains the given amount of ethylene oxide for every pound change in pressure. Therefore, the pressure excursion is equated to gas concentration. This system is very easy to monitor using pressure recorders. Gas analysis is not required, except for the certified charging gas.

The indirect method involves weighing the gas cylinders and calculating the weight differential (assuming there are no gas leaks from the chamber). The weight of the cylinder before charging and the weight of the cylinder after charging are calculated. This procedure assumes that an even dispersion of the ethylene oxide and diluent gas was released into the vessel, yielding a calculated concentration of gas in the sterilizing chamber.

The indirect method is limited because it does not compensate for the partial pressure contributions of water vapor and residual air, and assumes a homogeneous mixture of EO and Freon. It also does not consider or compensate for absorption of EO by the packaging materials or the product. These materials absorb EO at different rates than they do Freons. It also does not consider physical leaks in the sterilization system. Thus the indirect method gives, at best, only an approximation of the EO gas concentration.

B. Calculation of Ethylene Oxide Concentration Using Pressure Measurements

The theoretical calculation of the concentration of ethylene oxide in a sterilizer, after the initial charge of gas and at temperature equilibrium, is based on the ideal gas law (PV = nRT) [1]. The following assumptions are made:

1. The mixture of ethylene oxide, water vapor, and air (and the diluent gas when used) behaves as an ideal gas.
2. There is no selective loss of a component of the mixture, e.g., by means of absorption or adsorption.
3. The label information on the cylinders containing the gas is accurate, and the percentage by weight of the mixture of gas remains constant during admission to the sterilizer.
4. Gauge readings are absolute pressure readings.

The ethylene oxide concentration is calculated on the basis of the difference in total pressure resulting from the addition of ethylene oxide plus carrier or diluent gas, and the sterilizer chamber temperature.

The difference in total pressure due to the addition of ethylene oxide and diluent gas can be expressed as

$$P = P_{EO} + P_{DG} = \left[\left(\frac{n}{v} \right)_{EO} + \left(\frac{n}{v} \right)_{DG} \right] RT \tag{1}$$

Rearranging the above gas law expression (1) allows for the calculation of ethylene oxide concentration, regardless of the EO/single diluent combination, using the following equation:

$$EO_{conc} = \frac{K \times P}{R \times T} = \frac{4.4 \times 10^4 (M)(E)}{(M)(E) + 44(100 - E)} \tag{2}$$

where

EO_{conc} = EO concentration

R = gas constant

P = difference in total pressure due to EO and diluent

T = absolute temperature

K = constant for given diluent (see Table 1)

M = molecular weight of a diluent (see Table 1)

E = weight percentage of EO in diluent mixture

1. Example Calculations

To determine EO concentration in terms of mg/liter, we shall assume a process that uses 12% EO and 88% Freon 12. After gas injection, the rise in

TABLE 1   EO/Diluent Constants and Molecular Weights

EO/diluent	K (mg/g-mol)[a]	K (lb/lb-mol)[b]
10% EO/90% diluent	4.40×10^3	4.40
12% EO/88% Freon 12	1.20×10^4	1.20×10^1
20% EO/80% CO_2	8.80×10^3	8.80
100% EO	4.40×10^4	4.40×10^1

Molecular weight	
Ethylene oxide (EO)	44.0
Freon 12	120.9
Carbon dioxide	44.0

[a]Use when calculating mg/liter.
[b]Use when calculating lb/ft^3.

pressure was 40.5 in.Hg. If the temperature at the end of gas injection was 55°C, then:

P = 40.5 in.Hg = 1.35 atm
T = 55°C = 328 K
$R = 0.08205 \dfrac{\text{atm-liter}}{\text{g-mol-K}}$ (see Table 2 for gas constants)
$K = 1.20 \times 10^4$ mg/g-mol

The EO concentration is

$$EO_{conc} = \frac{K \times P}{R \times T} = \frac{(1.2 \times 10^4 \text{ mg/g-mol})(1.35 \text{ atm})}{(0.08205 \text{ atm-liter/g-mol-K})(328 \text{ K})}$$

$$= 602.5 \text{ mg/liter}$$

As an example of the determination of EO concentration in terms of pounds per cubic foot (lb/ft^3), assume a process that uses 10% EO and 90% CO_2. After gas injection, the rise in pressure was 2.89 kg/cm^2. If the temperature at the end of gas injection was 134°F, then:

$P = 2.89 \text{ kg/cm}^2 = 2.80$ atm
T = 134°F = 56°C = 329 K
$R = 1.3140 \dfrac{\text{atm-ft}^3}{\text{lb-mol-K}}$ (see Table 2 for gas constants)
$K = 4.40 \dfrac{\text{lb}}{\text{lb-mol}}$

The EO concentration is

$$EO_{conc} = \frac{K \times P}{R \times T} = \frac{(4.40 \text{ lb/lb-mol})(2.80 \text{ atm})}{(1.3140 \text{ atm-ft}^3/\text{lb-mol-K})(329 \text{ K})}$$

$$= 0.0285 \text{ lb/ft}^3$$

TABLE 2   Gas Constants (R)[a]

Pressure	Volume	Temperatures	R
atm	cm^3	K	82.057
atm	liters	K	0.08205
atm	ft^3	K	1.3140
bar	liters	K	0.08314
kg/m^2	liters	K	847.80
kg/cm^2	liters	K	0.08478
mmHg	liters	K	62.361
mmHg	ft^3	K	998.90
in.Hg	liters	K	2.4549

[a]Note: 1 atm = 760 mmHg = 29.92 in.Hg = 14.70 psia = 1.013 bar = 1.033 kg/cm^2 = 101.3 kPa (kN/m^3). Also, 1 liter = 1000 cm^3 = 0.03532 ft^2, and K = °C + 273. It is important to maintain the proper units when using the EO concentration equation and the gas constants.

C.   Derivation of the Ethylene Oxide Gas Concentration Equation

Since most operations record the pressure change during EO gas injection, the equation was derived to allow the calculation of EO concentration from the pressure rise due to EO gas injection, with or without a single diluent gas such as Freon 12 or carbon dioxide [1]. The purpose of this equation is to provide a simple and rapid method for calculating EO gas concentration in sterilizers.

The pressure rise can be expressed as in Eq. (1):

$$P = P_{EO} + P_{DG} = \left(\frac{n}{v}\right)_{EO} RT + \left(\frac{n}{v}\right)_{DG} RT$$

$$= \left[\left(\frac{n}{v}\right)_{EO} + \left(\frac{n}{v}\right)_{DG}\right] RT$$

The above formula can be expressed in milligrams per liter:

$$\left(\frac{n}{v}\right)_{EO} = \frac{g}{MW_{EO}} \text{ liter} = \frac{10^{-3}}{44}\left(\frac{mg}{liter}\right)_{EO}$$

$$\left(\frac{n}{v}\right)_{DG} = \frac{g}{MW_{DG}} \text{ liter} = \frac{10^{-3}}{M}\left(\frac{mg}{liter}\right)_{DG}$$

where

MW_{EO} = molecular weight of ethylene oxide = 44.0
MW_{DG} = molecular weight of diluent gas = M

Then the pressure rise can be rewritten as

$$P = \left[\frac{10^{-3}}{44} \left(\frac{mg}{liter} \right)_{EO} + \frac{10^{-3}}{M} \left(\frac{mg}{liter} \right)_{DG} \right] RT \qquad (2)$$

Since the weight percent EO (wt% EO) is usually known and the sterilizer volume remains constant, the expression derived above can be written as

$$Wt\% \ EO = \frac{\left(\frac{mg}{liter} \right)_{EO}}{\left(\frac{mg}{liter} \right)_{EO} + \left(\frac{mg}{liter} \right)_{DG}} \times 100$$

Solving for $(mg/liter)_{DG}$:

$$\left(\frac{mg}{liter} \right)_{DG} = \frac{\left(\frac{mg}{liter} \right)_{EO} 100 - \left(\frac{mg}{liter} \right)_{EO} wt\% \ EO}{wt\% \ EO}$$

$$= \left(\frac{mg}{liter} \right)_{EO} \left(\frac{100 - wt\% \ EO}{wt\% \ EO} \right)$$

Substituting the above for $(mg/liter)_{DG}$, Eq. (2) becomes

$$P = \left[\frac{10^{-3}}{44} \left(\frac{mg}{liter} \right)_{EO} + \frac{10^{-3}}{M} \left(\frac{mg}{liter} \right)_{EO} \left(\frac{100 - wt\% \ EO}{wt\% \ EO} \right) \right] RT \qquad (3)$$

Solving for $(mg/liter)_{EO}$ in Eq. (3):

$$P = RT \left[\frac{10^{-3}}{44} + \frac{10^{-3}}{M} \left(\frac{100 - wt\% \ EO}{wt\% \ EO} \right) \right] \left(\frac{mg}{liter} \right)_{EO}$$

Let wt% EO = E and rewrite:

$$P = RT \left[\frac{10^{-3}}{44} + \frac{10^{-3}}{M} \left(\frac{100 - E}{E} \right) \right] \left(\frac{mg}{liter} \right)_{EO}$$

Then rewrite:

$$P = 10^{-3} RT \left[\frac{1}{44} + \frac{100 - E}{(M)(E)} \right] \left(\frac{mg}{liter} \right)_{EO}$$

$$= 10^{-3} RT \left[\frac{(M)(E) + 44(100 - E)}{44(ME)(E)} \right] \left(\frac{mg}{liter} \right)_{EO}$$

Then:

$$\left(\frac{mg}{liter} \right)_{EO} = \frac{10^3 P}{RT} \left[\frac{44(M)(E)}{(M)(E) + 44(100 - E)} \right]$$

D. Direct Gas Measurement

Direct analysis of the EO in a sterilizing chamber can be performed by a variety of analytical systems [1]. Two of the most common systems use infrared (IR) spectrophotometry or gas chromatography (GC) detection.

1. Gas Chromatography

Gas chromatography (GC) has been the most widely used method for determining the level of EO in the sterilizing environment. When using EO mixtures, the chamber is under a positive pressure, making withdrawal of a gas sample easy. Sterilization processes that use 100% EO occur at subatmospheric pressures, making sampling more difficult, since the gas sampling system requires a vacuum to withdraw the sample. When dealing with explosive mixtures of EO or pure EO, only intrinsically safe instrumentation is permitted. Nonexplosive mixtures may be analyzed using any standard GC.

Sample removal is extremely important in order to assure meaningful data. Sample lines must be heated and insulated upon exiting the sterilizer. If cold spots exist in the sampling lines, the EO and water vapor will condense, yielding false data. These samples may be collected using gas collection bottles or lines attached directly to the GC if an automatic injection system is used.

Sample sites also present a problem. Representative sites are generally selected throughout the sterilizing chamber. Small capillary tubes serving as sample delivery lines are fitted to the gas sample ports. Care must be taken to permit these sample tubes to be flushed to assure that the sample being extracted is, indeed, from the chamber environment and not a residual in the sample delivery line. For this reason, it is not recommended to sample within the product or product packages. The flushing of the sample tube accelerates the gas penetration into these restricted locations and yields data that are not representative.

Prior to sample analysis, the GC unit must be calibrated with a certified standard gas. This certified standard may be either a diluted gas mixture or 100% EO. Most laboratories that are established to perform GC analysis are qualified to use 100% EO as the standard for calibration. However, certified mixtures are available from gas suppliers. The GC is calibrated at one point with this standard gas and expressed as mole percent. These calibration results are independent of temperature and pressure. The mole percent of the sterilization chamber is compared to the standard gas and is then converted into milligrams per liters.

$$\frac{mol\%}{100\%} \times \frac{44.0 \text{ g}}{mol} \times \frac{1000 \text{ mg}}{g} \times \frac{1 \text{ mol}}{22.41 \text{ liter}} \times \frac{(14.7 \text{ psia} + Y \text{ psig})}{14.7 \text{ psia}} \times$$

$$\frac{273°C}{(273°C + Z°C)} = XF$$

where

    Y psig = pressure of the sterilizing chamber

    Z°C = temperature in the sterilizing chamber

    XF = scaling factor

Therefore, the EO concentration from the GC data in mole percent multiplied by the scaling factor (XF) yields milligrams per liter.

2. Infrared Analysis

Most gases have a characteristic infrared spectrum that can be used to identify the gas and determine the amount of gas present. These spectra are usually rather complex. Each spectrum, however, usually contains a small number of strong bands. It is these strong bands that are used in this analysis.

These IR analyzers incorporate a fixed bandpass filter with a wavelength that corresponds to one of these strong bands in the infrared spectrum of the vapor being monitored. An optical path is also chosen that provides the sensitivity range required for that particular analysis.

The analytical wavelength for 100% ethylene oxide is 11.8 μm. When a Freon mixtrue is used, it has been found that a wavelength of 3.3 μm is more satisfactory and minimizes the interference with the Freon spectrum. The path length is 20.25 m. This system is theoretically sensitive to 0.4 ppm of EO using a 20-m cell.

Calibration of these analyzers must also be performed using certified standard gas. Calibration with the standard gas must consider the pressure differential between the calibration gas and the sterilizing chamber. Once the wavelength and path length are set, using the calibration standard, the instruments' response to absorbing the gas is directly correlated to concentration.

VIII. MOISTURE

Moisture is assessed by the indirect method or the direct method.

A. Indirect Method

The indirect method uses differential pressure measurements. This differential pressure is a valid measurement only when the pressure change is due entirely to the vapor pressure of water. If liquid water is emitted at the same time as steam pressure, an additional pressure rise will occur when the liquid water is vaporized. If there is an air leak into the vessel, a false pressure rise will be indicated. This air leak can cause an erroneously high amount of moisture. It is also very difficult to get an accurate measurement of this parameter when a product is in the vessel, because of the moisture-absorbing qualities of various products and packages. This is a process that works extremely well on an empty chamber, but it is very difficult to assess in a very practical manner within the loaded chamber.

If the indirect method is to be applied, measurements can be calculated using the properties of saturated steam found in engineering handbooks (Table 3). For example, the vapor pressure of saturated steam at 55°C is 117.85 mmHg. If the sterilization cycle is to be run at 55°C and a relative humidity of 50% is desired, a change in pressure due to the addition of steam will be 58.93 mmHg.

$$\text{Pressure change required (mmHg)} = \frac{\text{vapor pressure @ T}}{\text{saturated steam in mmHg}} \times \text{desired \%RH}$$

$$58.93 \text{ mmHg} = 117.85 \times 50\% \text{ RH}$$

where

T = temperature of sterilization process

TABLE 3

Temperature, °C	mmHg	Temperature, °F
0	4.579	32
5	6.541	41
10	9.205	50
15	12.779	59
20	17.51	68
25	23.69	77
30	31.71	86
35	42.02	95
40	55.13	104
45	71.66	113
50	92.30	122
55	117.85	131
60	149.19	140
65	187.36	149

Source: Ref. 2.

B. Direct Method

The direct method of assessing moisture uses analytical instrumentation such as dew-point hygrometers, infrared analyzers, or gas chromatography. Samples are withdrawn from the sterilizer chamber. When removing samples from the chamber, care must be exercised to assure that sample lines are properly insulated and heated so that the moisture does not condense in the sample lines. Reducing the pressure in the sample lines is important when using an analytical system that performs only at ambient pressure. If rapid changes in pressure occur, moisture will also be lost from the sample through condensation. These sample lines are usually closed loop circulating systems.

Calibration of these systems is performed with either a saturated water vapor standard or saturated salt solutions that yield headspace water vapor concentration other than saturation.

IX. VALIDATION OF ETHYLENE OXIDE STERILIZATION PROCESSES

Validation of the ethylene oxide process is divided into three segments: Engineering Qualification of the sterilizer, Calibration of all the instrumentation, and Process Qualification. When these three segments are completed successfully and all aspects of the process are documented, the process is certified for routine use for manufacturing goods.

A. Engineering Qualification

Engineering Qualification deals with the sterilizer and associated equipment used in the process. This segment is divided into two phases: Installation Qualification, and Operational Qualification.

1. Installation Qualification

Installation qualification requires an audit of the equipment as it has been installed in the facility. This audit includes checking all utilities and supplies to the equipment to make sure that they are in accordance with the manufacturer's recommended specifications. Engineering drawings must be evaluated to assure that (a) the equipment is assembled according to the manufacturer's prints, (b) the equipment is installed according to the installation schematics, and (c) all aspects of the equipment or documented with appropriate engineering drawings or sketches. These drawings are essential for future reference to compare the hardware validated to future configurations. This phase of the validation program is probably the most abused, because it is contrary to the way most engineering departments operate. Once the equipment is hooked up and it "runs," little more is ever documented. With the press to get things working, little attention is paid to documentation for future reference. Many validations have been performed with all the necessary tests on the hardware relating to product loads, with no record as to the exact configuration of the equipment when the validation was executed. Since any mechanical device will routinely malfunction, or wear out and be replaced, it is absolutely essential that a well-prepared Engineering Qualification document be assembled for each piece of equipment that is validated. If this is not done, the subsequent validation data are meaningless.

2. *Operational Qualification*

Operational Qualification deals with the operating parameters of the sterilizer as set by the manufacturer. These tests are performed with an empty chamber. The various parameters for the cycle are evaluated to determine if they perform as specified. Temperature controllers are set and evaluated to determine the deadband of the control switch, and the temperature distribution within the sterilizer. The unit is also sequenced through its operating steps to assure that the sequencing is appropriate. Every operating parameter is checked to see that it is in compliance with the manufacturer's operating specification. The validation team is often hampered because it does not have a detailed operating procedure. Through the use of a formal protocol, this procedure is tested. This testing specifies in detail both the equipment and how it is to operate. The operator performing this qualification should prove that the detail procedure is validated.

B. Calibration

The second major phase of the validation program is the calibration of all process sensing, controlling, indicating, and recording devices on the sterilizer. Recording instruments that appear on the control panel are typically calibrated, but many of the control instruments are often located out of sight and must not be ignored. They may have a tremendous impact on the cycle function. For example, with the dynamic environmental conditioning phase of an ethylene oxide sterilizing process, it is extremely important to calibrate the stall point of the vacuum pump before the actual pressure or temperature set points are calibrated. This measurement is critical to balance the steam input into the chamber in relation to the capacity of the vacuum pump to remove the steam from the chamber. All parameters that are measured by the control system must be calibrated. This is even more complicated when microprocessor control units are employed, because not only are there specific operating set points for those systems, there are also high-limit and low-limit alarm systems that must be calibrated. The calibration program will also vary depending on the type of microprocessor—whether it is a data processor or a process controller.

The calibration program should be performed with instruments referred to as secondary standards. The secondary standard is a standard that can be transported to and from the actual sterilization equipment because most instruments associated with the sterilizer must be calibrated at the sterilizer's location. Secondary standards are traceable to the National Bureau of Standards and should have an accuracy and a sensitivity of five times that of the instrument being calibrated.

Primary standards must have an even greater sensitivity. It is recommended that these primary standards be submitted to the National Bureau of Standards for calibration and recertification on a periodic basis. Primary standards are usually recertified annually.

It is extremely important that detailed procedures be established for the metrologist in charge of calibrating all the instruments on the sterilizer. Adequate records must be maintained. A means of tracking systems to prepare the metrologist for that required calibration at its designated frequency should be established. Some instruments may need to be calibrated quarterly, other instruments sensors may need to be calibrated semiannually; still other instruments, because of the criticality of the process, must be calibrated more frequently. As a history file is compiled on each sensor, it will become obvious if the frequency with which it is being currently calibrated is either excessive or not adequate.

C. Process Qualification

The third phase of validation deals with Process Qualification. Even though the unit has functioned appropriately with an empty chamber, it must now be proved that it sterilizes the product.

1. *Load Configuration*

There are several key aspects of Process Qualification. First, one must define the loading configuration used in the sterilizing vessel. Second, one must define the specific product and product package to be used in master cartons to build up to pallets. Packaging around the primary product is as important as any other parameter in the sterilization process. Temperature, relative humidity, and gas concentration are also important. Once the primary product is defined, and the package that contains that primary product is defined, master cartons or packaging configurations must be established and identified for the various loads to be sterilized. Many manufacturers have a vast array of products, so extensive that products must be mixed together in order to achieve effective throughput in the sterilization process. It is extremely important that the particular mix is built up with a rationale that is logical, based on mass of material being placed in the sterilizer, types of package around the product, and the actual product configuration itself. It is possible that a manufacturer may have in his catalog, literally, hundreds of different products. If these are all of the same generic type, such as catheters, sutures, and orthopedic implants, it is possible that they could, because of the similar geometry and similar material, be sterilized within one or two different sterilization processes. It is also possible that a manufacturer may manufacture only a few products, each being so different from the other products manufactured that all product processes will have to be qualified.

Categorizing product for the sterilizing load is an extremely important element and must be done by a knowledgeable and competent sterilization scientist. Once product categories have been identified, it is also possible to

vary the load. Load configurations should be extremely specific in their definition. However, there are certain tolerances that are permissible without
changing the overall impact on the biological effectiveness of the sterilization.
Generally speaking, a 25% increase or decrease in the load that is qualified
has little biological impact on the process. Much depends on how the material
is handled prior to Process Validation. If the material is adequately preconditioned in a special environment that assures adequate moisture penetration
to the product, and adequate temperature penetration and warming of the
product, then greater variables may be achieved in loading configurations.
However, if an increase in the load results in a greater compressing of packages on the pallet, for example, or if standard pallets are stacked so that
there is a chimney effect (spaces around the master cartons), allowing easy
permeation of gas throughout the pallet, and an additional 25% load would result in the pallet being packaged differently, removing these interstitial spaces,
a separate qualification program would be necessary. However, if the additional
boxes would still allow the pallet to penetrate the sterilizer, but would not impact the total orientation in the pallet, an additional process qualification would
not be necessary.

Once the load has been defined, then instrumentation should be placed in
the load so that the environment associated with the product is monitored.
Temperature and relative humidity are the most commonly monitored parameters.

2. Ethylene Oxide Gas Monitoring

Gas concentration is not generally monitored in the environment of the
product. The reason for this is that the capillary tube that is necessary for
withdrawing the gas sample from the sterilizer has a sufficient volume to cause
erroneous readings in the vicinity of the product. If this gas sampling tube
is monitoring the outside environment close to the product, then little technical problems are incurred. However, if the gas sampling port is placed
within the product, then the removal of that volume contained within the capillary tube may tend to draw ethylene oxide into the environment where the
product is and give an artificial indication of rapid penetration of ethylene
oxide gas into the product. Samples drawn continuously from the product
create a small delta pressure, causing a positive flow of gas from the environment into that sampling port of the product. If the environment within the
sampling area is large and unencumbered, then meaningful gas samples can
be withdrawn from the chamber. Samples are generally withdrawn from a
spectrum of locations within the chamber, typically warmer as well as cooler
than other locations. Samples should be withdrawn from both the front of
the vessel and the back, as well as from the top to the bottom of the vessel,
so that all geometric areas within the sterilizer are assayed.

3. Temperature Monitoring

Thermocouples may be placed and actually mounted into the product. Since
the thermocouple is an electrical reading coming out of the product, it can be
placed well into the product to indicate temperature heat-up of a particular
surface or environment within the product. Again, the number of thermocouples will depend on the complexity of the product and the complexity of
the loading configuration. As a general rule, no less than 10 thermocouples
should be used for mapping the temperature distribution within a chamber.
Larger chambers generally should contain many more than 10 thermocouples.

4. *Relative Humidity Monitoring*

Relative humidity sensors, used to monitor the chamber environment, can also be used to monitor the environment within the package or within the master carton and, in some cases, even within the product. Again, because this is an electrical reading, it does not have the same impact on the parameter that the removal of a gas sample has. However, the humidity element may indeed have an impact on the temperature within that particular environment in the load. Again, the humidity penetration should be measured at various geometric locations within the sterilizer. Specifications should be prepared that detail these specific parameters, the tolerances for those parameters, and the degree of biological effectiveness that is desired for the sterilization system. These parameters should be monitored and controlled and biological effectiveness should be achieved before the actual manufacturing process is terminated. Therefore, most Process Qualification cycles are performed at less than the operating time for the manufacturing process. A common practice in industry is to run one-half of the actual sterilization exposure for the validation run. Stated a different way, at the point where biological effectiveness is achieved, in order to assure that this effectiveness is carried out on every manufacturing process, a doubling of that particular exposure time is established for the routine process.

5. *Biological Monitoring*

Biological monitoring of the sterilization process uses calibrated bacterial spores. The bacterial spores most commonly used are *Bacillus subtilis*. The *B. subtilis* spores are very resistant to the ethylene oxide sterilization process. These spores are usually placed on a carrier substrate that allows them to be conveniently placed inside product samples. The location of choice is the position in the product that is most difficult to sterilize. The inoculated product samples are then packaged in a similar manner as the product. The samples are placed in positions in the load that also have been identified as difficult to sterilize.

Biological indicator (BI) systems have been developed using paper strips containing spores. The paper strips are packaged in biobarrier envelopes. Some BIs are packaged in self-contained culture systems. These systems are used in the same manner. They should be placed inside the product package rather than inside the product. Placement will depend largely on the configuration of the product and package.

Following the sterilization process, these monitoring systems are removed from the sterilizer and cultured in the laboratory. The U.S. Pharmocopeia recommends culturing in soybean casein digest medium at a temperature of 30–35°C. Specific culture recommendations may be supplied by the manufacturer of the monitor system. Some monitoring systems claim that high confidence levels can be achieved after 48 hr of incubation, while others claim that incubation should continue for up to 7 days.

BIs are much more convenient than inoculated product or inoculated simulated products. A Process Validation program should include product sterility data as well as BI data. Routine process monitoring can then include the use of biological indicators only. Normally, a minimum of 10 BIs are used for each sterilization cycle. For extremely large loads up to 1000 ft^3, several times as many BIs may be tested per cycle. This is dependent on the product application physical size and difficulty to sterilize. The BI data must be integrated into all aspects of the process control program to assure an adequate sterility assurance level (SAL). A common SAL is 10^{-6}, which means less than one chance in a million of an unsuccessful sterilization cycle.

6. Residuals

Sterilant residuals and sterilant reaction products must also be considered in the Process Validation program. Ethylene oxide, being a toxic substance, will render a sterile product unusable if excessive amounts remain in the product after sterilization. The ethylene oxide gas becomes trapped inside product voids. It is also absorbed and adsorbed by the product. Depending on the product material, it is generally easily removed. A common approach is to place the poststerilized product in a heated aeration chamber with very frequent air changes. Ambient storage will also allow the ethylene oxide gas to dissipate.

There are two ethylene oxide reaction products that are also considered toxic but to a much lesser degree than ethylene oxide gas. The ethylene oxide gas reacts with chlorine to form ethylene chlorohydrin and with water to form ethylene glycol. These reaction products are not easy to remove from the materials. Therefore, it is important to minimize the formation of these reaction products. In the case of ethylene chlorohydrin, product and package materials with chlorinated compounds should not be used if ethylene oxide gas is the sterilizing medium.

Ethylene glycol formation is dependent on the amount of moisture that is actually present as water. The pH of this water will influence the rate at which the ethylene glycol is formed. The reaction is usually quite slow. The approach is to minimize the actual pooled water in the product and package during the humidification process and to remove the humidity and ethylene oxide gas after exposure by evacuation of the chamber. This will effectively reduce the formation of ethylene glycol levels that affect the use of the product.

X. ETHYLENE OXIDE TOXICITY

Ethylene oxide is a toxic and hazardous chemical. It is this characteristic that renders it an effective sterilizing agent. Controlling this chemical to minimize and prevent human exposure is an important consideration in the application of EO gas when used to sterilize materials in the pharmaceutical industry. The Occupational Safety and Health Act of 1970 emphasized the need for standards to protect the health and safety of workers. The National Institute of Occupational Safety and Health (NIOSH) has disseminated information about the adverse effects of widely used chemical and physical agents, in an attempt to assist employers in providing protection to employees from exposure to these substances. NIOSH has taken the lead in disseminating information about ethylene oxide toxicity.

The acute toxic effects of ethylene oxide in humans and animals include: acute respiratory and eye irritation, skin sensitization, vomiting, and diarrhea. Known chronic effects consist of respiratory irritation, secondary respiratory infection, and anemia. No definitive epidemiologic studies and no standard long-term study assays are available on which to assess the carcinogenic potential. Limited tests by skin application or subcutaneous injections in mice did not reveal carcinogenicity. However, the alkylating and mutagenic properties of EO are sufficient basis for concern about its potential as a carcinogenic agent. Adequate data, for animals or humans, are not available on which to assess the potential teratogenicity of EO.

NIOSH is recommending that EO be considered as a mutogenic and potentially carcinogenic agent for humans and that occupational exposure to it be minimized by eliminating all *unnecessary* and improper uses of EO. The *Federal Register*, on April 21, 1984, proposed that the worker exposure limit be reduced from 50 parts per million (ppm) to 1 ppm in the worker's environment, based on a time-weighted average. This proposal was finalized on September 9, 1985 (Federal Register 50FR9800—March 12, 1985).

At the time of the proposal to reduce the level from 50 ppm to 1 ppm, little scientific evidence existed to support the contention that 1 ppm was necessary to protect the environmental health of the workers. Further assessment of ethylene oxide exposure and the adequacy of the available scientific data is being considered by NIOSH. Future studies are being proposed to assess the true occupational hazard of employees in the work environment.

If EO must be used as a sterilizing agent, improved techniques of exhausting the gas from the sterilizer and controlled aeration of the sterilized items must be implemented in order to comply with the new NIOSH regulations. Ethylene oxide sterilization should be supervised and the areas into which EO may escape must be monitored to prevent any unnecessary exposure of personnel. When proper control measures are instituted, the escape of EO into the environment is greatly reduced. Under such control, EO can be used as a gaseous sterilant in pharmaceutical facilities with little risk to the health of exposed workers.

REFERENCES

1. Association for the Advancement of Medical Instrumentation. 1982. Standard for BIER/EO Gas Vessels.
2. Weast, R. C., S. M. Selby (eds.). 1968. Handbook of Chemistry and Physics, The Chemical Rubber Co., p. E14.

14
Validation of Cobalt 60 Radiation Sterilization

GEORGE R. DIETZ

Isomedix, Inc., Whippany, New Jersey

I. INTRODUCTION

To validate: "To make legally valid; to support or corroborate on a sound or authoritative basis" (Webster, 1981 ed.).

Validation as applied to the radiation sterilization of medical devices includes:

1. The determination that the irradiated product is safe and performs its intended end use
2. The establishment of a proper radiation dose to assure that the desired degree of sterility assurance is consistently obtained
3. The establishment of a radiation cycle in the irradiator to assure that the prescribed irradiation dose is consistently delivered

Each of these aspects will be discussed in detail in this chapter.

II. HISTORICAL BACKGROUND

Although the Johnson & Johnson Company is generally recognized as the early developer and leader in ^{60}Co sterilization, the Westminster Carpet Company in Australia was actually the first to use gamma processing on a commercial scale for sterilization purposes. In 1960, it began to process goat hair for anthrax control. The final product was then used in the manufacture of carpets.

By this time, the Johnson & Johnson effort to adapt gamma processing for medical use was well underway, and by 1963 it was sterilizing sutures produced by Ethicon in North America's first large-scale commercial unit.

The remainder of the 1960s was relatively quiet as far as additional medical applications and new ^{60}Co facilities were concerned, although research continued. Cobalt-60 prices were high, and with relatively small volumes of product to process, unit costs were, for the most part, prohibitive. Microbiological testing, D-value results, and product bioburden evaluations began to suggest a particular radiation dose to assure sterility. Appropriate safety factors were added, and a sterilizing dose of 2.5 Mrad became the acceptable standard for sterilizing any product, regardless of its initial microbiological contamination or the intended end use of the product.

By the early 1970s, several small service irradiation companies emerged, offering radiation services on a more wide-scale basis. This enabled many companies to explore the potential use of radiation without the need for a rather large capital investment. Additional medical devices, usually small-volume, high-priced items such as orthopedic units, were introduced into radiation. The survival prospects of the service irradiation companies were helped at this point by the introduction of enzymes and phosphates into laundry detergents. Nearly all the enzymes underwent a gross filtration, followed by a final radiation step to further reduce microbial contamination. Almost concurrently, several large Teflon suppliers concluded that it was economically attractive to degrade Teflon scrap by radiation rather than heat. The degraded scrap was then air-milled to micrometer-sized particles, and was either used as a spray lubricant, or added to other plastics to enhance mold release during molding operations.

By the mid-to-late 1970s, medical device processing began to become significant in its own right. The main factors that contributed were

1. Excellent European experience in using radiation
2. Recognition by the Food and Drug Administration (FDA) that the reliability of gamma sterilization was excellent
3. The construction of larger-scale radiation facilities by service companies and several of the larger device manufacturers, wherein the economics of processing were more favorable
4. The formulation of radiation-compatible grades of materials by compounders and other suppliers
5. The doubt cast over the safety of ethylene oxide as a gaseous sterilant

Today, gamma sterilization is being used commercially in 36 countries on eight continents, in some 140 irradiation facilities. Of these, 38 units are operational in North America. An estimated 35–40% of all medical devices are now radiation-sterilized.

III. PRODUCT VALIDATION

A. Radiation Compatibility

The manufacturer must show that the final product—regardless of how it is manufactured or processed—is safe and performs according to its stated specifications. A product that has undergone the gamut of testing for a total manufacturing sequence—including the sterilization step—may not necessarily maintain its integrity if any of the manufacturing steps are changed. This is especially true if radiation is now to be considered for the sterilization steps.

Ionizing radiation, such as from ^{60}Co, generates free radicals that can cause chemical change. Usually, the free radicals recombine very rapidly, so that whatever physical change is to take place will do so immediately. There are notable exceptions, however, such as some grades of polypropylene, which will exhibit increased embrittlement over a period of many months. A number of possible changes may be only aesthetic, wherein there is a color change, or a different odor is noticeable. Some PVC formulations tend to discolor to a yellowish hue, while other plastics may characteristically yield a new odor. In either case, the product may still be quite functional; yet the marketing staff may find the aesthetic changes unacceptable.

A normal procedure in qualifying a product for radiation is to expose test samples to a dose of at least twice the anticipated minimum dose, and then to test the product functionally by routine test methods. At times a supplier may have a radiation-compatible grade of the polymer currently in use; at other times, a change in material might be required. Fortunately, with the growing use of radiation, plastics manufacturers or compounders have found it worthwhile to develop radiation-compatible materials, and grades of PVC, polypropylene, and other plastics are available, whereas a year or two ago they were not.

Since adverse effects tend to increase with an increased radiation dose, both minimum and maximum doses should be established for the product. The minimum dose will yield the desired degree of sterility assurance, while the maximum will be that dose beyond which the product might be unacceptable. These two doses must also be compatible with the irradiator. Depending on the design of the unit and the product density, it would not be unreasonable to expect a maximum/minimum dose ratio of 1.6. To realize this impact, and considering a 2.5 Mrad dose, the irradiator operator would probably target for a dose of at least 2.6 Mrad to compensate for dosimetry error. (A rad is a unit of absorbed energy, equal to the absorption of 100 ergs per gram. A megarad equals 1 million rads.) The 1.6 overdose would then yield a total or maximum dose of 4.2 Mrad to some items of product. Hence product testing should include items irradiated at this or higher levels.

B. Dose Setting

In 1976, the Association for the Advancement of Medical Instrumentation (AAMI) formed a Radiation Sterilization Subcommittee to explore scientific methods for establishing radiation doses. While the arbitrary 2.5-Mrad dose had "worked," there were drawbacks.

First, if all items received the same dose, it was conceivable that certain items, such as those that do not come into direct contact with the patient, could have a higher degree of sterility assurance than those products that do violate the body's barrier. From a practical standpoint, this didn't make a lot of sense.

Next, sterility is defined as the absence of viable organisms on an item. Yet sterility is really a probability. D-value curves all suggest that, regardless of the degree of treatment, there is always a probability of one in any total that will survive. Regulatory agencies then decided that for certain devices—those that did transgress the body's natural defenses—the probability of one survivor in any million units or a sterility assurance level/SAL of 10^{-6} was adequate to consider the product as sterile. Without compromising the safety of the patient, it was also feasible to consider SALs of 10^{-3}. Hence the 2.5 Mrad dose was vast overkill in many cases.

Next, it became recognized that radiation sterilization was superior in reliability because of the known assurance of dose delivery. Yet the arbitrary 2.5 Mrad minimum, with its associated 4.2 Mrad maximum, was a high enough dose so as to preclude radiation as a sterilant in many cases because of product degradation. Hence it was desirable to broaden the applicability through the utilization of lower, yet adequate doses.

Finally, if lower doses could be achieved, the economics would improve.

Accordingly, the AAMI Subcommittee developed several hypothesis on which its dose setting work would be based:

1. The sterilizing dose should be based on the frequency and radiation resistance of the naturally occurring organisms on the product.
2. The sterility assurance level (SAL) of a device should be based on the intended end use of the product.
3. Traditional poststerility testing methods had serious statistical limitations, and were not adequate.
4. Dose-setting methods to be established must be usable to both small and large health care manufacturers.

The efforts of the group were realized and are presented in the AAMI Recommended Practice, *Process Control Guidelines for Radiation Sterilization of Medical Devices.* (RS-3/84) The document has had widespread applications to dozens of products by many companies over the past several years.

This presentation does not intend to review the AAMI document because it is readily available for review in detail. Suffice it to say that at least four dose-setting methods that properly establish radiation dose are outlined. It is quite common that doses in the 1.5 Mrad range are sufficient to yield the desired SAL. The methods described are statistically sound to the point that poststerility testing of the product is not required by the FDA, provided that dosimetry confirms that the minimum target dose has been delivered. Authorization to utilize dosimetric release is normally obtained from the FDA via a 510K submission, supported by the appropriate microbiological results.

The completion of dose setting, then, together with radiation compatibility and product testing, constitutes validation in terms of product integrity and sterility.

C. Irradiator Validation

The aforementioned AAMI document also outlines a procedure for validating the irradiator. In comparison to other conventional sterilizers, an irradiator is the easiest to validate. To obtain a given radiation dose from a given amount of source, or ^{60}Co, the only variable is time.

Specifications must be agreed to for the sterilization of product. If the sterilizer is a contract radiation service company, then processing is still regarded as a manufacturing process, and the contractor becomes an extension of the principal's total manufacturing sequence. As such, the principal must agree to the contractor's Good Manufacturing Practices (GMPs) and Quality Control (QC) programs, or impose his own. Processing specifications should be developed that describe in detail how the service company is to handle, account for, and process the material through the radiation sequence. It is common to address at least the following areas.

1. Preirradiation Product Handling

Specifics should include methods of shipment to the contractor that comply with federal and state regulations. Quite often, the product is manufactured in a state other than that where the contractor is located, and the product is prelabeled as "sterile" when in fact it is not. Upon receipt at the sterilizer, an actual product count, usually by product code and lot number, is made.

Discrepancies between actual product count and what might be reflected on shipping documents should be resolved prior to further processing.

Methods of storage, product segregation requirements, and other staging requirements should also be addressed at this point.

2. Product Irradiation

Most large-scale irradiators utilize a large box or carrier to transport product through the irradiator. The carriers travel a fixed path, and their physical dimensions are such as to optimize utilization of the radiation energy.

Figure 1 shows a typical large-scale, fully automated ^{60}Co irradiator, as supplied by Atomic Energy of Canada, Limited. At least six of these state-of-the-art units are currently in operation, each capable of processing some 3–5 million cubic feet annually.

Figure 2 shows a product carrier with inner dimensions of about $2 \times 3 \times 10$ ft, or 60 ft^3. Product is stacked into these carriers according to a preset loading pattern, and transported through the radiation field.

Figure 3 shows the pre- and post-irradiation accumulation of carriers. As a finished carrier exits the irradiator, a sequencer automatically feeds a new carrier into the system.

This type of irradiator has a product holdup of approximately 1800 ft^3, and can process at a rate of about 400 ft^3/hr at typical sterilizing doses.

A product loading pattern should be established for each product, with the pattern designed to utilize the space within the carrier to the maximum extent possible. Once established, this identical pattern should prevail in each carrier while that particular product is being processed.

During processing, the contents of each carrier will not only receive the same dose, but the dose distribution throughout each carrier will be identical, and the maximum and minimum dose points will always be in the same relative position.

The dose distribution throughout an entire carrier is then mapped, using actual or simulated products. A sufficient number of dosimeters is placed in a matrix throughout the carrier to enable the points of maximum and minimum dose to be determined. Again, once this pattern of dose is determined, it will remain constant until there is a change in the product, or a source modification or reloading, or a major change is made to the conveyor system. When this occurs, a remapping is required.

Many units, including the aforementioned one, operate in a "shuffle-dwell" mode. That is, each carrier remains in a static position for a predetermined dwell time. Upon a signal from the control console, each carrier advances one position forward and again dwells for the prescribed time. This sequence continues until the carrier exits the irradiator.

The final step in the facility validation, then, is to establish the timer setting, which governs the length of time that the product remains in each dwell position. The setting for a particular minimum dose is usually easily calculated from previous experience with similar product, or even different product but with a similar density. If there is no experience to rely on, any setting can be utilized to establish some base point. From that, one can extrapolate the time required for the required dose, since time is the only variable in the system.

These three elements—product loading pattern, dose distribution mapping, and timer setting—constitute the steps for validation of the irradiator. Together with product validation studies, the product, the process, and the irradiator can be considered validated.

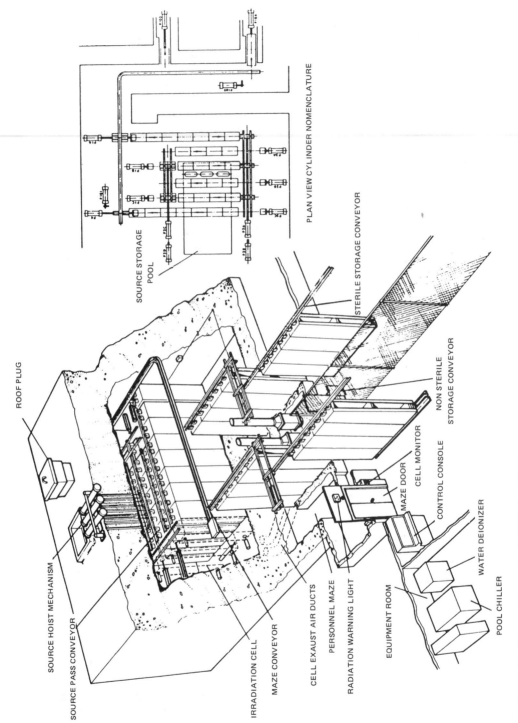

PLAN VIEW CYLINDER NOMENCLATURE

SOURCE STORAGE POOL

STERILE STORAGE CONVEYOR

NON STERILE STORAGE CONVEYOR

ROOF PLUG

SOURCE HOIST MECHANISM

SOURCE PASS CONVEYOR

IRRADIATION CELL

MAZE CONVEYOR

CELL EXAUST AIR DUCTS

PERSONNEL MAZE

RADIATION WARNING LIGHT

EQUIPMENT ROOM

MAZE DOOR

CELL MONITOR

CONTROL CONSOLE

WATER DEIONIZER

POOL CHILLER

FIGURE 1   General layout of IR89 irradiator.

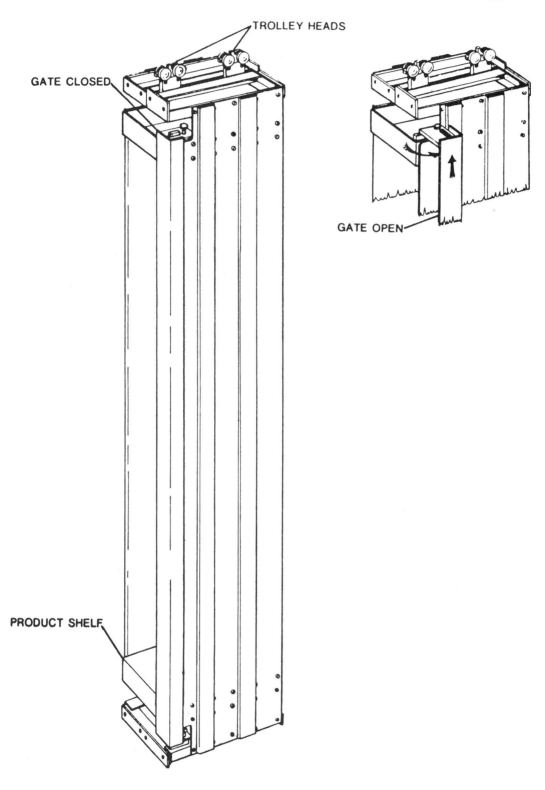

FIGURE 2 Product carrier.

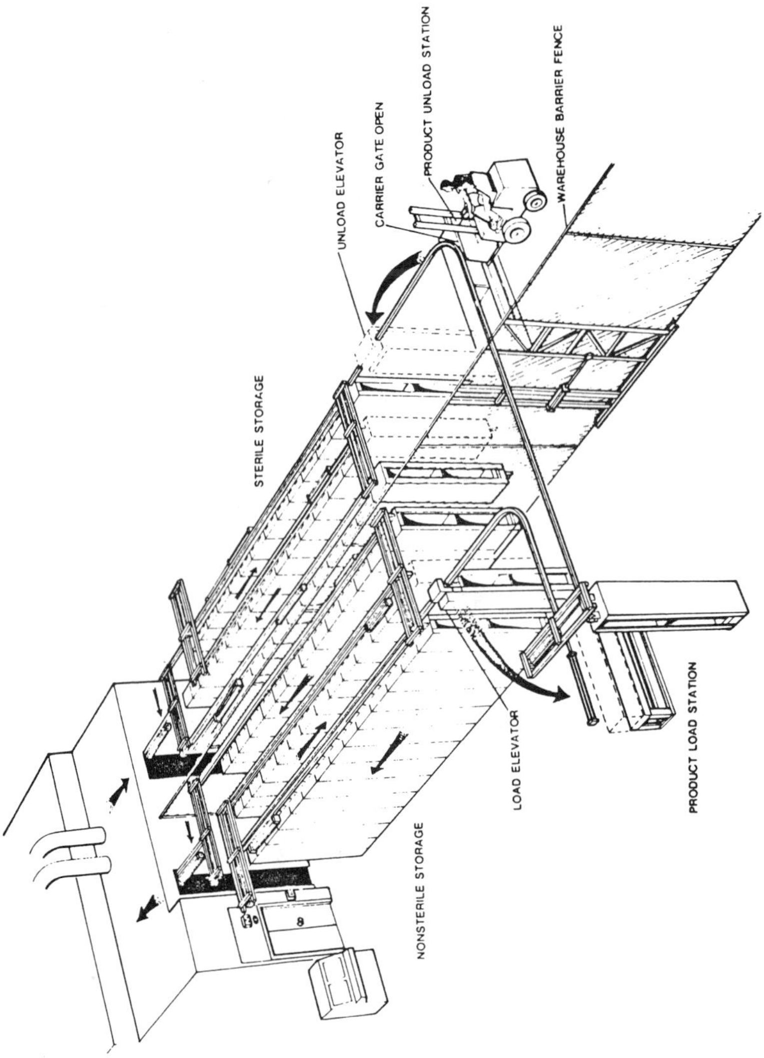

FIGURE 3 Storage conveyors.

For routine irradiation, specifications would cover dosimeter placement, their frequency of use, biological indicator and/or sample placement for sterility testing (if used), and any parametric monitoring requirements.

3. Postirradiation Handling

Finally, postirradiation handling specifications would include product accountability procedures, procedures for handling and shipping product, and specific requirements for the overall processing records.

IV. SUMMARY

The three general elements of validation of product for a ^{60}Co sterilizer are

1. Determination of product compatibility with the radiation process
2. Correctly establishing the minimum and maximum radiation doses
3. Assuring that the irradiator can consistently process between the two dose levels established above

The high degree of sterility assurance afforded by radiation, together with favorable economics and the absence of toxic residuals, has caused gamma processing to emerge as the preferred method of sterilization.

BIBLIOGRAPHY

Davis, K. W., Strawderman, W. E., Masefield, J., 1980. The DS gamma radiation dose-setting strategy for sterilizing medical products, in *Proceedings of the AECL 2nd Gamma Processing Seminar*. Atomic Energy of Canada Limited, Ottawa, Canada.

Davis, K. W., Strawderman, W. E., Masefield, J., and Whitby, J. L. 1981. DS gamma radiation dose setting and auditing strategies for sterilizing medical devices, in *Proceedings of the Second International Kilmer Conference on the Sterilization of Medical Products*. Multiscience, Montreal, Quebec, Canada.

Herring, C. M. 1980. Gamma sterilization dose determinations at American convertors, in *Proceedings of the AECL 2nd Gamma Processing Seminar*. Atomic Energy of Canada Limited, Ottawa, Ontario, Canada.

Masefield, J., Davis, K. W., Strawderman, W. E., 1977. A North American viewpoint on selection of radiation sterilization dose, in *Sterilization of Medical Products by Ionizing Radiation*, Vol. 2, Gaughran, E. R. L., and Goudie, A. J., eds., Multiscience, Montreal, Quebec, Canada. pp 322–330.

Masefield, J., Dietz, G. R., Owens, W. M., and Davis, K. W. 1980. Overview on gamma sterilization in North America, in *Proceedings of the AECL 2nd Gamma Processing Seminar*. Atomic Energy of Canada Limited, Ottawa, Ontario, Canada.

Masefield, J. 1982. Current North American practices in gamma sterilization, in *Proceedings of the International Symposium "Advances in Sterilization of Medical Products."* The University of New South Wales, Kensington, N.S.W., Australia.

Process Control Guidelines for Radiation Sterilization of Medical Devices (Proposed), AAMI Recommended Practice, RS-P, 1982, Arlington, Va., Association for the Advancement of Medical Instrumentation.

SMA Memo No. 16, 1982, Office of Small Manufacturers Assistance, Department of Health & Human Services, August 24.

15

Validation of Sanitization

JAMES D. WILSON

Abbott Laboratories, North Chicago, Illinois

I. INTRODUCTION

Sanitization of aseptic processing areas is a complex technology that has not received as much attention in the pharmaceutical field as terminal sterilization. Centering upon the omission, this chapter seeks to offer practical considerations that will aid industrial microbiologists in selecting those sanitizing agents and conditions that will achieve the desired end result—effective microbial control of aseptic processing areas.

Because of the diversity of agents, multiplicity of claims, and various control approaches, it is important to define relevant terms in sanitization clearly. An *antimicrobial* is an agent intended for minimizing growth or destroying microorganisms in vitro; antimicrobials include sanitizers, germicides, disinfectants, sterilizers, and microbiostats. Thus, the term antimicrobial is general and all-inclusive. For the purpose of this chapter, however, a *sanitizer* is specifically defined as any chemical that kills microbial contamination in the form of vegatative cells. A *sterilizer* may be defined as a chemical agent that destroys or eliminates all forms of microbial life in the inanimate environment. Needless to say, sanitizers by definition are not necessarily sterilizers. A *disinfectant* is an antimicrobial employed to destroy pathogens on inanimate objects. Microbicides may be classified by their specific activity as indicated by the prefix to *-cide*, e.g., bactericide refers to killing of bacteria, fungicide to fungi, virucide to viruses, and sporicide to spores. Static agents merely inhibit growth of microorganisms. To avoid confusion, it is necessary to understand that disinfection and sanitization are not interchangeable terms.

II. DISPELLING MYTHS ABOUT SANITIZERS AND SANITIZATION

A great deal of misunderstanding prevails regarding sanitizers and their application as sanitizing agents. Some of the more common fallacies in existence are tabulated in the following table.

Myth	Truth
1. Most sanitizers will kill spores.	1. Chemical sporicidal agents are the exception, not the rule.
2. The effectiveness of sanitization with chemical solutions is merely a function of agent concentration and time.	2. It is the application of an effective concentration for a specified time, at proper conditions, that produces efficacy. Dilute preparations of hypochlorite and povidone iodine may be more effective microbiologically than more concentrated solutions. Solution pH is extremely important in the employment of chemical sanitizers. The less organic manner present, the better many sanitizers work.
3. Many sanitization personnel believe it is axiomatic—"If it looks clean, then it is clean."	3. Visual examination is not a reliable means of evaluating a sanitization procedure from a microbiological viewpoint.
4. The splashing of a chemical agent on surfaces is an effective mode of sanitization.	4. Contact time must be sufficient for killing effect. Concentration, temperature, pH, contact time, and other factors are also important in efficacy.
5. Sanitizing agents are "sterile."	5. Some vegetative cells can survive in 10% povidone iodine, apparently as a result of encapsulation by organics or inorganic matter that protects the cells. Demonstration of intrinsic contamination of 10% povidone iodine solution with *Pseudomonas cepacia* surprised many in the chemical sanitizer field [1].
	Spores have been known to survive for years in alcohol. There have been numerous reports of contamination of quaternary ammonium solutions.
6. Laboratory evaluations of sanitizers are unreliable.	6. Laboratory evaluations are meaningful when appropriate controls and meticulous care are employed.

III. SELECTION OF AGENT

In choosing a sanitizing agent one should first consider the desired properties of an ideal sanitizer, but at the same time be cognizant that no sanitizer
achieves the ideal. Bacteriologists suggest that the ideal sanitizer: (a) kills
a wide range of microbes, (b) is nontoxic to humans, (c) is noncorrosive and
nonstaining to equipment, (d) possesses detergent action, (e) has stability,
(f) acts quickly, (g) will not be inactivated by organic matter, (h) produces
desired residual action, and (i) is inexpensive. Each agent will have its advantages and limitations. The microbiologist must select a single agent, or a
combination of agents, governed by the standards of his/her company, that
produces maximum effectiveness at a minimum cost.

A. Assessing Scope of Application

In assessing application scope, considerable research and evaluation is generally needed to determine the preferred sanitizer agent. A general consideration for selection of an agent must allow for determination of the surface areas
to be treated, with large surface areas limiting the choice of agents. Of primary concern is the nature of the material to be treated. Is the surface on
the inside or accessible from the exposed side? Type of finish (porous, smooth,
rough, grainy, etc.) plays a role (i.e., nonporous surfaces are easier to clean
and sanitize). For porous surfaces, addition of a surfactant should be considered to aid in penetration.

Method of application is another important step in assessment. The types
and amount of product residual should be determined. If product residual is
present, precleaning is essential as a requisite for sanitization. How will the
sanitizer be applied? Will spraying, mopping, fogging, or submerging be more
appropriate? What should be the contact time? Temperature and pH conditions
are also factors to be evaluated, since they can influence the rate of sanitization. Depending on the agent, elevation of temperature and/or reducing pH
may enhance activity. Does the product come into contact with the surface
being treated? The significance of the presence of agent residues and risk
areas of manufacturing contamination are of vital importance.

Surfaces such as ceramics, most glasses, and stainless steel are generally
resistant to most chemical sanitizers. Before an agent is selected, however,
a general survey of the compatibility (i.e., corrosiveness, staining, odor) of
the materials used in the processing areas as well as the coating of surfaces
for walls, ceilings, and floors should be determined. One may refer to references such as *The Handbook of Plastics and Elastomers* for guidance on
compatibility [2].

The choice of sanitizer and method of application, however, should be influenced more by the kind of microorganisms to be inactivated than by the
nature or surface of the material to be treated. Many sanitizers are effective
only against specific groups of organisms (Gram-negative bacteria, molds,
etc.). Strains of species may be found within such groups that are resistant
to or minimally affected by the agent.

Conditions for maximum effectiveness may differ among chemical sanitizers,
but important factors include (a) pH, (b) temperature, (c) humidity, (d)
nature of the diluent used, (e) concentration, (f) presence of organic matter,
and (g) contact time.

Acidic solutions generally exhibit more rapid killing power than neutral or
alkaline solutions (e.g., iodine, hypochlorite).

In general, sanitizing activity increases with rise in temperature, since the
effect on microbes is like a chemical reaction.

Agents such as quaternary ammonium compounds possess detergent properties that enable them to penetrate grease barriers, but highly reactive substances such as chlorine exhibit diminished efficacy in the presence of organic matter.

Sanitizer solutions may be microbicidal or just inhibitory, depending largely on concentration. Increased killing effect generally occurs with increased concentration of agent, but dilute concentrations of some agents can be metabolized by certain microorganisms (e.g., some species of *Pseudomonas* are noted for their oxidation of phenol compounds).

Since some laboratory assays (e.g., phenol coefficient method) are based on a contact time of 10 min, it becomes necessary to equate application techniques with respect to minimum control time to laboratory evaluation conditions if reproducible results are anticipated.

B. Frequency of Use

One would be remiss in assessing the scope of application if rotation of sanitizers was not considered. Since there is no single ideal sanitizer, it is prudent to consider two or more agents. Rotation of agents, theoretically, tends to preclude development of common environmental isolates or adaptation of microbes. Where rotation is deemed necessary, the rotation frequency should be determined. One approach is to rotate agents when specific test data show a need. Alternatively, arbitrary rotation on a time basis (weekly, monthly, etc.) can be employed.

When selecting a chemical sanitizer, the merits of four major groups should be considered. Based on classification by primary ingredient, they are (a) chlorinated compounds, (b) iodine compounds, (c) quaternary ammonium compounds, and (d) acid-anionic agents.

1. Chlorine-based sanitizers are probably most widely used. A great number of chlorine derivatives are commercially available. Among them are chlorine solutions in water, which cause the formation of hypochlorous acid. With chloramines and chlorine gas, increasing concentration kills bacteria faster. Increasing the concentration of hypochlorite solutions, on the other hand, decreases their sanitizing powers because of the effects of pH [3]. Others consist of solutions of salts of hypochlorous acid (e.g., calcium, potassium, sodium). The toxicity of dilutions of many solutions is very low, and their irritating and sensitizing properties are correspondingly low. Efficacy of some types may be reduced by organic matter, but chlorine-based agents are generally most economical.

2. Iodophors are basically a combination of iodine and solubilizing agent that release free iodine when diluted with water. At use concentrations they are nonstaining, relatively nontoxic, nonirritating, and stable. They possess quick microbial action against a wide variety of microorganisms. Iodophors, however, are also poor sporicides.

3. Numerous quaternary ammonium compounds are available. Chemists have developed and introduced sanitizers with new compounds having heavier molecular weight with improved cleansing and sanitizing properties. Many of the newly developed products sanitize at lower concentrations. These lowered concentrations have resulted in reduced sanitizer toxicity and irritating properties as compared to sanitizers used previously. Use dilutions are odorless, colorless, and stable when heated to 80°C, with optimum activity being observed in a pH range of 5 to 11. These are primarily most effective against Gram-positive bacteria. Gram-negative bacteria exhibit a greater resistance to quaternaries than other bacteria; most notable is the genus *Pseudomonas*. Optimum concentration may vary from one brand to another, but the carbon chain length of 14 is generally most effective [3].

4. Acid-anionic agents are combinations of organic or inorganic acids and surface-active agents. The acid is normally phosphoric, and the surfactant is usually of the alkyl sulfonate type. Bactericidal activity is provided by low pH and surfactant activity. Use solutions are typically odorless, stable, and noncorrosive to stainless steel while being active against a wide spectrum of microbes.

C. Advantages and Disadvantages of Major Types

Table 1 summarizes the advantages and disadvantages of the four major chemical sanitizers. Alcohols are not listed as a major group, they but have a broad range of bactericidal activity against vegetative forms. Their cleansing action and volatility can prove superior to agents that leave residues. Activity of alcohols has been recognized as increasing with branching (primary < secondary < tertiary), with isopropyl alcohol being slightly more potent. Alcoholic solutions of 60−90% (w/v) constitute effective concentrations, and 5 to 10 min are considered adequate contact time for most vegetative bacteria. A major limitation of alcohol lies in their lack of efficacy against spores. Nevertheless, the ability to evaporate without leaving significant residues and relatively rapid bactericidal capability have contributed to acceptance of alcohol as

TABLE 1　Properties of Major Groups of Sanitizers

	Hypochlorite	Iodophors	Quats	Acid-anionic surfactant
Activity	Good	Good	Varied	Effective at low pH (1.9−2.0)
Compatibility	Good	Stains porous and some plastic surfaces	Poor with detergent components	Controls water hardness film
Corrosiveness	Very on some metals	Slight?	None	To metals other than stainless steel
Cost	Low	High	High	Moderate
Dispensing	Easy	Easy	Easy	Easy
Effect on spores	Very good	Fair	Ineffective	Slow
Filming	None	Prevented	Forms	Forms
Odor	Marked	Absent	Absent	Some marked
Penetration	Fair	Good	Fair	Good
Rinsing	Essential	Essential	Essential	Not essential
Stability	Short	Good	Good	Good
Toxicity	Adverse on skin	Low	Low	Low
Water treatment	Good	Poor	Poor	Very poor

a final rinse treatment for sterile surfaces. Since spores have been known to
survive for years in alcohol, it is suggested that alcohol used in sterile application be filter-sterilized.

There has been an upsurge in popularity of hydrogen peroxide as a sanitizer in recent years. It is an elegant choice with regard to product safety,
and it is also stable in lower concentrations (i.e., 2–5%). The major deficiency
of hydrogen peroxide for use dilutions applied to inert surfaces is its poor
sporicidal properties and the requirement of surfaces to be free of inactivating
levels of catalase. Hydrogen peroxide, although having a moderate tolerance
to organic matter, is corrosive to some metals.

Phenolics have not retained their lofty position formerly held prior to the
Federal Environmental Pesticide Control Act of 1972, but properly formulated
phenolics are effective agents in general against vegetative microorganisms.
They do not kill spores under ordinary conditions of use.

D. Proprietary Claims

The variety of microorganisms to be controlled and different claims for the
source of available products have required regulation. Even so, commercialism
has created much confusion, with many of the available products being promoted
vigorously by exaggerated claims. In some instances, specious claims are conceived on technical chicanery. For example, Pauling observed and reported:
"Germicide X destroys the spore-forming Bacillus Y in 5 minutes." This does
not say spores of Bacillus Y [4]. In fact, further investigation revealed that
Bacillus Y had been tested in vegetative form, not spores. Another type of
claim occasionally seen is: "kills *Pseudomonas* in 2 minutes." Under what test
conditions (concentration, pH, etc.) were the data generated? Such claims
are meaningless unless the test conditions are known.

E. Vendor Evaluation

In selecting agents for a specific application, the number, types, and cost of
sanitizers on the market warrant close scrutiny of product labeling, vendor
brochures, and data sheets. Because of the jurisdiction of the Environmental
Protection Agency, the Federal Insecticide, Fungicide, and Rodenticide Act
requires that sanitizer chemicals provide the practical benefits claimed when
used as directed [5]. The manufacturer of a chemical bears the responsibility
for substantiating the validity and accuracy of product label claims prior to
product sale. Upon registration of a product with the agency, future production audits are required by the agency on a periodic basis.

To facilitate the decision-making process of microbiologists, a number of
standardized testing protocols have been developed and published in *Official
Methods of Analysis* (Association of Official Analytical Chemists, AOAC) [1].

IV. FACTORS INFLUENCING EVALUATION OF SANITIZERS

Whereas the ultimate test of efficacy of a sanitizer is the demonstration of effectiveness in application, the primary responsibility for evaluation belongs
to the microbiology laboratory [3].

A variety of analytical techniques for evaluation have been introduced
concomitantly with the evolution of chemical sanitizers. Yet apparent dispar-
ities and conflicts in results have contributed to confusion and misconceptions.

Also, the misinterpretation of bacteriostasis as bactericidal action has created confusion. Although many methods for testing sanitizer agents have been established, very few of them have given sufficient attention to the meticulous standardization of apparatus, equipment, media, test cultures, manipulative details, etc. Thus, the interpretation of laboratory results has been plagued by critics for lack of alleged provision in translating laboratory results directly to conditions of use.

Even with increased emphasis on standardization, there are many factors that can affect the result and, in turn, the interpretation of a microbiological sanitizer evaluation. The factors capable of influencing any chemical sanitizer test include the following:

1. *Culture*: Resistance of bacteria to chemicals may vary considerably among different species, different strains of the same species, and different subcultures of the same strain [3]. The physiological age of a culture may influence resistance to a chemical, with optimum age being determined for each culture, if known. Lastly, the daily transfer of cultures up to 30 days is important to minimize the effect of change in resistance when a large number of samples are routinely assayed.

2. *Inoculum*: Use of a 4-mm loop or micropipet can contribute significant variation in inoculum volume. A calibrated precision syringe is usually preferred over a loop or micropipet for greater accuracy. If daily transfers are not made, one should expect to observe "zigzag" patterns in resistance. Since the method of mixing inoculum and chemicals is treacherous, special care must be exercised to preclude deposition of inoculum on container walls above solution contact. Application of washed cells does not provide significant difference in resistance over unwashed calls.

3. *Composition of Medium*: The importance of composition of medium during culturing must be emphasized. The greatest single factor influencing the resistance of bacteria to sanitizers is the chemical composition of the medium [3].

4. *Temperature of Test Substrates and Incubation Temperature*: Test cultures should not be shocked with nonattempered substrates. Temperature of incubation should always be optimum for the culture under examination; however, an incubation temperature of 20°C is preferred by some scientists, because 20°C reflects the temperature of application.

5. *Time of Contact*: Exposure time should be realistic in terms of intended use or be translatable to use conditions.

6. *pH of Substrate*: Sanitizer activity on bacteria may be profoundly influenced by pH. Since the efficiency of chlorine solutions is dependent on concentration of undisassociated hypochlorous acid, pH does have a great influence and, therefore, must be controlled [3]. Thus, there is a corresponding increase in biocidal activity with a decrease in pH of hypochlorite solutions. For example, at pH 8.2, only 100 ppm available chlorine is required to provide equivalent activity to 1000 ppm of chlorine at pH 11.3 [3].

7. *Choice of Neutralizer*: An effective nontoxic neutralizer must be employed to stop bactericidal action instantly in evaluations in solutions. For sanitizer evaluations in broth tests, one should have positive supporting data that the neutralizers employed are effective. One must challenge solutions with low levels of inoculum to determine if inhibition is present. Without validation of neutralizer efficacy, one may develop a false sense of security.

8. *Osmotic Pressure*: A concentration of salt above 1% may inhibit the growth of nonhalophilic bacteria.

9. *Surface Tension*: Substances influencing surface tension can have an adverse effect on growth under certain conditions.

10. *Recovery Technique*: Validity of the recovery technique employed may affect the apparent result.

11. *Sample Size*: The practical or statistical significance of consideration should be given to a sample size where a high degree of confidence is desired.

12. *Nature of Substrate*: The physical state of the substrate used for growth and its stability are to be controlled in the laboratory.

13. *Type of Surface and Drying Technique for Surface Testing Methods*: Surface type, condition of surface, suspending medium used, and methods of drying cells may vary results considerably. Regardless of the nature of the variability or conditions of use, these factors can at least be standardized in the laboratory so that relative comparisons of efficacy for agents are valid.

V. QUALITATIVE SCREENING ASSAYS

A. Use Dilution Assays

1. Phenol Coefficient Determination

In vitro procedures published by the Association of Official Analytical Chemists (AOAC) for determining relativeness of a sanitizer to phenol provide a reliable basis for analyzing vendor claims and comparing products; moreover, they are a reliable means for certification of a sanitizer supplied by a vendor. The phenol coefficient method is a tube dilution procedure designed to determine the highest dilution of a sanitizer that will kill the test organism within a series of time intervals as compared to phenol.

The official AOAC phenol coefficient method is generally considered the primary bacteriological test method for chemical sanitizer agents [1]. The reader is referred to the AOAC Manual for preparation of reagents and materials except for the culture.

Culture: Hopkins strain 26 of *Salmonella typhi* (Schroeter) Warren and Scott, ATCC No. 6539 (formerly called *Bac. typhosus* and *Eberthella typhosa*) is the standard. Maintain stock culture on nutrient agar slants by monthly transfers. Incubate new stock transfer for 2 days at $35 \pm 1°C$, then store at $2-5°C$.

From the stock culture, inoculate a tube of nutrient broth and make at least four consecutive daily transfers ($\geqslant 30$) in nutrient broth, incubating at 37°C, before using the culture for testing. (If only one daily transfer has been missed, it is not necessary to repeat the four consecutive transfers). Use 22- to 26-hr culture of organisms grown in the nutrient broth at 37°C in test. Shake, and let settle 15 min before using.

Operating Technique: Make 1% (v/v) stock dilution of the substance to be tested (or any other convenient dilutions, depending on anticipated concern) in a glass cylinder or flask. Make final dilutions from the 1% stock dilution, directly into medication tubes, and remove all except 5 ml. (The range of dilutions should cover the killing limits of the sanitizer in 5—15 min and should at the same time be close enough for accuracy.) From 5% stock phenol solution (1—20), dilute further to make 1—90 and 1—100 dilutions, and place in medication tubes. Place these tubes, containing 5 ml each of final dilutions of disinfectant and of phenol, and the tube containing test culture in a water bath at 20°C and leave for 5 min. Add 0.5 ml of test culture to each of the dilutions at time intervals corresponding to the intervals at which transfers are to be made. (Thus, by the time 10 tubes have been seeded at 30-sec intervals, 4—5 min have elapsed, and a 30-sec interval intervenes before transference to subculture begins.) Add culture from a graduated pipet large enough to seed all tubes in any one set.

In inoculating medication tubes, hold them in a slanting position after removal from the bath, insert the pipet to just above the surface of the sanitizer, and run in culture without letting the tip touch the sanitizer. After adding culture, agitate the tubes gently but thoroughly to ensure even distribution of bacteria, and replace them in the bath; 5 min after seeding the first medication tube, transfer with a calibrated syringe 0.05 ml of mixture from the medication tube to the corresponding subculture tube. To facilitate transfer of uniform drops of medication mixture, hold the tube at a 60° angle, and withdraw the subsample so that the plane of the syringe or pipet is parallel with the surface of the liquid. After 30 sec, transfer the subsample from the second medication tube to a second subculture tube and continue the process for each successive dilution; 5 min after making the first transfer, begin a second set of transfers for a 10-min period, and finally, repeat for a 15-min period. (Note: The entire operating technique should take place in a laminar-flow hood.) Gently agitate the medication tubes before taking each interval subsample for transfer to subculture medium. Before each transfer, flame the mouth of every tube. Use a sterile syringe or pipet for each transfer.

Use care in transferring and seeding to prevent the pipet or needle from touching the sides or mouth of the medication tube, and see that no cotton threads adhere to the inner sides or mouths of tubes. Thoroughly agitate individual subculture tubes before incubation. Incubate subculture for 48 hr at 37 ± 1°C and read the results. Macroscopic examination is usually sufficient. Occasionally a 3-day incubation period, agar streak, microscopic examination, or agglutination with antityphoid serum may be necessary to determine feeble growth or suspected contamination.

Calculation: Express results in terms of phenol coefficient number, or highest dilution killing test organism in 10 min, but not in 5 min, whichever most accurately reflects the bactericidal value of sanitizer. Phenol coefficient (see following example) is a number obtained by dividing the numerical value of the greatest dilution (the denominator of the fraction expressing dilution of disinfectant capable of killing *S. typhi* in 10 min, but not in 5 min by the greatest dilution of phenol showing the same results).

Example

Dilution	5 min	10 min	15 min
	Sanitizer (X)		
1-300	0	0	0
1-325	+	0	0
1-350	+	0	0
1-375	+	+	0
1-400	+	+	+
	Phenol		
1-90	+	0	0
1-100	+	+	+

Phenol coefficient = 350/90 = 3.89

The test is satisfactory only when the phenol control gives one of the following readings:

Phenol	5 min	10 min	15 min
1—90	+ or 0	+ or 0	0
1—100	+	+	+ or 0

If none of the dilutions of sanitizer shows growth in 5 min and killing in 10 min, establish a hypothetical dilution only when any three consecutive dilutions show the following results: first, no growth in 5 min; second, growth in 5 and 10 min, but not in 15 min; and third, growth in 5, 10, and 15 min. The following example serves to illustrate this point.

Example

Dilution	5 min	10 min	15 min
Sanitizer (X)			
1—300	0	0	0
1—350	+	+	0
1—400	+	+	+
Phenol			
1—90	0	0	0
1—100	+	+	0

Phenol coefficient = 325/95 = 3.42

To avoid giving the impression of fictitious accuracy, calculate the phenol coefficient to the nearest 0.1. Thus, in the examples above, the phenol coefficients would be reported as 3.9 and 3.4 rather than 3.89 and 3.42.

Note: Although it is a commonly accepted criterion that disinfectants be at dilution-equivalent in sanitizer efficiency to phenol against *S. typhi* by calculating 20 × *S. typhi* coefficient to determine the number of parts water in which one part sanitizer may be mixed, this should be regarded as presumptive and is subject to confirmation by the use-dilution method. In fact, registrations with the Environmental Protection Agency now require data using the use-dilution method.

Using Staphylococcus aureus: Proceed as with *Salmonella typhi* except change the dilutions and test organisms. Use 22- to 26-hr culture of *Staph. aureus* FDA 209, ATCC No. 6538 having at 20°C at least the resistance indicated by following:

Phenol	5 min	10 min	15 min
1—60	+ or 0	+ or 0	0
1—70	+	+	+

Note: If conversion of the 20 × *Staph. aureus* coefficient is used to determine the number of parts water in which one part of sanitizer may be

incorporated to disinfect where pyogenic organisms are the objective, this
dilution is subject to confirmation by the use-dilution method.

Using Pseudomonas aeruginosa Official First Action: Proceed as with *Salmonella typhi*. Use 22- to 26-hr culture of *Ps. aeruginosa* PRD 10 (ATCC 15442),
having resistance to phenol at 20°C at least as follows:

Phenol	5 min	10 min	15 min
1—80	+ or 0	+ or 0	0
1—90	+	+	+

A major limitation of the phenol coefficient method is the procedure for con-
verting the phenol coefficient into safe use dilutions [3]. In lieu of multiplying the coefficient by the constant factor 20, the formula 2.5 coefficient X
(n + 1) should be used (where n = concentration exponent for the specific
organism to be used in challenging the sanitizer).

Despite the existence of regulatory statutes, it is important to properly
certify the vendor of a sanitizing agent. A number of testing failures on product of one of these standardized AOAC methods of analysis usually predicts
with certainty that such a product will be unsatisfactory in actual related uses.
Satisfactory results in determinations by any of these methods may not, however, provide the degree of confidence necessary for reliable microbial control.
Complete end-point methods are indeed the methods of choice; such methods
do have statistical limitations, but these limitations can be overcome by increasing the number of replicates. The current edition of AOAC *Methods of
Analysis* requires replicates and states the tolerance limits of each method.

2. MF Technique

One of the simplest effective analytical methods for evaluation of sanitizer
efficacy is the membrane filtration procedure. This method involves the direct
mixing of spores or cells with sanitizer and the subsequent filtering of the
solution at various time intervals. The primary advantage of this method over
any other solution culture method lies in the capability of completely eliminating
bacteriostasis.

Materials

1. Sanitizer
2. Cultures
    a. *Pseudomonas aeruginosa* ATCC No. 9027   (PA)
    b. *Escherichia coli* ATCC No. 8739   (EC)
    c. *Staphylococcus aureus* ATCC No. 6538   (SA)
    d. *Candida albicans* ATCC No. 10231   (CA)
    e. *Bacillus subtilis* var. *niger* ATCC No. 9372 (BS)
    f. *Aspergillus niger* ATCC No. 16404   (AN)
3. Sterile distilled water
4. 19 × 150 mm sterile screwcap test tubes
5. Sterile Butterfield buffer (modified) dilution blanks
6. Sterile 0.1% aqueous peptone solution
7. Poured, sterile Soybean-Casein Digest Agar (SCDA) Petri plates
    poured at least 3 mm deep (60 or 100 diameter)
8. Poured, sterile Potato Dextrose Agar (PDA)

9. Sterile pipets 25-ml, 10-ml, and 1-ml sizes
10. Sterile forceps or hemostats
11. Sterile membrane filtration units with 47-mm diameter, 0.4-µm pore size, solvent-resistant membranes
12. Incubator—30 to 35°C
13. Vacuum source
14. Sterile melted SCDA
15. Sterile melted PDA
16. Sterile, empty, 100-mm-diameter Petri plates
17. Sterile, empty containers of approximately 200 ml volume

Procedure for Determination of Sanitizer Efficacy

1. Preparation of challenge inocula
    a. Except for BS, streak slants (one or more) of appropriate agar (PDA for CA and AN, SCDA for all others) with specified microorganisms from stock culture. Incubate at 30 ± 1°C for 48—72 hr. AN may need extended incubation for good sporulation.

        Harvest cells by withdrawing approximately 3 ml of buffer from a 10-ml tube and pipetting onto a slant. Using a pipet, gently scrape the slant to suspend the cells. Withdraw the suspension and transfer it back into the tube for buffer. It may be necessary to serially transfer to one or more slants to build up the cell population.
    b. Do a microbial plate count of suspensions as necessary and dilute with appropriate buffer to obtain final working suspensions of 10,000—100,000 cells/ml.
2. Sample preparation
    a. Dilute the sanitizer to be tested according to the recommendations of the manufacturer. This is termed the "use dilution."
    b. Prepare further dilutions of the "use dilution."
    c. Adjust pH to 6.8—7.0 and attemper at 30°C.
3. Challenge test
    a. In duplicate, pipet 10 ml of each of the dilutions from steps 2a and 2b above into separate sterile test tubes (changing pipets after each transfer). Provide 12 tubes for each dilution and time intervals, as there are six challenge organisms.
    b. Using a calibrated syringe or pipet, inoculate each separate complement of dilution tubes with a different challenge microorganism, using an inoculum volume of 0.1 ml. Shake well (be sure cap is on tight) and let stand at 30°C.

        For positive controls, inoculate appropriate duplicate dilution blanks with challenge microorganisms.

        Assay at 5-, 10-, and 15-min intervals. Note: Use care in seeding and transferring to prevent pipet from touching sides or mouth of tube. Perform entire operation in a laminar-flow hood.
    c. Identify by tube number, inoculum, sanitizer, dilutions, etc.
    d. At the conclusion of each challenge time interval, pass the contents of each tube through a separate membrane filter unit. Wash each membrane with 3 × 100 ml portions of neutralizer solution. Remove each membrane from its filter unit and plate face up on the surface of an appropriate poured agar plate. Positive controls must be tested last. (Note: Stagger operations so that time intervals do not overlap.)

    e. Incubate all plates at 30 ± 1°C for 24–72 hr. Examine each day for signs of growth of the inoculum, count, and record.

4. Growth promotion controls. Positive control membranes must show confluent growth of each of the challenge microorganisms.

Table 2 and Table 3 demonstrate sanitizer efficiency of both benzalkonium test solution and controls.

3. Surface Test

Practical information on the efficacy of sanitizers can be obtained by evaluating their effectiveness on hard surfaces (or surfaces to be treated) and demonstrating activity against contaminated surfaces for various contact times. In the surface test, stainless steel strips are inoculated with the organisms, dried, submerged in sanitizer solution for various lengths of time, and cultured for growth. One method for determining activity is included in this chapter.

Material

1. Brushed stainless steel strips
2. Calibrated precision syringe
3. Tubes of 5.0 ml of sterile Letheen broth
4. Sterile Petri dishes (100 × 15)
5. Sterile soybean casein digest agar (melted)
6. Calibrated 1.0-ml pipets
7. Clean air center
8. Vortex mixer
9. Approximately 10,000 organisms/ml of the following designated cultures:
    a. *Staphylococcus aureus* ATCC 6538
    b. *Pseudomonas aeruginosa* ATCC 9027
    c. *Candida albicans* ATCC 10231
    d. *Aspergillus niger* ATCC 16404
    e. *Bacillus subtilis* ATCC 6633
    f. Organism(s) recovered from plant environment
10. Sterile soybean casein digest agar slants
11. Sanitizer to be tested
12. Sterile calcium alginate swabs or equivalent

Procedure for Sanitizer Evaluation from Surface Studies

1. Approximately 2 days prior to initiating disinfectant test, make a dilution of approximately 10,000 organisms/ml of each culture to be tested and perform plate count.
2. Sanitize the work station using a sanitizer previously demonstrated to be effective.
3. Prepare the following dilutions of the sanitizer solution at pH 6.8–7.0 (where feasible) to be tested:
    a. Recommended use concentration (concentration recommended by manufacturer).
    b. 1:10 dilution (1.0 ml of use concentration + 9.0 ml of sterile distilled water).
    c. 1:100 dilution (1.0 ml of the 1:10 dilution above + 9.0 ml of sterile distilled water).

TABLE 2   Results for Challenge Membranes

Benzalkonium Chloride

Microorganism	Time	Use Dilution (1:84)		1:840 Dilution	
		Plate 1	Plate 2	Plate 1	Plate 2
Staphylococcus	5 min	0	0	0	0
aureus	10 min	0	0	0	0
ATCC 6538 (SA)	15 min	0	0	0	0
Escherichia	5 min	0	0	0	0
coli	10 min	0	0	0	0
ATCC 8769 (EC)	15 min	0	0	0	0
Pseudomonas	5 min	0	0	0	0
aeruginosa	10 min	0	0	0	0
ATCC 9027 (PC)	15 min	0	0	0	0
Candida	5 min	0	0	0	0
albicans	10 min	0	0	0	0
ATCC 10231 (CA)	15 min	0	0	0	0
Bacillus	5 min	CF	CF	CF	CF
subtilis	10 min	61	290	CF	CF
ATCC 9372 (BS)	15 min	297	300	CF	CF
Aspergillus	5 min	CF	CF	CF	CF
niger	10 min	CF	CF	CF	CF
ATCC 16404 (AN)	15 min	CF	CF	CF	CF

Control

Microorganism	Time	Use Dilution			1:10 Dilution (of use dilution)		
		Plate 1	Plate 2	Ave.	Plate 1	Plate 2	Ave.
Staphylococcus	5 min	0	0	0	0	0	0
aureus	10 min	0	0	0	0	0	0
ATCC 6538 (SA)	15 min	0	0	0	0	0	0
Escherichia	5 min	0	0	0	0	0	0
coli	10 min	0	0	0	0	0	0
ATCC 8739 (EC)	15 min	0	0	0	0	0	0
Pseudomonas	5 min	0	0	0	0	0	0
aeruginosa	10 min	0	0	0	0	0	0
ATCC 9027 (PS)	15 min	0	0	0	0	0	0

TABLE 2   (Continued)

Microorganism	Time	Use Dilution			1:10 Dilution (of use dilution)		
		Plate 1	Plate 2	Ave.	Plate 1	Plate 2	Ave.
Candida albicans	5 min	0	0	0	0	0	0
	10 min	0	0	0	0	0	0
ATCC 10231 (CA)	15 min	0	0	0	0	0	0
Bacillus	5 min	0	0	0	CF	CF	CF
subtilis	10 min	0	0	0	217	300	300
ATCC 9372 (BS)	15 min	0	0	0	17	0	8
Aspergillus	5 min	0	0	0	40	CF	300
niger	10 min	0	0	0	14	16	15
ATCC 16404 (AN)	15 min	0	0	0	20	30	25

4. Clean each polished stainless steel strip with detergent and rinse well with distilled water.
5. Spot-inoculate four stainless steel strips with a known volume of a culture for each dilution of sanitizer. Each strip should contain approximately 100 organisms. Allow to air-dry for 30 min at approximately 20°C. Repeat this step for each test organism.
6. After drying, immerse two (or more) stainless steel strips from each culture in sanitizer solution to be tested, using a well-flamed inoculating loop or glass rod. Allow 5 min contact time between sanitizer and test organism at 20°C.
7. Repeat steps 5 and 6 but immerse in solution for 15 min.
8. Immerse two strips in sterile distilled water for positive controls and let stand at ambient temperature for 15 min. When testing more than one sanitizer, only one set of positive controls is necessary.
9. Swab each strip thoroughly with a premoistened calcium alginate swab and place in Letheen broth (or other suitable neutralizer).
10. Vortex tubes containing the swabs in Letheen broth for 30 sec.
11. Using aseptic technique, pipet 1.0 ml from the Letheen broth and plate into an appropriately labeled Petri dish. Repeat in duplicate for each tube of Letheen broth.
12. Using aseptic technique, pour approximately 15 ml of sterile soybean casein digest agar into the Petri dishes. Swirl to obtain an even distribution of inoculum. Allow medium to solidify.
13. Invert plates and incubate at 35°C for 48 hr, except for *Aspergillus niger*, which is incubated at 25°C for 5 days.
14. Calculate the number of organisms by counting colonies on each plate and multiplying by designated dilution factor.
15. Record number of organisms per plate and calculate to the average number of microorganisms recovered per dilution.

The results, shown in Table 4, show that the recommended use dilution is satisfactory for effective sanitization of surfaces.

TABLE 3   Sanitizer Efficiency Test

	Plate 1	Plate 2	Average	Challenge count
1. Inoculum microbial counts				
Staph. aureus	63	70	67	× Dilution Factor of 10^3 = 6.7 × 10^4/ml = 6.7 × 10^3
Esch. coli	84	110	97	× Dilution Factor of 10^3 = 9.7 × 10^4/ml = 9.7 × 10^3
Pseudo. aerug.	77	62	70	× Dilution Factor of 10^3 = 7.0 × 10^4/ml = 7.0 × 10^3
Candida albicans	146	126	136	× Dilution Factor of 10^3 = 1.36 × 10^5/ml = 1.36 × 10^4
Bacillus subtilis	41	59	50	× Dilution Factor of 10^3 = 5.0 × 10^4/ml = 5.0 × 10^3
Aspergillus niger	131	123	127	× Dilution Factor of 10^3 = 1.27 × 10^5/ml = 1.27 × 10^4
2. Positive controls				
Staph. aureus	CF	CF	CF	
Esch. coli	CF	CF	CF	
Pseudo. aerug.	CF	CF	CF	
Candida albicans	CF	CF	CF	
Bacillus subtilis	CF	CF	CF	
Aspergillus niger	CF	CF	CF	

Based on the results in the example given, the use dilution of 1:84 would be satisfactory.

Confirmatory tests by a method that employs the same surface or object to be sanitized should be considered for suitable candidate agents obtained via screening with the membrane filter technique.

CF = Confluent growth.

TABLE 4   Benzalkonium Chloride Evaluation—Surface Method

		Use concentration		1:10 dilution		1:100 dilution		1:1000 dilution	
		Plate 1	Plate 2	Plate 1	Plate 2	Plate 1	Plate 2	Plate 1	Plate 2
B. subtilis ATCC 6633	Strip 1	30	65	600	600	600	600	600	600
	Strip 2	150	170	600	600	600	600	600	600
C. albicans ATCC 10231	Strip 1	0	0	0	0	45	85	600	600
	Strip 2	0	0	0	0	130	180	600	600
A. niger WLRI 034	Strip 1	0	0	15	10	50	20	350	305
	Strip 2	0	0	30	15	45	85	445	195
S. aureus ATCC 6538	Strip 1	0	0	0	0	165	180	600	600
	Strip 2	0	0	0	0	155	135	600	600
P. aeruginosa ATCC 9027	Strip 1	0	0	0	0	265	235	600	600
	Strip 2	0	0	0	0	195	220	600	600
Plant isolate	Strip 1	0	0	0	0	0	0	600	600
	Strip 2	0	0	0	0	0	0	600	600
Negative control	Strip 1	0	0	0	0	0	0	0	0
	Strip 2	0	0	0	0	0	0	0	0

B. Chemical Evaluations

Chemists have contributed to the improved technology in chemical sanitizer analysis; however, it is relevant to note that the chemical condition of a substance may remain static, whereas the microflora of the substance may be dynamic. Bactericidal activity of a sanitizer is not solely a property of chemical composition, but is affected greatly by such physical factors as solubility, miscibility, degree of colloidal dispersion, ionization, surface tension, and other less well-defined properties [3]. Thus, in evaluating the effectiveness of an agent, one cannot rely solely on chemical assay for evaluation and ignore the microbiology, particularly with phenolics and quarternaries. Iodine and hypochlorite solutions or chlorine compounds provide greater assurance for security via only chemical assays than do other chemicals. However, even the titratable iodine and chlorine values can be somewhat misleading, because pH at use dilution is a very critical factor in the efficacy of both chemical agents.

C. Other Methods

Any method sanctioned by the AOAC must be considered acceptable for its intended use. These include: the use-dilution method, a carrier inoculum method to measure bactericidal activity against *S. aureus*, *S. choleraesius*, and *Ps. aeruginosa*; the available chlorine germicidal equivalent concentration test, a liquid inoculum capacity method to compare bactericidal activity with sodium hypochlorite against *S. typhosa* or *S. aureus*; the sporicidal test, a carrier inoculum method to measure sporicidal activity against the spores of *B. subtilis* and *Cl. sporogenes*; the fungicidal test, a liquid inoculum method to measure fungicidal activity against *T. interdigitale*; the germicidal and detergent sanitizers test to measure sanitizing activity against *S. aureus* and *E. coli*; the sanitizer spray products test, a carrier inoculum method to measure bactericidal activity against *S. aureus*, *S. choleraesius*, and *Ps. aeruginosa* and to measure fungicidal activity against *T. interdigitale*. Other appropriate methods may also be found suitable, but validation is necessary to assure adequate control.

D. Interpretation of Results

When laboratory evaluation does not yield a result that can be employed to predict practical value, the result is of limited value. Because microbiologists address death rates in exponential format, effects of sanitizers cannot be properly addressed by percentage reduction. If a direct measure of the objective of a sanitizer to kill vegetative bacteria is sought, then results of laboratory tests should be based on total kill of the population exposed. Interpretation of the total end-point method can be deceiving unless proper allowances are applied for the statistical limitations of sample size. When statistically significant data are developed for laboratory test results, good correlation between assays and in situ application can be expected. No great significance or absolute meaning can be assigned solely on the basis of a single reading of replicates; it is the relative comparison of sanitizers under controlled conditions that is all-important. To assure even greater confidence in determining proper use dilution, a safety factor may be added with supporting data.

VI. APPLICATION

A. Preparation Methods

The scheme for preparation of a sanitizer should be the same for a raw material.

The importance of proper safety precautions cannot be overemphasized, but the literature is replete with details of safety precautions for chemical sanitizers. Only the use of water meeting water-for-injection quality is recommended for application in diluting concentrated agents for use dilution. Mixing and compounding should be done in a suitable controlled area. All critical weighing or measuring steps should be witnessed and documented. Order of addition of agent to diluent is important. Some chemical concentrations can be added directly to water; others cannot. Acids, for example, should always be added to water.

Adjust pH, if necessary, to the preferred pH range for efficacy and compatibility. Generally speaking, the lower the pH, the faster bacteria are killed. Care should be taken when adding a "safety factor" not to diminish the effectiveness of the sanitizer by changing pH. More is not always better; thus, sanitization crews must be trained appropriately.

Once the use dilution batch is prepared, it should be subjected to qualitative microbiological screening tests and chemical assay as described herein (or an equivalent method) unless the method has been validated and data are available. Moreover, batches should be assayed periodically for contamination. Sterilization of sanitizers has not enjoyed widespread popularity, but microbiologists should determine the need for sterilization to avoid the potential for contamination of the area to be treated.

If a sanitizer solution is to be microbially filtered, care should be exercised to assure compatibility and eligibility of the material for filtration. For filters used to sterilize sanitizers, integrity tests are to be done before and after use. Furthermore, filters must be changed for each batch of sanitizer solution.

Documentation of manufacture of use dilutions of agents is important. Concentrate lot number (vendor), batch number, expiration data, operator(s), date of preparation, temperature, etc., are deemed minimal documentation requirements for preparation. Needless to say, all laboratory test results are required as an adjunct to the manufacturing record.

B. Technique Considerations

Critics of laboratory data typically allege that one can get almost any desired result in evaluation of a sanitizer. Exhibition of such cynicism is a manifestation of a basic misunderstanding of the problem. The many details involved in sanitizer evaluation methods and potential sources, however, do make them susceptible to bias.

Many different techniques have been studied, and the selection of one method over another is not critical. Regardless of the method employed, both the precision and accuracy of the method must be known. Resistance of each culture to a known sanitizer chemical should be determined concomitantly each time an analysis is run.

Standardization of equipment and materials, composition of media, pH, stock culture and test culture handling, preparation of exact sanitizer concentrations, accurate volume measurements, mixing of cells and agent, manipulative detail, and accurate timing establish a standard for adequate control.

Perhaps the greatest potential in the laboratory evaluation of agents centers around the circumvention of bacteriostasis. Stasis is frequently overcome by use of neutralizers in culture media.

Letheen broth is nutrient broth with added lecithin (azolectin) and Tween 80 (sorbitan monooleate). When testing cation surface-active agents such as quaternaries, or bacteriostatic phenolics, Letheen broth is the subculture medium of choice. For assay of oxidizing agents or heavy metals, fluid thioglycollate medium should be employed. Use of sodium thiosulfate solution to neutralize residual chlorine in solution is essential in testing efficacy of hypochlorite sanitizers in liquid form.

Since the required concentration of neutralizer varies with different test cultures used, neutralizer effectiveness verification or validation is essential to selection of maximum safe dilution for practical application in subcultures. Iodophors require both lecithin and thiosulfate to neutralize activity.

If there is suspicion of bacteriostasis in the use-dilution assay, all incubated tubes are reinoculated and reincubated.

If there is reason to believe that growth in a subculture tube may be contaminated, performance of Gram stains or subculture for identification is warranted.

C. Precautions

Responsibility for insuring that proper safety precautions are employed and that those working directly with agents are wearing minimum protection (e.g., masks, goggles, gloves) needs definition. Not only toxicity to the respiratory and digestive tracts must be considered, but also the vesicant and caustic action of agents on the skin and mucous membranes are of concern. Safety precautions should provide for assessment of the effects of prolonged and repeated contact with chemicals as well. Other practical precautions include:

1. Using only nonshedding materials in applying solutions to surfaces to obviate the addition of particulates.
2. Giving adequate consideration to removal of pyrogens for direct product contact lines, tanks, etc., particularly where steam or hot water is used to sanitize.
3. Watching for pitfalls in the temptation to increase concentration of the chemical in the absence of supporting test data. Chlorine and iodophor solutions, for example, may exhibit less microbiocial effect at more concentrated dilutions [6].
4. Observing a common isolate, even at levels below the alert level, in the environmental monitoring program may be a signal that a reservoir exists that has resulted in a low-grade infection. In such cases, complete dismantling of enclosed lines or similar systems may be necessary.

VII. RECOMMENDATIONS

Recommended practices for an effective microbial control program with sanitizers include:

1. Control air and water quality in the plant. Use only water-for-injection quality to prepare dilutions of sanitizing agents.
2. Confirm microbiological purity of each lot of chemical concentrate used to prepare use dilutions.
3. Thoroughly cleanse equipment immediately after use and sanitize equipment immediately prior to use.

4. Employ highly standardized test methods for microbial evaluation of sanitizers which can be correlated to actual use conditions, and periodically include environmental isolates in the challenge test panel.
5. Take advantage of the benefit in rotating chemical sanitizing agents.
6. Use only decontaminated mops, cloths, etc., to wipe down surfaces after application of sanitizing agent.
7. Assign the responsibility for sanitization to trained and reliable people. They need to know what is to be done, how to do it, and understand the key points of why the procedure is performed.
8. Assure that acceptable standards for materials transfer passage are enforced.
9. Develop an action plan that is appropriate for excursions beyond the warning level or management action level.
10. Document thoroughly the preparation, testing, use, and corrective action taken with sanitizing agents.
11. Exercise appropriate control to preclude recontamination following sanitization.
12. Look for documented references to product claims by vendors.
13. Agitate sterility test membranes obtained in assay of iodine solution for contamination during incubation to assure that microbial contaminants are not encapsulated.
14. Once a use-dilution has been validated both chemically and microbiologically, it will suffice to document the preparation of use dilutions (i.e., assays on each batch use dilution are not necessary).

Some specific areas or conditions where a particular type of sanitizer is recommended are tabulated below [7]:

Specific area or condition	Recommended sanitizer in order of preference
Aluminum equipment	Iodophor, quat
Bacterial spores	Hypochlorite
Bacteriostatic film	Quat, acid-anionic
Film formation, prevention of	Iodophor, acid-anionic
Fogging atmosphere	Hypochlorite, iodophor, quat
Hand sanitizer	Iodophor
Hard water	Acid-anionic, hypochlorite, iodophor
High iron water	Iodophor
Long shelf life	Iodophor, quat, acid-anionic
Low cost	Hypochlorite
Noncorrosive	Quat
Odor control	Quat
Organic matter, stable in presence of	Quat
Penetration	Iodophor, quat

Specific area or condition	Recommended sanitizer in order of preference
Prevention of film formation	Acid-anionic, iodophor
Residual film	Quat
Sanitization of equipment prior to use	Iodophor, hypochlorite
Sanitation of equipment to be stored	Quat
Shelf life	Iodophor, quat, acid-anionic
Stability	Iodophor, quat, acid-anionic
Stability of use solution	Acid-anionic, quat
Temperature changes, not affected by	Acid-anionic, quat
Visual control	Iodophor
Walls	Quat, hypochlorite
Water treatment	Hypochlorite
White porous surfaces	Hypochlorite, quat

VIII. SUMMARY

Sanitization is by definition elimination of viable microbial contamination of vegetative cells; it does not necessarily confer assurance of sterility. Use dilutions of acceptable chemical sanitizing agents are rarely sporicidal. Criteria for selection of a sanitizer include determination of label validity, verification of efficacy, application methods, frequency of use, preparation procedures, and microbiological evaluation. Confusion and misconceptions can be dispelled by sound microbiology. Efficacy of chemical agents depends on a multiplicity of factors. Microbiological assessment of the relative effectiveness of sanitizing agents must be based on validated methods and meticulously standardized procedures to successfully translate laboratory results to practical use conditions. Application of sanitizers must not be indiscriminate. Final selection of a sanitizer should be based consciously on weighing of advantages versus disadvantages of candidates for each application; a proper balance between incompatibility and microbiological efficacy must be sought.

In an effective microbial control program, recontamination of treated areas must be avoided following sanitization. Records of sanitization should be of the same caliber as a raw material.

REFERENCES

1. Association of Official Analytical Chemists. 1980. *Official Methods of Analysis*, 13th ed.
2. C. A. Harper, ed. 1975. *The Handbook of Plastics and Elastomers*. McGraw-Hill Book Company, New York.

3. Block, S. 1977. *Disinfection, Sterilization, and Preservation*, 2nd ed., Lea & Febiger, Philadelphia.
4. *Becton, Dickinson Lectures on Sterilization*. 1957. Seton Hall College of Dentistry and Medicine.
5. The Federal Insecticide, Fungicide and Rodenticide Act.
6. Berkleman, R. L., Holland, B. W., and Anderson, R. L. 1982. Increased bactercidal activity of dilute preparations of providone iodone solutions. *J. Clin. Microbiol. 15*: 635–639.
7. Forwalter, J. 1980. 1980 selection guide—cleaning and sanitizing compounds. *Food Processing*, February.

16
Validation of Sanitization in Air Locks

BARBARA M. GORDON

E. R. Squibb & Sons, Inc., New Brunswick, New Jersey

I. INTRODUCTION

Air locks are designed to provide a microbiological barrier between aseptic operations areas and adjacent, less clean, environments. They additionally provide a means of entry into aseptic areas for personnel and nonsterilized materials and equipment.

This chapter concerns methods for the validation and monitoring of the sanitization of equipment and materials passing through air locks into aseptic areas and discusses means of controlling contamination from personnel entering those areas.

A distinction must be made between three commonly, and often erroneously used terms: sterilization, disinfection, and sanitization. Sterilization and disinfection are absolute terms. The former designates a process that kills or inactivates all forms of life; the latter describes a process that destroys or inactivates infectious forms of disease-producing microorganisms and is often ineffective when applied to bacterial spores. The term sanitization refers to the reduction in the number of microorganisms to a safe or relatively safe level as determined by applicable regulations or the purpose of application. It is common practice to employ disinfectants for sanitization processes, hence effecting a greater reduction in microbial contaminants.

Terms such as bactericidal and bacteriostatic need to be defined. The suffix "cidal" refers to that which is destructive, while "static" indicates the prevention of growth or multiplication of a given group of microorganisms. The prefix describes the group of microorganisms affected; for example, bactericides, sporicides, and fungicides are destructive to bacteria, spores, and fungi, respectively. Bacteriostatic and fungistatic agents will prevent the growth and multiplication of bacteria and fungi, respectively.

Only those agents capable of destroying their target group of microorganisms should be employed for sanitization in air locks to prevent recovery and subsequent growth and multiplication of the organisms after being transported into the aseptic area.

II. AIR LOCKS

A. Types of Air Locks

An air lock, for this discussion, is a chamber between an aseptic area and an adjacent, less clean environment, and may range in size from a small double-door cabinet set within a wall to a room that can accommodate large pieces of equipment. The flow of HEPA (high-efficiency particulate air) filtered air under positive pressure inside the aseptic area, combined with appropriate sanitization procedures, is generally sufficient to maintain the clean air environment inside the air lock. Air locks may be equipped with high-intensity ultraviolet radiation lamps, which are utilized in conjunction with chemical agents for sanitization of equipment.

The air locks discussed thus far are utilized only for the passage of materials and equipment and should contain a clear demarcation over which personnel may not cross. In an elaborate system, there may be a full door creating a double-chamber air lock with an additional demarcation in the second entry chamber. The mode of operation of double-chamber air locks is described in more detail later in this chapter.

Air locks designed for use as an entryway for personnel are often just large enough for passage of one person. One type has several outlets through which filtered air is blown to loosen particulates from the operator's sterilized outer garments. Hence the term "air shower" is often applied to this type of air lock. There are those who believe that the "air shower" does more harm than good, in that the forced air serves merely to loosen particulates, thus increasing the degree of particulate shedding inside the aseptic area. A second type is without the "shower" and is referred to simply as a personnel air lock.

Entry air locks for personnel and equipment should be separate and distinct, since personnel are required to follow cleanup and gowning procedures to ready themselves for entry into the aseptic area. There would be no harm in personnel exiting via an equipment air lock, provided that they don fresh sterile garments prior to reentry through the proper passageway.

B. Personnel Air Locks

With all types of air locks, it is essential to remember that their primary role is that of a microbiological barrier between aseptic and nonaseptic areas, providing a passageway for materials, equipment, or personnel into or out of the aseptic area.

The main thrust of this chapter is directed at sanitization of equipment in the air lock, but since entry of personnel into the aseptic area is also through an air lock, the procedures to be employed will be discussed briefly. Humans may neither be sterilized, disinfected, nor sanitized. As a result, they represent a major threat of contamination to an aseptic environment. Sterilized clothing, shoe covers, gloves, hats, masks, and glasses must be available for all personnel entering the aseptic area. Personnel must be taught the proper procedures for donning these garments, since attire affords the best possible means of controlling microbial contamination. Standard Operating Procedures (SOPs) for gowning should be written and adhered to at all times.

Personnel preparing to enter an aseptic area should first remove jewelry and makeup, cover hair with a lint-free hat, and wash lower arms, hands, and face with a disinfecting soap such as Phisoderm. Ideally, these individuals should be dressed in a uniform made from a low-shedding fabric rather than street clothes. Beard and/or moustache covers made from the same type of fabric as the hat should be donned when required. They next pass through an air lock into a gown changing room, which may be divided into two sections by a bench type of barrier (see Figs. 1 and 2 for examples of the wash room and gown change room). The gown itself should be made from a nonshedding fabric and is often constructed in a jumpsuit style.

Gowning procedures may vary significantly from firm to firm as a result of their specific concerns. One example of a gowning procedure in a room with a bench type of barrier is outlined below:

1. Collect all required sterile garments and place on bench.
2. Cover one shoe with a sterile shoe cover (bootie) and swing leg over to other side of bench. Be sure that the bootie does not touch the floor on the less clean side of the bench. Repeat for other foot.
3. First put on the hood and then the gown, taking care not to allow any part of the garments to touch the floor. Close the zipper and adjust the gown so that the lower leg portion covers the top of the bootie, the sleeve covers the entire arm to the wrist, and the hood is securely tucked in at the neck.
4. Cover the nose and mouth with a surgical mask and fasten.
5. Examine appearance in a full-length mirror, looking for any openings in the garments, and make final adjustments as required.
6. Finally, put on sterile gloves covering elasticized sleeve of gown with upper portion of glove.
7. Enter the aseptic area via an air lock.

The doors to the air lock should be equipped with an automatic locking system to prevent the inadvertant opening of outer and inner doors simultaneously. With an air shower, both doors should be closed and locked until the fans have completed an automatically timed cycle. Once inside the aseptic area, 70% isopropyl alcohol or other disinfecting agent should be utilized continually to keep the gloved hands of the operators free of microbial contaminants.

C. Equipment Air Locks

Proper utilization of an equipment air lock requires the preparation of detailed Standard Operating Procedures (SOPs) and training of personnel. The firms' SOPs must clearly define rules and procedures for air lock entry and exit, and special clothing if any. The SOPs should also cite any restrictions placed on the air locks. For example, personnel may not enter an aseptic area via an air lock designated only for equipment. Another example is an air lock that provides only for exit of equipment and/or personnel from an aseptic area. This type of air lock does not require validation and therefore must not be utilized for entry of materials or personnel.

As previously cited, under no circumstances are the doors to both sides of the air lock to be opened simultaneously. Doing so may expose the aseptic area to the outer environment, thus compromising the integrity of the inner area.

An example of transporting equipment into an aseptic area is as follows: An operator moves the equipment into the air lock, taking care to avoid crossing the internal barrier, and immediately closes the entry door. Following prescribed SOPs, the operator then sanitizes the equipment and exits by the same door utilized for entry. After a designated waiting period, an operator from within the aseptic area enters the air lock, closes

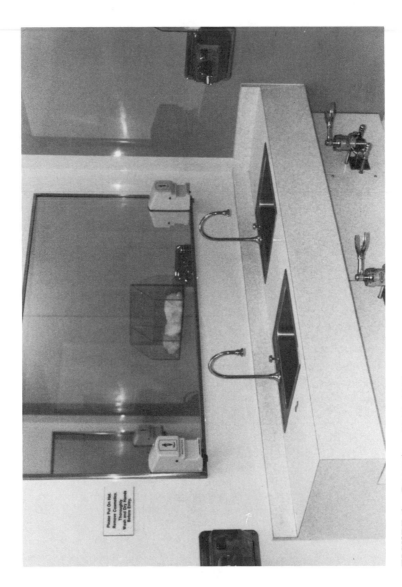

FIGURE 1   Preentry prep area.

FIGURE 2   Gown change room with step-over barrier.

FIGURE 3   Double-chamber equipment air lock.

FIGURE 4   Cabinet-type air lock.

the door, and sanitizes those portions of the equipment handled by the
first operator or having contact with the floor. The equipment is then
ready to be moved across the barrier. After a designated waiting period, the
equipment is transported into the aseptic area. All of the details concerning
the sanitizing agent, methods of preparation and application, waiting periods,
etc., must be contained in SOPs to assure uniformity of practice.

In the case of a double-chamber air lock (Fig. 3), the equipment is sanitized in the outer chamber and moved into the inner chamber without crossing
the internal barrier. The equipment is then sanitized again and the operator
exits by the same door utilized for entry. The procedures for additional
sanitization and transporting the equipment into the aseptic area are the same
as for a single-chamber air lock discussed above.

The small cabinet type of air lock (Fig. 4) operates with the same principles
as the larger air locks, but sanitization must be performed prior to placement
of the article into the chamber.

III. TYPICAL ITEMS TO BE SANITIZED

Ideally, materials and equipment should be sterilized and removed from the
autoclave or dry-heat oven in the aseptic area. Items that are nonsterilizable
because they are too large or labile to heat, steam, or ethylene oxide must be
sanitized in the air lock prior to transporting them into the aseptic area. Once
inside, any items required for routine operations should be allowed to remain.

Equipment and materials that are usually transported into aseptic areas
employing air locks include:

Laminar-flow hoods
Filling machines
Filled portable tanks
Tables and chairs
HEPA and other air filters
Cleaning tools and supplies
Maintenance cart
Machine repair parts, motors, etc.
Environmental monitoring equipment
Electronic parts and equipment
Balances and scales

IV. SANITIZING PRACTICES

A. Selecting a Chemical Agent

When selecting a chemical agent to be utilized for sanitization of equipment in
air locks, several properties must be examined, including desired level of
effectiveness, type of effect on microorganisms, degree of toxicity to operating
personnel, and residues adhering to sanitized equipment.

Agents that are chemical disinfectants, rather than sanitizers, are the
agents of choice and should be capable of killing bacteria, bacterial spores,
yeasts, and/or molds (cidal) rather than just stopping their growth (static).
A minimum of two bactericidal agents should be rotated on a regular basis to
prevent resistance development by indigenous flora. Methods for evaluation
to determine the most suitable chemical agent or combination of agents are
detailed elsewhere in this text.

B. Nonchemical Methods

The major nonchemical agent employed for sanitization of equipment in air locks is ultraviolet irradiation (UV). It is an efficient adjunct to chemical sanitization in that it sanitizes the air in the room in addition to the equipment surfaces. It is effective against virtually all microorganisms to varying degrees. UV irradiation is seldom utilized alone due to inherent deficiencies. For example, ultraviolet light is nonpenetrating and is effective only upon exposed surfaces. Those surfaces should be smooth and highly polished to assure adequate process lethality. Sublethal doses to organisms protected by cracks and crevices may result in cellular repair with subsequent recovery of the microorganisms.

Germicidal lamps are readily available commercially and transmit UV radiation with approximately 95% of wavelengths in the proximity of 2537 Å. Lamps may be installed on ceilings and/or walls, and portable UV lamps are also used. Both high- and low-intensity lamps are currently employed. The locations of the lamps must be carefully planned, and reflectors may be employed to utilize the light to the fullest advantage. It is equally important to arrange for the cleaning of lamps and reflectors on a regular basis. The lamps should be connected to timers and recorders for proper cycle documentation, and intensity must be measured with a calibrated meter.

The UV irradiation cycle length must be developed by determining reduction of selected organisms as a function of exposure time. Naturally occurring organisms isolated in bioburden studies should be included in the cycle development program.

C. Sanitizing Methods

All materials and equipment must be clean prior to entry into an air lock. The recommended method for application of a chemical agent is to use a gentle spray, making certain that the agent reaches difficult-to-clean areas such as wheels, gears, crevices, etc. The floor area in the air lock must be sprayed at the same time to prevent contamination of the equipment after sanitization is complete.

Standard Operating Procedures should include instruction on the operation of the spraying device and required time of contact between the chemical agent and the equipment prior to moving the item across the line or barrier within the air lock.

Alternative methods of application include total immersion of small items in the chemical solution or direct application of the agent with a cloth or wipe. The latter method may be implemented for articles that are smooth and contain no areas that could be missed in the process, but care must be taken to avoid increasing the particulate level on the article. A fresh, sterile cloth or wipe should be utilized for each piece of equipment to avoid an additional contamination source.

When ultraviolet irradiation is utilized, the chemical sanitization is performed first and then the UV lamps are activated for the selected cycle length while the agent is drying on the surface of the item.

V. BIOBURDEN DETERMINATIONS

A bioburden survey should be conducted to determine the number and kind of microorganisms naturally occurring on representative materials and equipment to be sanitized. The articles selected for the survey should include those

believed to have the highest bioburden, with attention paid to the environment
of the articles before transport to the air lock.

The information from the bioburden survey is useful in calculating the required concentration level of the chemical agent to be employed. The organisms isolated may be included as test challenges in the disinfectant efficacy
testing and the UV cycle development studies.

The results of a bioburden survey may reveal special problems: A particular piece of equipment is found to harbor an exceptionally large number of
microorganisms; or, due to the storage environment of a given piece of equipment, the bioburden is found to be different from the other articles tested.
In the case of the former, a presanitization program may be established to reduce the initial number of organisms prior to allowing entry into the air lock.
For the latter, including the organisms in the disinfectant evaluation and/or
ultraviolet irradiation cycle development studies would generate data concerning the relative resistance of these organisms to the chemical agent and UV
cycle employed.

After selecting the articles for the bioburden study, a form for documentation of data should be developed (see Table 1) and should include a diagram of
the item depicting sample locations chosen with worst-case conditions in mind
(i.e., cart wheels, crevices).

Bioburden sampling and testing methods must be developed and incorporated
into Standard Operating Procedures. Among these are Rodac plate sampling,
swabbing techniques, and immersion methods.

The Rodac plate method is the simplest, but is useful only for flat surfaces.
The sterile agar in a plate (usually 50 mm in diameter) comes into direct contact with the equipment surface, the plate is covered and incubated for a predetermined time at the recommended temperature (e.g., 30–35°C and/or 20–
25°C). The organisms are counted and may be identified by macroscopic and
microscopic morphology and may be fully speciated if required. Filled Rodac
plates are available commercially (e.g., BBL, Difco) containing a variety of
agars. Commonly utilized media are Standard Methods Agar and Standard
Methods Agar plus lecithin and polysorbate 80 (Tween 80), the latter useful
for neutralizing the effects of cationic surface active agents and phenolics.
Rodac plates have the distinct disadvantage of leaving a residue of media on
the surface being sampled.

Swab samples afford examination of corners, crevices, and other area in-
accessible to Rodac plates. The swab may consist of a variety of materials
such as cotton or dacron. A swab made from calcium alginate is a good choice
because the swab material dissolves in diluent, thus affording a better release
of organisms into the solution. The size of the sample should be consistent
(e.g., 100 cm^2) and a suitable diluent (e.g., USP phosphate buffer pH 7.2,
phosphate buffer with magnesium sulfate pH 7.2) must be employed. It should
be noted that any diluent selected must be tested for bacteriostasis with a
variety of control organisms. The quantity of diluent selected is dependent
on the total number of organisms present. For relatively clean surfaces,
2.5–3 ml of diluent per tube are recommended to provide 1 ml for testing of
aerobes and 1 ml for testing of anaerobes. An additional milliliter of diluent
may be added if testing for yeasts and molds is required. Even though it may
be determined that only selected locations shall be tested for anaerobes and/or
yeasts and molds, the quantity of diluent should remain consistent for all
samples.

The swab is prewetted with sterile diluent, rubbed over the area selected,
and placed into a fresh tube of premeasured sterile diluent. The samples

TABLE 1   Equipment Sample Information Sheet

DEPARTMENT:	STERILE FILLING	DATE: 12/15/83
SAMPLES TAKEN BY:	BG & KP	
TYPE OF EQUIPMENT:	UTILITY CART	

SAMPLE #	PLATE (P) OR SWAB (S)	SAMPLE LOCATION
1	S	Left rear wheel
2	S	Right front wheel
3	P	Top shelf, center
4	S	Second shelf, right rear corner
5	S	Bottom shelf, left front corner
6	S	Top shelf, underside, right rear
7	S	Handle
9	P	Second shelf center
10	S	Third shelf, left rear corner

DIAGRAM:

should be tested as soon as possible to avoid increase in numbers of organisms in the diluent. The tube is vortexed to release the organisms from the swab and the diluent is plated onto the appropriate media by the pour plate or spread plate method. Commercially available swabs with transport media may be utilized for direct plating. After incubation, the organisms are counted and identified.

The types of media employed are dependent on the disinfectant utilized. In some instances a neutralizing medium, such as Standard Methods Agar plus lecithin and polysorbate 80 (Tween 80), will be required to assure uninhibited bacterial growth. Five to ten percent sheep blood may be added to enhance the growth of anaerobic organisms. For the enhancement of yeasts and molds, a selective medium such as Sabaroud Dextrose Agar may be employed.

The effectiveness of media and methods should be determined prior to use. This may be accomplished by inoculating selected materials (e.g., glass, stainless steel, plastics) with a known quantity of bacterial cells and allowing to air-dry. Spray the inoculated materials with the chemical agent and recover the organisms employing the methods and media to be utilized for the testing of equipment. The study should be repeated without the chemical agent as a control.

VI. VALIDATION

A. Protocols

Prior to the initiation of any validation program, a validation protocol must be prepared and approved. Headings in the protocol should include: Introduction, Responsibilities, Procedure, and Acceptance Criteria.

The introduction should explain the purpose of the process to be validated and should include what is to be validated and why. The responsibilities section should detail the department and/or personnel required for each phase of the study, including the approval process for both the validation protocol and report.

The procedure section should describe sampling methods, including number and location of samples and transport of samples to the appropriate laboratory. Testing methodology should be detailed with reference to pertinent Standard Operating Procedures (SOPs) and documentation forms. This section should also list specific equipment to be sampled as part of the validation program, and should include the number of replicates required to complete the validation. All information relating to the sanitizing agent, its preparation, storage, and documentation should also be discussed and/or referenced.

Acceptance criteria must be established with limits clearly defined, and may include recommendations for investigation and correction if these limits are exceeded. Preliminary bioburden studies are helpful to determine realistic limits prior to the preparation of validation protocols.

B. Methods

The validation of a sanitization process is based on satisfactorily reducing the microbial load of the item sanitized. The methods employed for sampling and testing must be the same as those employed in initial bioburden determinations and media effectiveness studies described in Section V.

An example of a validation test program is described below:

1. The equipment is brought into the air lock and sampled for bioburden. Proper documentation of sample locations is essential (see Table 1).
2. The equipment is then sanitized according to standard procedures by operating personnel having no knowledge of which locations have or will be sampled.
3. After the prescribed waiting period has elapsed, equivalent but different areas on each piece of equipment are again sampled for bioburden. Once again, proper documentation of sanitizing agent and sample location is essential (see Table 2). All procedures and practices should be evaluated to ensure adequate sanitization, including preparation of sanitizing agent, time of exposure, concentration of solution, age of solution, and methods of application.

TABLE 2   Sanitized Equipment Sample Information Sheet

DEPARTMENT: ____STERILE FILLING____   DATE: ____12/15/83____

SAMPLES TAKEN BY: ____BG & KP____

SANITIZATION PERFORMED BY: __AT__ SANITIZING AGENT & CONC: XYZ,5%

DATE PREPARED: ____12/15/83____   EXPIRATION DATE: ____12/22/83____

TYPE OF EQUIPMENT SANITIZED: _____UTILITY CART_____

SAMPLE #	PLATE (P) OR SWAB (S)	BEFORE SANITIZATION	AFTER SANITIZATION
1	S	Left rear wheel	Right rear wheel
2	S	Left front wheel	Right front wheel
3	S	#1, rt fr corner	#1, lft fr corner
4	P	Shlf 2, lft center	Shlf 2, rt center
5	P	Shlf 3, lft center	Shlf 3, rt center
6	S	Handle, right	Handle, left
7	S	#3, lft fr corner	#3, rt fr corner
8	S	#2, lft rear corner	#2, rt rear corner
9	P	Shlf 1, lft center	Shlf 1, rt center
10	P	Under 1, lft center	Under 1, rt center

DIAGRAM: ,

4. If ultraviolet irradiation is employed, additional samples are collected after the appropriate UV cycle is concluded. Other factors to consider are cycle length, emission at 2537 Å, and light intensity. A monitoring program should be established for cleaning of bulbs, testing for proper emission, and measuring intensity with a calibrated meter, all on a regular basis.

5. All samples must be delivered to the testing laboratory as soon as possible to preclude bacterial growth in the diluent prior to testing.

C. Acceptance Criteria

As defined earlier, sanitization refers to the reduction in number of microorganisms to a safe or relatively safe level. The question of what level of contamination is "safe" or "relatively safe" must now be raised. The ideal answer is that all articles entering an aseptic area should be sterile, and that no level of contamination is "safe." For practical purposes, recognizing that sterility is not always achievable, acceptance limits must be determined based on usage of the equipment involved. Pathogenic organisms should be eliminated entirely, and the level of other environmental microbial contaminants should be held to a minimum. Acceptance limits for equipment in close proximity to product should be the same as or similar to those limits set by the firm when conducting environmental surface monitoring within aseptic areas. Limits may be less stringent for those areas of equipment far removed from product or filling lines (e.g., cart wheels, cleaning tools, and supplies), provided that there is no compromise to the aseptic environment.

D. Report

Upon completion of all validation data collection and evaluation, the validation report must be issued. The headings should include Abstract, Plan of Study, Experimental, Results, Conclusion, and Approval.

The abstract should be brief and describe the validated process. The plan of study should reference the validation protocol and describe the validation program in general terms. The experimental section should describe in detail the equipment sampled, number of samples taken, sanitizing agents utilized, and tests performed. Standard Operating Procedures should be referenced.

The results section may consist of tables of test data and should demonstrate the reduction of bioburden before and after sanitization. Acceptance limits cited in the validation protocol should be discussed with assurance that all have been met. The conclusion need state that based on the test results the process has been validated.

VII. CONCLUSION

The validation of a sanitization process must be conducted in a manner that proves the adequate and consistent reduction in number of microorganisms from selected equipment under a specified set of circumstances.

Sanitization validation studies must begin with preliminary bioburden surveys and selection of sanitizing agents best suited to destroy those organisms found or those likely to be found. Studies are then conducted to evaluate the agents to be utilized, including methods of application, and finally, the data collected are analyzed to determine effectiveness and reproducibility of the process. All procedures, methods, and results are documented to provide a permanent written record of the completed validation program.

BIBLIOGRAPHY

Bass, G. K. 1977. Methods of testing disinfectants, in *Disinfection, Sterilization, and Preservation*, 2nd ed., S. S. Block, ed. Lea & Febiger, Philadelphia. pp 49–77.

Beloian, A. 1977. Methods of testing for sterility and efficacy of sterilizers, sporicides and sterilizing processes, in *Disinfection, Sterilization, and Preservation*, 2nd ed., S. S. Block, ed. Lea & Febiger, Philadelphia. p 11.

Block, S. S. 1977. Definition of terms, in *Disinfection, Sterilization, and Preservation*, 2nd ed., S. S. Block, ed. Lea & Febiger, Philadelphia. pp 1025–1026, 1028.

Boucher, R. M. G. 1972. Advances in sterilization techniques, state of the art and recent breakthroughs. *Am. J. Hosp. Pharm. 29*: 661–672.

Christensen, E. A., Jepsen, O. B., Kristensen, H., and Steen, G. 1982. In-use tests of disinfectants. *Acta Path. Microbiol. Immunol. Scand. Sect. B 90*: 95–100.

Devleeschouwer, M. J., and Dony, J. 1981. An in vitro test for the evaluation of the efficacy of disinfectants. *Int. J. Pharmaceut. 9*: 49–58.

Gordon, B. M. 1983. Evaluation of diluents utilized for microorganism recovery. Unpublished data.

Prince, H. N. 1983. Disinfectant activity against bacteria and viruses: A hospital guide. *P & MC 2*: 54–62.

Shechmeister, I. L. 1977. Sterilization by ultraviolet radiation, in *Disinfection, Sterilization, and Preservation*, 2nd ed., S. S. Block, ed. Lea & Febiger, Philadelphia. pp 525–527.

17

Validation of Aseptic Processing Filters

JOHN J. ERRICO

Pfizer Inc., Groton, Connecticut

I. INTRODUCTION TO ASEPTIC FILTRATION

Aseptic filtration is frequently the method of choice for sterilization of fluids that are heat-sensitive and therefore do not lend themselves to autoclaving. In many cases, another influential factor is that large volumes of the sterilized fluid must be produced continuously on-line and energy/equipment economics dictate filtrative sterilization. The safety hazards associated with ethylene oxide sterilization have also contributed to the need for development of validated aseptic filtration techniques for products that are crystallized in bulk volumes.

This chapter deals with the practical needs of the pharmaceutical engineer in designing and validating aseptic filter configurations. The considerations addressed include appropriately specifying the needs of the process (flow rates, pressure drop, biological loading, filter longevity, hardware), verification of filter/stream compatibility, sterilization capability of the medium, mechanical integrity of the equipment, and appropriate sterilization methods for the filters themselves. Discussion of the needs of aseptic gaseous filtration will also be included. In addition, the process is not valid until the operating procedures are written, executed, and documented within the limits defined by the validation studies, so discussion of these objectives is presented as relevant and necessary.

A. What Is to Be Validated?

Since aseptic filtration is a process by which microorganisms are removed from the process stream by mechanical means, it is plagued with all the pitfalls of mechanical devices. The point to be made here is that since autoclaving relies on the delivery of heat in sufficient quantity to all parts of the system being sterilized, the task of validation is facilitated by the measurement of intensive properties of the system, such as temperature or pressure. In addition, there is no need to worry about the sterility of the sterilizing equipment, since it is itself sterilized in the process. On the other hand, aseptic filtration is vulnerable to numerous extensive pathologies, such as nonuniformity of filter manufacture, chemical attack on the filter medium, mechanical defect in the configuration, overpressurization, nonsterility of the filtration equipment, and excessive biological loading. In order to develop an appropriate validation rationale, we must envision the possibility of any or several of these effects as a challenge to the filter configuration, and then devise experiments that will demonstrate valid filter performance within control limits that will be procedurally enforced. There is no single means of validating an aseptic filtration system. It is a combination of validation studies that, when compelted, gives rise to a complex array of filter specifications, integrity test, sterilization, and operating procedures on a process stream-by-process stream basis.

The net effect on the validation is that a given process stream will emerge from the aseptic filter configuration such that the probability of its containing at least one microorganism is less than 10^{-6}. Further, we have not completely specified the problem until two other parameters have been quantified: How much process stream? What microorganisms? For purposes of this discussion, we will restrict ourselves to the above probability for the lifetime of the filter medium in the configuration and to microorganisms of size equal to or larger than *Pseudomonas diminuta* (ATC 19146, approximately 0.2 μm cross-section diameter).

B. Definition of Some Frequently Used Aseptic Filter Validation Terms

Aseptic filter configuration: the aseptic filter medium and hardware designed to support it in full assembly with gasketing, pipe connections, and instrumentation.

Upstream side: that portion of cavity and surfaces within the aseptic filter configuration which contacts the process stream prior to its passage through the aseptic filter medium.

Downstream side: that portion of cavity and surfaces within the aseptic filter configuration which contacts the process stream after its passage through the aseptic filter medium.

Aseptic filter medium: the membrane or other structure within the configuration that is permeable to the process stream and retains microorganisms at an acceptable efficiency for sterilization purposes.

Integrity test: a method, usually nondestructive, for verifying the absence of minute defects in the assembly of an aseptic filter configuration which could lead to bypass of the medium by the process stream.

Medium: see aseptic filter medium.

Note: All other terms used will be defined or explained as they appear in this chapter.

C. The "Ideal" Aseptic Filter

How do we find the best aseptic filter for the application? One way to approach this question is to describe the ideal filter for all applications and then identify what performance characteristics are important in aseptic filter selection.

1. Unlimited flow rates: The ideal filter configuration will provide flow rates that exceed normal process requirements well within the pressure drop limitations. There is, of course, no point in continuing validation studies on a candidate filter if flow requirements cannot be met.

The aseptic filter media usually capable of high flow rates are thin and have high void volumes, as a function of the process by which they are manufactured. If the volumes involved are small and configuration is not a restriction, the user may not have to focus on flow rate, since he can adjust filter area to accommodate his needs.

2. Inert: The ideal filter configuration reacts with nothing, nor does it leach anything at all temperatures, concentrations, pH, etc. Few materials that can be used in filter manufacture meet this requirement. Several polymers, such as Teflon, Kynar, and nylon, approach this quality and have been used in aseptic filter media manufacture. However, there are assorted materials other than the filter medium that the process stream contacts in the configuration, and the inertness of these too must be qualified.

3. Unlimited bioload removal: The ideal aseptic filter medium will be a sink for microorganisms. It will retain them to the extent that the entire filter surface is covered without passage of a single microorganism. A ballpark estimate of the quantity of challenge is 6×10^8 organisms/cm^2 of filter surface, assuming 0.2-μm organisms hexagonally packed.

Many of today's aseptic filter media are demonstrated to successfully retain several orders of magnitude greater challenges than this, which is theoretically superfluous but desirable to accommodate possible nonuniformity of distribution or nonviability of organisms in the challenge stream. Challenges in excess of 10^{10}/cm^2 frequently will result in complete blockage of flow through the filter.

4. Strength and thermal stability: The ideal filter will not tear or be punctured easily. It will withstand differential pressures in excess of available pressures. It will not fatigue or rupture under hydraulic shock and will withstand flow bidirectionally.

Steaming will not embrittle, wrinkle, shrink, stretch, or weaken the medium. Steaming will not change the filter's chemical compatibility or bioload performance. In practice, many media must be steam-sterilized at pressures below a specified maximum or they cannot be steamed at all. Few alternatives to steam sterilization of filter configurations are attractive, and so this quality must be carefully considered in the selection of candidate media.

5. Indefinite longevity: The ideal filter will not foul rapidly, and when it does, it may be cleaned, resterilized, and reused. The idea of the nonfouling filter is, of course, a myth. However, fouling rate must be carefully weighed against process economics in selection of a filter configuration. The answer may lie in appropriate prefiltration, in which a nonaseptic filter configuration of high dirt-loading capacity/low cost is employed to reduce the quantity of foulant reaching the more costly and (probably) more time-consuming-to replace, aseptic filter. An additional factor to consider in the optimization of prefiltration is that frequently a reduction in biological challenge to the aseptic filter will result in an additional margin of sterility assurance of the final stream through validation.

6. Low cost: The consideration to be given to filter cost will be a function of the process economics and the fraction of total processing cost that aseptic filtration really represents. In addition to this, a choice must be made between the purchase of cartridges for use in relatively low-cost housings, or flat stock aseptic filter media for use in membrane holders. For large-volume users, serious consideration must be given to the purchase of flat stock media for use in expensive multiplate membrane holders. Cost advantages of a given configuration must be weighed with indirect considerations such as reliability

of the supplier, turnaround time for replacement of a unit in the plant, existing equipment, and flexibility.

With a clear understanding of the performance goals our aseptic filtration configuration must meet, we can proceed to select candidates for validation.

II. DESIGNING THE FILTRATION PROCESS

The choice of filters as candidates for validation should begin with a quantitative assessment of the requirements of the aseptic filtration process.

A. Process Specifications

The following checklist of process specifications should be reviewed before screening candidate aseptic filter media:

> Desired flow rate (gal/min, liters/min, cc/min, etc.)
> Minimum acceptable flow rate
> Desired pressure drop (psi, dynes/cm^2, etc.)
> Maximum acceptable pressure drop
> Desired longevity of filter media (gal, batches, hr, etc.)
> Available means of sterilization (in-line steam, autoclave, ethylene oxide, etc.)
> Stream information (aqueous, solvents, percentages, pH, temperature, etc.)

1. Flow Rate Requirements

Flow rate requirements can often be verified without actual implementation of the process on a full scale by the use of flow decay studies. Flow decay experiments are used to predict the life of plant-scale filters and thereby determine if a candidate filter will provide feasible flow rates and how much filtration area will be needed. The apparatus needed to develop flow decay data is relatively simple, and a typical arrangement is given in Figure 1.

The procedure is to load a sample of the medium into a small filter holder such as a 47-mm holder available from several manufacturers. A sample of actual plant process stream, if available, is loaded into the pressure vessel. If no plant process stream is available, a laboratory pilot stream should be prepared. A regulated air supply is used to pressurize the vessel and maintain constant pressure on the upstream side of the filter medium, as measured by a calibrated pressure gauge. The pressure vessel may consist of an empty filter cartridge holder with sanitary fittings for ease of disassembly and cleaning. The volume of process stream to use should be in excess of the desired or expected throughput of the plant configuration calculated on the basis of cubic centimeters per square centimeter of filter area. In many cases, in order to be able to perform flow decay experiments with convenient (or in some cases, economic) volumes of process stream, it may be advisable to reduce test filter area size by using a smaller (25-mm or 13-mm) holder or by using restrictors that cover the filter surface except for an opening of known diameter.

The test is started by opening the pressure vessel discharge valve and venting off the filter holder so as to be sure all air is evacuated and free flow is established through the holder. A large, empty graduated cylinder is used to collect the filtrate and to obtain readings of the total throughput. The pressure gauge should be checked to be sure the desired pressure is being maintained and adjustments made to the regulator as required. Once flow is

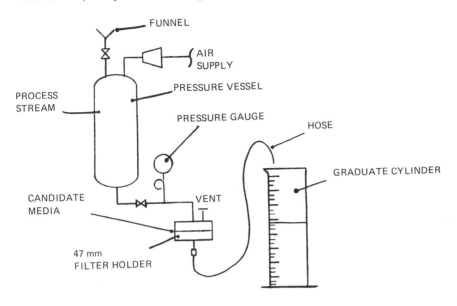

FIGURE 1 Flow decay test apparatus.

established into the graduate, the flow rate is determined by temporarily redirecting the flow into a smaller graduate, calibrated in smaller divisions,
preferably 0.1 ml, and timing the flow with a stopwatch. After the measurement, the flow is returned to the large graduate. The collected filtrate in the
smaller graduate should be returned to the larger graduate. A log is established with columns for time, filtration rate in cubic centimeters per minute,
total throughput collected in cubic centimeters, and confirmed differential
pressure in suitable units. The differential pressure to use in the experiment
should be approximately that which will be experienced in the plant. The log
entries should be made at intervals depending on how rapidly the flow is de-
caying. That is, there is probably little value in obtaining readings every
5 min if the flow rate is changing by only a few percent each time. The experiment should be continued for at least one half-life of the flow rate (i.e.,
the point at which the flow rate is one-half of the flow rate at startup).

Having completed the experiment, the data should be converted into specific
flow rate (cc/cm^2-min) and specific throughput (cc/cm^2) values suitable for
plotting. The raw flow rate and throughput data are simply divided by the
known test filter surface area in square centimeters. Figure 2 is a typical
flow decay plot. Note that the solid line representing the decay of specific
flow rate seems to drop as in an exponential decay function. Most flow decay
curves behave this way, and the reason can be shown mathematically.

If a slight decrease in specific flow rate, dF, is due to a slight increase
in foulant, df, on the filter surface, times a constant K_1, this can be written
as

$$dF = -K_1 \, df$$

However, if this is modified to indicate that the effect of fouling on flow rate
is greater at higher flow rates, then it will appear as

$$dF = -K_1 \, F \, df$$

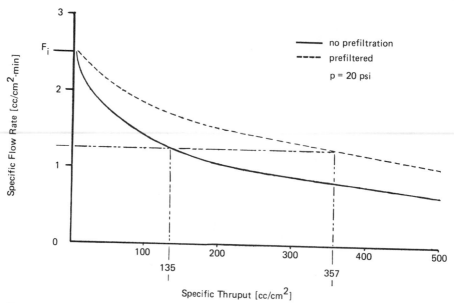

FIGURE 2   Flow decay plot.

Realize that a slight increase in filter fouling is due to a differential through-put, dF, of process stream in which the foulant was suspended, or

$$df = K_2 \, dV$$

By substituting and integrating,

$$dF = -K_1 \, F \, df = -K_1 K_2 F \, dV$$

$$\frac{dF}{F} = -K_1 K_2 \, dV$$

and combining constants,

$$\ln F = -aV + b$$

where b is simply the natural logarithm of the initial flow rate, F_i. Therefore,

$$\ln \frac{F}{F_i} = -aV \quad \text{or} \quad F = F_i e^{-aV}$$

This leads to a very useful way to compare the performance of one medium with another without having to refer to initial flow rates, which are really zero-foulant or "clean-stream" flow rates. The calculation of the specific throughput, $V_{1/2}$, at the half-life of specific filtration rate is a convenient way to do this. For most cases, this value can be obtained graphically or interpolated from the flow decay log. For some cases, where the volumes involved in carrying out flow decay are too large, statistical methods may be used to curve-fit the data available to the above equation and then realizing that at the half-life, and therefore

$$\frac{F}{F_i} = 0.5,$$

$$V_{\frac{1}{2}} = \frac{-1}{a} \ln_{F_i} = \frac{-1}{a} \ln 0.5 = \frac{0.693}{a}$$

An extremely high half-life would appear to be a flat flow decay curve or clean-stream performance. The absolute specific flow rate obtained in this case is a function of viscosity of the process stream pressure drop and the filter medium in question.

Not only can flow decay be used to evaluate aseptic media against aseptic media, but prefiltration efficiency can be measured. The recommended practice here is to pass the process stream through candidate prefilter media and evaluate the flow decay using a standard aseptic media. In this manner the projected life of the aseptic filter media based on half-life calculations can be used to economically optimize the prefiltration/aseptic filtrations scheme.

For example, refer again to Figure 2, in which a dashed flow decay curve has been plotted to represent the process stream after prefiltration through a candidate prefilter. Note that the half-life without and with prefiltration is 135 and 357 cc/cm^2, respectively. If the criterion for filter replacement is assumed to be the half-life, then the longevity of the aseptic filter medium could be extended significantly by prefiltering the process stream.

To calculate the breakeven point for prefiltration, we proceed as follows: If the aseptic filter medium costs x cents/cm^2, then the cost of aseptic filtration per cubic centimeter will be x/135. If the prefilter costs y cents/cm^2 of aseptic filter area, then the cost of prefiltration (assuming that the prefilter is replaced whenever the aseptic filter is replaced) plus aseptic filtration will be (x + y)/357. The breakeven point is when x/135 = (x + y)/357 or when y = 1.64x.

That is, it will be economically justified to perform prefiltration if the cost of the prefilter per square centimeter of aseptic filter is less than 1.64 times that cost for the aseptic filter itself, provided that the prefilter longevity is at least as great as the aseptic filter. It should be noted that x and y should be considered to be not just the purchased medium cost, but the total cost of implementation including labor, energy, depreciation of hardware, etc.

2. Pressure Drop Requirements

It was mentioned earlier that flow decay studies should be performed at the approximate differential pressure expected in the plant. If flow rate predictions are required for differential pressures other than that at which the flow decay was done, and the pressures are of the same order of magnitude, then reasonable estimates may be obtained by assuming that the flow rate is linear with pressure. In most cases the half-life (in cc/cm^2) will not be affected by differential pressure. There are cases, however, in which the nonviable foulant is submicrometer in size and a small percentage is able to pass through the medium. In such cases an increase in differential pressure could lead to a larger percentage of passage through the medium and an apparently higher half-life. This can be demonstrated by performing the following series of flow decay measurements:

1. Split the process stream sample into two parts, A and B.
2. Perform flow decay on part A at 20 psi, then perform flow decay on part B at 60 psi, saving the filtrates A' and B' separately. Calculate half-lives $V_{\frac{1}{2}}A$ and $V_{\frac{1}{2}}B$.
3. Perform flow decay on A' and B' at 20 psi. Calculate the half-lives $V_{\frac{1}{2}}A'$ and $V_{\frac{1}{2}}B'$.

If comparison of the half-lives shows that $V_{\frac{1}{2}}{}^{A} < V_{\frac{1}{2}}{}^{B}$ and $V_{\frac{1}{2}}{}^{A'} > V_{\frac{1}{2}}{}^{B'}$, then passage of foulant was evident at the higher pressure. If the foulant is undesirable, it may be important to perform these types of flow decay studies to determine a suitable pressure at which to operate the plant filtration. Indeed, an aseptic filter medium of smaller porosity may be necessary.

If foulant passage is not a problem, then operating pressures may be determined based on other restrictions. Most aseptic filter media are able to withstand up to 50 psi differential pressure in their configurations. If the equipment is capable of supplying pressures greater than this, it is advisable to install appropriate pressure relief valves or rupture disks to prevent medium rupture and as a good safety measure. In any case, the manufacturer's recommended maximum operating differential pressure should be known and never exceeded. Occasionally, a filter medium may have a recommended maximum differential pressure at high temperatures, for in-line steam sterilization applications, which will be discussed later in this chapter.

If variable supply pressures are available, the routine operating differential pressure should be selected to be no greater than the maximum recommended Δp or the integrity test differential test pressure for the filter, whichever is lower. The reasoning for this is that it is desirable to avoid exceeding those pressures at which the filter was demonstrated to be integral. If occasional unanticipated fouling occurs in the middle of a filtration cycle, then the pressure could be increased up to the maximum, if necessary, to complete the cycle (after which another integrity test would certainly be performed).

Another important design point in aseptic filtration is to eliminate hydraulic shock situations. Frequently this occurs wherever operating personnel are prone to building up supply pressure prior to opening the filter inlet valve. It may be necessary to install pneumatic robot arms on the valves with gradual opening. The user should avoid the use of reciprocating pumps to provide supply pressure. Under certain conditions, these pumps cause pressure pulses, which repeatedly strain and relax the filter medium in its configuration, causing filter fatigue and eventual failure.

3. Biological Requirements

A preliminary assessment of bioload requirements should be performed before accepting a candidate filter medium and configuration. The need for this is due to the requirement that the actual plant configuration undergoes a specific bioload, in organisms per square centimeter, which is less than that used in biological challenge validation experiments.

Representative process stream samples are obtained and viable organism counts per cubic centimeter are obtained. Based on these data and total expected process stream throughput and plant configuration surface area, a projected specific bioload can be calculated. If the result of this calculation is greater than 10^5 or 10^6 organisms/cm^2, then it is advisable to employ a prefiltration that will be capable of bioload reduction by 2 to 3 log.

Appropriate procedures for bioload determination will be discussed later in this chapter.

B. Selection of the Filter Configuration (Cartridge vs. Plate)

Frequently, aseptic filter media are available from the manufacturer in several configurations, and selection of the configuration usually must be made early in the validation program. One of the most significant choices to be made is that between cartridge and plate configurations.

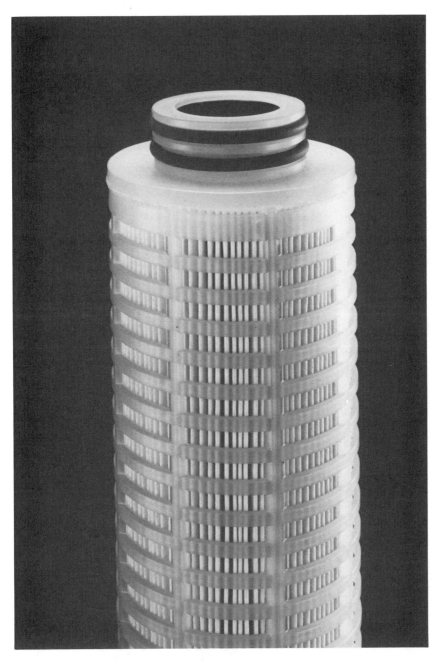

(a)

FIGURE 3 (a) Typical cartridge media with double o-ring seal, and outer support structure. (b) Typical cartridge holder with sanitary fittings.

(b)

FIGURE 3   (Continued)

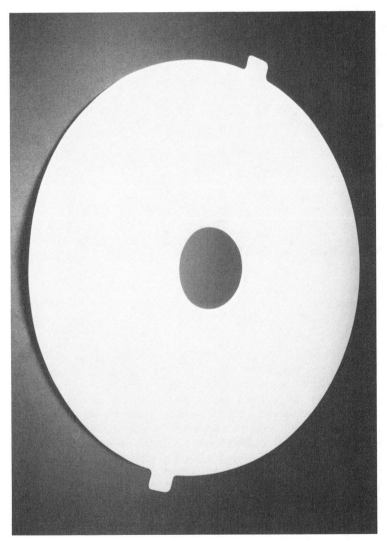

FIGURE 4 Typical sterilizing membrane media in flat stock for use in multiplate holders.

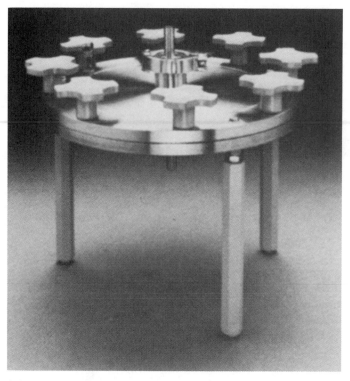

(a)

FIGURE 5 (a) Typical single plate (293 mm) holder. (b) Typical membrane filter holder.

Aseptic filter cartridges are produced by almost every manufacturer of
aseptic filter media in a variety of sizes, materials of construction, and
methods of construction. A typical aseptic filter cartridge and its holder are
shown in Figures 3a and 3b. The major parts of the cartridge are the end
caps, core, media support, media, outer support, and usually a double o-ring
seal. The medium is usually sealed to the end caps by a resin, which is frequently a source of chemical compatibility problems in solvent applications.
The medium must be seamed and sealed down the length of the cartridge, usually with the same resin. Some manufacturers are trying to avoid the use of
a sealant by developing methods of heat-sealing the medium to itself as well as
the end caps. Typically, cartridges contain 5 ft^2 of aseptic filter media for a
10- to 12-in. section or element. The limitation is that the medium and its
support are pleated and wrapped around the core, and the number of pleats
cannot be excessive or the pleats will be too closely spaced and filtration efficiency diminished.
      Aseptic filter cartridges are used in a housing usually constructed of 304
or 316 stainless steel. The housing usually has sanitary fittings at inlet and
outlet as well as threaded taps for installation of pressure instrumentation,
vents, drains, and integrity test apparatus.
      Aseptic filter media can also be purchased in disk or flat sheet form for use
in single plate or multiplate filter holders as shown in Figure 4. Standard diameters for disks are usually 293, 142, 90, 47, 25, and 13 mm. Single plate and

(b)

FIGURE 5   (Continued)

TABLE 1   Cartridge vs. Plate Configurations for Aseptic Filtration

	Cartridge	Plate
Cost of media	$15–$20/ft^2	$7–$11/ft^2
Cost of hardware	$200–$300/ft^2	Single plate: $2000–$2500/ft^2; multiplate: $2500 × A$^{.7}$/ft^2 (A in ft^2)
Volumes handled	Efficient for volumes 20 liters	Single plate: efficient for volume ⩾1 liter; multiplate: efficient for volumes ⩾100 liters
Surface area	5 ft^2 per element	Single plate: 0.55 ft^2 (293 mm); multiplate: 0.55–32 ft^2 (293 mm)
Strength of support	Medium support, generally from one side only	Single plate: flat support by backing plate or screen, one side only; multiplate: flat support by backing plates or screens, both sides
Chemical compatibility (other than media)	End caps, core, media support, O-rings, and sealants must be qualified either collectively or individually	Single or multiplate: usually gasket material is only component to be qualified
Ease of assembly	Fast replacement, few parts	Complete disassembly required, large number of parts, direct handling of medium required
Sterilizability	Steam, ethylene oxide, (possible ΔP limitation at high temperature)	Single plate: steam, ethylene oxide; multiplate: steam (ethylene oxide usually inconvenient or unfeasible)
Integrity test recommended	Diffusional flow, bubble point	Single plate: diffusional flow, bubble point; multiplate: if >5 ft^2, diffusional flow

multiplate holders are usually constructed of 304 or 316 stainless steel and are considerably more expensive than cartridge holders on a square-foot basis. The greater capital investment is offset by reduced filter medium cost, as flat stock is generally 50% of the cost of cartridge media on a square-foot basis. Figures 5a and 5b show photographs of typical single- and multiplate equipment. Table 1 presents a summary of characteristics of typical cartridge and plate configurations for the user's comparison.

III. CHEMICAL COMPATIBILITY

Candidate aseptic filter media must be screened on the basis of their chemical compatibility, or more descriptively, their mutual inertness with the process stream. The rationale for this portion of the validation must clearly have a twofold objective:

1. To demonstrate that the aseptic filter medium will not introduce any foreign components to the process stream
2. To demonstrate that the aseptic filter medium is not attacked by the process so as to diminish its strength and thereby integrity.

Though these objectives are definitely interrelated, the validation approach must assume that one effect could occur without the other and consider each independently.

A. Typical Methods

A number of methods have been employed in the evaluation of chemical compatibility of filter media toward objective 1.

1. USP XX Oxidizable Substances Test

After a preliminary flush of the aseptic filter medium with distilled water of a specified volume, the next 100 ml of flush is used as a sample and subjected to a permanganate titration according to the specifications of U.S. Pharmacopeia XX. The interpretation of results is limited in value for applications involving organic solvent streams or other potentially reactive components, since the distilled water exposure may not extract all components susceptible to the intended process stream.

Several methods are employed on the principle that process streams could not be considered to be compatible with the filter medium unless the solvent system of the stream itself, containing no solutes, could be demonstrated compatible. The following methods are therefore usually performed using the solvent system alone.

2. Weight Change

A relatively simple procedure is used to evaluate weight change of a representative sample of the aseptic filter medium or components of the configuration after exposure to the solvent system for a length of time. The component under test should be dried to a constant weight before and after exposure. Assuming that good technique is employed, typical weight change of 1% or less is observed for materials considered to be inert to the solvent system. Exposure time should be in excess of that expected in the plant configuration.

3. Extractibles

A sample of the solvent system is obtained after the exposure period recommended above and is subjected to one or more techniques that qualitatively
and quantitatively evaluate soluble components, such as ultraviolet spectral
analysis or gravimetric determination of extractibles.

In ultraviolet spectra analysis, the UV absorption spectrum of the exposed
stream is compared to a UV absorption spectrum for a blank or unexposed
solvent sample. Also, UV spectra may be prepared using spikes or suspected
extractable components in blank samples, and then compared to the exposure
sample UV spectra.

Gravimetric determination of extractibles should be performed on the exposure sample. Total weight of filter medium and volume of solvent system originally used will be needed to calculate percent extractibles on a weight basis
of filter medium. Significant extractible levels are in excess of 1%, but the
impact of this will have to be assessed in terms of the safety of the components
being extracted. To assist in quantitative analysis, it is appropriate to
calculate a level of extractibles that would result in the finished product with
a worst-case rationale that the leaching is continuous throughout the life of
the filter. If it is suspected that the leaching might be cured or diminished
with process stream contact, then this should be verified by performing staged
exposures and running UV on each stage of contact.

Now that we have briefly discussed those methods of verifying chemical
compatibility for protection of the process stream, we will discuss methods of
verifying that the filter has not been attacked, objective 2.

4. Integrity Test

Integrity testing of the filter medium before and after exposure to the solvent system or even the whole process stream should be performed as a means
of verifying chemical compatibility with the fluid. Since integrity test results
depend on the microscopic structural characteristics of the filter medium, it is
reasonable to use these results as evidence of inertness of the filter medium to
the process stream. It should be noted, however, that it is possible to obtain
integrity test results that show no apparent change but in fact are a result of
some minor degree of chemical attack offset by a "tightening" of the medium
due to swelling of the medium structure or some wetting phenomenon caused
by the process stream.

The details of integrity testing methods themselves will be discussed later
in this chapter.

5. Flow Rate Change

Frequently, filter media that are undergoing chemical attack by the process
stream will reflect a change in flow characteristics due to swelling, disintegra-
tion, or other affects. The most effective means of evaluating this change is
by monitoring specific filtration rate with the flow decay apparatus already
discussed. However, care must be taken regarding confusion of fouling effects
with incompatibility effects. Two possible ways to minimize this concern are
to either (a) prefilter the stream with another (known compatible) medium,
possibly even of smaller porosity than the medium in question or (b) arrange
the apparatus so that the filtrate can be continuously or periodically returned
to the pressure vessel, thereby not accumulating foulant on the filter medium
under test. Successful criteria for specific flow rate change evaluation should

be considered to be an essentially flat flow decay curve with ±5% change over the intended filter lifespan.

6. Physical Inspection

Aseptic filter media should be inspected visually after process stream contact for swelling, shrinking, color change, or any other physical characteristic that may change. In addition to physical inspection, scanning electron photomicrographs may be prepared to yield evidence of change in microscopic structure of the filter medium. This is an excellent method if the resources are available.

7. Process Stream Biological Challenge Test

One of the most effective means of proving filter compatibility is to verify that its chief performance characteristic, bioretention, has not been affected by process stream contact. The method is to inoculate a sample of process stream with an organism whose viability in that environment has been verified, and then to perform biological challenge to the aseptic filter medium. The details of biological challenge will be discussed later in this chapter.

B. The Recirculation Experiment

Refer to Figure 6, which depicts the apparatus necessary to perform filter medium exposure under dynamic flow conditions, which is representative of plant exposure conditions. The experiment compactly provides the user an opportunity to perform many of the compatibility evaluations described in the previous sections.

The procedure to follow in testing flat stock aseptic filter media is as follows, and only minor changes need be made to adapt the procedure for cartridge studies:

1. Dry the medium to constant weight in a vacuum oven, and record the weight for later use in weight loss determination.

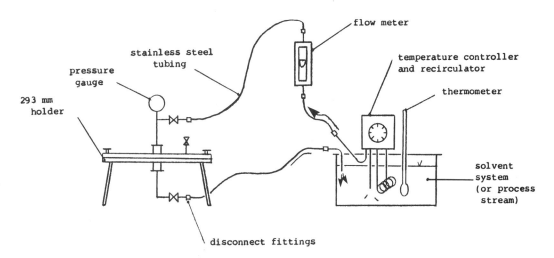

FIGURE 6   Recirculation apparatus for chemical compatibility studies.

2. Assemble the filter holder and medium and perform an appropriate integrity test, logging results.
3. Charge a measured volume of solvent system (or whole process stream) to the temperature bath, and adjust the temperature setting as desired for this study. (The temperature used should be approximately that to be experienced in the plant configuration.)
4. Recirculate the stream through the filter holder for an extended period of time (to exceed plant conditions). Flow rate control is desirable in order to achieve specific flow rates approximately equal to those ex-experienced in the plant.
5. Periodically, perform an integrity test on the filter configuration. (If the test fluid is not the same as the solvent system being used, disconnect the holder and drain residual fluid. The holder may then be connected to the test fluid supply and integrity-tested. After the test, the holder should be flushed with fresh solvent system, to avoid contamination of the bath with test fluid, and reconnected to the re-circulation apparatus.)
6. Sample the recirculating bath fluid periodically for use in UV, extractables, or oxidizable substances test. Replace the volume of sample with fresh fluid.
7. At the completion of the recirculation period, the filter medium should be redried for weight loss evaluation. The medium should then be visually and/or microscopically inspected.

The recirculation experiment is an efficient means of approaching chemical compatibility validation and can provide a fast screening method when many candidate media are involved.

IV. BIOLOGICAL CHALLENGE

A. Objective

The objective of performing biological challenge validation is to verify that the candidate aseptic filter medium is capable of retaining microorganisms in quantities exceeding the worst-case bioload indigenous to the plant process stream. Most aseptic filter manufacturers perform this testing routinely as a quality control on their manufacturing process and frequently claim retention capabilities of 10^8 organisms/cm^2 or better. As we noted previously, this is on the order of one layer of 0.2-μm organisms, shoulder to shoulder, on the filter surface. Though this may seem like more than enough retention power, it is advisable to generate bioload data on the process streams and verify that actual plant challenges are less than that stated above. Further, the user of the filter medium should consider it his responsibility periodically to verify the manufacturer's claims of bioretentivity by performing challenge studies such as that described in this section.

B. Bioload Determination

The purpose of bioload determination is to provide a statistical base to be used in calculations to demonstrate what the actual challenge to the filter configuration will be in the plant. The difficulty in accomplishing this lies in obtaining statistically representative samples of the process stream and then in recovering the organisms contained therein without significantly diminishing their original population. In addition to the above, it is essential that evidence be obtained that no organisms smaller than *Pseudomonas diminuta* (ATCC 19146) exist in the process stream, because this organism will be the validation challenge organism.

Guidelines for performing bioload determination are as follows:

1. Sample the process stream at a point in the process just prior to aseptic filtration. This will alleviate doubt as to the effect of time and equipment contacted if the stream were sampled considerably upstream of aseptic filtration.

2. If the operation is batchwise, and the batches each are homogeneous due to agitated process tanks, then a single sample per batch is sufficient. Otherwise, homogeneity of a given batch should be verified by sampling at the initiallization of flow and then at the middle and end of flow. The worst case or greatest bioload thereby derived should be assumed.

3. If the operation is continuous, as in distilled water production, then sampling should occur on a time frequency basis.

4. The total number of data points to obtain should be that number which (a) represents the process stream that will be filtered over the intended life of the aseptic filter or (b) until the calculated standard deviation of the bioload, expressed as organisms per volume, changes by less than 5% for each data point added, whichever is greater.

5. The sample size should be that in which the resulting plate is not overgrown with organisms and thereby uncountable, but not so small such that less than 10 organisms (1 log) are recovered.

6. Microorganisms should be recovered by filtration using sterilized 0.45-μm or 0.22-μm membrane filters. The resulting membranes should be aseptically transferred to a suitable nutrient media such as Trypticase Soy Agar and incubated at 30—35°C for several days.

7. Frequently, the procedures of sampling and microorganism recovery can be combined by connecting a sterilized 47-mm holder and filter with an inlet valve to the process stream pipeline. In this way the sample is filtered directly at the source and the membrane is removed in a laboratory for plating. A schematic of this arrangement is shown in Figure 7.

8. Alternatively, for streams with low bioload, a sample of the plant configuration's aseptic filter medium can be cut out and plated after a filtration cycle. Calculation of the bioload is then done from the known volume filtered and known total filter area of the configuration.

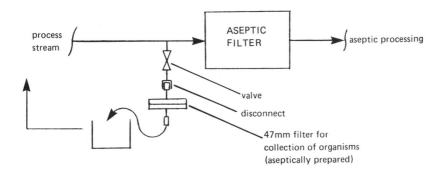

FIGURE 7   On-line bioload collection setup.

The final bioload, B, should be calculated as the mean value plus a factor, t, times the standard deviation of the data set, such that the probability of the calculated bioload being exceeded in a full life of the plant filter is less than 10^{-6}, assuming a normal distribution of individual bioload test results.

Let us say that a filter's lifespan is n batches, or segments, each of which we have sampled, tested, and know the bioload, b_i. We can calculate the average bioload, $\bar{b}$, and the standard deviation, σ. The probability that a single batch has a bioload greater than B is P. The probability that n consecutive batches have a bioload greater than B is P^n. To meet validation criteria, we desire that

$$P^n < 10^{-6} \quad \text{or} \quad P < \sqrt[n]{10^{-6}}$$

Thus the calculation is a matter of finding t, the number of σ's at which point the area under a normal distribution is equal to $1 - P$.

For example, given $n = 10$, $\bar{b} = 37$ organisms/ml, and $\sigma = 62.6$ organisms/ml, we calculate

$$P = \sqrt[n]{10^{-6}} = \sqrt[10]{10^{-6}} = 0.2512$$

and

$$1 - 0.2512 = 0.7488$$

Referring to a normal distribution table, we find $t = 1.15$.

$$B = \bar{b} + 1.15\sigma = 37 + 1.15(62.6)$$
$$= 109.0 \text{ organisms/ml}$$

Therefore, we have calculated that there is less than 10^{-6} probability that the plant aseptic filter will be challenged for 10 consecutive batches with a bioload of 109 organisms/ml or greater.

The calculation of bioload on an area basis should be performed, as it is this value that will later be compared with the validation challenge bioload B_{ac}. The area-specific bioload B_a

$$B_a = \frac{B \cdot V}{A}$$

where V is the total volume of process stream to be filtered and A is the total filter surface area.

If the value of B_a approaches or exceeds 10^8 organisms/cm^2, it is an indication that the plant configuration may be overchallenged. The best means of a multilog reduction in B_a is to employ a prefilter that is relatively inexpensive compared to the final filter. If prefiltration is not feasible or the bioload on a volume basis is already low, the filter surface area must be increased and/or the filtration volume must be decreased.

C. Design and Execution of the Challenge Test

The apparatus required to perform validation challenge testing can be varied, but a suggested configuration is given in Figure 8. The arrangement shown was designed to provide the ability to subject the candidate medium to the

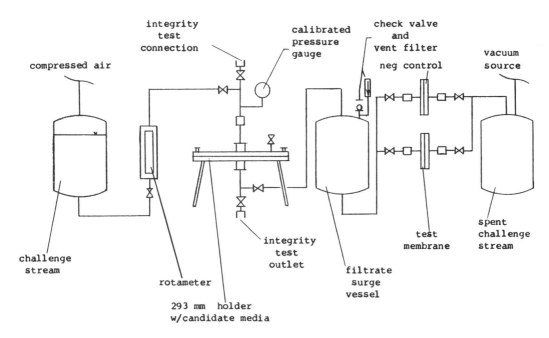

FIGURE 8 Biological challenge test apparatus.

specific flow rate that will be experienced in the plant configuration. In addition, the apparatus provides for integrity testing of the candidate medium, 100% sampling of the challenge stream filtrate, and negative control to invalidate results that were derived due to potential nonsterility of the test apparatus itself. The following guidelines for executing the challenge test should be followed.

The challenge stream should consist of *Pseudomonas diminuta* (American Type Culture Collection 19146) suspended in a volume of medium at a concentration such that approximately 10^8 organisms will be deposited on each square centimeter of candidate media. The suspension medium should consist of saline lactose broth of neutral pH. The challenge organism is supplied as a lyophilized culture with instructions for rehydration.

The approximate volume, V, of challenge stream to use is calculated as

$$V[ml] = \frac{10^8 \cdot A[cm^2]}{B_c[org/ml]}$$

where A is the candidate filter medium surface area and B_c is the estimated challenge stream bioload.

Just prior to the challenge test, a sample of the challenge stream is to be obtained for viable organism count. This is accomplished by serial dilution of an aliquot of the sample and performing an aerobic plate count with trypticase soy agar on each dilution. The value of B_c determined from this will be used in the final confirming calculation of the area-specific challenge bioload, B_{ac}. This value is to be compared to the area-specific bioload, B_a, calculated in Section IV, Section B, of the process stream. In order to be a valid challenge test, it is required that

$$B_{ac} < B_a$$

Now that we have established suitable criteria for the intensity of the challenge, we should establish flow rate and differential pressure criteria. Let us assume that the probability of a microorganism finding and penetrating a path through the aseptic filter medium is proportional to only not the population reaching the filter surface, but also to its total energy, kinetic and potential. We can say that the kinetic energy will be a function of the organism's velocity (cm/sec), and therefore to the area-specific filtration rate (cm^3/sec-cm^2). In addition, we can assume that the potential energy of the organism is proportional to the pressure drop it would undergo in passing through the medium. It would be a difficult task to determine what the relative contributions of each "driving force" is.

To be sure that the conditions of the validation challenge provide greater probability of bacterial passage through the filter medium than that in the plant, the area-specific filtration rate, the pressure differential, and the bioload of the plant configuration must be exceeded. This is the chief aim of the arrangement of the challenge apparatus in Figure 8.

Since the process stream may frequently have a different viscosity and foulant load than the challenge stream, it will be necessary to make certain adjustments. If the challenge stream is more viscous than the process stream, it will be necessary to significantly exceed the pressure differential that would be experienced in the plant to achieve the desired flow rate. If the process stream is more viscous than the challenge stream, it will be necessary to significantly exceed flow rates that would be experienced in the plant to achieve the desired pressure differential. Occasionally it will not be feasible to do this because the differences are so great that it would mean exceeding the design pressure of the equipment, or because the challenge bioload builds up an excessive pressure differential on the candidate filter even at low flow rates. If desired conditions cannot be reached due to these considerations, then it should be logged as such and the best approximation to these conditions possible should be used.

The procedure of validation challenge itself may be summarized as follows:

1. A 0.22-μm membrane is loaded into each small filter housing, one as a test membrane, and one as a negative control membrane.
2. The candidate aseptic filter medium is loaded into a 293-mm single-plate holder. Alternatively, a cartridge holder may be used.
3. All components of the assembly downstream of and including the 293-mm holder are sterilized by steam autoclave. Recommended conditions are 121–125°C for 60 min. (If techniques other than steam, such as ethylene oxide, are to be used, then no components must be allowed to remain that might prove cytotoxic to the challenge stream.)
4. The apparatus is connected together aseptically. The pressure gauge is calibrated, and the intended integrity test procedure applied to the aseptic filter candidate. Provided that the integrity test was successful, the challenge test may proceed.
5. As a negative control test, a saline lactose broth void of bioload is loaded into the pressure vessel and directed through the candidate filter and into the filtrate surge vessel. Next, the valves are arranged to filter through the negative control membrane by applying

vacuum to the spent challenge stream vessel. When complete, the control membrane valves are shut and the test membrane valves are opened.

6. The calculated volume of challenge stream is loaded into the pressure vessel and the validation challenge test is ready to begin.

7. Flow is established at the rotameter and pressure is built up at the 293-mm holder gauge as discussed above.

8. As soon as filtrate begins to fill the filtrate surge vessel, flow may be established through the test membrane by applying the vacuum source. Note that in this way the differential pressure on the candidate filter may be read at the pressure gauge directly and controlled independently of the filtrate sampling process. Note also that the check valve and vent filter on the filtrate surge vessel will allow it to exhale but not inhale potentially contaminated air.

9. At the completion of flow, both negative control and test membranes are transferred aseptically to trypticase soy agar plates and incubated at 30°C for a minimum of 72 hr.

10. The candidate filter medium holder is again integrity-tested, which must be successful for a valid challenge test.

11. As a precautionary measure against the biohazard present on the candidate filter medium, it is recommended that a suitable bacteriocide be flushed through the equipment before disassembly.

D. Validity of Results

Although considerable attention has been given above to the criteria for a valid challenge test, it may be helpful to recap them here and discuss relevant deviations.

1. The negative control must be successful for a valid test. Successful results are no growth whatsoever. If failure persists, it may be a function of inadequate sterilization conditions, improper assembly technique, or contamination in posttest handling.

2. The test membrane must show no growth whatsoever for a successful challenge test. Repeated failure that is not explained by control or integrity failure is grounds for disqualification of the candidate medium.

3. The validation challenge area-specific bioload, B_{ac}, must be approximately 10^8 organisms/cm^2. Failure to attain this order of magnitude should dictate improvement of culture technique or use of larger volumes of challenge stream.

4. The validation challenge area-specific bioload, B_{ac}, must be greater than the process stream area-specific bioload, B_a, as determined by the criteria of Section III, Section B. If this requirement is not met, then suitable prefiltration and/or surface area increase and/or volume reduction must be employed on the process stream. Of course, the addition of prefiltration will require redetermination of the bioload on the aseptic filter configuration.

5. Integrity test criteria must be met before and after the challenge test. The potential exists whereby the integrity test was not successful but all other criteria were met. This is an indication of some effect of test conditions on the medium or configuration and should be thoroughly investigated as a separate problem.

6. Flow conditions should exceed the area-specific filtration rate and pressure differential experienced in the plant configuration if possible. This will be highly process stream dependent.
7. The number of successful validation challenge tests required to qualify a candidate medium is not well rationalized. The key to this concern is arriving at a confidence in uniformity of manufacture of the medium itself. The area of manufacturing quality control will be discussed in a later section concerning filter purchase specifications.

For those readers who prefer that the question be answered mathematically, we could fall back on what we know about our plant bioload, B_a. Let us assume that the probability of passage is proportional to the intensity of challenge, with up to 10^8 organisms/cm^2 as a maximum. At that challenge level, we demonstrated that no organism will pass through the medium. At bioloads of B_a the probability of passage will be reduced by $B_a/10^8$. We could then rationalize that we should challenge test a fraction, $B_a/10^8$, of total medium used in plant. In other words, instead of challenging all of the filter medium we consume in the plant with a B_a bioload, we will intensify the bioload to 10^8 and challenge only $B_a/10^8$ of the media. This rationalization gives a clear advantage to low-bioload process streams and increases the incentive to reduce incident bioloads to begin with.

E. The Process Stream Challenge

As discussed in Section III, one of the most effective means of verifying filter compatibility with the process stream is to perform a challenge test using the process stream as the medium, inoculated with *P. diminuta* or an organism selected from the organisms indigenous to the stream. As this is a procedure that will be greatly dependent on the nature of the application, a brief set of guidelines for this study will be presented.

1. The process stream challenge should be performed essentially as a standard high-intensity challenge with exceptions as noted below.
2. The viability of the organism(s) selected should be verified prior to the challenge and suitable averages in challenge should be built into the calculations.
3. Processing parameters such as flow rate, pressure, contact time, number of batches, etc., should be scaled from the plant configuration.

V. VERIFYING CONFIGURATION INTEGRITY

A. Objective

The purpose of performing in-plant integrity testing is solely for the verification of the absence of channels of flow within the configuration that would permit the process stream to reach the downstream side of the filter without passing through the aseptic filter medium. This goal is clearly separate from the concept of biological challenge. It is considered that the medium in question has already been demonstrated to be capable of performance exceeding the bioretentivity criteria we have discussed, and that now we must have a repeatable, convenient, and nondestructive means by which to ensure that the medium is installed intact in the hardware. With the aseptic filter medium itself no longer a "candidate," we now consider the configuration a candidate each time it is assembled and used.

This goal is indeed a considerable task, challenged by all of the vulner-
abilities of the mechanical world. Honesty demands that a statement be made
here as to the limitations of currently practiced integrity test methods.

Let us say, for instance, that our aseptic filter configuration has some-
where within it a path of approximately 5.0-μm diameter leading from the upstream side to the downstream side. Certainly, this is a large enough path
for a small organism to traverse. If our process stream is assumed to be water
and the differential pressure on this filter is 10 psi, then we can estimate how
fast the process stream will flow freely through this path from a simplified
form of Bernoulli's equation for incompressible fluids,

$$\frac{p_1}{\rho} + \frac{v_1^2}{2g} = \frac{p_2}{\rho} + \frac{v_2^2}{2g}$$

where v_1, v_2 are the fluid velocities on the upstream, downstream sides and
p_1, p_2 are the respective pressures. The results of the calculation yields
$v_2 = 38.6$ ft/sec or a flow rate through the 5.0-μm path of approximately
0.01386 ml/min. If the filtration took place over 1 hr, this path would allow
0.83 ml to bypass the medium. If the bioload is typically 1 organism/ml, then
the probability of at least one organism finding and getting through this path
would be rather significant. As a matter of fact, we can assume that the arrival rate of microorganisms at this defect follows a Poisson distribution,

$$P_k(v) = \frac{(Bv)^k e^{-Bv}}{k}$$

where $P_k(v)$ is the probability of exactly k organisms arriving in stream leakage volume v, and B is the average bioload in organisms per cubic centimeter.
Then the probability of passage through this defect is $1 - P_0(0.83)$ or 0.564.

Therefore, the demand that integrity test methods be sensitive to extremely
small defects is real. In the discussions that follow, we will see that the net
probability of detecting a minute defect in an aseptic filter configuration is as
much a function of filter size and configuration as it is of the test method itself.
Further, it can be stated that, once faced with limits of detection, our best
defense again lies in reducing the incident bioload by appropriate prefiltration, and in the extreme case, redundant series aseptic filtration.

B. Principles of Integrity Testing

For an excellent treatment of the theoretical considerations of integrity test
design, the reader is referred to [1].

All of the commonly practiced methods of nondestructive integrity testing
of aseptic filters used in process stream sterilization are based on the measurement of some parameter of gas penetration through an aseptic filter medium
that has been wetted with some suitable test fluid. Other means of integrity
testing that have been used are based on performing a nonbiological challenge
test in which a stream containing particles of known size distribution is the
challenge stream. In many cases, the use of a nonbiological challenge test is
destructive and thereby limited in its application.

Wetted medium-based tests have been called by numerous names and associated sets of nomenclature. Some tests are based on the "bubble point," or
the rate of flow of a gas through the medium, or the rate of pressure loss on

one side of the medium. The means of achieving these measurements varies from test to test, and the results are not usually directly comparable. The results obtained are too dependent on choice of medium, wetting fluid, test pressures, temperature, technique, etc. However, two basic methods have emerged over the last 5 to 10 years as the most practicable and are widely popular: bubble point testing and diffusional flow testing.

1. Bubble Point Theory

The bubble point is that differential pressure at which the wetting fluid contained in the channels of an aseptic filter medium is driven out. The theoretical pressure necessary to accomplish this is derived from surface chemistry, where the Laplace equation for a spherical interface is

$$\Delta P = \frac{2\gamma}{R}$$

where R is the radius of the spherical curvature and γ is the surface tension of the wetting fluid.

Referring to Figure 9, representing the geometry of capillary rise phenomenon, we can see that

$$R = \frac{d}{2}\cos\theta$$

where d is the capillary diameter and θ is the angle of the test fluid surface with respect to the wall at the point of wall contact. Substituting this relationship into the Laplace equation gives

$$\Delta P = \frac{4\gamma \cos\theta}{d}$$

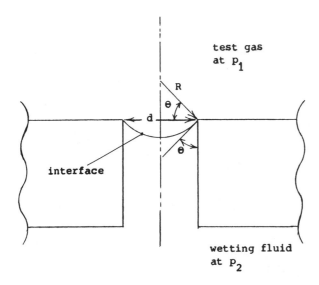

FIGURE 9 Depiction of the geometry of capillary rise in a hyrothetical channel of an aseptic filter.

As it is not possible to measure wetting angles and attempting to calculate ΔP absolutely, the bubble point measured in the plant will be chiefly dependent on pore size, wetting, and surface tension of the test fluid. More polar fluids will tend to give higher bubble points because of their higher surface tension. Candidate test fluids that will not wet the membrane must be disqualified. Most obviously, media of smaller pore size will yield higher bubble points. Note that this assumes the behavior of the channels in a medium to be like pores. This, of course, is only an approximation, as is the presumption that the size distribution is narrow.

All of the above considerations lead to emperical methods for the interpretation of bubble point. For a given material of construction and wetting fluid, the bubble point is most dependent on pore size and for this reason was the original and still is the most popular method of manufacturer's quality control. The relative simplicity and speed of the test allows it to be used for in-process control of membrane casting operations. Further, the test has been correlated by virtually every manufacturer to some form of biological challenge test. Typically, a hydrophilic filter medium of rated 0.22-μm porosity will exhibit bubble points in excess of 40 psi with water as test fluid and possess a bioretentivity in excess of 10^8 organism/cm^2.

2. Diffusional Flow Theory

In the previous section describing bubble point theory, a secondary effect that occurs when a test gas used in integrity testing is in contact with the liquid surface of the test fluid and is soluble in that fluid was ignored. Diffusional flow is the flow of test gas through a filter medium wetted with a test fluid at differential pressures below the bubble point. The phenomenon can be described best by Fick's law,

$$J = -D \frac{dc}{dx}$$

where J is the molar flux of the dissolved gas, D is the diffusivity of the gas in the liquid, and dc/dx is the concentration gradient of the gas in the direction of the diffusion.

The test gas under pressure, and in contact with the test fluid surface, dissolves and begins to diffuse in the direction of decreasing concentration, until it reaches the lower-pressure side of the media, where it evolves. If it is assumed that the fluid is at saturation concentration c_2 at the lower pressure, then the concentration gradient will be

$$\frac{dc}{dx} = \frac{c_1 - c_2}{t}$$

where t is the thickness of the filter medium. Further, the concentration c_1 and c_2 can be estimated from Henry's law, where at low mole fractions,

$$c = \frac{p}{M \cdot H}$$

where p is the partial pressure of the gas above the liquid surface, M is the molecular weight of the liquid, and H is the Henry's law constant for the gas in the liquid.

Substituting into Fick's law,

$$J = \frac{-D}{MHt} (p_1 - p_2)$$

Therefore, the diffusional flow rate of a test gas through a wetted medium is related to the pressure differential, the thickness of the medium, and the diffusivity and solubility of the gas in the liquid. It should be noted that both diffusivity and solubility are likely to be affected by temperature changes, and so this effect should be verified to assess the need for some degree of temperature control during testing.

As in bubble point testing, empirical methods must be utilized for interpretation of diffusional flow results. Diffusional flow is infrequently used by manufacturers as an in-process quality control because of its relative independence of porosity.

Figure 10 depicts a typical diffusional flow (DF) curve. Note the almost linear response of DF with Δp, as expected below the bubble point pressure. However, the linearity is lost as Δp approaches the bubble point value. A sharp transition from diffusional flow to bulk flow is an indication of a narrow pore size distribution. That is, a broad distribution having a higher percentage of larger channels would begin transition at lower pressure because these channels would themselves have lower bubble points and allow bulk flow earlier on the curve. Note that the curve is plotted as area-specific diffusional flow vs. Δp.

The design of a diffusional flow integrity test procedure requires that several specifications be made:

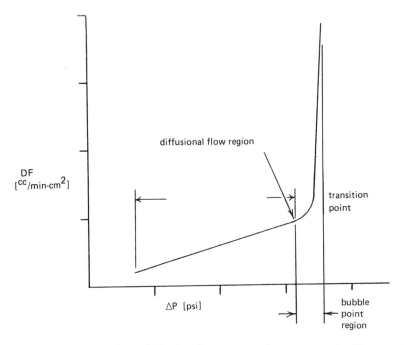

FIGURE 10   Typical diffusion flow curve for an aseptic filter medium.

1. Aseptic filter medium: manufacturer and model number.
2. Configuration: cartridge, multiplate, single-plate, etc. This specification is necessary because one support structure may result in different diffusional flow than another (possible because of wetting geometry).
3. Wetting fluid: the fluid that will be used to intrude the medium channels.
4. Test fluid: occasionally, the fluid suitable for wetting the medium will not be suitable for establishing diffusional flow readings and must be flushed out by a test fluid so as to replace the wetting fluid. In most cases, however, the wetting fluid is suitable as the test fluid. It is desirable that the wetting and test fluids be compatible with the process stream so as to avoid contamination risks.
5. Test gas: Usually compressed air is satisfactory, but safety considerations may dictate that compressed nitrogen be used.
6. Test pressure: Establish the diffusional flow curve and select a standard pressure at which the measurement will be done such that the flow is reproducible and sensitive. Typically, approximately 80% of the expected bubble point pressure is used so as to maximize sensitivity to small defects without getting too close to the transition point and thereby avoiding erratic results.
7. Control limit: an important and controversial diffusional flow specification above which the filter configuration should be considered to be defective. A rationale for establishing this value will be discussed in a later section.

Diffusional flow integrity testing has particular value in testing plant configurations due to the relative sensitivities of bubble point and diffusional flow to minute defects.

3. Bubble Point and Diffusional Flow Procedure

This section will discuss the step-by-step methods of performing these integrity tests in a generic approach. The two techniques are presented together because the bubble point is determined as an extension of those steps necessary to measure diffusional flow.

Figure 11 shows schematically an appropriate arrangement of connections and values on an aseptic filter configuration about to be integrity tested. Note that the equipment required is simple, and does not require any modification of the aseptic filter configuration but only the connection leading to and from it. The procedure is as follows:

1. Drain the filter free of any residual process stream. Close the inlet valve.
2. Connect the upstream connection to the wetting fluid source and fill the entire configuration, venting the filter to remove all air pockets. Allow free flow of the wetting fluid through the configuration. At this point, the wetting fluid may be directed through the downstream connection and/or outlet valve. It may be necessary to restrict the outlet valve in order to build enough pressure in the filter to vent all air pockets.
3. Close the wetting fluid source and the upstream connection valve. Disconnect the wetting fluid source.

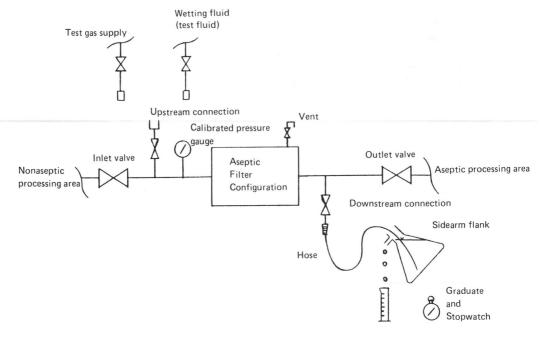

FIGURE 11   Integrity test apparatus.

4. (If the test fluid is different from the wetting fluid, then perform
    this step, otherwise proceed to the next.) When the pressure in the
    filter reaches atmospheric, connect the upstream connection to the
    test fluid source and purge the wetting fluid from the filter. The
    amount of purge required is a function of filter size and should be
    validated to give consistent results from test to test. When purging
    is complete, close the test fluid source and disconnect it.
5. Close the outlet valve.
6. Connect the upstream connection to the test gas supply and apply a
    small (<5 psig) pressure of test gas to the configuration. Be sure
    the downstream connection is full open and the test fluid is flowing
    freely out of the hose to the desired disposition.
7. When the flow of test fluid begins to slow, insert the hose into the
    tilted sidearm flask and fill the flask until flow emerges from the
    sidearm. Maintain pressure well below test pressure.
8. Allow flow from the flask until the rate appears to bottom out.

At this point, the procedure for diffusional flow reading will be described.
However, if only bubble point is to be measured, then the operator would
proceed directly to step 11 below.

9. Smoothly increase test gas pressure on the configuration until the
    diffusional flow test pressure is reached. The emergence of test gas
    from the hose in the sidearm would constitute an unsuccessful test.
10. Using a stopwatch and graduate cylinder, measure the diffusional
    flow in cubic centimeters per minute. Repeat measurements until the
    flow rate is unchanged. Usually, two significant figures of precision

are required for the measurement. Criteria for considering the flow rate unchanged should be set up and consistently followed (e.g., less than 10% change in flow rate per minute means no change). The criterion for a successful diffusional flow test is a final measurement that is below the specified control limit.

11. Incrementally increase the test gas pressure until a sharp change in flow rate emerging from the sidearm is observed. Depending on the size of the filter and its downstream holdup volume, the test gas will follow shortly after. The pressure at which the sharp increase in *flow*, not necessarily the observance of bubbles of test gas, is the observed bubble point pressure. The criteria for a successful bubble point test is an observed bubble point equal to or greater than the manufacturer's recommended minimum bubble point.

12. At completion of either test, the downstream connection valve should be closed to avoid suckback of the test fluid into the configuration as the test gas is disconnected and vented.

The procedure lends itself to automation because of the well-defined sequence of operations that must be performed. The necessary equipment basically constitutes a series of robot arms, a pressure transmitter, a flow transmitter, and a programmable controller. As one might guess from the procedure, discerning a bubble point can be somewhat eyeball dependent and is one of its major drawbacks. However, the problem of consistency could be put to rest by programming measurable criteria for a bubble point using extrapolation of the diffusional flow region. Several manufacturers already market "automatic" integrity testers, which may be worth pursuing if the user's engineering resources are limited.

Notice that in measuring bubble point or diffusional flow using this procedure, the testor is observing the flow of the test gas through the aseptic filter medium indirectly by displacement of the test fluid. This leads to several points of which the user should become aware if he is not already.

Once diffusional flow is established, the downstream test fluid begins to be displaced and could be depleted if the operator waits too long to complete the measurement. This could be incorrectly interpreted as a failure.

It may be necessary on some filter configurations to vent the downstream side during wetting if the geometry of the unit has large air pockets, so as to get a supply of test fluid into the downstream side. This is particularly true of multiplate filters in which the center annulus is such a cavity.

The increase of pressure on large-surface-area filters while diffusional flow is in progress leads to a bulk flow of test fluid in addition to that caused purely by diffusional flow. This flow comes about by (a) a net volumetric yield of the configuration due to compression of the medium's support structure causing displacement of test fluid, and (b) the drainage of additional test fluid through the medium that was trapped on the upstream side. The operator must be sure to allow the bulk flow to dissipate before attempting to measure diffusional flow.

C. Troubleshooting Integrity Test Problems

The causes of unsuccessful integrity testing are varied and frequently can be categorized as a test problem or a real problem. Test problems are summarized as follows:

1. Test design: Refer back to Sections V, B.1 and B.2, and re-evaluate the selection of test specifications, especially test fluid, test pressure, and control limit or expected minimum bubble point recommended by the manufacturer. Generate a diffusional flow curve for the medium and establish that its behavior has not changed since previously evaluated. Be sure the control limit was established for the particular configuration under test.

2. Equipment: Recalibrate the pressure gauge frequently. In critical applications this should be done before every test.

3. Technique: The three most common flaws in technique that can lead to test failure include:

    a. Improper wetting and venting of the configuration, leading to "dry" zones of medium that allow bulk gas flow or inadequate evacuation of trapped air causing insufficient downstream supply of test fluid;

    b. Test pressure overshoot, resulting in the drying out of a larger percentage of channels than expected, allowing bulk test gas flow; and

    c. Insufficient equilibration time, causing premature measurement of difussional flow, giving higher and often unacceptable results. This factor is also important in attaining more reproducible and tightly grouped results for a medium type.

Once the user has satisfied himself of the validity of his test results, a number of causes of real integrity problems must be considered:

4. Defective medium: It is frequently difficult to "autopsy" a defective medium, especially in cartridge configurations where the medium is not easily observed. However, repeated failures attributed to this cause should prompt investigation with the manufacturer. For disk media, the failed membranes may be removed from the filter and inspected with a lightbox.

5. Defective support: Cartridge housings should be inspected for defects in the O-ring socket such as dings and dents. Single- or multiplate holders should be inspected for sharp edges or severe dents in the support screens.

6. Defective gasketing: Inspect and/or replace worn or cut O-rings and gaskets. Teflon is especially prone to deformation and should be frequently replaced or an elastomer substitute sought where feasible.

7. Heat distortion: Many cartridges and disk media marketed will not withstand autoclave steaming, much less in-line steam sterilization. If many failures are taking place, the procedure for sterilization should be reviewed carefully so as to be sure that excessive steam pressure is not being used. In-line steam sterilization is sometimes more likely to damage cartridges because their support and sealants may soften at elevated temperatures and yield to the differential pressure if excessive. Multiplate filter holders are particularly prone to relaxation of the plate stack torque due to deformation of gasketing multiplied over the stack height. In this case, retorqueing the plate stack after sterilization may be the only reasonable remedy.

D. Integrity Test Sensitivity

It should be clear to the reader at this point that the bubble point measurement is a pressure measurement that is the result of the average behavior of all of the media channels in the configuration, while the diffusional flow measurement is the aggregate effect of all of the media in the configuration. Bubble point should be considered an intensive property with diffusional flow an extensive property of the medium.

Let us review the problem of the 5-μm channel through an aseptic filter medium in terms of integrity test sensitivity. It was established in Section V, Section A, that this channel does indeed offer significant probability of biopassage under relatively moderate bioload challenge. Assuming that this filter was subjected to a diffusional flow integrity test with air at 40 psi test pressure, calculate the expected contribution to the total diffusional flow based on orifice flow computations [4]. We will calculate the velocity, v, of air, a compressible fluid, through the orifice as

$$v = \sqrt{2g_c\left(\frac{k}{k-1}\right)p_1\bar{v}_1\left[1 - \left(\frac{p_2}{p_1}\right)^{k-1/k}\right]}$$

where k is the heat capacity ratio, c_p/c_v, p_1, p_2 are the upstream and downstream pressures (psf) and $\bar{v}_1$ is the specific volume (ft^3/lbm) of air at p_1. The critical ratio for air is approximately 0.53, and in our integrity test, $p_2/p_1 < 0.53$, which indicates that the sonic velocity will be reached. Therefore we use 0.53 as the value of p_2/p_1 in the above equation and obtain $v = 286$ ft/sec or 0.103 ml/min through the 5-μm hole. Realizing that this flow will be added to the background diffusional flow, we must try to evaluate how this would impact pass/fail criteria.

Table 2 shows the estimated impact of various size defects with various size configurations where the above integrity test is run and on a diffusional flow value of 2.0 ml/ft^2-min is expected. The table entries give the contribution of the defect as a percentage of expected flow. Note that 0.5 ft^2 represents the approximate surface area available in a 293-mm, single-plate configuration, while 5 ft^2 represents a typical cartridge, and 25 ft^2 represents a

TABLE 2 Contribution of Defects to DF as Percent of Expected DF for Various Surface Areas[a]

Defect size (μm)	Defect flow (ml/min)	Expected DF		
		0.5 ft^2	5 ft^2	25 ft^2
5	0.103	10%	1%	0.2%
50	10.3	1030%	103%	20%
100	41.1	4110%	411%	82%

[a] 40 psi differential and expected DF of 2.0 ml/min-ft^2 are assumed.

typical high-volume, multiplate filter. The conclusions that can be drawn are that the sensitivity of a diffusional flow integrity test to a given size defect is

1. A function of test pressure, which governs the rate of test gas flow through the defect, and is roughly proportional to $\sqrt{\Delta p}$;
2. Inversely proportional to total filter surface area, as the expected total DF will be greater;
3. Inversely proportional to the area-specific expected DF for the same reason; and
4. Inversely proportional to the difference between expected or typical DF value and control limit DF.

The last point should be discussed further. If, for example, we have specified a control limit of 3.0 ml/ft^2-min for this integrity test as our pass/fail criterion, we would have the result that, on the average, any defect in Table 2 contributing 50% or less to the expected DF would go undetected. Therefore, the 5-μm hole would not be detected in any of the configurations, nor would a 50-μm hole be detected in a multiplate.

Where does all of this leave the bubble point? Unfortunately, its sensitivity to a minute defect must be considered to be far less than diffusional flow. It is probable that a bubble point would be unaffected by defects that contribute 100% or even 200% to the DF, simply because the DF is not measured and compared to some norm. Just how sensitive the bubble point is to a given size defect is really a function of conclusion 1 above plus the time necessary to displace all downstream holdup so that the operator will observe gas bubbles prematurely and call the test a failure.

Sensitivity of the integrity tests to various parameters is summarized in Table 3.

E. Setting Control Limits

Minimum acceptable bubble points are usually recommended by the aseptic filter manufacturer as correlated to bioretention data. We have already discussed

TABLE 3 Factors of Comparison: Diffusional Flow vs. Bubble Point Integrity Tests

Parameter	Differential flow	Bubble point
Test fluid	Affected	Affected
Test gas	Affected	Unaffected
Medium porosity	Unaffected	Affected
Medium thickness	Affected	Unaffected
Temperature	Variable effect	Variable effect
Filter area	Area-specific	Unaffected
Differential pressure	Pressure-specific	Pressure is measurement
Support configuration	Moderately affected	Unaffected
Minute defects	Moderate sensitivity	Poor sensitivity

the limitations of sensitivity of integrity testing in detection of minute defects. Aware that bubble point is thus empirically derived, we will not concern ourselves with the statistical treatment of an integrity test that has limited value in plant configurations.

The diffusional flow test is sensitive to several conditions and therefore must be completely specified in terms of configuration, test fluid, media, test pressure, etc. For each test specified, there must be an associated control limit so that when it is exceeded by a DF measurement, the filter will be considered as nonintegral. One possible rationale is as follows:

1. A configuration identical to the plant configuration is subjected to biological challenge as described in Section IV. Integrity testing is performed before and after by the diffusional flow method.

2. After repeated experiments of this kind, the integrity test data from successful challenges are gathered into a data base on which we will base our control limit. The mean and standard deviation of the data are calculated.

3. Presume that the total diffusional flow, DF, that will be measured in the plant configurations themselves will be the sum of the contribution, DF_D, of a defect of given size plus the pure diffusional flow, DF_0, or $DF = DF_D + DF_0$.

   In order to detect a defect, the DF measured must be greater than some preset control limit, CL, or

   $$DF > CL$$

   Therefore

   $$DF_D + DF_0 > CL$$

   or

   $$DF_0 > CL - DF_D$$

   Therefore, the probability that we will detect the defect is equal to the probability that the pure diffusional flow is greater than the control limit less the flow contributed by the defect. If a normal distribution of pure diffusional flow results (DFs) is assumed, then a table can be generated showing the probability of detection of a given size defect vs. control limit for a given size configuration.

   Table 4 shows the probability of detection P_D, of a 50-μm defect in a 5-ft^2 configuration using the 40-psi diffusional flow test with air, vs. control limit, CL. The DF data base from challenge experiments is assumed to be a mean of 2.0 ml/min-ft^2 with a standard deviation of 0.3.

4. Select the control limit that will provide the highest probability of detection, but that is no closer than 2 standard deviations from the mean. This cutoff is inclusive of 95% of the data base assuming a normal distribution.

However, we must review our original objective, which is to attain less than 10^6 probability of passage or an organism larger than 0.22 μm. The probability of this can be stated as the probability of *not* detecting a channel large enough for an organism to pass through, multiplied by the probability of an

TABLE 4   Probability of Detecting a 50-μm Defect in a 5-ft^2 Cartridge Using DF at 40 psi and Assuming DF Data Base Average of 2.0 ml/min-ft^2 with σ = 0.3

CL	2.3	2.6	2.9	3.2	3.5	(ml/min-ft^2)
P_D	>0.999999	>0.999998	>0.999878	>0.996207	>0.952540	

organism actually being contained in the estimated volume of process stream bypassing the media. This is stated mathematically as

$$P = (1 - P_D) \cdot P_B$$

where P is the total probability of passage, P_D is the probability of defect detection, and P_B is the probability of bacterial presence in the volume leaked through the defect. This formula points out that bioload reduction is the other key to attaining the desired probability of passage. In other words, if the user calculates a probability of nondetection for a given size defect as 10^{-4} but the bioload is so low as to result in 10^{-2} probability of an organism in the bypass volume, then the validation requirement is satisfied.

What about the case where the probability of biopresence in the bypass volume is high, say, 10^{-1}, and the probability of nondetection is as high as 10^{-1}?

F. Series Redundant Aseptic Filtration

The approach to high probability of passage application is to perform two aseptic filtrations in series with the understanding that

$$P = P_1 P_2$$

where P_1, P_2 are the individual probabilities of passage for each filter configuration and P is the overall probability of passage. The expanded equation is

$$P = (1 - P_{D_1})^2 P_{B_1} P_{B_2}$$

It is reasonable to calculate the bioload that will challenge filter 2 based on estimated bypass volume and total filtration volumes through the defect in filter 1.

Let us assume that P_{B_2} has been reduced to 10^{-3}, which could be a typical result if 99% of the process stream actually went through the aseptic filter media. Then

$$P = (10^{-1})^2 (10^{-1})(10^{-3}) = 10^{-6}$$

and validation criteria would be met.

The second important use for series redundant aseptic filtration is in situations where integrity test failure is intolerable or the process stream cannot be refiltered. In this case, the question is one of probabilities in that the likelihood of failure of two configurations in series is the square of the probability of a single filter failure.

VI. STERILIZATION OF FILTER CONFIGURATION

A. Objectives

Up to this point, our discussions have concentrated on the validation effort required to demonstrate the effectiveness of sterilization of an aseptic filter configuration. Clearly, the aseptic filter medium represents the dividing line between sterile and nonsterile equipment surfaces that contact the process stream. Therefore, it is our task to complete the validation by demonstrating the effectiveness of the procedure(s) by which the filter configuration is itself sterilized. To further specify our objective, we need concern ourselves with sterilizing the surfaces downstream of the aseptic filter medium only. To be consistent with the statistical objective of aseptic filtration, the probability of survival of an organism on the downstream side of the filter must be demonstrated to be less than 10^{-6}.

A second but equally important objective of this portion of the validation is that the sterilization technique be demonstrated to be nondestructive to the filter configuration. The only acceptable means of accomplishing this is to perform the previously discussed validation studies of chemical compatibility, biological retention, and configurational integrity *after* exposure to sterilization procedures identical to those that will be used on the plant configuration.

Frequently, it is the latter requirement that places limitations on the effectiveness of sterilization techniques selected, and some careful optimization of the sterilization procedure will be needed to avoid damage to the media. This is typically true of heat sterilization techniques, which often must be limited in temperature and exposure time. As a result, the validation studies may have to be designed to examine two boundaries of failure, one concerned with effective sterilization at minimal exposure conditions and the other concerned with medium integrity at maximal exposure conditions. Since we have described the criteria for assessing the latter in previous sections, the discussion that follows will provide guidelines for the evaluation of sterilization technique.

B. Sterilization Techniques

1. In-Line Steam Sterilization

Feasibility: In-line steam sterilization is probably one of the most widely desirable and accepted methods of filter sterilization. It has the advantages of being achievable without the need for autoclave equipment and hazardous chemical sterilants such as ethylene oxide (ETO) and formaldehyde. Since it can be accomplished in situ, the risk of recontamination during assembly or installation is thereby eliminated. Steam sterilization is perhaps one of the least costly and simpler techniques to validate and execute.

There are, unfortunately, some major disadvantages of this method, one of which has already been mentioned as susceptibility of the medium to damage by heat exposure under differential pressure. This is typical of cellulosic media, in which heat exposure can result in embrittlement, shrinkage, and other evidence of deformation. In recent years, the availability of polymer-based media has alleviated this problem. Media constructed of

materials such as nylon, Kynar, and Teflon are considerably more tolerant
of the severity of in-line steam sterilization.

Another disadvantage of in-line steam sterilization is the potential development of large pressure differentials in systems where steam is introduced from
the upstream side and the medium itself is hydrophilic. Frequently, the medium becomes thoroughly wetted as steam condenses on the initially cool surfaces. In order to get immediate bulk flow of steam to the downstream side of
the configuration, which, as mentioned above is the target of sterilization, the
medium's bubble point must be exceeded. Provided that the medium is tolerant of extended heat exposure, the downstream side will build pressure as the
medium is heated to steam temperature. If the particular configuration is extremely slow in heat-up time, the user may decide to introduce steam from
both upstream and downstream portions of the filter. However, it is important
that a slightly higher pressure be maintained on the upstream side to avoid
rupturing the medium in systems where support is unidirectional.

Procedure: The basic in-line steam sterilization procedure that is to be
validated consists of the following steps:

1. Apply steam to the upstream side of the configuration at 15–20 psig
    while venting trapped air until steam begins to vent.
2. Drain condensate from the physically lowest points on the upstream
    and downstream sides of the configuration.
3. Allow steam pressure to build according to a calibrated pressure gauge
    or transmitter connected to the downstream side of the filter. The
    target pressure range should be 15 psig plus the tolerance of calibra-
    tion for the gauge as a minimum, and the saturated steam pressure
    recommended by the medium manufacturer as a maximum.
4. Maintain these conditions for a period of time determined necessary by
    the validation rationale, below.
5. Cool down the filter by closing off all downstream vents to avoid in-
    halation of potentially nonsterile air and then introducing cool air or
    water through the upstream side, gradually.

Validation Rationale: The rationale to be used to demonstrate less than
10^{-6} probability of survival of an organism on the downstream contact surface
of the configuration can be summarized as the following tasks:

1. Estimate the total bioload on the internal surfaces to be sterilized. This
is most appropriately accomplished by "swabbing," in which a sterile cotton
pad soaked with nutrient medium is contacted with a known surface area prior
to sterilization. Plating techniques are used to generate a colony count, which
is multiplied by 2 on the assumption that only one-half of the organisms were
picked up on the swab. The count per unit area is multiplied by a total estimated surface area to yield total estimated bioload. Swabs should be done
on various portions of the configuration, and the highest counts thereby obtained should be assumed for bioload estimation.

2. Distribute thermocouples throughout the downstream side of the configuration. Be sure to monitor the lowest drainage point for condensate as
well as the most massive portions, which are likely to be greater heat sinks.
Usually, type T thermocouples are sufficient, though accuracy should be
verified and documented.

3. Distribute biological indicators on the downstream side for additional
evidence of thorough steam distribution, although these will not be mathematically considered in the final probability computation. The indicators should
contain on the order of 10^{-5} or greater *B. stearothermophilus* spores.

4. The in-line steam sterilization should be carried out as per normal procedures, using the calibrated downstream pressure gauge as the only process control instrument. During the cycle, a data logger records the thermocouple outputs at frequent time intervals. The steam pressure attained on the gauge should be at least 15 psig plus gauge accuracy, but minimized for reasons that will become apparent below.

5. The thermal lethality [5] at 121°C, F_{121}, is calculated for each thermocouple position from

$$F_{121} = \int 10^{(100-T)/Z} dt$$

where T is the actual temperature attained (°C), Z is the slope of the thermal resistance curve, at 121°C, for *B. stearothermophilius*, usually 10°C, and dt is the time derivative. (Note: The value of thermal resistance, D_T, for an organism is the time required to decimate a population at a reference temperature, T, and is determined experimentally. The value of Z is actually that ΔT required to change the value of D by one $\log_{10}$).

6. The probability of survival, P, is calculated from the lowest value of F_{121} obtained for a thermocouple position as

$$\log P = \log B - \frac{F_{121}}{D_{121}}$$

where B is the total estimated bioload on the surface to be sterilized, and D_{121} is the thermal resistance of *B. stearothermophilus* at 121°C.

7. The criterion for a successful validation is $P < 10^{-6}$ and all biological indicators negative upon incubation. The procedure must be enforced so as to guarantee that the F_{121} value delivered to the filter is always greater than that observed in the studies by (a) using the maximum steam pressure of the studies as a minimum control pressure for routine operation, (b) using the time cycle of the validation studies as the minimum time at which the minimum control pressure is maintained, and (c) all venting and drainage manipulations are reproduced as they were performed in the studies.

8. Should validation criteria not be met because $P \geqslant 10^{-6}$, then cycle time and/or steam pressure must be reduced. If this is insufficient or unfeasible, attempt to reduce B by presanitization techniques. However, such techniques will have to be incorporated into the filter preparation procedure and demonstrated to be reproducible. Should validation criteria not be met due to a positive biological indicator, repeat the test with thermocouples placed in the failed position to verify a cool point.

2. Steam Autoclave Sterilization

Steam autoclave sterilization is the preferred technique where in-line steam is unfeasible. It is particularly desirable to use this approach when the medium in use is prone to failure when differential pressure is applied at elevated temperatures.

The rationale for steam autoclave sterilization should be addressed as part of the protocol for steam autoclave validation (see Chap. 10). The key difference between the in-line rationale and autoclaving is that the controlling process parameter becomes autoclave pressure rather than the downstream gauge. All other aspects of in-line steam sterilization validation bioload studies apply to the autoclave technique, including heat distribution studies, biological indicators, and probability calculation.

3. *Ethylene Oxide (ETO) Sterilization of Aseptic Process Filters*

This technique should be reserved for use where the filter configuration contains aseptic filter medium that is susceptible to heat. The process is considerably more complex than those of in-line and autoclave steam sterilization, and therefore the controlling parameters are more extensive and difficult to measure. In addition, the possibility of residual ethylene oxide and its by products must be addressed to avoid potential process stream contamination. The toxic and flammable hazards of ethylene oxide make it a least desirable approach, and prevention of operator exposure must be guaranteed.

The controlling parameters of ETO sterilization are ethylene oxide concentration, relative humidity, heat penetration, gas penetration, and exposure time. Sterilization of filters is most effectively controlled in an autoclave. In-line ethylene oxide sterilization is undesirable for the previously mentioned safety considerations. Also, control and measurement of relative humidity in-line is difficult to validate.

For rationale of autoclave ETO sterilization, the reader is referred to Chapter 14.

4. *Other Techniques*

Chemosterilants: The use of a sterilizing fluid will require validation of complete contact with the internal filter surfaces and media. This may be demonstrated by impregnating the filter medium with spores of known resistance to the sterilant, in quantities exceeding the worst bioload.

Radiation: This technique is generally unfeasible for filters in steel housings but could become an important technique in future filter designs. An important subject to address in this regard will be the effect of radiation on the polymers of which many useful filter media are constructed.

Dry Heat: This is generally unfeasible because of the high temperatures required (200°C).

VII. ASEPTIC VENT AND GAS FILTRATION

A. Objectives

So far, we have discussed aseptic filtration of liquid process streams without reference to any of the special problems imposed by the validation of gaseous filtration. The objective of validating the aseptic filtration of gaseous streams for purposes of the following discussion is identical to that of liquid streams. That is, we will restrict ourselves to filtration requirements wherein the gaseous stream must be sterile to the same probability as that for liquid streams because it actively contacts the aseptic product, or in some cases, contains the product. This specifically excludes discussion of gaseous aseptic filtration for environmental purposes where a high degree of bioload removal is desired, but is likely to be recontaminated by personnel working in the atmosphere.

Some of the specific needs for aseptic filtration of gases take place whenever the processing involves operations such as vent breathing of process vessels, milling, conveying, drying, pneumatic transportation, and other applications involving direct aseptic product contact. The following paragraphs will provide some guidelines to the application and validation of these operations.

B. Recommended Techniques

1. Vent Breathing of Aseptic Processing Tanks

Probably the most important application of gaseous aseptic filtration is in process tanks where changes in liquid volume must be accommodated and the entry of potentially nonsterile atmosphere must be prevented. A relatively simple but automatic means of achieving this is shown schematically in Figure 12. Note that the process tank is maintained at a net positive pressure in this arrangement, and all air (or nitrogen) entering the vessel must come through the aseptic filter cartridge. At static conditions, the pressure regulator maintains a pressure p on the tank. The pressure switch, PS, has a set point of slightly higher than P, or $P + \Delta P$, and the three-way solenoid valve is open from filter to tank. Net gas flow is zero. During tank draining the pressure regulator maintains pressure P on the tank, with gas flow through the aseptic filter cartridge. During filling operations the headspace pressure increases to $P + \Delta P$, at which point the pressure switch repositions the solenoid to vent tank pressure. Note that a safety rupture disk should be positioned in a bypass to the vent line in the event of excessive tank pressure.

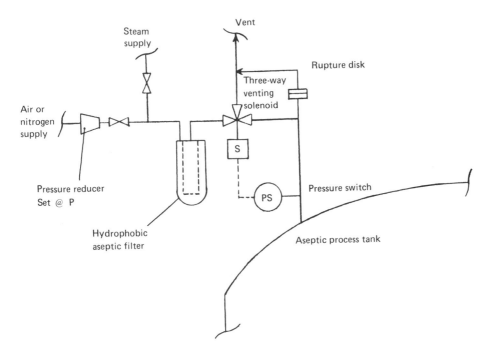

FIGURE 12   Vent breathing of aseptic process tanks.

The choice of aseptic filter media for venting applications should be limited to hydrophobic media capable of in-line steam sterilization. The use of hydrophobic media will enable the user to establish bulk air flow through the filter more readily after steam sterilization is complete.

The ordering of test/sterilization operations for venting applications is suggested as follows, because of the difficulty associated with integrity testing in situ:

1. Assemble the filter configuration and integrity test off-line.
2. Install the configuration and perform steam sterilization in situ.
3. Establish air flow and proceed with operations.
4. After use, remove the configuration and integrity test off-line.
5. Repeat with a new cartridge each cycle.

2. Bulk Gaseous Aseptic Filtration

Applications that require bulk quantities of aseptic gases for milling, drying, conveying, etc., operations will require a careful design effort dependent on the number of cubic feet per minute required and pressure constraints imposed. Many of the media manufacturers give air flow vs. pressure differential data for their hydrophobic media, which is frequently misleading when considering the media alone. Data tables and charts that show flow vs. pressure figures for completely assembled configurations should be used, because significant pressure drops are frequently more a function of inlet/outlet nozzle size and housing type than the medium itself.

Once the required filter area has been calculated, it is a good idea to apply a safety factor of 2 or even 3. Single-cartridge element housings may be piped in parallel to achieve the desired area, but several manufacturers catalogue multiple-cartridge housings suitable for gas filtration.

C. Validation Considerations

The objectives of validation of gaseous process stream aseptic filtration are the same as those for liquid process streams. Several problems, however, cause additional difficulty in the areas of biological load determination, biological challenge, and integrity testing. Some guidelines are provided below.

1. Bioload Determination for Gaseous Streams

Inherent difficulties associated with obtaining representative data on gaseous streams are due to (a) the large volumes, (b) sampling on-line, and (c) maintaining viability of the organisms. Three methods traditionally employed in obtaining samples are briefly described below:

Impingement: A small sample line in the main line is used to direct the gas stream directly at a TSA plate, allowing the heavier organisms to impinge on the plate as the gas stream changes direction. Care must be taken to avoid overexposure of the plate, which will desiccate and cause poor recovery of the organisms.

Media-Bubbling: A flask containing a suitable growth media such as trip-ticase soy broth (TSB) is fitted with a bubble tube and vent. The gas sample is allowed to bubble through the medium such that organisms will remain. To improve medium contact, the flask should be packed with a bed of gas beads. Later, after a known volume of gas has been bubbled through, a sample of the medium can be plated on tripticase soy agar (TSA) for colony count.

Filtrative Collection: Direct filtration of the gas stream followed by plating techniques may prove satisfactory, but care must be taken to maximize viability of the organisms. One way of accomplishing this is through the use of nutrient-containing membranes.

2. Biological Challenge for Gaseous Streams

Biological challenge is frequently not possible for gaseous streams and two substitutes are available: (a) nonbiological challenge where particles of known size and quantities are injected into the inlet gas stream and are counted at the outlet, or (b) liquid stream challenge.

It should be pointed out that the substitution of liquid stream challenge does have the inherent weakness that conditions conducive to biological passage may not be duplicated. For instance, gas volumetric flow rates are considerably higher than those of liquids for a given media and ΔP. As a result, an organism flowing with a gas stream will have considerably more kinetic energy, which may improve its probability of passage.

3. Integrity Testing Gaseous Aseptic Filters

The use of hydrophobic media will usually dictate that the integrity test design be extremely careful. A solvent will be required as the wetting fluid. The test should be designed for a solvent most acceptable to the user, and this means it is necessary to determine the appropriate test pressure and DF limits. A diffusional flow curve should be generated for this purpose. If erratic DF values are obtained with the solvent, several alternatives are available: (a) Resort to a solvent with a higher boiling point and viscosity, or (b) use the solvent as a wetting fluid to be purged out by the test fluid, which may be chosen as water.

VIII. CONTROLLING THE PROCESS

A. Objectives

The key objective of the user must be to ensure that all constraints defined the validation studies are met in process implementation by documentation and control.

B. Filter Purchase Specifications

Earlier in this chapter, we referred to the uniformity of media manufacture as being one of the most vulnerable aspects of validation. Surely, minor changes that could be implemented by the manufacturer to improve the process may in fact have significant impact on the user and invalidate considerable efforts. In setting up Purchase Specifications with a manufacturer, the user should be sure to include all parameters for which the user is dependent on filter-to-filter uniformity as part of the validation rationale. These will typically include:

1. Appearance
2. Dimensions: filter area, thickness of medium, seal dimensions
3. Chemical compatibility: extractibles, oxidizable substances, component-by-component material of construction
4. Flow rates with a standard fluid

5. Bioretentivity on a specific area basis under agreed test conditions
6. Sterilization procedures: alternative procedures that will not affect medium integrity or bioretentivity specifications
7. Integrity specifications: minimum bubble point and maximum diffusional flow specifications with test fluids acceptable to the user

C. Instrumentation

1. Pressure gauges used in routine steam sterilization and integrity test operations in the plant must be calibrated routinely and documented.
2. Diffusional flow measurements using automatic mass flow devices must be done with calibrated instruments.
3. All instruments that are used to measure parameters on which the validation rationale rests must be calibrated to tolerances that guarantee conformance to these limits defined in the validation studies.

D. Documentation and Operator Training

1. All procedures should be unambiguous and provide step-by-step instructions for the operator.
2. Each aseptic filter configuration should be considered an entity unto itself and have an associated log showing all assembly, cleaning, integrity testing, sterilization, and batch filtration data with operator signatures.
3. Individualized instruction using actual configurations should be held routinely for operating personnel.

IX. SUMMARY

In this chapter we have examined the rationale and practical methods of validating aseptic filtration as a sterilization process.

In Section I the objectives of the validation process were defined as those steps necessary to guarantee that the probability of producing a nonsterile filtrate is less than 10^{-6}. The "ideal" filter was presented and goals for chemical compatibility, flow rates, bioretention, strength, and longevity were described.

In Section II the procedure and interpretation of flow decay testing was presented as a useful tool in predicting and comparing flow performance of candidate media. Some economic criteria for filter selection were discussed as well as of comparison of cartridge vs. plate configurations.

In Section III the appropriate methods of demonstrating chemical compatibility were described with the chief goals of protecting the process stream from contamination while verifying that the performance of the candidate medium is not compromised. Criteria of UV, extractibles, gravimetric, flow rate, and integrity test evaluation of chemical compatibility were discussed. The recirculation test was offered as a means of exposing the candidate media to the process stream.

In Section IV the rationale and procedures for executing bioretentivity studies on candidate media were discussed. Bioload determination and a method of calculating a worst-case value for a stream were described. Biological challenge procedures and interpretation of results were presented.

In Section V, the considerable task of verifying configuration integrity was approached. Detailed test procedures and the theory of their operation were given. Comparison of bubble point vs. diffusional flow was presented. Probability calculation for detection of defects was explained. Some important approaches to troubleshooting integrity test failures were given.

In Section VI we discussed the methods of sterilization of aseptic filter configurations.

Section VII offered an effective approach to vent filtration. In addition, the special problems associated with validating large-volume gas filtrations were discussed.

Section VIII provided guidelines to implementing the process. A substantially successful validation effort is frequently underminded by weaknesses in control. Some objectives to be met in filter purchase agreements, operator training, and documentation were discussed.

REFERENCES

1. Reti, A. 1976. An assessment of test criteria for evaluating the performance and integrity of sterilizing filters.
2. Adamson, A. 1973. *A Textbook of Physical Chemistry*. Academic Press, New York.
3. Bird, R. B., Stuart, W. E., and Lightfoot, E. N. 1960. *Transport Phenomenon*. John Wiley & Sons, New York.
4. Perry, R. H., ed. 1976. *Engineering Manual*, 3rd ed. McGraw-Hill Book Company, New York.
5. Pflug, I. J. 1972. Heat sterilization, in *Industrial Sterilization*, G. Briggs Phillips and W. S. Miner, eds. Duke University Press, Chapel Hill, N.C.

18

Validation of Unique Filtration Processes

CAROLE S. GENOVESI

Wyeth Laboratories, West Chester, Pennsylvania

I. INTRODUCTION

The title "unique" filtration processes is an attempt to differentiate the types of filtration discussed here from those covered in Chapter 17. Although the filtration systems examined in the following pages can be used as part of an aseptic processing technique, the net result of the use of these filters is not necessarily a sterile product, especially in ultrafiltration and crossflow filtration, where the retained portion of the process is often of more interest than the filtrate.

Nevertheless, all considerations cited in Chapter 17 as to sterilization, chemical compatibility, configuration integrity, process specifications, documentation, and control of aseptic systems are equally applicable to the systems covered here and will not be further addressed in this chapter. The material in the following pages attempts to highlight a number of problems and considerations that are "unique" to each process discussed. The reader is encouraged to refer to the preceding chapter for a comprehensive discussion of the validation of any filtration system.

II. CROSSFLOW FILTRATION

A. Definitions

Conventional filtration processes operate with the filter in a "dead-end" mode; i.e., the flow of the process stream is perpendicular to the filter surface. This flow pattern causes a buildup of insoluble material on the filter surface, and, over a period of time, produces a progressively increasing drop in the flow rate and/or an increase in differential pressure (ΔP) across the filter. This means that conventional membrane filtration (CMF) is necessarily a batch process. As particles accumulate in or on the membrane, the pores become clogged, reducing the effective surface area of the filter.

Filter performance is commonly measured in two ways, efficiency and flux. Efficiency, or the ability to remove suspended particles of a particular size, may actually increase as the pores become clogged and their apparent diameter decreases. Flux, however, which is defined as the volume of filtrate per unit area of filter surface per time (i.e., gal/ft^2/day or liters/M^2/hr), will be reduced in direct proportion to the number of pores that are lost due to clogging. Therefore, to maintain a constant flux with a dead-end system, the differential pressure across the membrane must be increased as the number of available pores decreases. Eventually, depending on the size and concentration of the particles in the process fluid, the filter will reach a state where the flux is no longer acceptable or the pressure requirement is too high, and the membrane must be replaced.

However, if the system is configured so that the process flow is parallel to, rather than perpendicular to, the filter medium, much of the reduction in flux due to pore clogging can be eliminated. This process is termed crossflow filtration (CF) (Fig. 1). By utilizing a high fluid circulation rate parallel to the membrane, CF minimizes the accumulation of particles at the filter surface. A steady-state operation can then be achieved, as the moving process fluid carries away particles at the same rate as they are deposited on the membrane. Comparisons of otherwise identical systems demonstrate throughput increases of several orders of magnitude with membranes operated in a crossflow mode [1].

Most ultrafiltration (UF) systems operate in a crossflow manner. These UF systems are used to remove dissolved material, 1000 to 1,000,000 MW, from solutions, and will be discussed in Section IV. However, the principles of crossflow, first described for ultrafiltration, were later applied to extend the life of microporous membranes, which remove undissolved particulates (0.1 μm +) from suspensions.

Microporous crossflow filtration has several advantages over conventional filtration methods in addition to the increase in throughput. Crossflow is particularly advantageous if the solid phase of the suspension is to be recovered as a product. Other advantages include the following:

1. Filter flux is not a strong function of the size of the retained particles. In conventional filters, smaller particles (those approaching the pore size of the filter) cause clogging faster than larger ones because the smaller particles can enter the pore structure of the membrane and block the passages, while

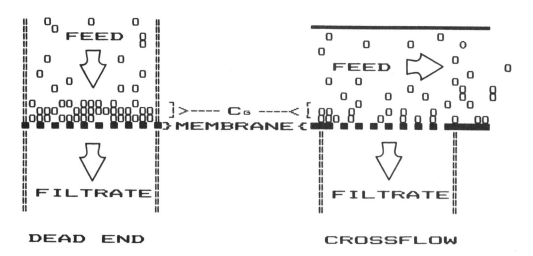

FIGURE 1 Comparison of conventional and crossflow filtration.

the larger sizes remain on the surface, forming a cake. In crossflow, the smaller particles are carried away by the recirculating fluid, and are not given the opportunity to be forced into the pores. Suspensions containing high concentrations of submicrometer particles will filter quickly, and additives such as flocculating agents are not needed, an important factor when recovery of the suspended materials is desired.

2. Most crossflow systems can be backflushed or cleaned with chemical agents to recover the initial high permeate flow rate if clogging does occur.

Crossflow filtration, however, can consume more energy than conventional filtration because the energy required to move the solution parallel to the filter must be supplied in addition to the driving pressure for the filtration. This requires consideration by the user as to which type of system is more economical for the process requirements.

B. Specifications

As with conventional filtration, specifications for crossflow filter systems depend on the nature of the solution to be filtered and the desired operating parameters. In addition, the end product of CF is not necessarily the filtrate, and secondary systems may be required for recovery of the retained solid material, or cleaning of the filter.

Crossflow systems are now commercially available in several configurations: turbulent-flow tubular, hollow fiber or pleated designs, and laminar-flow spiral-wound or annular flat-channel designs. Each can be obtained in a variety of media from various manufacturers, and most suppliers can provide a pilot size for test purposes. It is strongly recommended that one or more different pilot units be used to determine empirically which type is best for the specific process.

C. Process Considerations

To understand the mechanics of crossflow it is necessary to examine the concepts of concentration polarization and other factors that affect filter performance, retentivity, and flux.

1. Polarization

The buildup of particles at the filter surface is the major reason for flux decline in any filtration system. While the tangential nature of the crossflow process stream minimizes this surface accumulation, it is not eliminated completely.

Polarization at the filter surface occurs because, during filtration, particles in the solution are transported to the membrane surface and retained there while the liquid passes through the filter. A concentration gradient (C_G) of particles is established, with the highest concentration next to the membrane surface and the lowest concentration on the side of the gradient nearest the incoming process stream (Fig. 1). A steady state is reached when the number of particles driven toward the membrane is balanced by the particles being recaptured by the moving fluid.

Classical mathematical models for polarization behavior were developed to describe conditions during the operation of an ultrafiltration system, and were concerned with the behavior of dissolved solutes of molecular sizes. When these models are employed for studying the behavior of retained particles rather than molecules, calculated flow rates are often low by several orders of magnitude. This is one of the reasons that pilot studies using the intended process stream are essential for filter evaluation.

The transport of particles away from the membrane surface is accomplished by two different mechanisms:

1. In narrow-channel laminar-flow systems, the liquid flows across the membrane surface in an extremely thin film. Theoretical models of laminar-flow systems suggest that permeate (filtrate) flux (J) is an exponential function of the shear rate ($\dot{\gamma}$):

$$J = \dot{\gamma}^{x} \tag{1}$$

The shear rate is directly proportional to the velocity of the fluid, and inversely proportional to the diameter or depth of the flow channel.

In a circular channel: $\dot{\gamma} = \dfrac{8V}{D}$ D = channel diameter   (2)

In a rectangular channel: $\dot{\gamma} = \dfrac{6V}{b}$ b = channel height   (3)

Shear rate is the factor that controls wall shear stress (τ^{W}), a measure of the force acting on the particle in the vicinity of the membrane:

$$\tau^{W} = n\dot{\gamma} \qquad n = \text{viscosity of the liquid} \tag{4}$$

Increasing the wall shear stress by increasing the shear rate will reduce the tendency of the particles to accumulate at the filter surface, and thereby prolong a high flux rate. Obviously, a high shear rate can be obtained at a lower circulation rate by decreasing the height or diameter of the flow channel.

2. In tubular or pleated turbulent-flow configurations, the circulation rate is adjusted so that the Reynolds number (N_R) is greater than 3000:

$$N_R = \frac{PVD}{n}$$

V = average velocity

P = density of fluid

n = viscosity

D = diameter of flow channel   (5)

Experiments have shown that a laminar-flow condition exists when the Reynolds number is less than 2000, whereas above 3000, flow is turbulent. In the transition region between Reynolds numbers 2000 and 3000, flow is unstable and may be one or the other [2]. Laminar flow is not desirable in tubular systems, due to the formation of a boundary layer, which allows particles to accumulate at the filter surface.

2. Process Parameters

Other factors that affect permeate flux and system efficiency include: membrane characteristics, percent solids in feed, pressure, temperature, pH or other chemical effects, and circulation rate. Most of these have been discussed in detail in Chapter 17. Some factors peculiar to CF, or not mentioned in that chapter, are discussed below.

Membrane Characteristics: Microporous membranes are made of many different materials: cellulose (several types), polypropylene, polycarbonate, PTFE, and nylon are common. Each material has recommended pressure limits and allowable sterilization techniques. The manufacturer will also provide a list of solvent compatibilities. However, these compatibility determinations are made at specific temperatures, pressures, and solvent concentrations and may not be valid under all conditions. Reaction of the membrane material with a solvent or with one or more components of the process stream (e.g., chlorine with some polypropylenes) can produce membrane fouling. Fouling, unlike polarization, is usually an irreversible process caused by adsorption of substances to the membrane, or by deterioration of the membrane itself. Effects of fouling include weakening of the membrane, downstream release of particulates, loss of efficiency, or rapid flux decline. The membrane chosen should be compatible with the process fluid and tolerant of the most extreme conditions of pressure and temperature anticipated in the system.

Solids Concentration: Many crossflow applications require that the process stream be concentrated severalfold. A determination of the concentration/permeate flux relationship must therefore be made. A pilot system should be run with varying concentrations of solids to determine the most efficient concentration range for the particular filter and process stream. In general, the decrease in flux for an 8- to 10-fold concentration is moderate, but varies with the nature of the retained particles. This has been observed for both laminar and turbulent-flow systems.

Pressure: Permeate flux is not a strong function of pressure. The typical curve is shown in Figure 2. The flux is directly proportional to the pressure at very low pressures. However, a plateau is reached where the flux does not increase with further increases in pressure. This plateau pressure tends to decrease with increasing particle concentration. The plateau should be determined using the pilot system. As much of the energy utilized in operating a crossflow system is used to pump the process stream across the membrane, operating at too high a circulation rate or at a pressure above the plateau value is uneconomical.

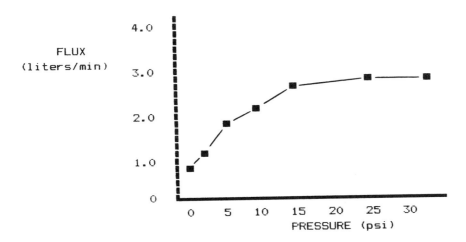

FIGURE 2   Flux as a function of transmembrane pressure.

It should be stressed that steady-state flux data are important in determining the effectiveness of a crossflow system for a particular process. Usually, the initial flux rate is high, and then falls until a pseudo-steady state is reached (Fig. 3). This is not a true steady state, as flux will slowly decline over time (see Sec. D, Sec. 2). The steady-state data, rather than the initial flux readings, should be used to evaluate the filter.

Temperature: Permeate flux increases with increasing temperature. This is attributed to the temperature/viscosity dependence; i.e., the flow rate through the pore is inversely proportional to the fluid viscosity. It is most important to control process fluid temperature during crossflow pilot studies. Otherwise, the variation of flux with temperature will conceal the effects of other factors.

Circulation Rate: It was indicated earlier that permeate flux is dependent on shear rate, which is controlled by channel size and circulation rate. Although classical concentration polarization models predict this dependence, they are not quantitatively accurate, and pilot trials should be run to determine the correct rate for each application. For instance, in the operation of one tubular system, adjusting the circulation rate to obtain a Reynolds number of 2100 produced the most satisfactory flux [3]. In other systems, the circulation rate may need to be raised to a N_R of 3000 or more to obtain turbulent flow conditions. When adjustments are made to upstream and downstream valves to control the pressure drop across the membrane, care must be taken to maintain the Reynolds number needed to assure turbulent flow and minimize particle polarization. Each type of system has requirements for minimum and maximum flow to obtain the greatest efficiency. The supplier should be consulted as to the correct parameters for each specific system.

D. Validation Techniques

Because of the multiplicity of uses to which crossflow filtration has been adapted, outlining a general validation procedure is difficult. The considerations

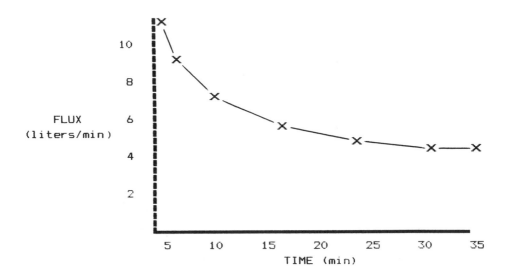

FIGURE 3   Flux as a function of time.

addressed in Chapter 17 are applicable to any filtration system, and crossflow
adds several other parameters.

1. Increasing Solids Concentration

If the crossflow filter is to be operated in a recirculating rather than a
one-pass mode, the concentration of the retained substances in the recirculation stream will increase. These substances may be the desired end product,
or they may be unwanted and discarded. Process parameters will dictate the
methods for removing, diluting, or collecting the retained material. This may
be continuous removal, such as recirculating the retentate through a settling
tank or diverting some portion and replacing it with fresh process material.
A batch-type arrangement is also possible, with the filtration process stopping
at predetermined intervals to replace or regenerate the feed. The process
is then resumed using the same filter. This means that, in addition to validating that all process parameters are under control, it must be demonstrated
that the increasing slurry concentration, viscosity, or other changes that
occur over time do not compromise the integrity or efficiency of the filtration
system. This may necessitate a study that is considerably longer than the
typical chemical or process compatibility studies described in Chapter 17 for
filters used in a batch process.

2. Cleaning

Unlike conventional filters, the crossflow filter is sometimes intended to be
used over extended periods of time, often years. Although the CF filter is
not subject to particulate polarization to the same extent as a conventional
filter, some loss of permeate flux will be encountered after the steady state
is reached. In many processes, especially when the retained species are rigid
particles, a backflush with filtrate or clean solution under pressure is sufficient to recover a large percentage of the initial flux.

In systems where this method is used, the backflush apparatus is usually
an integral part of the filter installation. This adds more work to the validation, in that the backflush technique and equipment must be considered as
part of the system and validated. Some considerations concerning backflush
include:

1. How often is it performed?
2. On what basis will the interval be chosen—pressure increase, flux
    reduction, sampling of filtrate or retentate, or other considerations?
3. Is it possible for the backflush to affect the integrity of the membrane,
    joints, or seals?
4. What safeguards are taken to assure that such events do not occur?

If the retained particles are colloidal or deformable, backflushing alone may
not be effective in regenerating the filter. Most crossflow filters can be renewed by rinsing or backflushing with a chemical cleaning solution. The
cleaning solution may consist of detergents, strong acids, alkalies, or other
agents, depending on the nature of the membrane and the makeup of the retained species. This type of cleaning can be done easily when the filter is
used on a batch basis, as in the concentration of bacterial cultures. The filter need not be cleaned at the same time the product is present. It is only
necessary to demonstrate and document that the cleaning process has no effect
on the filter or system integrity, and that the cleaning agent is completely
removed by whatever rinsing method is used.

However, if the filter is part of a process that is normally operated in a continuous-flow manner, the system can be designed in several ways to accommodate the cleaning process:

1. Duplicate or parallel filters, so that one can be cleaned while others remain on stream
2. Scheduled shutdowns, during which the cleaning is performed
3. Replaceable modules, which are removed from the system to be cleaned

Any of these methods require that the user validate the following:

1. No cleaning agent or agent residue can reach or affect the product.
2. The cleaning agent has no adverse influence on system effectiveness or integrity. This includes the membrane as well as gaskets, seals, tubing, piping, and related devices such as gauges or sensors.
3. The agent is effective in producing a regeneration of filter capabilities.
4. No long-term effects occur from repeated use of the agent. These could include leaching of metals from pipes, deterioration of pump seals, or changes in the porosity or retentive ability of the filter. If such effects are unavoidable, a documented schedule for replacing the component before the deterioration occurs should be included.

3. Integrity Testing

Most crossflow filters can be tested in the same way as conventional filters. There are some types that cannot be tested. If other system requirements necessitate the use of a nontestable filter, a method must be found to ensure filter integrity at suitable intervals. This usually involves monitoring one or more aspects of the permeate stream for evidence of the component the filter is intended to retain. Validation must document the interval, validity of test method, sample size, sampling methods (including preparation of equipment), documentation of results, and alert and action levels and the actions to be taken.

For filters that can be integrity-tested, the test apparatus may or may not be incorporated into the filter system. Unless the process fluid can be used to perform the test, the same consideration given to the validation of cleaning agents must be applied to the solution and equipment used to integrity-test the filter.

4. Summary

1. Continue the study for a sufficiently long time period, especially if the crossflow system is to be used on a continuous rather than a batch basis. Many long-term effects of conditions or chemicals do not appear until after considerable use.

2. To ensure that the system chosen is correct for the intended use, take advantage of the scaled-down pilot models offered by most manufacturers. Test the pilot system at the extremes of the proposed process.

3. Take all components of the system into consideration during validation. This includes pumps, backflush, or cleaning apparatus, and integrity test equipment.

4. Ensure that all parameters are controlled, even if they do not affect the condition of the product; e.g., temperature may have no effect on the stability of the product, but may affect the flow characteristics or retention of the membrane.

5. Control manufacturer specifications. Because the crossflow concept is relatively new in microporous filtration, manufacturers are constantly changing and improving their systems. This includes the membrane material, type of sealer (epoxy, resin, melt-seal), membrane support structure, integrity tests, and recommended cleaning procedure. For example, a change in O-ring material that is not validated can affect previously determined integrity, retention, or extractable data. Assure that the manufacturer will make no unannounced changes that may affect the validation parameters.

6. All procedures should be fully documented. Operator instructions, especially, may be more involved than with conventional filtration.

III. PYROGEN REMOVAL BY FILTRATION

A. Introduction

A pyrogen is any substance that causes a temperature rise when injected. They are usually high-molecular-weight lipopolysaccharide (LPS) complexes associated with the cell walls of Gram-negative bacteria, and are often referred to by the generic term "endotoxins." Depth filtration with asbestos-containing filters has long been known to be effective in removing pyrogens. However, since the Food and Drug Administration (FDA) has banned the use of asbestos in the processing of parenterals, charge-modified depth filters (CMD) have proven effective replacements in many processes (Sec. III, Sec. B).

Endotoxin isolated from Gram-negative bacteria contains three chemical regions: Lipid A; a central polysaccharide core; and an O-antigenic side chain. Recent studies have indicated that the Lipid A is responsible for most, if not all, of the pyrogenic activity [4]. This portion of the molecule also provides the basis for depyrogenation by membrane filters that can absorb endotoxin by the hydrophobic interaction of Lipid A with the uncharged membrane surface (Sec. III, Sec. C).

Endotoxin molecules in solution may exist in different states of aggregation. In the most aggregated form, as in the presence of magnesium or calcium, units exist with a diameter up to 0.1 μm. The addition of chelating agents breaks the aggregates into rod-shaped subunits, each 8–12 Å in diameter and 200–700 Å in length, with a molecular weight of 300,000 to 1,000,000. Use of a surface-active agent such as sodium deoxycholate reduces the endotoxin to its smallest subunit, with a molecular weight of approximately 10,000. Endotoxins in any state of aggregation can be removed by ultrafiltration (Sec. III, Sec. D).

B. Charge-Modified Depth Filters

The mechanism by which asbestos functions to remove pyrogens has been extensively studied and duplicated in charge-modified depth filters, composed of cellulose and modified inorganic filter aids. These filters combine the large effective surface area of asbestos filters with a positive zeta potential for the capture of small particles and charged molecules. The endotoxin molecules or aggregates have a net negative charge and, under many conditions, will be captured by the filter. However, while water and some pharmaceutical products can be depyrogenated in this way, the absorptive process requires a positive charge on the medium and a negative charge on the endotoxin molecule. This requirement limits the useful pH range to 4.5–8.0, which excludes many pharmaceutical products. Also, the presence of competing negatively charged substances in the solution will quickly limit the capacity of the filter.

1. Validation Considerations

Filter Media: Most inorganic filter aids such as sand, perlite, and diatomaceous earth naturally exhibit a negative zeta potential, which is not useful for particle capture. They can be modified, however, by treatment with a cationic colloid to produce a positively charged filter medium [5]. This material, when combined with cellulose, provides both mechanical straining and electrokinetic capture. Most CMD filters can be sterilized by steam in an autoclave or in-line, or by chemicals. Sterilization will sometimes produce a discoloration of the filter, which may leach out into the process stream, so if sterilized filters are to be used, extractable data should be acquired from filters that have been subjected to the sterilization process.

Because they are depth filters, CMD are excellent prefilters, producing a sizable log reduction in both bacterial and particulate counts. However, as with all depth filters, they are subject to unloading due to pressure surges, may shed filter material downstream, and are usually not testable by common integrity test methods. For these reasons most suppliers recommend that CMD filters not be used as a final filter, but as part of a total processing system.

Most manufacturers will provide a recommended ΔP at which the filter should be changed. This ΔP is based on a steady-state pressure. If the system design is such that backpressure or pressure surges are possible, the filter should be validated at the extremes of the expected pressures, or provisions made in the system design, e.g., check valves, so that rapid pressure changes do not reach the filter.

Type and Level of Contamination:
1. Particulate: If the process solution contains a heavy load of particulates, the CMD filter will reach maximum operating pressure in a very short time. In addition, many particulates in solution exhibit a negative charge, which will use up the available positive charge sites on the medium and thereby permit eventual endotoxin breakthrough. Conventional depth filters or serial CMD filters may be needed to obtain proper flow rates or batch sizes with acceptable pyrogen removal. An average particle burden study as part of the design process would be useful in the determination of prefilter needs. Pilot studies with the process fluid should be used to determine the maximum particle load compatible with successful filter operation, and the system should be validated at this level.

The size of the particulate contaminants is also important, and an average particle size determination will help predict the useful life of the filter. Large particles are trapped by mechanical straining in the filter, and do not usually bind positive sites in the filter media. Small particles are captured by electrokinetic means and can compete with the endotoxin molecules for the charged sites. By treating charge-modified media with alkali to destroy the charged sites, investigators have shown that, for particles greater than 1 μm in diameter, the main removal mechanism is mechanical rather than electrostatic [6].

2. Pyrogen: Studies indicate that a minimum of a 2.5–3 log reduction of endotoxin activity can be expected from a properly functioning CMD filter [4]. This is sufficient for most parenteral products but may require the use of serial prefiltration for highly contaminated water or raw material systems. The flow rate of the solution through the filter may require adjustment for high endotoxin concentrations. Too rapid a flow rate will not allow the solution to remain in contact with the medium for sufficient time for total binding of the endotoxin to occur, even though surplus binding sites are available [4]. A pilot study using process fluid contaminated with endotoxin at the highest

expected level can be used to adjust flow rates so that the desired removal efficiency is obtained for the entire batch.

While purified endotoxin is used in most cases to test the removal capabilities of CMD filters in pilot trials, the chemical structure of natural endotoxins may vary, and it is important that the filter be validated with the actual endotoxins encountered in the process fluid. Small changes in endotoxin molecules can cause alterations of electrokinetic properties and therefore in the ability of the filter to adsorb the pyrogen.

Properties of the Solution: In addition to the physical properties of the solution—i.e., temperature, viscosity, and compatibility with the filter media, which may affect any filtration process—two other factors are of immediate concern when using a CMD filter. Because the electrokinetic properties of molecules are affected by the environmental conditions in which they exist, any change in the process solution that would influence the electrokinetic properties of either the fluid or the suspended molecules must be considered in the validation studies.

1. pH: Table 1 shows the typical effect of pH on the capability of charge-modified filters to remove endotoxin. The loss of efficiency above pH 8.5 is to be expected if the major capture mechanism is electrokinetic attraction. The study shown consisted of 0.9% NaCl contaminated with 10^5 pg/ml of *E. coli* endotoxin. It should be mentioned that the same study showed no elution from the filter of *previously* adsorbed pyrogens when the pH is abruptly changed, even when the second solution was above pH 8.5 [4].

2. Organic Contaminants: Most of the CMD studies reported in the literature have been performed using water or low-molecular-weight salt solutions [4, 6]. Recently reported work with CMD filtration of potable liquids and solutions containing water-soluble organic compounds describes two effects of organic contaminants on filtration efficiency: (a) Anionic contaminants such as dextran sulfate can prevent adsorption of endotoxin by binding the positive sites on the filter media; and (b) cationic molecules such as B-lactoglobuline (at pH 3.7) can prevent endotoxin adsorption to the filter by adsorbing upon the endotoxin molecule and superimposing a positively charged layer on the negative charge of the endotoxin.

TABLE 1 Effect of pH on Endotoxin Removal by CMD Filters

pH	Endotoxin level of filtrate (pg/ml)
4.5	< 30
6.5	< 30
7.0	< 30
7.5	< 30
8.0	< 30
8.5	240
9.5	480

The author of the study, which was concerned with particulate removal, concludes that previous studies reporting the removal of particulates smaller than the pore size of the CMD from organic liquids were based on the erroneous calculation of pore size, and that the removal efficiency of charge-modified filters in organic solutions is based on mechanical straining and not electrokinetic effects [7]. As CMD pyrogen removal relies entirely on electrokinetics, the possibility of this sort of contamination occurring during the filtration process should be given consideration in the validation.

C. Membrane Filters

The use of microporous membrane filtration for pyrogen removal is a relatively recent innovation in pharmaceutical processing. Although large endotoxin aggregates, those approaching 0.1 µm in diameter, can sometimes be removed by simple mechanical straining, endotoxin molecules will more commonly pass through a 0.2-µm sterilizing filter. Table 2 shows a survey of various membrane types and their endotoxin removal capability in deionized (DI) water. Log reduction value (LRV) is defined as:

$$LRV = \log_{10} \frac{\text{challenge endotoxin concentration}}{\text{filtrate endotoxin concentration}}$$

The table indicates the existance of two pyrogen removal mechanisms, based on different methods of attraction: electrokinetic interaction and hydrophilic adsorption [8].

1. Electrokinetic Interaction

The first mechanism is the electrokinetic interaction of the endotoxin molecules with charged groups on the membrane surface, the same process as in charge-modified depth filters. Membranes manufactured from polyamides,

TABLE 2   Endotoxin Removal by 0.2-µm Membrane Filters[a]

Polymer type	Hydrophobicity	Surface charge	Endotoxin LRV
Polypropylene	Hydrophobic	Zero	1–3
Polyethylene	Hydrophobic	Zero	2.5–3.5
Polyvinylidenedifluoride	Hydrophobic	Zero	0.8–1.0
Polytetrafluoroethylene	Hydrophobic	Zero	1.2–2.0
Cellulose nitrate	Hydrophilic	Negative	<0.1
Cellulose acetate	Hydrophilic	Negative	<0.1
Polycarbonate	Hydrophilic	Negative	<0.2
Polysulfone	Hydrophilic	Negative	<0.2
Polyamide	Hydrophilic	Positive	>3.5

[a]Experimental conditions: membrane porosity = 0.2 µm, P = 1.3 psi, flow rate = 0.8 ml/min/cm^2, challenge concentration = 30 ng/ml *E. coli* LPS.

or with amines bonded to the surface, will exhibit a net positive charge in solutions below pH 8 and thus adsorb the negatively charged endotoxins (Fig. 4). In this example, unmodified nylon membranes have a negative zeta potential at pH 6 and above; below pH 6 they have a positive charge. By treating these membranes with a cationic resin, a charge-enhanced membrane (CEM) is produced that retains a positive charge from pH 3 to 10.

Charge-enhanced membranes are subject to the same limitations as charge-modified depth filters: There are a limited number of charge sites on the membrane. However, a charged membrane has several advantages over a depth filter:

Membrane filters have pore sizes that can be accurately defined.
Membrane filters do not release fibers downstream, a requirement for
    parenteral final filters.
There is little product hold-up in the filter.
The membrane can be tested for integrity by common methods, and can
    be used as a sterilizing filter as well as for depyrogenation.

On the negative side, the membrane is not technically a depth filter, and therefore does not have the particulate or endotoxin load capability of a CMD. This will generally result in higher pressure drops and reduced filter life compared to a depth filter. Process parameters will dictate which type is the better choice for a particular process.

Use as a Final Filter: If the charge-enhanced membrane is to be used as a final sterilizing filter, and also for the removal of pyrogens, careful studies

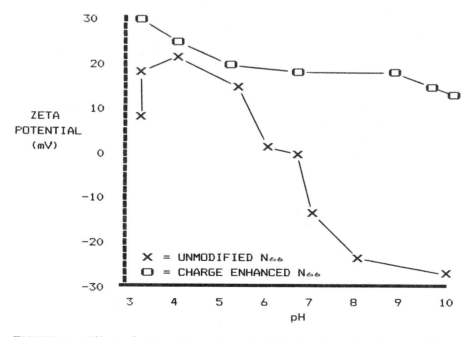

FIGURE 4   Effect of pH on the zeta potential of enhanced and unmodified nylon membranes.

for the matching of filter surface area to batch size must be performed. If
the process fluid has been adequately prefiltered and contains few large particles, the pressure drop across the filter will not increase appreciably during
the filtration. Breakthrough of the endotoxin will occur when the majority of
the charged sites are exhausted, but the pores will not block and there will
be no indication that the filter capacity has been exceeded.

When using a charge-enhanced membrane in this "adsorptive mode," i.e.,
for the removal of very small particles or endotoxins, it can be advantageous
to use two filters in series. When the tests of the filtrate from the upstream
filter show that the electrokinetic sites are exhausted, the downstream filter
is moved to the upstream position and a new filter is placed downstream, thereby achieving both economy and a high degree of safety [9].

The relative benefits of using a charge-enhanced membrane as a final filter
have not been completely defined. In most cases, it is better to use the CEM
in conjunction with a filter with a negative zeta potential, such as unmodified
nylon or cellulose, especially in the filtration of water. Many water supplies
contain positively charged contaminants:

1. Very fine asbestos fibers—a large proportion, possibly exceeding 30%
    nationally, of water supplies contain more than 10,000 asbestos fibers
    per liter [10]. These fibers can pass through many municipal water
    systems and will not be captured by a positively charged filter.
2. Aluminum hydrates or cationic polyelectrolytes, which may be carried
    over from their use in water treatment.

Use as a Prefilter: Charge-enhanced membranes are very efficient for prefiltration. They have been shown to increase the life of a final filter as much
as sixfold. Because the charged membrane enhances removal efficiency, a
membrane several pore sizes larger than expected will remove small particles
while maintaining a high flow rate (Table 3). One manufacturer claims a
99.97% removal of endotoxin from a challenge solution containing 0.016 g of
E. coli endotoxin by use of a 1.2-μm CEM filter, with a final pressure drop
of less than 1 psi [9]. Other benefits of charge-enhanced membrane prefiltration include:

1. The pressure drop across the final filter usually remains low or un-
    changed throughout the filtration process. Often the final filter can
    be reused by replacing the prefilter only.
2. Fewer bacteria or particulates reach the final filter, resulting in
    increased system reliability.

TABLE 3   Removal of *Ps. diminuta* Organisms by 1.2-μm CEM and
Unmodified Nylon Filter Media

Challenge, organisms/ft^2 media	Removal efficiency, %	
	CEM	Unmodified nylon
2×10^{10}	>99.99	<50
2×10^{12}	>99.99	<50
2×10^{12}	>99.90	<50

The optimum CEM prefilter for any final filter is best determined by pilot runs at production conditions. Generally, the choice is a prefilter two to four grades coarser than the final filter—e.g., for a 0.2-μm final filter, a prefilter of 0.65—1.2 μm. By testing the final filter with several grades of prefilter, the correct combination of filters can be chosen to result in the desired flow rate and final filter longevity.

Compatible Fluids: Fluids from which charge-enhanced membranes can effectively remove pyrogens in the pH range 3—10 include:

1. Water
2. Aqueous solutions with less than 0.2—0.5 N concentration of highly ionized salts
3. Aqueous solutions with high concentrations of nonionized compounds
4. Mixtures of water with solvents—e.g., water with 70% or more of the lower alcohols
5. Ionizing liquids in general [9]

It should be noted that charge-enhanced membranes, like charge-modified depth filters, will remove any negatively charged molecules from the solution. If the product of interest is such a molecule, there is a possibility that all or part could be retained by the filter.

Long-Term Use: If charge-enhanced membranes are to be used on a long-term basis, such as for low-level pyrogen removal from water, a beneficial side effect may be noticed. The quarternary ammonium groups at the membrane surface that provide the positive zeta potential in at least one brand of CEM have demonstrated bactericidal activity. Laboratory tests have shown growth inhibition of *Ps. diminuta* and *S. marcescens* on a CEM disk. This ability to prevent the growth of some bacteria can be expected to reduce the generation of pyrogens during long-term use.

2. Hydrophobic Adsorption

Hydrophobic microporous membrane filters have recently been shown to adsorb bacterial LPS. The polymers comprising these membranes lack hydrophilic ionizable groups capable of interacting with anionic endotoxins. All known bacterial endotoxins have a hydrophobic Lipid A core, and it is probable that hydrophobic interaction between the membrane and the core is responsible for this adsorption of endotoxins [8]. Adsorptive hydrophobic microfilters (AHM), being devoid of charged sites, should not be subject to the pH range limitations of the filters, which depend on electrokinetic adsorption for pyrogen removal.

Effect of pH: Since hydrophobic adsorption does not involve charged groups, pH should not affect LPS adsorption. In actual practice, adsorption is relatively independent of pH from 1 to 8, but is reduced at pH 9 and shows almost no activity at pH 12. This is due to the fact that, as pH increases, the endotoxin negative charge density also increases. As the charge density increases, the number of associated neutralizing cations and bound water molecules increases, forming an insulating layer between the Lipid A core and the membrane surface groups. If this layer is thicker than the distance over which hydrophobic interaction can occur, adsorption of the endotoxin will not take place [8].

Effect of Flow Rate: Table 4 shows a typical LRV for endotoxin removal over a 10-fold flow rate change. During these trials, which were done with

TABLE 4   Influence of Flow Rate on Endotoxin Adsorption by Polypropylene Filters

Flow rate ($ml/min/cm^2$)	Endotoxin LRV	Equivalent flow through a 10-in. cartridge LPM (gal/min)
0.5	3–4	4.5 (1.2)
1.0	3–4	9.3 (2.5)
5.8	3–4	54.0 (14)

a challenge of 50 ng/ml *E. coli* endotoxin in DI water, a LRV of greater than 3.6 was maintained up to 10 μm endotoxin adsorbed/square centimeter of filter media, and an LRV of greater than 2 was still recorded after 32 μg/cm^2, even at the highest flow rate. This rate of removal would allow approximately 10,000 liters of product to be depyrogenated by 2 logs or more in a single filtration step with one 10-in. cartridge [8]. Effective prefiltration to remove particulates will allow the use of flow rates based on process considerations.

Endotoxin: Depending on the makeup of the solution, endotoxins can exist in sizes from molecular species as small as 10,000–20,000 MW up to whole Gram-negative cells. A 10,000 MWCO ultrafiltration membrane is required to remove all endotoxins in solutions containing chelators or surfactants when mechanical straining is the only removal mechanism. If adsorptive hydrophobic filters are used, singly or in series, endotoxin levels can be reduced 3 to 4 logs, which is usually sufficient for most parenteral applications. The advantage of using microfiltration is that a 10-fold greater flow rate is obtained at one-fifth the pressure drop needed for UF. A knowledge of the maximum endotoxin levels likely to be encountered in the process stream will aid in choosing between UF and microfiltration as the most economical method.

Validation: Adsorptive hydrophobic filtration is a relatively recent discovery in pharmaceutical filtration. Very little has been published about these filters and, other than studies with purified endotoxin in DI water, little empirical data has been generated concerning their removal capabilities. The initial test results described above show great promise. Because these filters are 0.2 μm or 0.1 μm in pore size, they remove more than just endotoxin from the process fluid. The decision must be made early in the process design as to whether the filters will be used only to depyrogenate, or in a dual role utilizing both sterilizion and pyrogen removal capabilities. In either case, it should be demonstrated that changes in particulate or organism load of the process stream do not affect endotoxin removal ability. Because the filters do not depend on charged sites to effect adsorption, their action is not subject to competition by charged molecules. However, the process fluid could contain substances that also undergo hydrophobic adsorption, and will compete with the endotoxin for the bonding space. This competition would result in unanticipated endotoxin breakthrough if the possibility were not taken into consideration and eliminated or controlled.

D. Ultrafiltration

Ultrafiltration will be discussed in detail in Section IV. Only the aspects of the process that are concerned with pyrogen removal will be covered here.

Section IV should be consulted for definitions and information on types of ultrafiltration systems.

1. Endotoxin Aggregation State

An ultrafilter is a screen filter. It retains substances by having a pore size smaller than the diameter of the species to be retained. For this reason it is necessary to determine the size of the endotoxin molecule in the solution to be filtered in order to assess the practicality of using UF, and to choose an appropriate membrane.

In aqueous solutions, the LPS molecules are arranged in a bilayer vesicular structure, with the hydrophilic components exposed to the aqueous environment and the Lipid A hydrophobic portions in the center of the double layer. These vesicles are apparently stabilized by divalent cations, because when the cations are chelated by addition of EDTA, the aggregates, which can be as large as 0.1 μm, begin to break up into smaller, micellelike structures with molecular weights of 300,000 to 1,000,000. These appear under electron microscopy (EM) as small rods or disks. Addition of detergents or bile salts further reduce the aggregates into the basic endotoxin subunits [11]. These are invisible under EM, but have been shown by sedimentation velocity, density, and viscosity to be 10,000 to 20,000 MW [12].

Ultrafilters are rated, not on pore size, but on molecular weight cutoff (MWCO) or nominal molecular weight limit (NMWL), which is the molecular weight of the smallest molecule that will be at least 95% retained by the membrane. This value is a guide, not an absolute, as the shape and deformability of the molecules also determine retention.

Table 5 illustrates the removal of *E. coli* endotoxin from water and salt solutions with and without chelating agents and detergents. It can easily be seen that even a 0.025-μm filter usually used for virus filtration, can retain highly aggregated endotoxin molecules. The vesicular aggregates are retained on a 0.025-μm membrane, the micelles on a 1,000,000-MWCO membrane, and the small subunits on 10,000 MWCO [13]. This is important because the majority of parenteral solutions have solutes of less than 10,000 MW, which will pass through the membrane. Depyrogenation studies using UF have been performed successfully on:

Water
20% glucose
4% amino acid with 12.5% xybitol
Sodium cephalothin (aqueous)
30% aqueous chloramphenicol succinate
20% aqueous fructose
400 ng/ml sodium carbenicillin

A 10,000 MWCO membrane was used to depyrogenate these solutions of both 500 ng/ml *E. coli* endotoxin and 500 ng/ml pyrogenic material from wild-type water organisms [14, 15]. No pyrogens were detected in any filtrate, and no reduction was found in solute concentration in the filtrate.

Depyrogenation of high-molecular-weight solutions depends on the aggregation state of the LPS molecules. In most aqueous solutions, the endotoxin molecules are highly aggregated and could possibly be removed by a 100,000- or even a 500,000-MWCO membrane, which would allow passage of the product molecules.

If the endotoxin and solute molecules are of a similar size, it may be possible to manipulate the effective size of the endotoxin aggregate by addition

TABLE 5   Removal of *E. coli* Endotoxin from Various Solutions by Ultrafiltration

Solution	Endotoxin concentration (q/ml)	Endotoxin (q/ml) recovered in filtrate from:				
		0.2 μm	0.025 μm	10^6 MWCO	10^5 MWCO	10^4 MWCO
Water	10^{-6}	10^{-6}	$<10^{-10}$	$<10^{-10}$	$<10^{-10}$	$<10^{-10}$
0.9% NaCl	10^{-6}	10^{-6}	$<10^{-10}$	$<10^{-10}$	$<10^{-10}$	$<10^{-10}$
5 mM MgCl2	10^{-6}	10^{-6}	$<10^{-10}$	$<10^{-10}$	$<10^{-10}$	
5 mM EDTA	10^{-6}		10^{-6}	$<10^{-10}$	$<10^{-10}$	$<10^{-10}$
0.5% Na cholate	10^{-5}			10^{-10}	10^{-7}	$<10^{-10}$
1.0% Na cholate	10^{-5}			10^{-6}	10^{-7}	$<10^{-10}$
2% Na cholate, 5 mM EDTA	10^{-5}			10^{-5}	10^{-5}	$<10^{-10}$
1% Deoxycholate	10^{-5}			10^{-5}	10^{-5}	$<10^{-10}$

or removal of cations, detergents, or chelating agents in order to facilitate separation of the endotoxin from the solute. The size of the endotoxin aggregate in the product solution is easily determined by passing the solution through successively lower MWCO membranes and sampling each filtrate. The membrane that removes all endotoxin, does not remove product solute, and produces an acceptable flow rate should be selected for pilot tests in a process environment.

2. Water

The only approved methods at present for producing USP water-for-injection (WFI) are distillation and reverse osmosis (RO). However, other water types (e.g., USP purified water) may be produced by UF. In fact, the USP specifies the production method only in the case of WFI. All other grades of water are defined only by their final quality.

Ultrafiltration of deionized, carbon-filtered water has been shown to be effective for removal of bacteria as well as pyrogens. In extended studies, the water quality exceeded requirements for USP WFI at almost all times. A final sterilizing-grade microporous filter placed after the UF would guarantee sterility. The successful use of UF for water depyrogenation has been demonstrated in many trials [11,13–15]. UF functions with about 50% of the operating costs of a recompression still, and approximately 10% of the capital costs.

A UF system used for water depyrogenation is configured differently from that used for solution filtrations. Because most solutions will contain particulates and organisms as well as endotoxins, high crossflow rates are necessary to prevent membrane fouling. In water depyrogenation, the particulates (assuming adequate prefiltration) are present in very low concentrations, and a relatively low crossflow rate is needed to maintain flux. Also, in many cases, UF can operate solely on line pressure (25 psi), and booster pumps can be installed to increase downstream pressure where necessary.

3. Advantages

Uncomplicated: Compared to a still, or even an RO unit, UF is relatively simple to operate. Low pressure drop, high flow rates, and modular construction reduce maintenance, cleaning, and setup time.

Efficient: Because UF does not depend on charge interaction, removal efficiency is not dependent on either the endotoxin concentration or the volume of solution filtered. UF will continue to remove endotoxin molecules as long as the solvent will pass through the integral filter.

Inert: Endotoxin removal by UF involves no phase change, addition of chemicals, increase or decrease in temperature, or other alterations that could affect the product. It is nondestructive to sensitive fluids and is not affected by pH changes or solvent differences, except those that might change the aggregation state of the endotoxin molecule.

Selective: By choosing a MWCO that will allow passage of the product solute while retaining the endotoxin, UF can be used to remove pyrogens from parenteral solutions. RO and distillation are suitable only for water.

4. Validation

Cleaning: Most UF systems can be cleaned with an 0.1 N NaOH solution to destroy any retained LPS. This may be done on a batch, time, or as-needed basis. As with the crossflow filters, the cleaning procedure should be included in the validation. Initial filtrate from the cleaned unit should be assayed for pyrogen content and pH to assure cleanliness and removal of the cleaning agent.

Integrity Testing: The UF integrity test is similar to the bubble point test described in Chapter 17 for sterilizing-grade filters. The gas is introduced on the upstream side of the membrane, and the downstream side is examined for bubbles. The test is usually conducted at low pressures, since only major damage can be detected in this manner. In fact, unlike a standard bubble point test, the pressure is merely raised to the test level, and the absence of bubbling indicates integrity. The pressure is not raised until bubbles appear. A higher-sensitivity integrity test may be carried out by challenging the filter with endotoxin. This type of validation is more representative of integrity and performance [16].

IV. ULTRAFILTRATION

A. Fundamentals

Ultrafiltration (UF) is molecular filtration. It discriminates between molecules of different sizes and, therefore, between different molecular weights. Ultrafiltration will retain suspended solids, emulsified oils, colloids, and dissolved macromolecules while passing dissolved sugars, inorganics, solvents, and water. The "pore size" of a UF membrane is rated by the molecular weight cutoff (MWCO), which is the size of molecule, usually determined with globular proteins, that is at least 95% retained by the membrane. This is not a rigorous limit. The MWCO varies with the shape of the molecule, the concentration of the molecule, filtration pressure, duration of filtration, pH, and ionic strength. Generally a UF membrane can accomplish adequate separation in cases where the solute molecules to be retained are a minimum of one to two orders of magnitude larger than the solvent (permeate) molecules.

The advantage of UF over other separation processes include:

    No phase change
    No heat
    Low energy cost
    Low capital cost
    Simple process equipment
    Minimum labor requirement

B. Uses

Ultrafiltration can be utilized for one or more of the following processes.

1. Concentration of a Solute

Ultrafiltration is excellent for the concentration of substances such as proteins and enzymes whose structure and activity are likely to be altered by other concentration procedures such as precipitation or evaporation. UF can be conducted rapidly at a low temperature, so that degradation does not occur. Concentration by UF is also useful for very dilute solutions, which would be impractical, time-consuming, and expensive to concentrate by other methods. For cell concentration, UF provides the same or better recovery, with faster processing times and at a fraction of the cost of a continuous centrifuge, and produces no potentially hazardous aerosols.

2. Purification of a Solvent

Ultrafiltration can depyrogenate and remove organisms, particulates, organic material, and dissolved macrosolutes.

3. Separation

Solute X can be separated from solute Y (assuming adequate molecular weight difference) by using a membrane that allows passage of one but not the other.

4. Diafiltration

Water or another pure solvent is added to the feed stream at a rate equal to (or less than) the permeate flow. This is analogous to cake-washing, and can either improve the recovery of the membrane-permeable solute, or increase the purity of the retained species.

C. Membranes

An ultrafiltration membrane should possess the following characteristics:
   1. High permeability to the solvent under modest pressures.
   2. Sharp retention cutoff characteristics. The membrane should be capable of retaining all molecules above the MWCO in size, and/or passing all molecules below the specified value. This depends on the pore size distribution of the membrane, since solutes smaller than the minimum pore size will pass through, and solutes larger than the maximum pore size will be 100% retained. The spread of pore sizes between the smallest and the largest will determine the sharpness of the cutoff. UF membranes tend to have sharper cutoffs as the membrane thickness decreases [17].
   3. Good mechanical durability, chemical and thermal stability.
   4. Minimum dependence of permeability on solute type or concentration.
   5. High fouling resistance, i.e., little tendency for reduction in permeability due to intrusion of the solute molecules into the membrane, or to occlusion of the pores due to the adhesion of molecules to the membrane itself. Most serious fouling problems are caused by materials such as oil or some proteins, which have large hydrophobic surface areas and tend to aggregate in an aqueous environment. The same hydrophobic bonding that contributes to aggregation will cause the molecules to cling to the surface of the membrane. One way to avoid this is to use a membrane that is extremely hydrophilic, and remains wetted even in the presence of hydrophobic particles. The most hydrophilic membranes are those with the sulfonate (SO_3) group on the surface. The natural substance heparin, for instance, which functions to keep the walls of the blood vessels wetted, is a sulfonate polymer [18].
   Fouling will be most pronounced with solutes whose sizes lie in the lower part of the pore size distribution scale, since these will have the least difficulty in entering the membrane structure, and a high probability of lodging in the pore constrictions. It is sometimes necessary to use a membrane that has a mean pore size below that of the solute molecule to be retained.
   In addition, a partially fouled membrane may show a change in retention characteristics. As the lower part of the pore size distribution is inactivated by fouling, most of the flow will pass through the larger pores, and the filter

will be less retentive. As fouling progresses, even the larger pores will be partially blocked, and an effectively finer pore size filter may result. For these reasons, pilot trials of any system should be monitored from a new, clean filter through several cleaning or regeneration cycles before the filter MWCO is determined.

6. Reproducibility of flow and retention characteristics from lot to lot. Because UF is under constant development and subject to manufacturer's changes and improvements, the membrane supplier must be made aware that any changes in the manufacturing technique should be communicated to the user, so that tests can be run to assure that no change has occurred in the validation parameters.

Ultrafiltration membranes are generally gels formed by the submersion of a viscous mixture in a coagulating solvent (casting). They are manufactured from a variety of polymers, including cellulose acetate and nitrate, polysulfones, and polyesters. The noncellulosic membranes are highly resistant to acids, bases, alcohols, detergents, and oxidizing agents. UF membranes were developed in the early 1900s, but were not used except experimentally for many years because of fouling problems. It was not until the discovery of the anisotropic nature of these membranes that real progress could be made. We now know that the casting process invariably gives rise to the formation of a dense "skin" with very small pores on the top of the membrane, where the solvent evaporation first takes place. When skinned membranes are used with the skin side in the downstream direction ("upside down"), they foul quickly and have a low flow rate. Before the discovery of the anisotrophy, membranes were used in the wrong position equally as often as in the correct attitude, giving rise to a reputation for poor reproducibility of results.

An anisotropic membrane has several advantages over an isotropic membrane, which has nearly constant diameter pores throughout its thickness. The "skin" on the anisotropic membrane (Fig. 5) is typically $0.1-1.0$ μm thick, and is supported by a highly porous sublayer for strength. The presence of the skin allows high filtration rates at relatively low pressures. This can be seen in the equation for flux, J:

$$J = \frac{\pi r^4 \, \Delta P}{8nL} \tag{6}$$

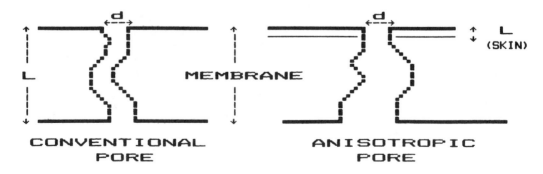

FIGURE 5 Comparison of conventional and anisotropic pores.

where

   r   = radius of the pore

   ΔP = pressure differential

   n   = viscosity

   L   = length of the pore

Referring to Figure 5, it is obvious that the effective pore length, L, for the anisotropic pore is much less than for the constant pore size membrane, and flux is thereby maximized with no increase in pressure.

Because the skin is so thin, a UF membrane is probably as close to a true membrane filter, as opposed to a depth filter, as is practical today. This has several fortunate consequences:

1. Sharp cutoff in the size of the molecules retained. A depth filter owes much of its retentive ability to the tendency of particles to become trapped in the long, tortuous passages through the membrane. This also leads to a rather diffuse cutoff, as the passages have widely varying diameters. The UF filter is a screen filter. The pore size of the skin alone determines which molecules will be retained.

2. Resistance to fouling, as most retained species remain on the surface, where they can be washed or dissolved away in the cleaning process.

Most ultrafiltration membranes are composed of hydrophilic polymers, and often cannot be allowed to dry out without irreversible changes in properties, or complete destruction. Some cellulose esters are sensitive to hydrolytic degradation in acidic or basic media. Many of these are swollen or altered by organic solvents, concentrated electrolytes or detergents. Only a few can withstand steam sterilization. Where sterility is required, most must be treated chemically with formaldehyde, ethanol, a dilute bactericide, or by radiation. In all cases, the user should not depend on the manufacturer's table of compatibilities, except as a general guide. Pilot trials need to be performed under process conditions, and the following limits determined:

1. Chemical resistance. All species in the process fluid should be identified, along with their possible concentration ranges. This includes compounds to be used for cleaning or regeneration, as unexpected reactions can occur between chemical agents and any process solution remaining in the filter.

2. Thermal stability. The most extreme conditions to be encountered during the process filtration should be defined.

3. pH limits. The acceptable operating limits should be set, and it should be determined if the filtration process causes changes in pH during filtration.

D. Flow Dynamics

A schematic representation of the ultrafiltration process is shown in Figure 6. A recirculating feed stream containing molecules of various sizes is pumped across the membrane surface at a velocity determined by the feed pressure differential. This continuous flow of solution across the membrane is used in all UF systems as a means of sweeping the membrane surface to control fouling.

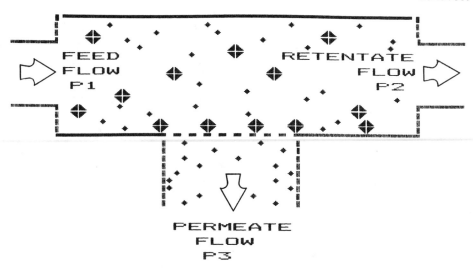

FIGURE 6   Schematic representation of the ultrafiltration process.

The pressure gradient $(P_1 - P_2)$ responsible for the crossflow is referred to as the hydrodynamic pressure gradient, ΔP_H.

As the feed stream passes over the membrane, membrane-permeable molecules pass through the membrane and exit in the permeate stream at pressure P_3, which is often atmospheric. The driving force for permeate flow is the pressure exerted through the membrane at each point on the surface. This transmembrane pressure gradient, ΔP_T, is at a maximum at the inlet side, and at a minimum at the outlet:

$$\Delta P_T \text{ (inlet)} = P_1 - P_3 \tag{7}$$

$$\Delta P_T \text{ (outlet)} = P_2 - P_3 \tag{8}$$

$$\Delta P_T \text{ (inlet)} > P_T \text{ (outlet)} \tag{9}$$

Although variable along the membrane, ΔP_T is usually stated as an average:

$$\text{Avg. } \Delta P_T = \frac{P_1 + P_2}{2} - P_3 \text{ or roughly } \frac{P_1 + P_2}{2} \tag{10}$$

The transmembrane pressure gradient can be related to the hydrodynamic pressure gradient by the equation:

$$\text{Avg. } \Delta P_T = P_1 - P_3 - \frac{\Delta P_H}{2} \tag{11}$$

This indicates that if P_1 and P_3 (inlet and permeate) pressures are fixed, changes made to ΔP_H to control fouling will also effect ΔP_T [19].

1. Concentration Polarization

When the feed stream is pumped through the UF system, solvent and solute molecules are forced toward the membrane under the influence of ΔP_T. Because the membrane retains the solute, the solute concentration at the membrane surface will increase as a consequence of the removal of the solvent, which passes through the membrane. This results in the development of a boundary layer concentration gradient, C_G, with the maximum solute concentration located next to the membrane. The formation of this gradient is referred to as concentration polarization. As a result of their increased concentration at the membrane surface, the solute molecules have a tendency to diffuse back into the lower-concentration area of the bulk stream. Under steady-state conditions, the convective movement of the solute toward the membrane is balanced by an equal diffusive movement of the solute away from the surface.

In ultrafiltration, the colloids and macrosolutes do not simply increase in concentration at the membrane surface. Instead, they tend to form a secondary membrane, sometimes referred to as the gel layer or cake [19]. Besides affecting the membrane retention characteristics, the polarization limits the useful transmembrane pressure. As ΔP_T is increased, an initial increase in flux will result. This increase will carry more solute to the membrane surface, which will increase the thickness and resistance to flow of the gel layer, which will level off the flux.

If ΔP_H remains constant, the increasing solute concentration in the feed stream due to removal of the solvent through the membrane will increase the depth of the gel layer, as fewer molecules diffuse back into the stream. For a constant feed stream concentration, polarization can be delayed by increasing the velocity of the feed stream, so that diffusive flow is maximized. The best approach to coping with polarization is to minimize its effects by proper equipment design and utilization of crossflow techniques.

There are four basic factors that affect permeate flux:

Operating Pressure: As discussed above, flux generally increases with pressure, although there is a plateau pressure beyond which flux does not increase due to pore compaction and polarization. Any increase in flux associated with increased pressure after the plateau is counteracted by an increase in the boundary layer thickness.

Feed Flow Rate: Flux generally increases with an increase in feed flow rate. The higher velocity helps to clean the membrane surface and reduce polarization. The flow rate chosen should be a compromise between increased flux and increased power consumption costs.

Temperature: Flux increases with temperature due to lower viscosity and higher molecular activities. Unless the process fluid is temperature-sensitive, the operating temperature should be as high as possible, but below the recommended upper limits for the membrane.

Feed Concentration: Flux decreases with increasing feed concentration. There is usually a concentration for each feed beyond which it is not economical to continue processing. Generally, the flux rate varies inversely with the logarithm of the concentration of the retained solute [20].

The filtration capacity of a specific system can be increased by either increasing the membrane area or increasing the energy expenditure for feed flow velocity and/or pressure. Both have associated costs, and an economic study is required to determine the optimum solution.

2. Calculations

There are several simple equations that may be helpful in determining the reliability and performance of ultrafiltration systems. These equations describe different ways of viewing the operation of the system, and can be used to ensure that parameters are following expected trends during processing.

Flux (J)

$$J = \frac{\text{volume permeate/time}}{\text{area of membrane surface}} \tag{12}$$

Solute Retention (R)

$$R = \frac{\text{feed concentration} - \text{permeate concentration}}{\text{feed concentration}} \tag{13}$$

Concentration or Volumetric Reduction Factor (NX): NX is especially useful in dewatering applications.

$$NX = \frac{\text{system feed rate}}{\text{permeate flow rate}} \tag{14}$$

Recovery (r) *for Batch Processes*

$$r = \frac{\text{volume permeate}}{\text{volume initial}} \qquad (\text{x } 100 \text{ for percent}) \tag{15}$$

Average Membrane Rejection Coefficient ($\bar{Q}$) *for Batch Processes*

$$\bar{Q} = 1 - \frac{\ln(1 - V_P C_P / V_0 C_0)}{\ln(1 - r)} \tag{16}$$

where

r = recovery (Eq. 15)

V_P = total permeate volume

V_0 = original process volume

C_P = concentration of solute in bulk permeate

C_0 = concentration of solute in original process volume

Membrane Rejection at a Specific Point in Time ($Q;$)

$$Q; = \frac{(1 - C_{PI})}{C_I} \qquad \begin{array}{l} C_{PI} = \text{concentration of solute in permeate} \\ C_I = \text{concentration of solute in retentate} \end{array} \tag{17}$$

E. Membrane Configurations

Ultrafiltration membranes are usually manufactured in modular form. The modules are arranged singly, in series (one after the other), or in parallel (flow through all simultaneously), to form the UF system. This flexibility contributes to the usefulness of ultrafiltration. There are two general module configurations, narrow-channel and wide-channel (Table 6). Both types of modules utilize crossflow to extend the filter life and minimize the flux reduction and change in retention characteristics associated with polarization [21].

1. Wide-Channel

Tubular: Tubular modules consist of a porous support tube with the membrane cast on the inside surface. The tubes are usually 6 to 25 mm ID. The tubes may be single, or manifolded inside a support structure. Tubular modules usually require no prefiltration and provide a high, stable flux and reliable operation due to ease of regeneration or cleaning. Backflushing, chemicals, or detergents may be used, or small sponge balls may be pumped through the system to scrub the membrane clean. Tubular systems can operate at high pressures, and are therefore useful for feeds with a high concentration of solids or particulates. However, the energy required to maintain turbulent flow is also high, typically 1 kW-hr for 50–500 liters of filtrate.

2. Narrow-Channel

Hollow Fiber: The hollow-fiber configuration employs the same basic system as the tubular, except that each tubule is typically less than 1 mm ID. Prefiltration is usually required, because the fibers are susceptible to plugging due to the narrowness of the channel. Holdup volume is low, as is power consumption. Typical uses for hollow fiber modules include water filtration prior to reverse osmosis, and concentration of cell suspensions. Hollow fibers are somewhat limited in pressure capacity, but can be used to concentrate feed solutions up to about 30% solute concentration.

Spiral Wound: Of the two types of flat sheet membranes, the spiral wound is the most commonly used. Two (or more) flat membranes are sealed together on three sides like an envelope, with spacer screens between the sheets. The fourth side is sealed to a permeate collection tube. A spacer sheet is then placed on the "envelope," and the layers are rolled up, with the collection tube in the center. The feed stream moves along the spacers, then through the membrane to the collection tube. Spiral-wound modules allow high-pressure operation, but need prefiltration and can have cleaning and solute recovery problems due to screen clogging. They have the lowest energy requirement of any module, producing 500–30,000 liters of filtrate per kilowatt-hour.

TABLE 6   Comparison of Different Ultrafilter Configurations

Configuration	Holdup volume	Pre-filtration	Power usage	Ease of cleaning	Resistance to damage	Typical life (yr)
Tubular	High	No	High	Good	Good	2–6
Hollow fiber	Low	Yes	Low	Fair	Good	1
Plate and frame	Low	Yes	Low	Fair	Good	1–2
Spiral wound	Low	Yes	Low	Poor	Poor	1–2

Spiral-wound systems are compact, with lower capital costs than other types, and will process feeds with up to 40% solute concentration.

Plate and Frame: Plate-and-frame modules consist of flat membranes interleaved with support screens. They will withstand high pressures and can accommodate high solute concentrations with low holdup volume, but are difficult to clean and require prefiltration for optimum performance. Energy expenditure is high, typically 1 kW-hr for each 250−350 liters of filtrate.

F. Operating Modes

The flexibility of UF allows processing configurations designed to meet the needs of the user.

1. Batch

A batch process is the concentration of a fixed volume of feed by continual recirculation through the filter until the desired solute concentration in the retentate has been reached, or until the desired volume of permeate has been filtered. The feed rate is usually maintained high in relation to the permeate flow rate to ensure that the solute concentration in the recirculation loop is not significantly higher than that in the holding tank. High feed velocity also reduces the polarization caused by the increasing solute concentration.

2. Feed and Bleed

The retentate containing the concentrated solute is constantly removed while fresh feed solution is continually added. No holding tank is required for this mode.

3. Single-Pass

There is no recirculation loop. The process material is concentrated to its final level after one pass through the filter.

4. Series or Staged

The recirculation stream (bleed) from one module is used as the feed material for a second module. This method allows concentration of the solute in easy stages. The modules may all contain the same MWCO membrane, or the sizes may change, depending on the required result.

5. Parallel

Two or more modules may be operated on the same feed stream. This allows rapid processing of large volumes [22].

G. System Tests

1. Integrity

The UF integrity test is similar to the bubble point test described in Chapter 17 for sterilizing filters. Air (or other gas) is introduced on the upstream side of the membrane, and the filtrate line is examined for bubbles. The test is usually conducted at low pressures, since only major damage can be detected in this way. In fact, unlike a standard bubble test, the air pressure is merely raised to the test level, and the absence of bubbling indicates integrity. The pressure is not increased until the bubbles appear.

UF membranes can also be tested by feeding a marker substance to the membrane, and testing the filtrate for the presence of the marker. Substances used for the test can include dyes, macromolecules of known molecular weights, or the process fluid itself. In the case of water or other solvents that may have very dilute solutes, pure dextrans of known molecular weights can be used as indicators. Dextrans are used as plasma extenders in humans, and can be hydrolyzed with dilute acids to oligosaccharides, which will leave no detectable residue in the UF system [23].

2. Test Procedures

Flux: A clean system check should be run with water or other clean fluid when the system is new. Most manufacturers recommend an initial cleaning and sanitization procedure before testing. After the cleaning procedure, the flux should be determined using the clean solvent. If water is used, it should be deionized water. Inlet and outlet pressures and fluid temperature should be specified for the test, and the results recorded for future reference. The flux should be measured after a 15-min stabilization period. This will provide a baseline value, which can be used later to assess the effectiveness of the cleaning procedures.

1. Pretreatment: Determine if the feed material requires pretreatment. This could include prefilters, bag filters, or settling to remove suspended material; clarification to remove fats and oils; or other methods. It is usually wise to use prefiltration as a precaution in the initial pilot study, as lack of needed pretreatment may lead to premature fouling and cleaning problems. Once the basic system parameters are established, a set of comparison trials without prefilters can be run to determine if the pretreatment is necessary.

2. Mass Balance: Determine how the system is to be monitored. Flow may be calculated by weight or volume, concentration by direct measurement, turbidity, or other methods. If the mass of the permeate plus that of the concentrate does not total that of the initial process material, it indicates something wrong either with the measurement technique or with the system.

3. Initial Study: In order to determine the correct system operating parameters for a specific process, a series of pilot studies should be run with the process fluid. A typical study of this kind recommended by one manufacturer of hollow-fiber modules includes the following:

An initial cleaning cycle
The flux test
A recirculation rate study
A cleaning cycle
A repeat of the flux test [22]

The recirculation rate study consists of stabilizing the process temperature and feed inlet pressure at specific values, and then varying the outlet pressure to observe the effect on flux. Because the permeate flow rate is related to the combined effects of recirculation flow rate and pressure, it can be changed by adjusting the outlet pressure while maintaining a fixed inlet pressure.

The trial should be run at varying recovery percentages:

$$\% \text{ recovery} = \frac{\text{volume permeate}}{\text{volume original}} \times 100$$

A procedure for a sample recirculation rate study is as follows:

1. Stabilize the feed fluid temperature at 70°C. Start the system and maintain 25 psi inlet pressure and 5 psi outlet pressure until 20% recovery is reached.
2. Return the permeate line to the holding tank to maintain the system in a steady state during the test. Wait 2—5 min before collecting flux data to allow the system to stabilize.
3. Measure and record the flux at this pressure, and take samples of the filtrate and retentate.
4. Increase the outlet pressure to 10 psi, then 15 psi, and finally 20 psi, allowing the system to stabilize and repeating step 3 after each pressure increase.
5. Decrease the outlet pressure to the initial value of 5 psi, and check the permeate flux. If this value does not agree with that of the recorded in step 3 (±10%), it indicates a high-fouling process stream, and consequently that prefiltration is necessary or that a different membrane or a higher recirculation flow rate should be used.
6. From these data, determine the differential pressure that produces the greatest flux. Adjust the system to this pressure, remove the permeate line from the holding tank, and continue to concentrate the feed. It is very important that a constant temperature be maintained during these trials.
7. Continue to concentrate until 50% recovery is reached. Repeat steps 2—6 at this point.
8. Repeat steps 2—6 at 75% recovery and at 90% recovery.

The system should then be cleaned according to the manufacturer's recommendation. Following the cleaning cycle, repeat the clean fluid flux test to determine the effectiveness of the cleaning procedure.

The data should be analyzed by plotting on semilogarithmic graph paper. The X axis is the log of the concentration factor (cf), a dimensionless number representing the degree of concentration of the retained components in the feed stream:

$$cf = \frac{\text{volume feed}}{\text{volume concentrate}} = \frac{\text{volume feed}}{\text{volume feed} - \text{volume permeate}}$$

or

$$cf = \frac{1}{1 - r} \qquad \text{where } r = \text{recovery (Eq. 15)}$$

The Y axis is the flux in gal/ft^2/day or liters/m^2/hr. Determine the pressure differential where the greatest flux was obtained, and analyze the samples to see if membrane performance was acceptable at all concentration levels.

A second trial should be run in the same way to check the reproducibility of the data.

3. Cleaning

There are three general methods for cleaning a UF system.

Reverse Flow: Usually used in tubular or hollow-fiber systems, the reverse flow method involves reversing the direction of flow through the feed channels to clean away material deposited on the membrane. Use of this method involves no extra validation effort except assurance of integrity, since all activity is carried out upstream of the membrane.

Backflush: The nature of some process streams requires a reverse flow through the membrane with permeate, buffer, or cleaning agents to remove fouling material. Most UF systems either have an integral backflush apparatus or can be easily modified. This must be validated in the same way as the crossflow backflush apparatus.

Cleaning Agents: Depending on the membrane, many types of cleaning agents can be used. These include dilute acids and bases, oxidizing agents such as H_2O_2, and enzyme preparations such as Tergazyme. The system should be thoroughly rinsed after cleaning. If water is the rinse agent, soft water should be used, as hard water can cause precipitation and fouling with some cleaning agents. A soft water rinse is also required if sodium hypochlorite is used as a sanitizing agent.

4. Storage

Most hydrophilic membranes cannot be allowed to dry out. If not in use, they should be stored as recommended by the manufacturer. Storage solutions include 10% ethanol, 1–2% formaldehyde solution, or other bacteriostatic agents. If flat membranes are used, they should be marked so that the "skin" side is obvious, to avoid confusion later.

V. SUMMARY

This chapter has provided an overview of the problems that may be encountered in choosing, installing, and validating various types of filter systems. It should again be emphasized that the material in Chapter 17 covering specifications, design, and theory of validation has not been repeated here, and that chapter should be read in conjunction with this one.

In Section II, the theory and practical applications of microporous crossflow filtration were discussed. Special attention has been given to the ways in which this process differs from conventional sterilizing filtration. The removal of bacterial endotoxins by filtration was discussed in Section III. Three types of filters for this purpose were described, with the specific advantages and drawbacks of each. Section IV covered the subject of ultrafiltration, describing the types of membranes, operating systems, and test procedures used to separate solutes on a molecular level.

VI. DEFINITIONS AND ABBREVIATIONS

AHM   Adsorptive hydrophilic (micro)filtration (filter): a membrane that removes endotoxin by hydrophobic interaction with the Lipid A portion of the LPS molecule.

Anisotropic membrane   A membrane that displays a marked change in pore size from one surface to the other. The surface with the smaller pores is generally used on the upstream side.

CEM   Charge-enhanced membrane (filter): a membrane whose natural charge has been made more electropositive by treatment with a cationic resin or by other chemical means.

Cf   Concentration factor.

CF   Crossflow filtration (filter): any filter system in which the process stream is introduced tangential to (parallel to) the membrane surface.

CMD   Charge-modified depth (filter): a depth filter (as opposed to a membrane) that has been treated to produce a net positive charge in the media.

CMF   Conventional membrane filtration (filter); use of a microporous membrane filter in a "dead-end" mode, with the process stream flowing perpendicular to the membrane.

DI   Deionized water.

EDTA   Ethylenediaminetetraacetic acid.

EM   Electron microscopy.

Flux   Volume of filtrate produced per unit area of filter surface per time, such as $gal/ft^2/day$.

GNB   Gram-negative bacteria.

MF   Microporous filtration (filter): a membrane filter that will remove suspended particles 0.1 μm and larger.

MW   Molecular weight.

MWCO   Molecular weight cutoff.

ng   Nanogram (10^{-9} g).

NMWL   Nominal molecular weight limit.

Laminar flow   A flow condition in which all elements of the fluid are moving in parallel planes.

LPS   Lipopolysaccharide.

LRV   Log reduction value: $\log_{10}$(challenge concentration)/(filtrate concentration).

Permeate   That portion of the process stream which passes through the membrane.

Retentate   That portion of the crossflow filtration process stream which does not pass through the membrane.

Reynolds number   A nondimensional quantity that indicates if flow in a confined space is laminar or turbulent.

RO   Reverse osmosis: a process used to separate solutes of less than 1000 MW from a solvent.

Shear rate   The velocity gradient of a circulating fluid at the flow channel surface.

UF   Ultrafiltration (filter): a filter capable of separating solutes of 1000— 1,000,000 MW from a solvent.

WFI   Water-for-injection.

Zeta potential (as used)   The effective net charge (can be positive or negative).

VII. SYMBOLS

ΔP	Pressure differential
ΔP_H	Hydrodynamic pressure gradient
ΔP_T	Transmembrane pressure gradient
N_R	Reynolds number
V	Velocity
P	Fluid density
n	Viscosity
D	Diameter of flow channel
b	Height of flow channel
τ^w	Wall shear stress
$\dot{\gamma}$	Shear rate
J	Flux

REFERENCES

1. Bickmore, W. D., Champa, R. A., and Olson, W. P. 1977. *Pharm. Technol. 6*:55.
2. Sears, F. W., in *Mechanics, Wave Motion and Heat*, Chap. 15, pp 410–411.
3. Popp, D. M. 1983. *Filtration and Separation*, March/April.
4. Gerba, C. P., Hou, K. C., Babineau, R. A., and Fiore, J. V. 1980. *Pharm. Technol.*, June.
5. Ostericher, E. A. 1977. U.S. Patent No. 4,007,113.
6. Hou, K. C., Gerba, C. P., Goyal, S. M., and Zerda, K. S. 1980. *Appl. Environ. Microscop., 40*: 892–896.
7. Raistrick, J. H. 1982. *Proc. World Filtration Conf. III*, Vol. 1. 310–315.
8. Robinson, J. R., O'Dell, M. C., Takacs, J., Barnes, T., and Genovesi, C. 1982. Removal of endotoxins by adsorption to hydrophobic microporous media, presented at the PDA Annual Meeting, Philadelphia, Pa.
9. N_{66} *Posidyne Filter Users Manual*, Pall Corp., Glen Cove, N.Y.
10. Kanazek, Conforti, and Jackson, 1980. *Environ. Sci. Technol. 15*, August.
11. Nelson, L. L. 1978. *Pharm. Tech.*, May.
12. Hannecart-Pokorni, E., DeKegel, D., and Dupuydt, F. 1973. *Eur. J. Biochem. 38*.
13. Sweadner, K. J., Forte, M., and Nelson, L. L. 1977. *Appl. Environ. Microscop.*, October. pp 382–385.
14. Zimmerman, G., Kruger, D., and Woog, H. 1976. *Drugs Made in Germany*, Vol. 19. pp 123–128
15. Koppensteiner, G., Kruger, D., Osmers, K., Pauli, W., Woog, H., and Zimmerman, G. 1976. *Drugs Made in Germany*, Vol. 19. pp 113–123.

16. Tutunjian, R. S.   1981.   Ultrafiltration in the pharmaceutical industry, presented at the Pharmaceuticals and Cosmetics Expo, Chicago.
17. Michaels, A. S.   1968.   In *Progress in Separation and Filtration*, Vol. 1.   pp 297—334.
18. Gregor, H. P., and Gregor, C. D.   1978.   *Sci. Am.*, July.
19. Breslau, B. R.   1982.   Ultrafiltration—Theory and practice, presented at the Corn Refiners Assoc. Conf.
20. Amicon Ultrafiltration Catalogue.
21. Hayward, M. F.   1982.   *Proc. World Filtration Conf. III.*   pp 572—583.
22. Romicon, Inc., Pilot Plant Manual, Food and Pharmaceutical Applications, Rev. F-0779.
23. Olson, W. P., Eras, M. H., and Parks, R. G.   1982.   *Proc. World Filtration Conf. III.*   pp 484—490.

19

Validation of New Formulations

J. PATRICK JEATER* and ROBERT A. JACOBS

Wyeth Laboratories, Paoli, Pennsylvania

I. INTRODUCTION

The validation work that should be performed on new products to assure that manufacturing processes do what they purport to do can be divided logically into four parts:

1. Developmental validation
2. Prospective validation
3. Retrospective validation
4. Revalidation

The first of these parts refers to validation information that should be gathered during the development of a product before full-scale manufacture, the second to data gathered at full scale; the third may be performed by analyzing data and information gathered consistently over a long time period during which many production-sized batches have been manufactured; and finally, revalidation is the appropriate term when some specific changes to the product formula or its method of manufacture have taken place.

The minutiae of the tasks involved with this validation work may differ from company to company depending on the manner in which the responsible departments are organized and, moreover, the names of these sections may vary among companies.

The following example of the organization of the departments involved in validation work may help with comprehending the thoughts behind this chapter.

The Pharmacy Research and Development department is responsible for product formulation work at an R&D scale with batch sizes of up to approximately 20 kg or liters. The Pilot Plant, which may also be a Pharmacy R&D division, usually processes requests when clinical trial materials are required over approximately 20 kg or liters and is involved when products are to be taken from R&D weights and volumes and are to be increased to full-scale

---

Current affiliation: ICI United Kingdom, Macclesfield, Cheshire, England.

manufacturing. The fact that both of the above groups ultimately report to the same individual ensures some continuity of purpose and action.

The Manufacturing, Quality Assurance, and Engineering departments are inextricably involved with prospective, retrospective, and revalidation sections of new product validation, and their relationships to the R&D department do not need to be elaborated upon here.

This chapter provides an approach to the validation work that is considered to be necessary from the point where a product undergoes clinical trials through market introduction and up to a change in production batch size. That all of this work should come under this chapter heading is supported by Rifino [1]. He considered that changes in batch size, equipment for production, excipients, raw material, and several other items should cause a product to be considered "new" and therefore be considered cause for further validation work.

Figure 1 illustrates the four stages of validation work that were outlined earlier overlaid on a timetable of events. This timetable stretches from the filling of an Investigatory New Drug (IND) application to a point after production at full scale. The length of time covered in this diagram varies depending on the information required by the federal Food and Drug Administration (FDA). A glossary of abbreviations encountered in this chapter follows:

ALP   Automatic Liquid Packaging
FDA   Food and Drug Administration
GTR   General Technical Report
IND   Investigatory New Drug
NF   National Formulary
NDA   New Drug Application
RPP   Report for Pilot Plant
RPPE   Report of Pilot Plant Experience
RPS   Report for Product Specifications
SOP   Standard Operating Procedure
USP   United States Pharmacopeia

The remainder of this chapter gives details of the validation work thought to be necessary at the various stages shown on Figure 1.

II. DEVELOPMENTAL VALIDATION

First, it must be assumed that after the filing of the IND, a formulation strategy has been chosen. Although the Marketing department may suggest the type of formulation that would be desirable (e.g., freeze-dried, dry powder, etc.), an R&D function probably will have decided upon a type of formulation.

The value of the concept of Developmental Validation type work was detailed by Samyn [2]. Noting that the future need to validate the process of new drug production has a heavy impact on Research and Development functions, he described a method of investigating critical steps in product manufacture.

A critical step was defined as "one that is likely or probably to be a cause of an unacceptable product," and the blending step in a low-dose product was provided as an example.

It was pointed out that R&D information describing strengths and weaknesses of formulas and manufacturing attempts was of great importance. The information, therefore, should form the basis on which future validation is

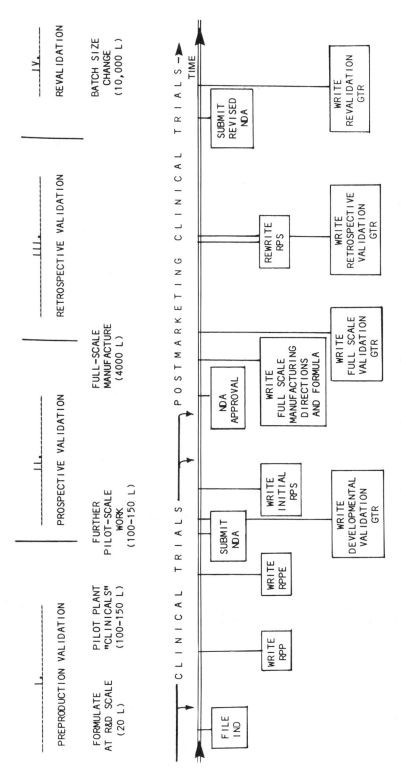

FIGURE 1   Validation and other milestones in new product manufacture.

built and must therefore exist as a formal report. This basic philosophy may be carried out starting with pilot-scale batch sizes.

The process of validation begins in the Pilot Plant upon receipt of a technical report that is called a Report for the Pilot Plant (RPP). It should be realized that the names for these types of report will vary from company to company. (A general synopsis of the reports that should be used in the process of validating a new product is shown in Table 1.) This document is written by the Pharmacy R&D department and contains the recommended formula and manufacturing directions as its most important information. Both items have their origin in the IND sections entitled "Articles Used as Components of," "Statement of Composition," and "Manufacturing Directions." Other details given in the RPP can include the processing history, physical and analytical data, and some limited stability data.

In agreement with Samyn's [2] points about "strengths and weaknesses," the processing history will document success *and* failures encountered during the development of the final formula and manufacturing directions. That the failures should be documented may be surprising, until it is remembered that a successful product may be in production for a long time period. Almost inevitably the personnel involved with the product will change, and expertise and information should not be lost as a result. For example, the reasons for choosing a sterile freeze-dried product over a solution dosage form should be described. Physical data include results from tests for such properties as clarity, color, and viscosity upon reconstitution. A variety of analytical testing is performed, including assay, content uniformity, and moisture content, for example. Stability studies have also been initiated on the formulation and, although not complete, some data may be included.

The information contained in the RPP is used for two purposes: first, to control the manufacture of the product that is to be used in clinical trials; and second, for the scale-up and validation work that is performed by the Pilot Plant subdivision. Equipment and batch size differences that exist between the formulation group of Pharmacy R&D and the Pilot Plant may mean that the manufacturing directions will need to be "interpreted" for use with the larger-scale equipment. For example, the former may use a beaker with stirring bar, while the latter will use a tank and agitator equipped with a tachometer. Some detailed, mathematically oriented comments about the scale-up factors associated with this type of work have been given by Carstensen and Mehta [3] in their article specifically related to manufacture of solution dosage forms. While changes may be made to the manufacturing directions, the number of changes in the formulation are minimized and limited to situations where the formulation fails to meet analytical specifications, or exhibits poor manufacturability or stability.

The formula and manufacturing directions supplied in the Report for Pilot Plant are usually used in the manufacture of supplies for clinical trials. However, it should be noted that the manufacture of clinical supply materials is usually divided between the Pilot Plant and the formulations group. The formulations group manufactures supplies for small-scale studies, i.e., less than 30,000 dosages, while the Pilot Plant handles the larger volumes. Both groups may make minor improvements in the manufacturing directions during the manufacture of clinical supplies, although formal scale-up work may not yet have begun. Further, it can be the case that clinical lots are useful for scale-up purposes.

The scale-up process will involve as many trials as necessary to establish what will be a satisfactory, reproducible, full-scale method of manufacturing an acceptable product. Hence, these trials will encompass changes (improvements and optimization) and of course, validation carried out in the same manner as that used for production batches. Batch sizes, which are usually in the 100–150-kg or liter range, are normally determined by equipment size, raw material availabilities, and economic consideration for these pilot-scale batches. Process changes, improvements, and optimization are carried out in this scale-up phase during the evaluation of the selected manufacturing method. Obviously, the method must yield a product that is satisfactory from physical and chemical standpoints. For example, this should include evaluation of such criteria as distribution of active ingredient (for freeze-dried or aseptic solid dosage form), chemical uniformity, and identity.

Mixing times and speeds should be established for optimal distribution of actives and excipients. Agitator speeds and filter porosities should be evaluated to produce a formulation with optimum characteristics from manufacturing and stability standpoints. In the same time period, attempts are usually made to minimize the number and complexity of processing steps. Validation work is usually performed once the final manufacturing procedure has been established. Usually one lot of product is validated at the pilot scale.

The completed scale-up work is then reported in a technical document that is referred to as a Report of Pilot Plant Experience (RPPE). This document contains processing details, physical and analytical data, and the recommended formula and manufacturing directions. As is the case with the Pharmacy R&D report (RPP), mentioned earlier, this report also documents both failures and successes for the same reasons given earlier.

For continuity, the physical and analytical data provided in this document should be the same as those given in the Report for Pilot Plant. The recommended formula and manufacturing directions are integral parts of this document and are used to generate the Report for Product Specifications (RPS) and parts of the New Drug Application (NDA). The specific sections concerned in the latter include "Articles Used as Components of," "Statement of Composition of," and "Methods and Processes" [4].

Validation performed at Pilot Plant scale is aimed at evaluating the same parameters that would be investigated at full scale. These include, but are not limited to:

1. Mixing: The agitator rpm and mixing time must be determined. Details of agitator shape and size should be provided. Analytical data concerning the distribution of active ingredients in suspensions, for example, would be generated.
2. Blending: Length of time of blending, rotational speed of the blender shell (in the cases of twin shell or twin cone blenders), intensifier or pin bars if used, and percent loading of the blender are of major concern. Blend analysis should be performed, including uniformity of active ingredients, particle size analysis, and density measurements, especially with aseptic powders.
3. Communition: The machine parameters of concern here are chamber speed, blade configuration, feed rate, and screen size. For certain products, heat buildup and protection of the material before and after milling should also be taken into consideration. Of course, particle size analysis, and bulk density (and perhaps uniformity of active ingredients) should be used as product measures.
4. Drying: Temperature, temperature distribution, and the length of drying time should be measured. If a vacuum cycle is to be used, the

TABLE 1 Validation Reports: Origin and Content

Report title	Report generated by	Information contained therein	Information used for
RPP (Report for Pilot Plant)	Pharmacy R&D Formulation group	Chosen formula and small-scale manufacturing directions	Manufacturing of clinical supplies
		Cleaning procedures	Help with pilot studies in scale-up/validation/FDA documentation
		Processing history successes/failures	
RPPE (Report of Pilot Plant Experience)	Pharmacy R&D Pilot Plant Subdivision	Recommended formula and scaled-up manufacturing directions	NDA general formula/manufacturing directions
		Processing history successes/failures	Report for Product Specifications (RPS)
			Generation of validation document
			FDA documentation

RPS (Report for Product Specification)	Pilot Plant sub-division with approval by: Quality Assurance Engineering Manufacturing Other R&D groups	Formula Manufacturing directions Packaging directions/components Testing standards Raw material specifications	Generation of full scale Formula Manufacturing directions Packaging specifications Testing standards Cleaning
PPVR (Pilot Plant Validation Report)	Pharmacy R&D Pilot Plant sub-division	Validation information at pilot scale	Information for FDA
GTR (Prospective Validation / General Technical Report)	Pharmacy R&D Pilot Plant sub-division	Full-scale validation work	Information for FDA
SOP (Standard Operating Procedures)	General Administration groups	Procedures for operation, cleaning (etc.) equipment	Training, etc.

vacuum and the length of time of application of vacuum should be monitored using Karl Fischer or loss-on-drying techniques for example. A useful comparison of various moisture measuring techniques is given by Vemuri [5].

Using the data gathered during the monitoring of these and other parameters, a validation document is generated. This document is a separate entity from the technical report that is written about the experience gained during scale-up. The information from both reports is used in two additional ways: first as a basis for the formula and general manufacturing directions that may be used for submission to the FDA as part of an NDA; and second in generating a Report for Product Specifications. This RPS document is the backbone of the system used to control production at full scale.

As an example of typical validation and scale-up work, consider a new freeze-dried antibiotic formulation. This starts with the receipt of an RPP. The Pilot Plant may then interpret the manufacturing directions covering this freeze-dried formulation, and a decision to combine the validation and scale-up work is then developed. Batch sizes are chosen based on availability and cost of active ingredients and on equipment size and availability. Two scale-up trials may be performed, one to determine manufacturability and adjust the manufacturing directions and a second to incorporate modifications, validation, and manufacture of stability samples. All phases of the manufacture of the second lot would be validated. Some of the parameters monitored for validation of a freeze-dried antibiotic would be mixing, drying, and freezing times, vacuum levels, and shelf temperature. From these data, separate validation and scale-up General Technical Reports (GTRs) will be written.

Some of the safeguards inherent in this system are highlighted at this point. The Report for Pilot Plant documents the experience gained at small scale (volumes up to 20 liters, for example). The Report of Pilot Plant Experience documents work up to 100–150 liters using equipment with the same configurations as those to be used at full scale.

Another responsibility for Pilot Plant is validation of the cleaning procedures for equipment used in the manufacture of clinical/experimental dosage forms. The need for such work is obvious when taking into account the hazardous nature of some experimental compounds and the potentially serious consequences of cross-contamination of clinical materials if cleaning procedures are not sufficient to guarantee that the amount of residual active compound has been reduced to a safe level. Many of the methods for validating cleaning procedures at the full scale are used in validating at the pilot scale.

Within Pharmacy Research and Development three approaches have been taken for determination of residual active components:

1. Measurement of the amount of active in a given amount of rinse water or solvent rinse.
2. Swabbing various parts of the equipment used with a solvent-impregnated swab and quantitating the residual active.
3. The manufacture of a placebo batch after cleaning has been performed. This should involve the use of all of the pieces of equipment used in the active batch. Measurement of the active in the final dosage of the placebo batch thus clarifies the efficiency of cleaning of all parts.

It should be realized that there are other approaches that can be taken, including the reduction of bioburden by cleaning activities.

III. PROSPECTIVE VALIDATION

At this point it is assumed that data for the Report of Pilot Plant Experience (RPPE) and Developmental Validation documents have been gathered, although the actual documents may not have been completed and signed by the appropriate individuals in the approval system. From this work, the general manufacturing directions necessary for the New Drug Application (NDA) can be written.

It is best to write these directions in general terms so that later, minor changes to the manufacturing directions can be carried out without revising the NDA. Ideally, the Validation Department, if it is separate from the department responsible for writing the directions, should be cognizant of these directions to ensure that when approval is granted, they contain nothing untoward that requires alteration before validation work can be performed.

During this time period, a document called a Report for Product Specifications (RPS) is written. This document is broken down into several stages covering the following items:

1. Formula
2. Manufacturing directions
3. Packaging components
4. Testing standards and raw material specifications

This document is important since it covers all of the items that can possibly be changed to affect product quality with respect to analytical and physical parameters. Hence, it is an important method of change control. As it is such an important document, it is circulated for approval signatures to the upper management of R&D, Quality Assurance, and Manufacturing. It is conceivable that other disciplines, for example, Regulatory Affairs, Engineering, Packaging, and Purchasing, may be involved with the system of approval, depending on the nature of the RPS.

The depth of the involvement of the Validation Department will vary from company to company. For example, the involvement with the formula segment will be small if the validation department is production-oriented. Conversely, involvement may be large if the validation group reports through an R&D department.

The formula will obviously be basically that which has been successful from the clinical trials and which has been scaled-up in pilot-scale validation trials. The formula itself is written with generic names with quantities for a single dose and those for the likely production batch size. An example is shown in Table 2. It will be noticed here that examples of NF or USP generic ingredients are given and that the formula may vary slightly depending on the assay of the active and pH adjustment ingredients. Indeed, in other instances, the percentage of diluents may be altered slightly to aid with manufacturability of the product.

The manufacturing directions section of the initial RPS will also be written employing generic instructions. An example of a typical set of manufacturing directions is given in Table 3.

An example of the involvement with packaging directions can be taken from operation of an Automatic Liquid Packaging (ALP) machine where liquids are aseptically filtered and filled directly into plastic bottles that are formed, filled, and sealed on one machine. Typically, Validation involvement for this type of process should be to ensure that the correct types of liquid and air

TABLE 2 Freeze-Dried Formulation

	Per dose	Ingredient	Per 500,000 dosages
	2.0 mg	Active ingredient[a]	1.0 kg
	100.0 mg	Lactose, USP[a]	50.0 kg
	1.0 mg	Potassium dihydrogen phosphate[b]	0.5 kg
	4900 mg	Water-for-injection	2450.0 kg
Solution wt.	5003.0 mg	Total	2501.5 kg
Dry wt.	103.0 mg		51.5 kg

[a]If the active ingredient assays less than 98% on an "as-is" basis, adjust up to 98% and reduce the lactose accordingly.

[b]This ingredient is used for pH adjustment. Less than 0.5 kg should be used.

TABLE 3 Freeze-Dried Formulation: Manufacturing Directions

1. Add water-for-injection into a suitable holding tank equipped with an agitator.
2. While agitating slowly, add the active ingredient and lactose.
3. Agitate slowly for 30 min.
4. Collect a sample for dissolution testing.
5. Continue agitating and adjust the solution pH to between 7.0 and 7.2 by the addition of potassium dihydrogen phosphate.
6. Connect the tank outlet aseptically to sterilize 0.2 μ filter system.
7. Pass the solution through the filter system and into a sterile holding tank.
8. Aseptically collect and submit a sample of sterile solution for Quality Assurance testing.
9. Fill sterilized vials with approximately 5 ml of filtered solution (as determined by assay in step 8) and partially plug with a suitable closure.
10. Load filled vials from step 9 onto trays and then into a freeze-drier.
11. Freeze-dry under normal conditions.
12. Automatically seat the closures.
13. Remove trays from freeze-dryer.
14. Seal vials with aluminum crimps.
15. Sample for Quality Assurance testing.

filters are employed, that correct flow rates are used, and that the filters are challenged with *Ps. diminuta* (or some other suitable microorganism), extractables tested where necessary, and suitably sterilized before use.

Involvement with the testing standards can extend to assistance with specifications related to the numbers of particles remaining in liquid products that have been filtered. Involvement of Validation personnel with analytical testing standards can be contentious, since this may be considered to be the domain of the analytical chemist. Obviously, since areas of expertise and organizational control vary among companies, the amount of Validation involvement will also be different from company to company. Nevertheless, each test procedure must be validated.

The same comment can also be applied to the final part of the overall RPS system, the raw material specifications. Although it has not always been the case, it is not difficult to see that a new source of raw materials could be construed as the cause of a revalidation exercise. One comment to this effect [6] noted that the same raw material from three different suppliers revealed remarkably different properties. One effect of the Validation group on testing standards, therefore, could be to add tests to help monitor for differences that may adversely affect manufacturability and stability of the product.

One final point that has not been covered in the past five items: cleaning. This topic has recently assumed a greater importance [7], and indeed it is mandatory to have cleaning procedures in written form and to perform tests on final rinse waters, for example, to show absence of active ingredients. The instructions may appear in standard operating procedure (SOP) format and may even become part of the manufacturing directions under certain circumstances. Validation of cleaning procedures at scale-up and at full scale should be performed, taking into consideration that the cleaning agents and methods of cleaning [manual, automatic clean-in-place (CIP)] may be different at each scale.

An initial RPS for a new product therefore entails a great deal of work from several departments, including the Validation department. It can be seen that careful attention to details will be necessary before approval of a procedure is given. Once approved, the appropriate parts of the document are then used for the writing of a master copy of the formula and manufacturing directions that will be used for full-scale manufacture of product. In this copy of the formula and manufacturing directions, trade names are normally mentioned as the primary name in addition to the generic names given in the RPS documents. This is because drums of raw material that may be used for trade-sized batches are normally labeled most prominently with trade names. For example, microcrystalline cellulose may be labeled Avicel, and Polysorbate 80 as Tween 80. The trade names appear as the more prominent labels, and it is these that are normally used in the formula and manufacturing instructions that are followed in production work.

The first few batches of any new product manufactured at full scale should be allocated an increased amount of investigatory and supervisory time, preferably by the persons who have been performing the scale-up work. The first few batches can be labeled accordingly (for example, "Pilot Batch"), to indicate to all who are concerned that the manufacture of these batches will be overseen by the responsible scale-up personnel. The "Pilot Batch" label also enables extra instructions to be written in if necessary by the appropriate responsible individuals or staff. The number of batches that are labeled "Pilot," and indeed the number of batches that are required for validation purposes, varies depending on the "newness" of the product and the complexity

of the problems related to production. It is obvious that the minimum requirement to show repeatability for validation work must be two batches. But the
necessity for an upper limit or the "at least three" figure that has been received wide publicity is a debatable issue. Whatever the number of replicates
chosen, the choice should be governed by sound scientific judgment of particular circumstances.

It should be noted at this point that this full-scale work may be performed
before the NDA has been formally approved. If this occurs, it is obvious
that the company will have taken a calculated risk so that the new product
may be introduced to the marketplace as soon after NDA approval as possible.

Hence, this full-scale validation work could assume some added importance
because of this risk.

There are several steps that are taken during this full-scale validation
work, and these will now be described in some detail. These steps are listed
below:

1. Review formula and manufacturing directions and decide which steps
   in the manufacturing procedure are "critical."
2. Decide type and number of samples to be taken at the critical steps
   in the product manufacture.
3. Before production, ensure that the apparatus to be used is suitable
   for the purpose and is checked or calibrated. (This assumes that a
   suitable calibration scheme is in operation—an important point.)
   (See step 6.)
4. Sample all raw materials.
5. Sample in-process materials.
6. Time, measure, and check all apparatus during production when filled
   with product; investigate cleaning procedures.
7. Analyze in-process, final product, and cleaning samples.
8. Check results for suitability.
9. Write report.

A. Review of Formula and Manufacturing Directions

In reviewing the formula, decisions must be made regarding the sampling and
analysis of the raw materials to be used for the product. The raw materials
should be examined to determine if they are typical of their kind. At this
point, other samples of the same material used for other formulations that
have already been validated may be useful for comparison purposes. This is
discussed further in Section D. Manufacturing directions should be reviewed
so that decisions can be taken regarding (a) the "critical" steps that require
investigation, (b) those that do not have significant impact on the product,
and (c) equipment parameters that should be monitored. Many sets of manufacturing directions can be shortened to help produce a better idea of the
work to be tackled. For example, the instructions given in Tables 3 and 4
may be summarized as follows:

Freeze-dried formulation	Dry powder fill formulation
1. Prepare solution	1. Prepare solution
2. Filter-sterilize the solution	2. Filter-sterilize solution and acetone
3. Fill solution into containers	3. Crystallize

Freeze-dried formulation	Dry powder fill formulation
4. Freeze-dry	4. Centrifuge
	5. Oven-dry
	6. Fill into containers

This has the effect of breaking down manufacturing directions into a set of unit processes that can then be investigated using a set of broad protocols for each process. During the process of reviewing the manufacturing directions, it will become obvious that there are several items that need qualifying for use before the manufacture of these products. In these examples those items include:

1. Water-for-injection system (step 1, Table 3)
2. The filter used for "sterilization" (step 6, Table 3, and step 9, Table 4)
3. The vent filters used on holding tanks (step 7, Table 3, and step 12, Table 4)
4. The freeze-dryer (step 11, Table 3)
5. The oven (step 13, Table 4)
6. The dry powder filler (step 15, Table 4)

These items should be the subject of separate Installation and Operation Qualification reports that can be referred to in the reporting of the validation work performed on these new products. For example, the validation of a sterile dry powder fill facility was covered by Prout [8]. Indeed, details on validation of most of these items are the subject of other chapters of this book.

TABLE 4   Dry Powder Fill Formulation Manufacturing Directions

The first eight steps in this procedure are identical to those given in Table 3.

9. Add the acetone through a sterile 0.2 μm filter to the solution from step 8.

10. Add a suitable number of sterile crystals of active ingredient to the solution to induce crystallization.

11. Allow to stand for 2 hr.

12. Pass the crystalline suspension from step 11 through a centrifuge and collect the crystals in sterile stainless steel bins.

13. Vacuum-dry the product for 24 hr at 36°C (±1°C).

14. Collect and submit a sample of the dried product for Quality Assurance testing.

15. Fill the dried product into suitable, sterile vials. (Product in vials should weigh 103 ± 3 mg.)

16. Collect and submit samples of filled vials for Quality Assurance testing.

B. Sampling Plans

Decisions must next be made about the number and type of samples to be taken at the critical manufacturing steps and what analysis needs to be performed. Considering the production of a blend of sterile solids, two types of samples are normally necessary, the first for content uniformity of active ingredients and the second for particle size analysis and possibly bulk or tap density measurements.

The content uniformity sampling can be problematical. Ideally, analysis for the active ingredient should be performed on a quantity of the blend equivalent to one pharmacologically active dose. In this case about 5000 mg is required, but if the blend is at all affected by static electricity, the analytical results can be erroneous, because the active ingredient can adhere to spatulas, sample bottles, sample thieves, etc., reducing the apparent active content in the analytical sample. Because of this it is always advisable to take at least duplicates of all content uniformity samples, and maybe even "train" the analyzing chemists in what to expect by testing samples from developmental work.

The number of content uniformity samples to take can lead to many arguments. Many sampling plans hinge on the $\sqrt{n + 1}$ example, and this is always a useful standby plan. However, if there are likely to be problems with a sampling method yielding too few samples to be of use, sample plans can be devised depending on the method of production. If a product is filled into drums after a sterile blend, for example, then these can be sampled at top, center, and bottom—in duplicate, of course—to yield a statistically significant number of samples for analytical purposes. In the freeze-dried formulation detailed in Tables 2 and 3, sampling is performed at step 4 to ensure that the, ingredients have dissolved. A further sampling step could be to ensure that the pH adjustment additive is in solution. Step 8 is present to ensure that the product that was passed through the filter system is sterile and for assay and content uniformity of the active ingredient. The minimum number of samples to be taken here for sterility testing purposes is detailed in USP [9]. Finally, the finished product in vials is also tested at step 15.

With the dry powder fill product (Tables 4 and 5), in addition to the samples already taken at steps 4, 8, 14, and 16, samples could be taken before and after the seeding with crystals; at various times during the 2-hr crystallization step; before and after centrifuging; and at various times during the 24-hr drying cycle.

C. Equipment Suitability

Before production, it is necessary to ensure that all equipment that is to be used is suitable for the purpose intended. This includes:

1. Materials of construction. Do the ingredients of the product react with the equipment? For example, type 304 stainless steel vessels are not suitable for use with sodium chloride solutions.
2. Cleaning. Has the equipment been checked for residuals of previous actives and the cleaning agents? Did a supervisor check that the cleaning was performed correctly? Was the appropriate paperwork completed to verify this?
3. Instruments. Have they been calibrated? If they are new, have they been added to the instrument calibration list? Are all of the

TABLE 5   Sterile Dry Fill Formulation (from crystallization)

Per dose		Ingredient	Per 500,000 dosages
2.0 mg		Active ingredient	1.0 kg
100.0 mg		Lactose, USP	50.0 kg
1.0 mg		Potassium dihydrogen phosphate	0.5 kg
4900	mg	Water-for-injection	2450.0 kg
7500	mg	Acetone	3750.0 kg
Solution wt. 12503	mg	Total	6251.5 kg

Note: The only difference between this and the freeze-dried formulation (Table 2) is the acetone.

instruments that are required by the manufacturing directions, etc., fitted to the equipment, and are they of sufficient accuracy and easily readable?

D. Sampling Raw Materials

With some dosage forms, sampling raw materials will give an indication of the starting point for some of the in-process test results (if the processing does not call for dissolving the materials). With others, this sampling may help with determining the effect of the processing on the materials.

In some cases, more than one "receiving" of a raw material may be used. For example, where a large proportion of a product is one ingredient, such as propylene glycol, two different suppliers of the raw material may be used in one batch. In this case, if the material from both suppliers has passed the vendor inspection by Quality Assurance, there should be no problems with sampling and testing. Actives that are of the high-potency, low-dose type, found in oral contraceptives, for example, should be sampled and tested by groups specifically trained to examine and test such items.

Overall, a broad picture of raw material evaluation should be developed so that no untoward raw materials are employed in the manufacture of a new product for trade. With new products, pilot-scale validation work will give an invaluable handle on this raw material work. If raw material data bases can be built up over a cross section of products that use common raw materials, this, too, can be helpful.

E. Sampling In-Process Materials

Although some of this area was covered in Section B, and this may seem like stating the obvious to the trained worker, broadly it should be noted that:

1. Blending requires that ingredients are uniformly distributed.
2. Comminution steps will affect the particle size distribution and hence density figures.

3. The drying steps will affect the moisture/solvent content of the materials, but may also have a deleterious effect on the physicochemical composition of actives and other ingredients.
4. Crystallization steps will affect particle size, bulk density, and crystal morphology.
5. Filtration steps should remove microbial and particulate contamination and should not introduce extractables or fibers into the product.

So that an accurate picture of changes or similarities can be produced throughout the processing, in-process sampling of materials should be carried out, noting what is likely to occur with the product at individual steps. This obviously starts with the raw materials section, and comparisons can always be made with pilot-scale work.

F. Measuring Equipment Variables

All equipment variables should be checked when the equipment contains the complete quantity of materials to be manufactured. This will ensure that there are no differences between the operation of the equipment empty and when filled with product. In the examples given in Tables 3 and 4, the following items should be considered:

1. The metering of the water-for-injection should be checked against the weight/volume in the tank.
2. The rpm of the agitator and the type of agitator blade used should be noted.
3. The calibration of the timers used to control the steps that call for "agitate for 30 min" and "dry for 24 hr" should be confirmed.
4. The flow rates of solution through the filters must be controlled.
5. The rpm of the centrifuge and the volume flow rate of the fluid to it must be within specified ranges.
6. The temperature in the dryers, both cold and hot, should be uniform and within specified ranges.
7. The suitable number and weight of sterile seed crystals needed to induce crystallization need to be identified.

Other equipment variables that should be controlled during manufacture include, but are not limited to, comminuting mill chamber speeds, feed rates and screen sizes; amp/watt draw to determine crystallization end points; the length of blending, rotation speed of a blender shell, and the suitability of the blender volume. The fill level of various blender types can be an important matter with a serious effect on the distribution of active ingredients. Too much or too little product can both lead to insufficient interparticle movement and inadequate blending.

IV. RETROSPECTIVE VALIDATION

Having performed and documented validation of developmental and initial full-scale batch sizes, retrospective validation is required when the product has been in production for some time, for example, a period of about 2 years with a successful product. Indeed, it can be argued that this is a requirement of the *Federal Register* [10].

Product sterility is one of the several tests with parenteral products, and the details related to this are included in other parts of this text. It represents an area where retrospective validation is inappropriate.

However, there are several other parts of parenteral product manufacture that can be reviewed from a retrospective standpoint. This can start with the calibration of instruments and programs used for maintaining up-to-date standard operating procedures (SOPs) associated with production equipment.

During the manufacture of a product, there may be a series of steps of the type "Sample the product and submit the sample for Quality Assurance testing." The relatively simple freeze-dried product instructions given in Table 3 include three sampling steps (steps 4, 8 and 15). Additionally, checks on the weight of product may be made at various intermediate steps in manufacture. Therefore, it should be apparent that there is a wealth of information that is gathered for every batch of product manufactured. This is the type of data that can be used for retrospective validation.

Starting with the first full-scale production batch of a new product, a data base of the results from in-process and final dosage testing should be built. These results lend themselves to study using control charting techniques, since the testing standards set for a product while it is still in the R&D stage will have upper and lower acceptance limits specified for the important ingredients. Action and ultimate unacceptability limits have been set up. When a new product data base is built up on this systematic fashion, right from the start of production, it is easy to interrogate it periodically (for example, every 20 batches) in addition to the careful scrutiny afforded individual batches. Control charting techniques can provide an insight into the basic variability of the parameters tested and can allow trends to be spotted before a product gets out of control.

Simms [11], at a Pharmaceutical Manufacturer's Association meeting in 1980, provided information about the validation of existing products on which a great deal of production experience has been gained. However, as detailed in this book and elsewhere [12], there are basic precautions that should be taken so that the results from a retrospective look at data are meaningful. This technique can only be enhanced if prospective validation is performed in development stages and at full scale when the product is still "new."

V. REVALIDATION

The final element of the four parts of new product validation is revalidation. There are many reasons for performing revalidation work; the list below shows some of the more important. Changes to any of these parameters should usually require revalidation:

1. Batch size—increase or decrease
2. Manufacturing equipment
3. Equipment operating parameters
4. Location
5. Raw material manufacturer
6. Method of formulation

7. Formula
8. Analytical technique

Some of these issues were brought out by Rifino [1], who indicated that a product should be considered to be "new" when factors 1, 4, and 7 exist. Points 1, 2, 4, 5, 6, and 7 were also mentioned by Jeater [4] at the same Pharmaceutical Technology Conference session. Overall, there can be no real doubt that when any of the above items change, the product should be considered "new" from a validation standpoint. Elaboration and examples can be given for many of these points.

Batch sizes may need to be changed for many reasons. Increase or decrease in product demand, scale-up from pilot to full scale, and changes in economic ordering quantities of materials are three common explanations. It is reasonable to expect possible blending differences between products manufactured in a 2-ft^3 and a 75-ft^3 blender, for example. How is a change from a 50- to a 75-ft^3 blender viewed, however? What should be done with different sized batches within the same blender? Obviously, companies will differ in their opinion, but the basic premise must be that changes in batch size warrant revalidation or that the product should be considered as new.

Examples of changes to manufacturing equipment and equipment operating parameters with sterile dosage forms are not unusual. A change from a cellulose acetate sterilizing filter to a nylon membrane is one such example. The new type of filter may also be usable at a higher flow rate, and this may allow filling at a faster rate.

An example of an operating parameter change may be necessitated by the mesh size of raw materials from two different suppliers which are passed through a milling step during processing.

The fact that moving a manufacturing location requires revalidation of products as "new" is easily recognized. Most changes in location will mean that equipment will change, and this amplifies the reason for the work.

As discussed earlier in this chapter, changes in raw material suppliers can lead to several problems. The basic premise should be that tight controls are required on the quality of raw materials. Tests should be in position in the Quality Assurance department to monitor the critical parameters of raw materials. If changes are deemed to be necessary in raw material supplier for economic reasons (for example), then studies should be started to revalidate what has essentially become a new product. Differences that are noticeable in critical parameters on the same material from two suppliers can mean that one set of manufacturing directions will not be suitable for material from both suppliers. This comment can be particularly applicable to products that utilize low-dose, high-potency active ingredients. A recent book [13] contains a chapter that may help to shed further light on this topic.

Method of formulation changes are normally so radical that "new product" status should be afforded to the changed product. Such an example can be made with a change of procedure from freeze-dry to sterile dry fill methods of manufacture.

Formula changes may appear to best be treated simply as "new" products, but how should a reduction of active ingredient overage from (say) 3% to 1.5% be treated? It is certain that the answer will differ among companies, but ideally this change should be treated as a revalidation candidate.

Finally, changes to analytical techniques may impinge on validation work. It is well known that equipment used for analyzing products are constantly improving, and that techniques and standards are being changed because of this. So it is possible that products that have been judged to be validated using old analytical methods may become unsatisfactory or unavailable using revised or new methods. Consequently, such products may need to be revised and revalidated.

Any of the items mentioned above will cause the product to be considered as "new." This means that an RPS must be written, justified with a supporting GTR, and the whole process of validation and regenerating data bases will be restarted.

REFERENCES

1. Rifino, C. B. 1982. Process validation of a new solid dosage form product; presented at Pharmaceutical Technology Conference, Validation Session; New York, September.
2. Samyn, J. C. 1980. New product validation begins in Research and Development; in *Proceedings of P.M.A. Seminar on Validation of Solid Dosage Form Processes*; Atlanta, Georgia, May. pp 105–116.
3. Carstensen, J. T., and Mehta, A. 1982. Scale-up factors in the manufacture of solution dosage forms. *Pharm. Technol.* 6(11):64–77.
4. CFR 21, Chapter 1, Subchapter D, part 314.1. pp 85–96.
5. Vemuri, S. 1983. Measurement of moisture contents in tablet granulations. *Pharm. Technol.* 7(9):119–123.
6. Jeater, J. P., and Cullen, L. F. 1982. Revalidation, when, how, why?, presented at Pharmaceutical Technology Conference, Validation Session, New York, September.
7. *GMP Trends.* 1982. Manufacturing controls section. GMP Trends, Inc., Boulder, Col., November 15.
8. Prout, G. 1982. Validation and routine operation of a sterile dry powder filling facility. *J Parenteral Sci. Technol.* 36(5):199–204.
9. Sterility tests—Quantities for liquid articles. USP XX, Section 71, p. 880.
10. C.G.M.P. for finished pharmaceuticals. 1978. *Fed. Reg.*, Part II, Suppl. D., #211.68, Automatic, Mechanical and Electronic Equipment.
11. Simms, L. L. 1980. Validation of existing products by statistical evaluation; in *Proceedings of P.M.A. Seminar on Validation of Solid Dosage Form Processes*; Atlanta, Georgia, May. pp 81–99.
12. Agalloco, J. P. 1983. Practical considerations in retrospective validation. *Pharm. Technol.* 7(6):88–90.
13. Berry, I. R. Process validation of raw materials, in *Pharmaceutical Process Validation*, Loftus, B. T. and Nash, R. A., eds. Marcel Dekker, New York. pp 203–249.

20

Component Preparation Processes

DOMINIC A. VENTURA* and STEPHEN W. GOODSIR

Wyeth Laboratories, West Chester, Pennsylvania

I. INTRODUCTION

A product can only be as good as the container/closure system in which it is packaged. Although this statement is applicable to all dosage forms, it holds a special meaning for parenteral products, which must be maintained sterile and particulate-free throughout their shelf life.

With the advent of validation in the pharmaceutical industry, manufacturers of sterile products have placed emphasis on sterilization since it is one of the most critical aspects of the process. Validation of the component preparation process in many instances has lagged far behind. This may be due in part to the seemingly complex and unending nature of the task.

Unlike sterilization validation, component preparation process validation has no generally accepted method(s) of challenging a given system or procedure. Moreover, because of the diversity of the processes, one cannot expect definitive guidelines or methods from government agencies. The validator is expected to assess the parameter(s) that can be affected by the process and then develop baseline data by which future batches can be measured. For the most part, the validator has been left to his or her own wiles to develop defensible data based on sound judgment and scientific principles.

The purpose of this chapter is to inform the validator of some of the measures that may influence the component preparation process and offer guidelines on which a sound validation program can be built. This chapter will illustrate a general approach to the task. The validator must adapt the validation program to his or her own operation by developing a logical, scientific approach.

No attempt will be made to judge the merits of a specific process. A given process is offered only as an illustration or example. Further, it is presumed throughout the discussion that before process validation is initiated, qualification and calibration of the equipment and instruments have taken place. Such procedures have been discussed elsewhere in this text. Without a comprehensive understanding of the function of the equipment, no sound judgments can be rendered regarding the process to be studied and evaluated.

---

*Current affiliation: Elkins-Sinn, Inc., Cherry Hill, New Jersey.

With these considerations in mind, the chapter is divided into two sections to illustrate the major packaging components of a parenteral product: rubber closure processing and glass component processing.

II. RUBBER CLOSURE PROCESSING

A. General

It has been stated in the literature that the "selection of an appropriate closure for a parenteral product initiates the validation process" [1]. Unfortunately, when one assumes the task of validating existing rubber closures that have been successfully marketed with given products, the validator is required to work with materials previously specified. The composition, design, and processing of the closure should have been carefully considered during the original selection process. The in-depth testing required by today's approach to validation may not have been conducted during the development work with the product and closure at hand. Even under the best of circumstances it is very likely that only basic information may exist regarding the chemical, physical-mechanical properties, or functional characteristics of the closure.

Recently, task groups of the Research Committee of the Parenteral Drug Association have presented comprehensive reviews covering the extraction, performance, and identity characteristics of elastomeric closures in *Technical Bulletin No. 1* and *No. 2* [2,3].

These documents are invaluable to the validator in that they serve to define in precise terms many of the properties and characteristics that are used in the description of closures as well as providing applicable tests and procedures that may be used to evaluate them.

Depending on the type of closure and the intended use, consideration of the following aspects of these properties and characteristics are of interest. Some of the physical and mechanical tests, such as the tensile strength, ultimate elongation, and modulus of elongation, are best applied to the compound itself, since they are of little value in closure specifications.

1. Chemical properties
   a. Composition
      (1) Elastomer
      (2) Vulcanizing agent
      (3) Accelerator
      (4) Activator
      (5) Fillers
      (6) Plasticizers
      (7) Antioxidants
      (8) Lubricants
   b. Extractables (leaches)
   c. Coatings
2. Physical and mechanical properties
   a. Tensile strength
   b. Ultimate elongation
   c. Modulus of elongation
   d. Compression set (permanent set)
   e. Durometer
   f. Solvent resistance
   g. Particulate matter levels

3. Functional characteristics
    a. Dimensions
    b. Coring
    c. Plunger movement, i.e., break-loose and extrusion pressure
    d. Needle penetration
    e. Vacuum retention
    f. Moisture vapor transmission

In the case of rubber closures, many, if not all, of these properties or characteristics have been determined by the rubber manufacturer and, with the possible exception of the quantitative analysis of the rubber, the manufacturer is usually willing to share this information. The vendor should realize that in today's regulatory climate the pharmaceutical manufacturer has a heavy burden placed on him not only to understand and guide his own operation, but to possess in-depth knowledge of the components that he purchases and uses. In some instances, this may require the vendor to reassess what was once considered proprietory aspects of his business.

Before the validator begins to trace the component through his own operation in anticipation of validating washing and processing, he should fully understand what took place at the manufacturer regarding the component and its formulation. This may include, but is not limited to, the following considerations.

1. Formulation
    a. Control methods for formulation and blending operations
2. Molding
    a. Uniformity of compound distribution in mold
    b. Type of mold release or trimming agent
    c. Method, i.e., transfer molding (for small parts), etc.
    d. Controls on presses—timers, heat sensors, etc.
3. Post-molding
    a. Autoclave extraction cycles
    b. Oven post-cure
    c. Inspection

The post-molding processing, for example, could have a pronounced affect on the closure. Autoclave extractions may remove residue or extractables from the compounds, while a high-temperature oven "post-cure" treatment may have been used to compensate for a relatively short molding cycle. Perhaps a low-temperature oven exposure was used to dry the closure prior to shipment. Since the curing reaction is dependent on time and temperature, the state of cure of the molded closure can be readily affected by any of these operations.

Also, any change in the vendor's inspection process could affect the quality of the components. Therefore, the validator must be aware of the extent to which the closure is inspected and for what qualities.

The key word for any components received from the vendor should be consistency. If any or all of the above operations are employed, the vendor must understand that any subtle change in processing could have an affect on the property(ies) or characteristic(s) of the closure used by the customer. The vendor must notify the customer if there are changes in the formula of a given compound. The customer must be informed if a new high-temperature washer/dryer were substituted for more conventional equipment that had been used in the past. A change such as this might improve the extractable or particulate matter quality of a given part, offering an advantage to the customer. But it could also result in a deleterious effect.

B. Warehousing

Once the validator has developed an understanding of the manufacture and handling of the closures by the vendor, he should then proceed to review the warehousing of the closures in his own plant.

In most instances, warehousing of rubber closures by the vendors are held to a minimum. The influence of the storage period at the closure manufacturer's facility is of relatively short duration in comparison to that typically experienced by the parenteral manufacturer. Care must be taken in providing the closures with a suitable environment, in which they are not influenced by their surroundings.

A closure may be adversely affected by such conditions as heat, cold, moisture, ozone, and even attack from chemicals that are stored or dispensed in close proximity to the stored closure. Of these, heat is the most likely condition to affect the component, since heat can reverse the cross-linking of the vulcanization process. This will, of course, alter the physical and mechanical properties of the compound. The adverse affects of heat are discussed further in Section F.

Care must be taken in how the cartons of components are stacked to avoid distortion. Most elastomers possess a memory such that prolonged deformation even under ideal storage conditions can result in stoppers that do not track properly through a stoppering machine or cannula covers that are bowed and cannot be properly mated with a needle.

Improper warehousing can also promote "blooming" of the elastomer. Unfortunately, most of the current rubber components in use by the industry have a tendency to "bloom," i.e., a phenomenon wherein ingredients or complexes of ingredients crystallize on the surface. Many times the rubber formulations are actually designed to perpetuate such "blooms." Helizone, an antiozonite, must bloom to the surface of a compound in order to be effective. Paraffin, although not usually designed to bloom, can be found on the surface of most parts prepared with paraffin-containing compounds. Both these wax-type compounds are particularly sensitive to variable temperature storage, especially cold. The solubility of the waxes in the rubber compound are reduced by exposure to cold, causing the waxes to bloom to the surface.

Another common constituent of rubber is sulfur. The sulfur is usually present in the rubber compound in an excessive quantity, so that a more than adequate amount exists to promote vulcanization during the molding process. The excess sulfur will often bloom, especially when the parts are exposed to elevated temperatures, such as could be encountered in the summer months in an uncontrolled warehouse.

Fortunately, material that blooms to the surface of the rubber stock during warehousing can be removed during the subsequent washing operation. Some parts, such as stoppers, are received from the vendor coated with Teflon or silicone. These parts will be simply divided into suitable containers and sterilized. Any bloom present would be carried along with the stopper. During the dry heat or steam sterilization the bloom may be dispersed over the surface of the part, especially if the material has a relatively low melting point, such as a wax. Although this material will not be apparent on the closure after sterilization, the material could recrystallize after the closure has been installed on the product container, leading to an unacceptable product.

Improper or prolonged warehousing could also affect the coating itself. Studies have shown that the silicone is readily absorbed by the rubber during storage [4]. This would result in a part that could affect the feed rate or jam a stoppering machine.

Because rubber parts age, it is best to purchase and use these components in as short a time frame as possible. A first-in, first-out (FIFO) system is mandatory for all elastomeric components. A maximum storage time in the warehouse should be developed. If parts are held for extended periods of time, the validator may suggest appropriate retests to measure the aging characteristics of the rubber. These periodic retests, in keeping with the established incoming test program, would focus on changes in physical and mechanical properties, such as tensile strength, compression set, and modulus of elongation. This is done to ensure that the stored component is of the same quality and will endure the processing and subsequent sterilization cycles in the manner as "fresh" components. These retests may be specific for a given property, characteristic, constituent, or even coating used on the rubber stock. The absorption of silicone by the rubber cited previously is a prime example with one considers the time delay between manufacture, or in this case, coating of the stock, and its intended use. A minimum acceptable level of the coating must be established so that the parts can be tested periodically to ensure that this level is maintained. This testing can be performed at specific intervals or immediately before the part is used in the production of the final package.

Where subassemblies, such as lined seals, are concerned, or where further mechanical functionality is no longer of concern once the part is introduced to the other component(s), one need not be concerned beyond that point. This is best illustrated by a stopper in a vial. The lubricant must only be present on the surface of the stopper in sufficient quantity to guide the stopper through the assembly equipment into the vial. Once the stopper is seated and a seal is applied, the lubrication has completed its task. This is not true, however, in the case of a closure that must remain mechanically functional or be prepared to be functional during the entire shelf life of the product package. A syringe plunger faces this challenge. Therefore, the quantity of lubricant, e.g., silicone, at the interface between the rubber and the syringe barrel (glass or plastic) must remain constant. If too little silicone is present, the break-loose and extrusion characteristic of the plunger becomes too high to administer the injection properly. Conversely, too much silicone can lead to a low break-loose and extrusion. This may result in product leakage around the plunger while the package is on the shelf, or blow-back may occur during use, i.e., product may be expelled around the plunger instead of through the needle when the plunger is activated.

C. Washing

When considering the washing of small rubber parts for use in contact with dry or liquid parenteral products, one must consider that there are a variety of commonly used devices employed throughout the industry. Many of these devices use unique approaches to cleaning and therefore sometimes pose unique problems to the validator. In most instances, the more involved the process, the more considerations must be addressed.

Unfortunately, many washing methods violently agitate the rubber parts together. While this may serve to cleanse the part of molding residues or particulate matter contamination, such as lint, cardboard fiber, etc., these techniques do little to prevent the generation of particles from the rubber itself. Once the closure has been abraded and the "skin" of the part has been broken, elastomer particles may be generated not only by the washing procedure itself, but throughout subsequent operations, such as may be encountered in the assembly of the part within the final container. The closure may shed particles during sterilization and is especially vulnerable if the product is terminally sterilized. Even lubrication of the part with silicone will not eliminate this potential. In some cases the silicone may only attract the particle to the surface of the rubber long enough for assembly of the package, at which time the particle could be liberated by the contents of the vial. In the case of liquid products this becomes a vial that is rejected for visual particulate matter, or, where a dry powder for reconstitution is concerned, a potential product complaint. In either event, care must be taken during the validation of the process to ensure that the washing process is effective but not abusive. Often, slight adjustments in a given cycle can improve the particulate matter quality of the part. It is therefore critical to determine the optimal process before validating.

The machines used to wash pharmaceutical rubber run the gamut from simple domestic laundry-type washers that process thousands of small parts at one time to more sophisticated devices that treat each part individually [5]. By washing each part individually, it is contended that many of the problems encountered with the mass washing techniques, most notably the transfer of particles from one part to another, is eliminated. Between what may be considered these two extremes are several types of commercially available industrial washers, including those with rotating cages or drums and those that work on the principle of overflow.

Some of the devices are equipped with a microprocessor-controlled mechanism that can wash, rinse, siliconize, and dry the parts automatically with the selection of a program or the insertion of a punch card. This is a definite advantage from a routine operating standpoint, since the process, once selected for the given stock, cannot be altered by the operator. This, of course, provides a controlled, reproducible process, which is essential to minimize batch-to-batch variation, enhancing the validation effort. However, it may leave the validator with yet another challenge if samples are to be selected while the program cycle is engaged. If the cycle is interrupted periodically for sample selection, care must be taken to assure that the interruption in the cycle or alteration of the timing sequence does not significantly affect the outcome of the process. This can be accomplished in part by comparing the levels and nature of particulate matter of parts prepared with and without the required sampling pause.

One of the most common abuses of the mass-type washers comes from overloading the equipment. Conversely, but on a diminutive scale, is the possibility of underutilization of equipment by the use of less than optimal loads in the device. Therefore, as part of the evaluation, the validator must consider the influence of the quantity of parts to be washed. This is most important, for example, in devices that rely on the overflow principle.

An example of one such device functions by floating the parts to be cleaned in a water bath. The water is purged with high-pressure air and a steady stream of water from beneath the "floating" parts, thus causing the particulate matter to be directed to the surface of the bath, at which point they are discharged into the overflow drain. Theoretically, the device works best when the parts are free-floating, since stationary parts could act as a filter bed and thus prevent the migration of the liberated particles to the surface. In the case of small rubber parts of compact design, or parts that are dense due to the use of a metal insert (plungers with metal bushings), it may be impractical from a standpoint of production capacity to completely float the parts. In many instances, depending on the part, a compromise will have to be established.

Regardless of the device or process, the following physical attributes should be taken into consideration:

1. Physical appearance
2. Dimensional characteristics
3. Durometer values
4. Particulate matter determination
5. Water quality
6. Residue
7. Physiochemical test

These parameters are discussed in the following summaries.

1. Physical Appearance

The parts should be inspected visually and/or microscopically throughout the various stages of the washing cycle. Any changes in the color, coating (if applicable), or surface should be noted. Also, the part should be examined for any "surface tack" that may have been imparted by the washing operation.

2. Dimensional Characteristics

Upon completion of the washing cycle, the critical dimensions of the part should be compared to that of the "as-received" part to determine if swelling or distortion has resulted from the process. Standard dimensional tolerances are available [6].

3. Durometer

Depending on the size and the configuration of the part, a softening of the part as a result of washing cycle may be detectable by the use of a Shore durometer according to ASTM Method D2240-81 [7]. Since the durometer functions by pressing the metallic point actuator of a calibrated spring against the surface of the rubber stock, a flat surface, such as a stopper flange, is needed to accomplish this test.

4. Particulate Matter Determination

The parts being washed should be monitored for particulate matter throughout the washing steps if possible. This may be accomplished using a visual test (membrane filter) such as is described in USP XX [8], or by automatic particle counting techniques. Hopkins [9] also offers a sampling method that involves shaking the rubber parts in filtered water and then collecting contained particles on a filter membrane for microscopic study. This approach would be generally applicable to any small rubber part. A particle counter such as a HIAC could be used to count the particulates in place of visual membrane technique. This would be particularly helpful in the case where many samples are being tested, such as a validation program on a specific piece of equipment. By comparing the nature of the particulate matter on the part before and after washing, one can determine the effect of the cleaning method on the naturally occurring particulates.

Nishimura [5] has employed a method to actually challenge the washing system by providing a "controlled contaminant." For his study of cleaning of conventional-style, 20-mm, gray butyl vial stoppers, Nishimura prepared red-colored talc of a known size, which was dispersed as a 1% (w/w) aqueous suspension. Following immersion in the suspension, the stoppers were dried at 100°C for 60 min with their plugged sides up. Although apparently quite successful as a tool in Nishimura's evaluation, the validator must carefully consider the nature of the part being tested by developing the artificial contaminant and the ability to clean the contaminant from the processing and washing system once the experiment is completed. The washing system may also be evaluated using a given lot of the actual component that is to be routinely processed. The system can be challenged by selecting a lot that exhibits an extraordinarily high level of particulates. This eliminates the possibility of the contaminant acting in an atypical manner during the washing process.

5. *Water Quality*

For the washing of injectable components, only the highest quality of water should be used. It is presumed that at least the final rinsing step employs water that meets the USP water-for-injection (WFI) tests. The particulate matter content of the water should be monitored throughout the process cycle. This can be accomplished by sampling the rinse water following each stage of the process and comparing the clarity of the water to a standard, i.e., WFI. The two other factors that are important are the length of time the parts are exposed to the water and the temperature of the water throughout the washing and rinsing cycles.

6. *Residue*

If cleaning agents, such as trisodium phosphate, sodium pyrophosphate, or sodium lauryl sulfate are employed in the washing operation, the final rinse water should be checked for the presence of these agents. A simple but effective means is to check the conductivity of the rinse water. In addition, a pH check of the rinse water can be performed. A simple shake test to ensure absence of foaming may be used to indicate when the cleaning agent has been removed.

The quality of the cleaning agents should be analyzed by both chemical and toxicity tests as part of the incoming acceptance tests. In addition, when the materials are further diluted or used in a solution, the strength of the solution should be monitored.

7. *Physiochemical Test*

USP XX [10] provides physiochemical test procedures that are "designed to determine pertinent physiochemical extraction characteristics of elastomeric closures." The effect of the washing operation may be determined by water extracts of treated closures with those of untreated closures. The test covers turbidity, reducing agents, heavy metals, pH change, and total extractables. Subsequent variations in the wash cycle may also be evaluated using this test.

D. Lubrication

Following the washing and rinse cycles, many closures require the application of a suitable lubricant such as silicone. The quantity applied and the method of application may vary with the part as described earlier. The level of silicone can be detected by a suitable method such as that provided in ASTM Method D3733-78 [11].

If the silicone is to be applied in the form of an emulsion, care must be taken that the emulsion is not affected by the application method. High-temperature heating or boiling of the emulsion could cause the emulsion to separate or "crack." Presuming that a bath or dip technique is employed, the cracked emulsion would mean that the silicone may not be applied uniformly to the parts being processed. This could result in parts with an overabundance of silicone while others in the same process vessel have little or none at all. In order to prevent this situation, it is suggested that the quality of the silicone emulsion be monitored before and after use. A centrifugation test can be used to confirm the acceptability of the emulsion by determining the degree of separation.

As far as the part is concerned, the following tests may be considered:

1. *Physical appearance*: Particular attention should be paid to the surface sheen indicating completeness or evenness of the application.
2. *Dimensional characteristic*: In particular, swelling may have occurred as the silicone was absorbed by the rubber.
3. *Silicone level*: The level of silicone can be detected by a suitable method such as is provided in Ref. 11.
4. *Particulate matter*: Determination—refer to Ref. 8.

E. Drying

Following the washing and/or lubrication procedure, if the parts are not to be sterilized immediately, the parts must be dried to remove any residual water. Wet components could promote the growth of organisms and formation of pyrogens. This would change the established bioburden level of the part and therefore influence the conditions needed to sterilize the part.

Drying is accomplished primarily by air drying at room temperature or by exposing the parts to a warm air cycle in the washing device or a warm air oven. Both procedures have certain advantages and disadvantages, which must be recognized by the validator as follows:

1. *Air drying*: From an overall influence on the part, the air drying technique is probably the least likely to promote change. The parts are usually transferred from the washing vessel to shallow bins or trays or simply spread out on drain boards. If the parts are protected by laminar flow or filtered air, little concern need be given this part of the operation. If, however, the environment in the immediate vicinity is less than ideal, it is suggested that the particulate matter levels be compared before and after drying.
2. *Oven drying*: Oven drying represents more of a challenge to the validator, since the time and temperature involved affect certain properties and characteristics of the closure. Having already discussed the aging phenomenon imparted by even relatively short exposure to high-temperature conditions, the validation program should be tailored according to the severity of the conditions.

Since the part is liberating water during the oven drying and is thus producing a cooling effect, the part will be slow to reach the temperature at which the oven is set. However, one way to determine the actual temperature of the parts is by conducting a thermal profile of the load. Presuming, of course, that the oven in which the load is processed has been qualified, a multipoint profile is performed by placing the thermocouple at different locations within the bins or trays of closures. This will determine the quickest and slowest points to heat within the load. By testing those parts that received the most sustained heat, one can be assured that the parts are representative of the worst-case situation. These parts should be evaluated for:

1. *Physical appearance*: Using the same approach discussed for parts during washing.
2. *Dimensional characteristics*: As per washing, except that particular care should be taken if an oven heat cycle has been encountered.

F. Sterilization

Regardless of whether an elastomeric component is sterilized prior to assembly, as part of a subassembly, or terminally as part of the finished closure/container system, the heat imparted by the sterilization process can have an adverse affect on the part. For example, closures prepared with natural rubber compounds are susceptible to decomposition from heat. Exposure to what is considered minimum sterilization time/temperatures can quickly advance the state of cure of the rubber to the point where reverse or a breaking of the cross-linking begins to occur.

This process can affect all of the physical and mechanical properties cited earlier, as well as functional characteristics such as dimension or plunger movement, or even chemical properties such as the extractables. In addition, particulate matter can be generated as the aging effect of the rubber is accelerated by the heating process.

III. GLASS COMPONENT PROCESSING

A. General

Most containers of parenteral products are made of glass and, as such, glass vial, syringe, and ampul processing is a major process validation concern of the parenteral manufacturer. Prior to evaluating the critical process steps performed in-house, it is essential, as with other components, that a thorough knowledge of the actual component and method of vendor manufacturing be acquired. Since different types of glass are commonly used as well as various vendor treatment procedures, definition of these variables are required to avoid negating process validation efforts because of component or manufacturing changes occurring at a later time.

PDA *Technical Bulletin No. 3* [12] addresses the differences between available glass used for parenteral products and the two common methods of designation: USP classification and manufacturer's designation. The USP classifies glass intended for parenterals as Type I, II, or III (most commonly used for dry powders). Type I is a borosilicate glass (low alkalinity), whereas Types II and III are soda-lime glass. Type II differs from Type III in that it is surface-treated to reduce the alkalinity of the internal surface. Treatment processes include either an aqueous ammonium sulfate rinse or gaseous sulfur dioxide exposure. The latter method is somewhat more difficult to control uniformly. The criticality and acceptability of the actual treatment process should be determined at the time of the glass selection. Most vendors will supply untreated ampuls or vials for purposes of controls in compatibility/ stability studies, which can be used as worst-case challenge samples.

Additionally, an ammonium bifluoride wash of the finished container may also be performed by the vendor [13]. The purpose of this procedure, which is unlike the surface neutralization wash, is to remove surface imperfections and aid in removal of general particulate matter by sloughing off the exposed surface layer. Whatever the particular type of glass or vendor treatment, it is imperative that the pharmaceutical manufacturer ensure lot-to-lot reproducibility, since the glass type and treatment can have a significant effect on the product stability.

Beyond the actual glass manufacturing process, the pharmaceutical manufacturer should also consider the packaging and handling processes. Ampuls, vials, and syringes are essentially clean at the time of molding/annealing. Annealing, or lehring, as it is known, is the process of heating and then cooling the glass for the purpose of softening and making the glass less brittle. Following lehring, all attempts to minimize contamination during further handling are warranted [14]. Glass ampuls, vials, and syringes may be packaged in clean rooms using nonshedding materials and shrink-wrapped with polyolefin [15]. The general quality of such procedures should be determined prior to validation of in-house processing; i.e., a baseline of incoming component quality is necessary to accurately determine the efficacy of subsequent in-house procedures and ultimately their actual need and/or criticality.

This assessment should include monitoring for both visual and microscopic particulate matter. General cleanliness using general and specific analyses to check for water-insoluble contaminants, especially mold release agents such as mineral oil, should be performed.

As previously discussed, reproducibility of specific vendor treatments should also be determined. Such testing may include, at minimum, residual sulfate testing using barium chloride to confirm sulfur-type dealkalinization procedures when sulfur dioxide treatment is required. If possible, the actual efficacy of the sulfur treatment should also be checked by using USP Type II test procedures to determine component-to-component variations. This test can also be used to confirm treatment of Type I glass, which may be performed in containers made from glass tubing rather than molded glass [15]. (The USP does not address this possibility, since only bulk glass testing is required to confirm the use of borosilicate glass.)

Assuming that the aforementioned variables have been addressed, the pharmaceutical manufacturer can start evaluating his or her own in-house processes. This should begin with a close inspection of the internal handling procedures, including warehousing, shrink-wrap removal and the general environmental quality in which the exposed components will be handled [16,17]. Evaluation of these procedures will assure minimal contamination of as-received components with nonviable and viable particulates. Regardless of the efficiency of component cleaning and sterilization processes that would eventually be performed, it is still good practice to avoid taxing these processes with excessive particulate burden or bioburden on the components. Although bioburden resulting from inadequate environmental control and hygiene may be eliminated after sterilization, it may also result in excessive pyrogen levels, which may not be removed during processing.

Having defined these procedures and having implemented adequate controls, the actual glass processing can be evaluated. The overall ideal validation objective to define, monitor, and control the process is applicable regardless of the actual equipment.

B. Glass Washing/Treatment

Various types of washing equipment are available, and no attempt will be made to discuss the specifics of each model. The following generic discussion should apply to most designs and is presented as a general approach to identify possibly critical processing aspects of washing equipment.

The foremost concern is the area in which the washer is placed. It is imperative that environmental control of this area be maintained during and subsequent to all validation trials. Ideally, the area will be qualified to conform to Class 10,000* or better criteria. Typically, the first step in washing is an air wash, since removal of particulates is much easier prior to wetting. The pressure of the air and orifice size of each nozzle should be determined in order to assure uniform cleaning. Quality of the air (especially compressor contaminants) and the design and placement of washing nozzles should be recorded. If the nozzles enter the vial, the depth of penetration should be measured. To ensure uniform cleaning, air pressures should be specified for each individual ampul or vial size to be cleaned. Changes in component neck diameters can dramatically effect the degree of cleaning when nozzle diameters approach the size of the container orifice [15]. Exposure times should be determined for both batch and continuous processes. In order to set minimum and maximum operating parameters, test samples should be prepared and evaluated at the extreme settings. Test samples can be prepared by adding various dry powder water-soluble dyes to the individual ampuls, vials, or syringes, or by adding an alcoholic solution of a dye and allowing the solvent to evaporate. Efficacy of the air wash can then be assessed by measuring the concentration of dye in the solvent spectrophotometrically after reconstitution within the cleaned component. Another approach is to use electronic, microscopic, or visual particulate counting of appropriate test materials [5].

Washing equipment may be designed to allow for an ammonium bifluoride treatment that usually consists of a 1- to 2-sec wash followed by a 30-sec hold, which allows the reaction to occur between the bifluoride and glass. This reaction is reported to achieve sloughing of a fine layer of glass surface, which can be subsequently removed by washing [18]. Roseman reported that the depth of reaction is less than that of a sulfur dioxide treatment that may have been performed by the vendor [18]. Nonetheless, it is prudent to demonstrate via appropriate reactivity testing that the actual in-house process has not comprised any former treatment. The adequacy of the bifluoride treatment should be considered for each ampul, vial, and syringe size, since variation in container volume/surface area may necessitate changes in the amount of bifluoride solution which is applied. Validation should include control of the solution concentration, rate and length of delivery, and residence time before rinsing. The efficacy of the rinse has been characterized by electron microscopy [15], but an indirect method can also be used that requires only simple physical or chemical testing of the container. Soluble silicate levels of water-filled containers can be measured by atomic absorption, or physical visual inspection for glass insolubles can be performed [19]. To ensure adequate flushing of the bifluoride and resultant fluoride, a sensitive selective fluoride

---

*Less than 10,000 particles greater than 0.5 μm per cubic foot.

electrode can be used [13]. A conductivity meter can also be helpful, since it will detect silicates as well as fluoride. Some washing systems may not be amenable to adequate rinsing, especially if the ampul, vial, or syringe is not inverted during the rinsing cycle. A careful benefit-to-risk assessment should be made concerning the need for a bifluoride treatment based on the ability to adequately rinse.

In some systems the bifluoride wash is replaced with a detergent or surfactant wash. Again, adequate process control of the length of wash and detergent level should be achieved. The need for a detergent should be based on the general quality of the received component. Pooled aqueous washings of received components can be subjected to specific and general chemical tests per USP XX WFI monograph testing [20]. Additionally, organic extracts can also be tested by ultraviolet (UV) or infrared (IR) spectroscopy for general organic contamination. Pooled samples can be evaporated and total solids can also be determined. These same samples can then be used to assess the efficiency of the washing process.

Residual detergent or surfactant testing should also be performed to define the adequacy of subsequent rinse cycles. The actual analytical testing used is determined by the chemical nature of the detergent/surfactant. Conductance measurements can be used for anionic and cationic agents, and many nonionic compounds can be quantitated by UV spectroscopy, high-performance liquid chromatography (HPLC), or gas chromatography (GC). A simple shake test using WFI and measurement of foaming will, in most cases, suffice to demonstrate acceptable removal of detergents.

If quantitative data are needed, several dilutions of positive test samples can be used. The degree of clarity will depend on that of the starting solution. Most washing systems employ a steam or hot water rinse. Others cycle between cold and hot water, compressed air, or steam. The latter may help free contaminants by the rapidly induced expansion and contraction of the glass. Regardless of the actual technique, the quality of the rinsing agent is paramount. Good-quality water yields good-quality glass. Steam and/or water pressures and flow rates should be controlled as well as cycle times. Generally, WFI-quality water or clean steam (condensate) should be maintained. Filters, if required to control particulate matter, should be checked for adequate flushing to remove extractables prior to use and/or change. The frequency of filter changes should also be determined.

Again, washing/rinsing nozzle sizes should be defined and evaluated for each component size. Volumes and rates of delivery should be assessed and controlled via flow meters or regulators, timers, relays, etc. The monitoring and control would ideally be through a dedicated microprocessor. Fluid temperatures should also be controlled/monitored. Most important in these evaluations is the effect of equipment speed for continuous processing. The most detailed validation can become meaningless if the validated line speed is altered without first assessing its effect on the previous parameters.

Ultrasonic cleaning baths are increasingly popular and require unique monitoring and control. As with conventional washers, the quality of the wash/rinse water is paramount. Water change frequency vs. cycle speeds should be evaluated via the bath quality (particulate matter, total solids, UV absorbance, conductivity, etc.) and container quality. Obvious parameters, such as immersion time and drainage time (prior to drying) should be evaluated and controlled. Process control should include temperature readings on the bath and suitable amperage monitoring of the ultrasonic horn (generator).

Regardless of the type of washer, the design and materials of construction should be closely evaluated. Typically, 316 stainless steel is the major material of construction. Specific grades or alternates may be required due to a particular product's sensitivity to trace metals. Piping, valves, filters, manifold and gasket materials should also be examined with product in mind from both a direct contamination standpoint as well as from a sanitation standpoint. Maintenance procedures and schedules should be an integral part of the validation phase.

The validation of an effective washing of ampuls, vials, and syringes can be a difficult and complicated task. Removal of both fine and coarse particles, general contaminants, and often pyrogenic material must be accomplished.

C. Siliconization

Silicone treatment of glass parenteral containers is a common practice performed for a multitude of reasons. Siliconization of glass minimizes its reactivity with product, reduces potential adsorption problems, improves withdrawal of contents, and adds to the pharmaceutical elegance of the product [21].

Silicone oil, silicone/water emulsions and dispersions, and silicone solutions with organic solvents are all used for siliconization. Application is usually by immersion or spray techniques followed by a thermal cure to improve the durability of the coating. Although each process has unique considerations, there are general parameters that should be assessed regarding control of the processing and end results.

The first aspect that should be evaluated is the actual siliconizing medium that is used. Concentration of silicone in dispersions, emulsions, and solutions should be evaluated and controlled. Gravimetric or density measurements are usually adequate analytical methods that can be used. The chemical quality of the silicone and/or emulsifying agents should also be considered and appropriate specifications established. Emulsion and dispersions should also be evaluated for droplet size and uniformity. Centrifugal separation tests or direct particle size measurement can be used for this purpose. Although in most cases the siliconized glass container will eventually be exposed to depyrogenating and/or sterilizing temperatures, consideration of the microbial and pyrogenic quality of the siliconizing agent should also be made.

When immersion into silicone or silicone solutions is the method of application, temperature, immersion and drainage times, as well as the angle of inversion, should be controlled.

Spraying processes should be monitored for nozzle orifice size, delivery pressures, spray and drainage times, and temperatures. Once coated, the curing time for each individual type container should be controlled by time-at-temperature monitoring.

Prior to any of the aforementioned controls, it is essential that the efficacy of the process be demonstrated. This, of course, depends on the purpose(s) of the siliconization as noted earlier. Ideally, product testing can be correlated to the quality and quantity of the silicone application. The latter can be determined by removal of the silicone coating with organic solvents (methyl ethyl ketone, ether, Freon, etc.) and analysis after evaporation of the residue (gravimetric, atomic absorption, or infrared spectroscopy) to determine the degree of siliconization on a vial-to-vial basis. Various methods can also be used to determine the quality of the coating, i.e., whether the coating is integral and/or durable. Coating integrity has been measured qualitatively by Tollen's reagent and formaldehyde and inspecting for deposition of silver on the glass surface as well as the measurement of adsorbed in situ denatured albumin [22].

Specific quantitative tests designed to measure the extent of adsorption may be warranted if the drug is of low concentration [19]. The durability of the coating can also be determined by freeze/thawing the containers and repeating the adsorption measurement test [22].

Particulate measurement can also be used to evaluate the efficacy of the process and especially the cure cycle. Difference in the amount of shed silicone particles has been observed from variation in the concentration of silicone solution used and cure cycles [18]. This technique can also be used to determine the durability of the coating if done before and after freeze/thawing experiments.

As discussed in Section II, siliconization of syringes may be performed to permit satisfactory break-loose and extrusion of the plunger action. Precise physical measurements of the break-loose and extrusion pressures should be made to assess the adequacy of the silicone-treated syringe. Ideally these measurements will correlate to the previously noted processing variables.

IV. SUMMARY

Although the processes discussed in the two sections of this chapter were distinctly different, by now it should be apparent that the validation guidelines offered are not only applicable to rubber and glass components, but also provide insight that may be used to validate any given component process.

From a practical standpoint, not all variables associated with the component or process can be explored, nor is it necessary to do so. The key to component preparation process validation is to consider the influence of the component on the product, provide a complete description of the equipment, clearly define the process, and determine the test criteria *before* a protocol outlining the validation experiments is drafted. In this manner the major constituents of the jigsaw puzzle are all in proper place awaiting only the keystone, which is, of course, the result gained from the study.

In order to demonstrate what may be considered a typical validation approach, a protocol for washing rubber stoppers in an overflow-type washer, described earlier in this chapter, was selected. The protocol shown in Table 1 assumes that all necessary conditions associated with the washer have been

TABLE 1   A Typical Component Processing Validation Protocol

1. Date (time) of Study _____ (Exact information) _____

2. Validator(s) _____ (Record names) _____

3. Objective (intended purpose of study)— to wash and siliconize rubber stoppers

4. Project Assignments

    a. Validation Unit— Prepare protocol; conduct test program; monitor trial; collect samples; analyze data; prepare final report

TABLE 1   (continued)

      b. Production Unit—Review protocol; provide stoppers, detergent, water; prepare equipment; run equipment

      c. Quality Assurance Laboratory—Review protocol; conduct necessary physical and chemical test as indicated

5. Equipment Identification

      a. Name/Serial No. ____ (Equipment title and no.)

      b. Location ____ (Room location)

6. Stopper Identification

      a. Manufacturer ____ (Actual molder of the part)

      b. Size ____ (13, 20, 28 mm, etc.)

      c. Rubber Compound ____ (Mfr. formulation no.)

      d. Lot No. ____ (Mfr. identification on carton)

      e. Date Manufactured ____ (Date actually molded)

      f. Date Received ____ (Date received in-plant)

      g. Date Released for Use ____ (QA date)

      h. Stoppers per Processing Basket ____ (Actual no. recorded)

7. Equipment Operation

      a. Cleaning and Preparation Record ____ (Copy provided)

      b. Standard Operating Procedure (SOP) ____ [Enter applicable procedure(s)]

      c. Time record for processing steps (Include time between cycles)

      d. Temperature record ____ (Monitor throughout run)

      e. Air flow ____ (Air pressure maintained)

      f. Water flow ____ (Record rates)

8. Sampling Plan—Processing Solvents, 50 ml Samples

      a. WFI upstream from equipment

      b. Hot water wash/detergent wash

      c. Hot rinse water

      d. Silicone emulsion

9. Sampling Plan—Stoppers—use clean bags and scoops

      a. Immediately upon removal from carton

      b. Following hot water/detergent wash

      c. Following hot water rinse

      d. Following silicone emulsion soak

TABLE 1   (continued)

---

10.   Test Criteria—Water Efficient

    a.   Physical appearance—7a, b, c, d

    b.   Particulate Matter determination—7a, b, c, d

    c.   Water quality—7a, b, c

11.   Test Criteria—Stoppers

    a.   Physical appearance—8a, 8b, 8c, 8d

    b.   Particulate matter determination—8a, 8d

    c.   Dimensional characteristics—8a, 8d

    d.   Silicone level—8d

---

qualified and calibrated and that the rubber closures are of an existing style and formulation previously used by the manufacturer. In each case the minimum process condition from the tolerance ranges (min./max.) provided in the standard operating procedures (SOPs) that detail the operation of the washer were chosen.

Completion of the protocol testing should result in a formal report documenting the rationale, data, and conclusions.

In the introduction of this chapter it was stated that a product can only be as good as the container/closure system in which it is packaged. By having combined the proper process for the container/closure system with a well-designed validation program, the validator can take satisfaction in the knowledge that he or she has provided assurance that future batches of product consistently meet the same high standards of quality.

REFERENCES

1.   Wood, T. 1980. Validation of elastomeric closures for parenteral use: An overview. *Bull. Parenteral Drug Assoc. 34*(4).
2.   Extractables from elastomeric closures: Analytical procedures for characterization/identification. *Technical Methods Bulletin No. 1,* 1980, Parenteral Drug Association.
3.   Elastomeric closures: Evaluation of significant performance and identity characteristics. *Technical Methods Bulletin No. 2,* 1980, Parenteral Drug Association.
4.   Green, G. E. 1977. Warehousing of pharmaceutical closures. *Bull. Parenteral Drug Assoc. 31*(2).
5.   Nishimura, T. 1979. A novel system for washing parenteral rubber closures individually. *Bull. Parenteral Drug Assoc. 33*(2):96.
6.   *Vanderbilt Rubber Handbook.* 1968. R. T. Vanderbilt Co., New York.
7.   Rubber property—Durometer hardness, ASTM D2240-1, 1981. *Annual Book of ASTM Standards.* American Society for Testing and Materials, Philadelphia.
8.   Large volume injections for single dose infusion, in *The United States Pharmacopeia, 20th Rev.* 1979. Mack Publishing Co., Easton, Pa. p 863.

9. Hopkins, G. H. 1972. Improved machine design for stopper washing. *Bull. Parenteral Drug Assoc. 27*(3) 114.

10. Physiochemical test procedures, in *The United States Pharmacopeia, 20th Rev.* 1979. Mack Publishing Co., Easton, Pa. p 918.

11. Silicone content of silicone polymers and silicone-modified alkyds by atomic absorption, ASTM D3733-78, 1978. *Annual Book of ASTM Standards.* American Society for Testing and Materials, Philadelphia.

12. Glass containers for small volume parenteral products: Factors for selection and test methods for identification. *Technical Methods Bulletin No. 3,* 1982. Parenteral Drug Association.

13. Hinson, A. L. 1971. Fluoride washing of glass containers. *Bull. Parenteral Drug Assoc. 25*(6) 266.

14. Anschel, J. 1977. General guidelines for the processing of glass containers for parenteral products. *Bull. Parenteral Drug Assoc. 31*(1): 47.

15. Stafficker, C. F. 1963. A comparison of blown bottles and tubing vials. *Bull. Parenteral Drug Assoc. 17*(5): 31.

16. McGinn, A. B. 1972. Control of particulate matter in preparation of parenteral containers. *Bull. Parenteral Drug Assoc. 26*(1): 26.

17. Carenberg, C. 1973. Toward cleaner glass bottles. *Drug Cosmet. Inc. 112*: 49.

18. Roseman, T. J. 1976. Glass for parenteral products: A surface view using the scanning electron microscope. *J. Pharm. Sci. 65*(1): 22.

19. Passl, W. J. 1979. Interactions of parenteral solutions with sulphur treated glass bottles. *J. Pharm. Pharmacol. 31*: 721.

20. Water for injection, in *The United States Pharmacopeia, 20th Rev.,* 1979. Mack Publishing Co., Easton, Pa. p 850.

21. Theodorakis, M. C., et al. 1980. A study on particulate formation of silicone-coated glass surfaces. *Int. J. Pharm. 6*: 333.

22. Mizutani, T. 1982. Adsorption of some antibiotics and other drugs on silicone-coated glass surfaces. *J. Pharm. Pharmacol. 34*: 608.

BIBLIOGRAPHY

Anderson, P. R., et al. 1975. Effect of surface treatments on the chemical durability and surface composition of soda-lime glass bottles. *J. Non-Crystalline Solids 19*: 251—262.

Anisfeld, M. 1978. Design for a small-volume parenteral manufacturing facility. *J. Parenteral Drug Assoc. 32*(6).

Douglas, R. W., et al. 1949. The action of water and of sulphur dioxide on glass surfaces. *J. Soc. Glass Tech. 33*: 289—335.

Green, H., et al. 1979. The container size/volume relationship in particulate contamination. *J. Parenteral Drug Assoc. 33*(6): 319—325.

Larsson, N. 1978. SEM-Study of rubber stoppers for parenteral drugs. *Pharm. Ind. 40*(11a).

Nail, S. L. 1979. Evaluation of the effectiveness of ammonium bifluoride treatment in the cleaning of parenteral glassware by an automatic particle counting technique. *J. Parenteral Drug Assoc. 33*: 177—183.

Passl, W. J., and Renshaw, E. 1982. Chemical resistance of glass bottles for intravenous infusions. *Pharm. Ind.* (10a): 955—977.

Rifkin, C. 1968. Panel discussion: Siliconization of parenteral packaging components. *Bull. Parenteral Drug Assoc. 22*: 66—69.

Smith, G. 1976. New process for treatment of parenteral closures. *J. Parenteral Drug Assoc. 30*(2).

21

Validation of Packaging Operations

CHARLES S. LEVINE

Astra Pharmaceutical Products, Inc., Westboro, Massachusetts

I. INTRODUCTION

In the pharmaceutical industry, the term "packaging" has many different definitions. Packaging can bring to mind visions of employees gathered around a table placing product into corrugated cases and sealing the cases with tape, or highly automated equipment filling parenteral solutions into sterile containers in an aseptic environment.

To attempt to cover the validation of such a myriad of processes in one chapter is a difficult assignment. However, by dividing these processes into four categories, the information can be presented in an organized manner and emphasis can be placed on those areas demanding the most attention. The four categories are

1. Filling
2. Sealing
3. Inspection
4. Labeling and final packaging

It is important that each category be clearly defined before proceeding.

The filling of parenteral solutions into sterile containers requires extensive evaluation of the aseptic environment. These aspects of a parenteral filling operation are discussed in detail in other chapters.

Our view of the parenteral filling operation will examine the process of accurately filling a specified quantity of product into a container without any product abuse or spillage.

The sealing process will examine the two processes that are most commonly used in parenteral dosage forms: flame sealing (ampuls); and glass/rubber container closure systems (vials).

The U.S. Pharmacopeia (USP) requires all small-volume parenteral products to undergo 100% inspection for particulate contamination [1]. The inspection for particulate contamination will be the focal point for our discussion of inspection processes. The review will include both visual and automated inspection methods.

The final packaging process is considered to be that which begins after particulate inspection and continues until the product is packed into cases. The packaging process could include such things as labeling, cartoning, and secondary container sealing. Validation should address only those packaging processes that are automated.

Any process undergoing the scrutiny of validation generally should depend heavily on a machine operating within its designated parameters. This is not to say that the performance of operating and maintenance personnel should be overlooked. The validation of strictly manual processes should not be considered in lieu of in-process or finished product testing.

When discussing the validation of automated or semiautomated processes, the first question asked should be "Is this piece of equipment new, or has it been in use for a substantial period of time?" If you are dealing with a piece of equipment or process that is currently in operation, there may be sufficient data to statistically validate the process or equipment in question. Review of test results, however, will not provide a complete picture. Review of current standard operating procedures, maintenance records, and calibration records is necessary to ensure that the process is suitable for pharmaceutical production. A piece of equipment that has a history of frequent breakdowns and repairs cannot be considered a validated process. In many instances, such maintenance histories are not readily available to either Quality Assurance or Validation personnel.

New equipment provides Validation personnel with an opportunity to develop a proper equipment history file, which will ensure access to such information in the future. Before starting any validation testing, it is extremely important to ensure that:

1. The equipment is properly installed.
2. The equipment has undergone mechanical startup (on site) by the equipment vendor or manufacturer.
3. Preliminary performance tests are performed.

Whether the equipment is custom-designed or prototype, the validation tests should be conducted for long time intervals. Many design defects will not appear during short test intervals such as 30 min or 1 hr. In one instance, a vial filler was not able to maintain the desired fill volume. The problem did not arise until the sixth hour of filling. This problem was the result of an improperly polished piston shaft, which began to bind after 6 hr of operation.

Most of the discussion in this chapter will concentrate on the validation testing required for new or modified equipment.

It is not yet common in our industry to associate validation with packaging operations. The history of Food and Drug Administration (FDA) recalls has shown a majority of product recalls to be a result of packaging problems. Currently, the FDA emphasizes the validation of sterilization processes and spends little time investigating the validation of "packaging" operations. Under the current economic and political climate, the FDA will not be able to devote attention to new areas of emphasis such as packaging operations. By validating packaging processes, everyone will find long-range profits by shortening new equipment learning curves and achieving higher operating efficiency in a shorter period of time.

II. FILLING

The validation of a filling operation involves significantly more than just measuring the fill volume, especially when validating a new filler. The integration of new equipment into pharmaceutical operation is always a traumatic experience. Vendor participation in the initial equipment startup is vital.

When compared to autoclaves, however, the startup of a new filler is rather simple. Though most production personnel are interested only in the ultimate volume control aspects, it is important to understand the theory of operation when validating a new filling system.

There are primarily two pump systems currently used in parenteral filling. They are the "positive displacement volumetric liquid fillers" and "time/pressure" filling.

A. Positive Displacement Volumetric Systems

A typical positive displacement volumetric system can be compared to a one-cylinder engine in that the stroke and bore of the piston determine the volume of liquid dispensed by each cycle of the piston. During the upward stroke of the piston, the valve assembly allows the product to enter the cylinder. The valve assembly then rotates to allow the product to be expelled into the container. Figures 1 and 2 demonstrate these cycles.

A well-designed positive displacement volumetric (PDV) system will deliver product of various viscosities with a high degree of accuracy. However, the accuracy is greatly dependent on the delivery system.

The major hazard encountered is air or gas in the delivery system. This is normally encountered at the start of a filling operation when bleeding the supply tubes.

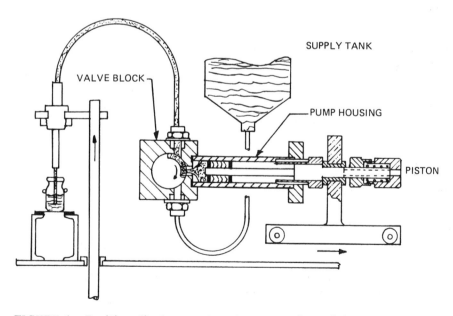

FIGURE 1 Positive displacement system, container-filling stroke.

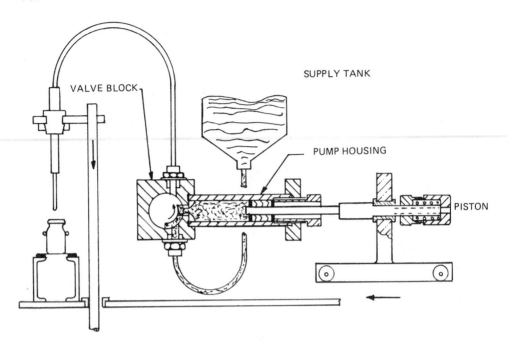

FIGURE 2   Positive displacement system, cylinder-filling stroke.

When filling products that have been purged with a gas, changes in temperature may cause dissolution of the gas, creating bubbles.

Typically, PDV systems are constructed of stainless steel or glass. Finish tolerances are extremely important in providing a smoothly operating and accurate system. One of the major disadvantages of this system is that the product is in contact with moving parts.

One variation of this concept is the TL pump manufactured by T—L Systems Corporation of Minneapolis, Minnesota. The "Rolling Diaphragm Liquid Metering Pump" (U.S. Patent no. 3880053) incorporates two concepts [2]:

1. A flexible diaphragm covers the piston, which provides a system without moving parts.
2. The intake and discharge valves compress flexible tubes, again eliminating moving parts.

These concepts enable one to accurately fill (±0.5%) a variety of products (parenteral solutions, corrosive chemicals, suspensions, and blood) that previously could not be filled using a PDV system.

B. Time/Pressure Systems

A new delivery system that utilizes an entirely different principle is time pressure filling. The principle is stated as follows: "Liquid of a given temperature and viscosity will flow at a constant rate through a fixed opening, provided the pressure is constant. Having established a constant rate of flow, time is the necessary variable to produce a specified fill volume [3].

With the time pressure (T/P) filling system, no moving parts are in contact with the product. The system pressure is controlled to ±0.01 psi by an in-line pressure sensor located between the pressurized storage vessel and the filler. The pressure sensor, which provides a signal to the pressure controller, must be located downstream of any sterilizing filters. The pressurized product flows through flexible tubing that is routed through a flow control valve. The flow control valve is actuated by a signal from a microprocessor. The valve will remain open for a predetermined period of time in order to deliver the desired amount of product. Figure 3 shows the product flow from the pressurized storage vessel to the flow control valve.

C. Validation Conditions

What does validating a filling system mean? In the classic example of a steam autoclave, it normally means accumulating a minimum F_0 and destroying a specified population of microorganisms. A validated filling system cannot be defined as precisely.

1. A filling system must be able to accurately fill a specified volume of product repeatedly.
2. The filling system must be able to fill the product without splashing, foaming, or damaging the containers.
3. The filling system must be able to deoxygenate the product containers, if required.

Regardless of the type of filling pumps used, one concept must be strictly adhered to during the validation of a filling system. The worst conditions must be simulated as part of the ultimate challenge. When validating a load configuration in an autoclave, the worst case is normally the largest load by mass.

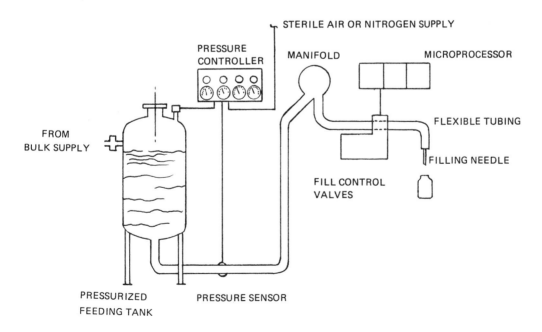

FIGURE 3 Time/pressure filling system.

Surface tension	min	
Surface tension	max	
Not degassed		
Degassed		
Supply pressure	min	
Supply pressure	max	
Operating speed	min	
Operating speed	max	
Product viscosity	min	
Product viscosity	max	
Container size	min	
Container size	max	

	1	2	3	4	5	6	7	8	9	10	11	12
Container size max.	X											
Container size min.		X										
Product viscosity max.			X									
Product viscosity min.				X								
Operating speed max.					X							
Operating speed min.						X						
Supply pressure max.							X					
Supply pressure min.								X				
Degassed									X			
Not degassed										X		
Surface tension max.											X	
Surface tension min.												X

FIGURE 4   Sample matrix, on which the extreme condition of each of 12 variables could be listed.

The worst condition for a filling system is the extreme of several variables. For the most part, each type of filling system requires that the same variables be evaluated.

The first step of any validation is to establish the utilization list for the equipment or system under evaluation. From this list, choose those products whose physical characteristics represent the extreme conditions, e.g., maximum and minimum viscosities. Also, a product from each product type should be selected, e.g., nonaqueous products and suspensions. When designing a comprehensive validation program, one might simply develop a matrix that includes the extreme condition of each variable. Filling one product to evaluate each combination of variables would be extremely time-consuming and expensive. As can be seen from the matrix in Figure 4, 132 combinations would be required to validate a 12 × 12 matrix. By selecting the proper combination of variables, the same knowledge can be gathered in much shorter time.

When evaluating a pump system's ability to meet the first criterion of a validated system (accurately fill a specified volume of product), the variables that present the greatest challenge are viscosity and type of product (suspension or nonaqueous solution). The more viscous products represent the greatest challenge. For example, if a pump system can accurately fill 50 ml of a viscous product, it will certainly fill 50 ml of a less viscous product with the same or better accuracy.

Similarly, a suspension or nonaqueous solution represents different challenges to a filling system and should be evaluated separately. When considering suspensions, the mixing system plays an extremely important role in fill volume accuracy. If the mixing system is incorporating air into the suspension, the fill weights will be correspondingly low.

Other variables that can affect fill volume accuracy are machine speed and delivery system pressure. Normally, the machine speed at which a filling system can accurately fill is limited by its mechanical design. Once the upper or lower limit of the mechanical design is exceeded, the fill volume accuracies deteriorate. It may seem contradictory, but lowering machine speeds could cause inaccurate filling. This is a common occurrence with equipment that has been designed for high-speed operation.

Maintaining a threshold pressure is all that is required to ensure accurate fill volumes, except when using a T/P filling system. The pressure control system of T/P filling systems should be monitored during routine operation so that pressure control data can be correlated with fill volume data.

The length of the filling operation is one variable that is expensive and time-consuming but cannot be ignored. As previously mentioned, we are concerned primarily with new equipment in this chapter. The only way to verify that the moving parts of a PDV or TL pump system have been properly machined is to repeatedly operate the filling system over an extended period of time. If parts are not machined properly, those points of metal-to-metal contact will bind or restrict the shaft movement, which will result in fill volumes below the target levels. It is impossible to predict the operating interval required to guarantee a nonbinding filler. Situations have been documented where binding first appeared after 6 hr of consecutive filling.

The volume of product being filled into each container is vital to establish a comprehensive validation program. The acceptance criterion for fill volume accuracy should be established from the Quality Assurance tolerances for the product being filled.

Both the largest and smallest volumes should be evaluated, for two different reasons. The smallest volume normally has the tightest tolerances for fill volume and the largest volume has the potential to starve the filler because of an inadequately sized delivery system. When dealing with a pressurized delivery system, the volume of product delivered per unit time can be calculated by the Darcy equation,

$$Q = C \sqrt{P \left(\frac{62.4}{p} \right)} \tag{1}$$

where

Q = quantity in gallons per minute

C = flow coefficient of the filling device (from manufacturer)

P = pressure drop across the filling device in pounds per square inch (with a T/P system, the line pressure should be substituted)

p = density of fluid in pounds per cubic foot

A different equation must be used if the viscosity is different from that of water or if the flow is not in the fully turbulent region.

Verification that the delivery system can adequately supply the filler obviously must be conducted at the maximum machine speed.

In summary, worst-case conditions can generally be evaluated by conducting an extended filling operation with the following variables:

	Conditions 1	Conditions 2
Product	Most viscous	Most viscous
Product volume	Smallest	Largest
Machine speed	Fastest	Fastest

Now that we have established these worst-case conditions and have begun collecting fill volume data, how do we determine if the acceptance criteria have been met?

D. Statistical Evaluation

Normally, Quality Assurance will establish fill volume tolerances for each product regardless of the filling equipment. Many fill volume tolerances are established by the USP [1]. Table 1 summarizes the requirements of the USP for "volume of injection in containers." As you will note, the USP requirements make no demands for statistically sound sampling. Today's filling equipment is sufficiently accurate to fill product within the tolerances established by the USP.

Normally, Quality Assurance fill volume tolerances have evolved over the years. They are established so that no units are filled with less than the labeled amount. In order to accomplish this, the target fill (T) is determined by adding three standard deviations (σ) to the labeled amount (L) as shown in Eq. (2) and represented graphically in Figure 5.

$$T = 3\sigma + L \tag{2}$$

TABLE 1 USP Requirements for Volume of Injection in Containers

Labeled size (ml)	Excess volume (ml)	
	For mobile liquids	For viscous liquids
Required minimum volume—label claim:		
0.5	0.10	0.12
1.0	0.10	0.15
2.0	0.15	0.25
5.0	0.30	0.50
10.0	0.50	0.70
20.0	0.60	0.90

30.0	0.80	2%
50.0 or more	1.20	3%

Volume in container	No. of samples	Transfer technique	Method of determination
Methodology:			
Less than 3 ml	5 or more	dry syringe	graduated cylinder or weight
3–10 ml	3 or more	dry syringe	graduated cylinder or weight
Greater than 10 ml	1 or more	dry syringe or emptying	graduated cylinder or weight

Source: Ref. 1.

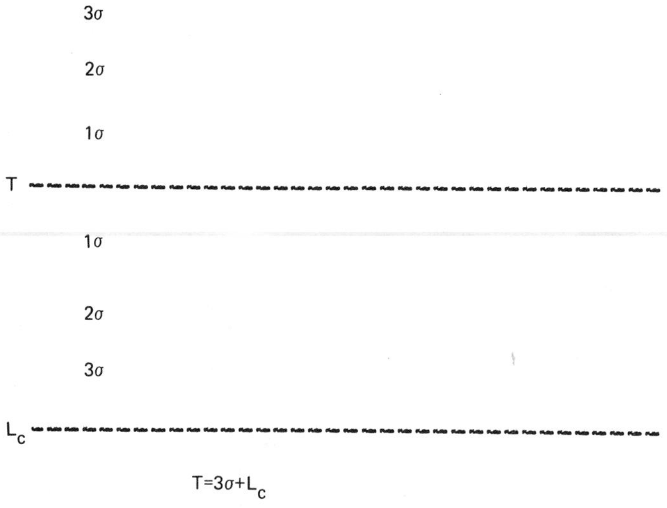

3σ

2σ

1σ

T ▬▬▬▬▬▬▬▬▬▬▬▬▬▬▬▬▬▬▬▬▬▬▬▬▬▬▬

1σ

2σ

3σ

L_c ▬▬▬▬▬▬▬▬▬▬▬▬▬▬▬▬▬▬▬▬▬▬▬▬▬

$$T = 3\sigma + L_c$$

FIGURE 5   Target fill.

When a product is transferred from an existing filler to a new filling system, there is an abundance of data from which the standard deviation could be established. One must be cautious when selecting historical data, because all the conditions of the filling operation may not have been properly documented; i.e., it is important to select data from time periods during which no filler adjustments were made. It is also desirable to group the data by filling head to avoid incorporating adjustment variations between filling heads.

If the target fill for the new filler is established using Eq. (2), we are now ready to analyze the data to establish its acceptability.

Fill weight monitoring lends itself to a statistical process control method called $\overline{X}$-R charts. There are many publications and texts available that explain the use and theory of $\overline{X}$-R charts. The *Quality Control Handbook*, by J. M. Juran, provides an excellent discussion.

The basic purpose of a control chart is to detect "assignable" causes of variation in the process. There are two types of causes that create variation in a process. These are "assignable" and "random" [4]. "Random" causes are due to slight variations in numerous variables whose overall effect is minimal and economically impractical to eliminate [4]. Assignable causes are due to large variation in a few variables whose overall effect is significant and economically vital to eliminate [4].

A control chart can be used in two different ways:

1. To determine if an "unknown" process is in a state of control (control with no standard given)
2. To determine if a "known" process remains in a state of control (control with standard given)

The limits of a control chart are normally set at ±3 standard deviations. If only "random" causes are present, 99.7% of all the individual values will fall within the control limits, which are normally referred to as the Upper Control Limit (UCL_x) and the Lower Control Limit (LCL_x).

TABLE 2 Control Limit Factors

n	A_1	A_2	B_3	B_4	D_3	D_4	E_1	E_2
2	3.759	1.880	0	3.267	0	3.268	5.318	2.660
3	2.394	1.023	0	2.568	0	2.574	4.146	1.772
4	1.880	0.729	0	2.266	0	2.282	3.760	1.457
5	1.596	0.577	0	2.089	0	2.114	3.568	1.290
6	1.410	0.483	0.030	1.970	0	2.004	3.454	1.184
7	1.277	0.419	0.118	1.882	0.076	1.924	3.378	1.109
8	1.175	0.373	0.185	1.815	0.136	1.864	3.323	1.054
9	1.094	0.337	0.239	1.761	0.184	1.816	3,283	1,010
10	1,028	0.308	0.284	1.716	0.223	1.777	3.251	0.975

Source: Ref. 4.

The steps to be followed when determining the state of control of a process are as follows:

1. Periodically take a series of samples in subgroups to establish a data base. The number of samples and frequency will depend on the speed of the filling equipment. It is normally desirable, at each sampling interval, to sample three units from each filling head so that each filling head may be evaluated separately if necessary.

2. During the filling process, record any process change that affects the data collected, i.e., volume adjustment on one of the filling heads.

3. Compute trial control limits from the data base collected in step 1. The average ($\overline{X}$) and range (R) of each subgroup is calculated. The grand average ($\overline{\overline{X}}$) and average range ($\overline{R}$) are then calculated.

The trial control limits are calculated by the following formulas [4]:

	Upper limit	Lower limit
Subgroup average	$\overline{\overline{X}} + A_2\overline{R}$	$\overline{\overline{X}} - A_2\overline{R}$
Subgroup range	$D_4\overline{R}$	$D_3\overline{R}$

The values for the multipliers A_2, D_3, and D_4 are listed in Table 2. The value n is the number of samples in each subgroup.

Compare the data points to the control limits for both $\overline{X}$ and R. If both statistics are within the limits, consider the process under control. If either statistic is outside the control limits, it indicates that the process is not in control. If an average ($\overline{X}$) is outside the control limit, this is an indication that a general change has occurred that affects all the samples. If a range (R) is outside the control limits, this is indicative of increased variability due to a change in material, personnel, or the process.

The use of X-R charts during the validation of new filling equipment not only provides specific acceptance criteria, but also serves as a tool for troubleshooting problems.

The importance of documenting all changes during the process cannot be overemphasized. This information will be vital to troubleshooting any problems.

III. CONTAINER SEALING

There are numerous statements in the literature that define containers for injection. The USP [1] is one such reference, and *Remington's Pharmaceutical Sciences* [5] describes a test for leakers. However, there has also been a significant amount of discussion in the literature concerning the inadequacies of various leak detection methodologies. T. G. Crouthamel, of the FDA [6], presented the results of an investigation in which ampuls exhibited dried drug substance on the tip of flame-sealed ampuls. Approximately 2% of these ampuls exhibited this leakage despite having undergone dye leak testing. Investigation by the firm found that the leaking ampuls had a stacked, ordered morphology of crystalline material that differed from the smooth morphology of normal vitreous glass. This change in morphology, which can occur when glass is held at high temperatures (flame sealing), is known as "devitrification" in the glass industry. The firm also found that fractures can occur in the area of devitrification. The fractures vary in width from 0.5 μm to 2.5 μm and follow a torturous path through the ampul tip.

When asking why these leakers were not detected, one should consult a publication by McVean et al. [7] for a nomogram following Poiseuille's law:

$$t = \frac{8 \times L \times V \times n}{\pi \times r^4 \times \Delta P} \tag{3}$$

Using this formula, McVean et al. established the minimum time t (sec) required for a volume V (cc) of a test solution of viscosity n (dyne-sec-cm^{-2}) to penetrate a capillary of length L (cm) and radius r (cm) when the pressure differential is ΔP (dyne = cm^{-2}).

Reading the nomogram (Fig. 6), one can see that a crack of 0.2 μm would require 50 hr in the dye bath at 2 atm of differential pressure.

One should also note that nomogram assumes that 0.00001 ml of dye solution will be detectable in the leaking ampul. This leads to a second problem encountered in dye leak testing, the dye solution itself. The selection of the dye solution is critical. The dye must be stable in the presence of the products being evaluated. Some dyes will revert to different optical isomers at

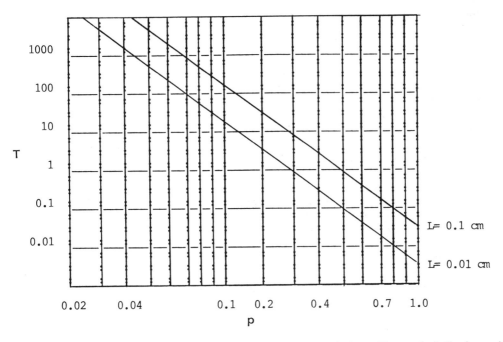

FIGURE 6 Radius of leaks. Nomogram for length of time, T, needed (in hours) for dye testing with a pressure differential of approximately 2 atm; L denotes the length (in centimeters) of the capillary leak. It is assumed that the amount of dye solution that must penetrate in order to ascertain visual detection is 10 (−5) ml and that the viscosity of the dye solution is 1 cps. The radius of the capillary leak, p, is expressed in microns [7].

various pH ranges, which will affect the visibility of the dye in the ampul. The breakage of ampul in the dye bath could also affect the dye concentration and pH. Thus, it is critical to monitor these parameters if one is reusing the dye solution.

There are two dye leak procedures normally utilized in the industry:

1. Vacuum dye leak procedure
   a. The ampuls are submerged in the dye solution in a vacuum chamber.
   b. The ampuls are vacuum-drawn and released.
   c. The ampuls are removed, rinsed with water, and dried.
   d. The ampuls are visually inspected for the presence of dye.

It has been reported by W. J. Artz et al. [8] that repeatedly releasing and drawing vacuum increases the effectiveness of the procedure, and that the use of a fast release is more effective than slowly releasing the vacuum.

2. Autoclave dye procedure
   a. The ampuls are submerged in the dye solution in an autoclave.
   b. The ampuls are autoclaved.
   c. The autoclave is slow-exhausted.
   d. The ampuls are rinsed, dried, and visually inspected.

The autoclave must be slowly exhausted to avoid boiling the dye solution. As the pressure in the autoclave is reduced, all of the ampuls must be submerged in the dye solution. Artz et al. [8] have found the autoclave dye procedure to be slightly more selective than the vacuum dye procedure because the extreme conditions during autoclaving may damage the weaker or more poorly sealed ampuls.

Before attempting to validate such a procedure, one should ask, "can a procedure whose effectiveness is questionable, and very difficult to quantify, be validated in the true sense?" The answer to this question is "No!" The procedure must be carefully developed to ensure that all ampuls receive the same treatment each time the procedure is performed.

There are a number of experiments that can contribute the final characterization of the dye leak test.

An earlier question must be answered: "Is the dye solution stable when diluted by the product?" Solutions of the product with varying concentrations of dye solution should be prepared and analyzed using visible spectroscopy. The solutions should be filled into ampuls, and the ampuls sealed and placed in a controlled storage area. Ampuls from each group should be removed and analyzed at varying intervals depending on the normal delay in the manufacturing process. I would recommend daily pulls the first week and weekly thereafter for 4 to 6 weeks. Once the stability of the dye solution has been established, the concentration of dye detectable by trained inspectors should be established.

Again, ampuls with varying concentrations of dye solution should be prepared. These seeded ampuls should be placed among groups of ampuls that have previously passed the dye leak test. The acceptable ampuls (group A) should have been previously inspected and accepted 100% of the time by a minimum of five trained inspectors. A sufficient number of seeded ampuls from each concentration (groups B, C, D, etc.) should be mixed with the group A ampuls so that the frequency of detection can be established.

The seeded population is now inspected by a minimum of five trained inspectors and the frequency of detection for each concentration is established. Upon completing the experiment, a plot (Fig. 7) should be developed indicating a threshold concentration above which 100% detection is always obtained.

This threshold concentration can be inserted onto the equation for Poiseuille's law to calculate the time required for passage of the dye solution. The dimension of the capillary openings in sealed ampuls is not so easily determined.

It is recommended to use a value that was experimentally determined by Greiff et al. [9] using laser imaging. Greiff's examination of machine-sealed ampuls showed the presence of helixlike channels in the ampul tips with a diameter of less than 5 μm.

The length of the channel could be determined simply by cutting the neck of the ampul and using calipers to measure the thickness of the tip.

As has been previously shown, devitrification cannot be detected by the dye leak procedure because of the excessive time period required to pass dye through fractures ranging from 0.15 to 0.5 μm. The calculations using Poiseuille's law will indicate the time required to detect leakers other than those caused by devitrification.

There is, however, a method now available that appears to be able to detect devitrification microfractures. Densok [10] of Japan claims that their pinhole inspection machine for ampuls can detect "pinholes" (0.5 μm and larger) in glass parenteral ampuls using electrostatic capacitance.

This detection method is based on the principle that a sealed ampul represents a greater capacitance than an unsealed ampul when placed between two electrodes of extremely high voltage differential.

To demonstrate this principle, Figure 8 shows the ampul in contact with the ground electrode B and the high-voltage electrode A at the point of inspection. The glass wall acts as a capacitance (C_a) between electrode A and the contents of the ampul, and again as capacitance (C_b) between the contents of the ampul and electrode B. The current as calculated by Ohm's law for the electrical circuit shown in Figure 8 is

$$I = \frac{V}{\frac{1}{2\pi f C_a} + R + \frac{1}{2\pi f C_b}} \qquad (4)$$

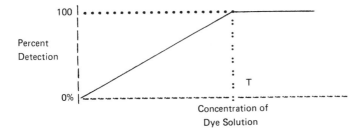

Percent
Detection

Concentration of
Dye Solution

FIGURE 7

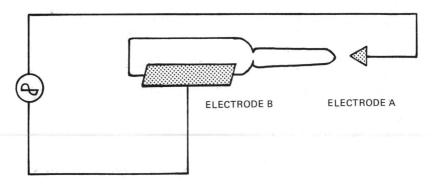

FIGURE 8

where

    I = current

    V = voltage

    f = frequency

    R = resistance

When a pinhole or leak exists, the capacitance C_a is zero and thus the current that passes between the two electrodes (see Fig. 10 for the resultant electrical circuit) is

$$I = \frac{V}{R + \dfrac{1}{2\pi f C_b}} \tag{5}$$

The Densok leak detector is capable of detecting an ampul leaker via this current differential. Densok has equipment available that challenges the entire ampul and not just the sealed tip.

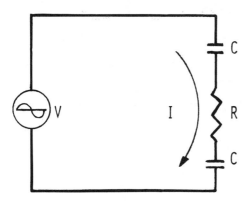

FIGURE 9 Ampul without pinhole.

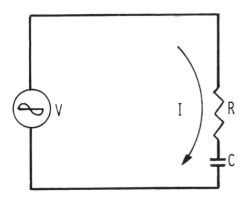

FIGURE 10 Ampul with pinhole.

The detection sensitivity is adjustable and should be established by each firm for each ampul size and each product.

The minimum requirement for electric conductivity of the solution is $5 \ \mu \mho \ cm^{-1}$.

The ideal method of setting the sensitivity is to artifically prepare ampuls with pinholes of the desired diameter. However, this is nearly impossible and not very practical. The best method available to most firms is to collect rejects from the dye leak test or ampuls that exhibit crystallization of the product on the exterior of the ampul. Ampuls that exhibit minimum leakage should be used, as this will represent the greatest challenge.

Once the sensitivity is set so that all rejects are removed by the leak detector, it may be desirable to increase the sensitivity slightly to provide a safety factor, since the test leakers were not selected with the greatest precision.

If a firm has the use of an electron microscope, it can select ampuls that exhibit devitrification from those ampuls that passed the dye leak test. This will provide the most positive control for the establishment of the sensitivity setpoint.

One should note that leakers cannot be repeatedly tested in the Densok leak detector, as the high voltage will eventually damage the ampul and increase the size of the leak.

Once the sensitivity has been established, the validation is relatively straightforward. A large group of ampuls that passed the dye leak test should be seeded with dye test leakers. The test group should be passed through the Densok leak detector and all leakers removed by the detector. No limit should be placed on ampuls that passed the dye leak test but were rejected by the Densok leak detector.

The Densok is a major step forward in leak detection, because we now have a process that we can quantify and challenge objectively.

B. Glass/Rubber Closure Systems

The validation of glass/rubber closure systems presents a problem different from verifying that ampuls are properly sealed. Once a glass ampul is properly sealed, the only way its integrity can be affected is by physical damage. The same cannot be said for glass/rubber closure systems. The stability of seal throughout the life of the product presents a problem that cannot be addressed by most stability programs, which evaluate the product by its physical, chemical, and, in some cases, its microbiological qualities.

Performing sterility tests during the product's shelf-life is insufficient because:

1. Statistically, a positive sterility test several years after manufacture is not conclusive; likewise, negative sterility results do not prove that the closure system has performed its intended function.
2. Many products contain preservative systems.

From the product development discipline, two tests have been used in conjunction to validate a container closure system [11].

The leak test defined by the Defense Personnel Support Center [12] has been utilized as a purely physical test of a container closure system. The test requires that the containers be placed in an inverted position for 2 hr at room temperature and then 4 hr at 49 ± 3°C. If the containers exhibit no evidence of leakage, they are considered to be acceptable.

If this test is utilized to evaluate container closure systems during product shelf life, significant data can be collected concerning the stability of the container closure system. If all are acceptable, up to 24 months, and later some failures appear, a change has occurred in the container closure system. It may not, however, be indicative of container closure system failure.

The second test that has been documented [11] in the validation of container closure systems requires filling containers with soybean-casein digest medium and precisely processing the filled containers according to normal production conditions.

If an aseptic filling process is used, a significant portion of the containers should be incubated at 30–35°C for 14 days prior to entering the test regimen and examined macroscopically for microbial growth. The USP growth promotion test [1] should also be performed at this time.

The remaining containers are stored at 23–25°C and annually the containers are removed and macroscopically inspected for growth. In addition, the USP growth promotion test [1] should be performed at each inspection interval.

A portion of the stored containers are placed in the inverted position. Annually, these vials are totally immersed in a suspension of *E. coli* which contains 10^8 colony-forming units per milliliter. The units are submerged for 10 min at 23 ± 2°C, removed without rinsing or drying, and placed in a biological hazard bag and incubated for 7 days at 30–35°C in the inverted position.

In conjunction, a growth promotion test should be performed on the negative units with less than 100 colony-forming units of *E. coli*. This biological test, though severe, does provide evidence that the container does maintain sterility under normal and abnormal conditions.

These tests are not practical for production control. It is critical that a test be performed that can correlate the biological test results to the consistent performance of the sealing process. One such test currently in use is a closure displacement test. Utilizing a digital micrometer and a spring force tester, it is possible to measure the force required to compress the capped closure at a specified distance (0.005 in). The greater downward force required, the more the rubber closure has been crimped by the metal cap. With such a test we now have a tool that can quantify the capping process during both the product development phase and normal production. Such a tool should be used during equipment setup and as an in-process test.

Values for the required downward force should be established for each container/closure/cap system. The concept requires that only a lower control limit be established for the closure displacement test. Extreme downward capping pressures will result in broken containers, which will be obvious to operating personnel. Having an operating criterion that can be related directly to Product Development studies is vital to any validation program.

Products terminally sterilized via steam are normally cooled with water prior to unloading from the autoclave. It must be shown that the container/ closure system maintains its integrity during the cooling process. Container/ closure integrity can be proven by adding a stable chemical entity to the cooling water and analyzing the product for the chemical entity. It is important to choose a chemical that meets the following criteria:

1. Nondestructive or corrosive to the autoclave system
2. Detectable in trace amounts in the presence of product

If the sterilization and cooling conditions can be reproduced in a laboratory system, containers filled with media can be sterilized and cooled with water containing extremely high microbial levels.

Before conducting such a laboratory experiment, it is necessary to validate the load configuration to ensure the sterility of the medium in the containers. Also, the growth-promoting property of the medium and the microbial level of the cooling water should be verified as part of the laboratory experiment.

This experiment, successfully completed, would prove that the container/ closure system does maintain its integrity during the sterilization and cooling process.

IV. INSPECTION

The requirement for inspection of each container of injectable product for contamination by visible foreign matter is clearly stated in USP XX, page 861 [1]. The reason for this requirement can be found in numerous medical papers [13–27] that discuss the possibility of human injury as a result of injected particulates. The papers conclude that thrombosis, phlebitis, renal infarction, brain damage, and death due to pulmonary insufficiency can occur. Thus, one can easily see why it is necessary to maintain the proper level of particulate control. Normally, statements as general as those that are made in the USP allow a degree of freedom that results in continuous development and improvement in the techniques utilized to accomplish the task in question. Such has been the case with particulate inspection. Most inspections today are performed by any of three general techniques:

1. Visible inspection with manual handling
2. Visible inspection with automated handling
3. Automated inspection

A. Visible Inspection

Visible inspection techniques have been studies in depth because inspection, being a critical part of the pharmaceutical process, is completely a human endeavor. Many psychophysical experiments have evaluated the relationship of luminance, contrast (object to background), and speed of vision to detection by the human eye.

Some important facts to consider when designing or validating the visible inspection process are the following:

1. For a high-contrast circular image against a background luminance of 110 ft/ambers, 90% of maximum visual acuity can be observed. This means that a 26-μm particle can be detected at a 20-cm viewing distance [28].

2. If the time required to detect an object exceeds 0.2 sec per pause, the probability of detection is decreased [29].

3. When inspecting for glass particles, the probability of detection increases sharply because of reflection [30].

The psychophysical theories are valuable, but the most important fact to remember is that visual inspection is probabilistic in nature. Units rejected by one inspector may be accepted by another. Thus, the primary variable that must be addressed is the inspector. How does one certify that an inspector is properly trained? There are several statistical techniques that can be used. These are discussed later in this section.

B. Presentation Devices

In order to increase the productivity of the inspection process, many firms have introduced automated presentation devices. The overall inspection time is reduced because the handling is entirely automated. The inspector's function is to simply view the containers as they pass through the field of view and remove the defective units by either manual or power-assisted means. These presentation devices can be operated at various speeds, some as high as 175 units/min. The units are normally equipped with a transportation mechanism that brings the units into the field of view, which has a black background and an adjustable source of illumination. It is critical to establish the optimal illumination prior to any attempts to validate the inspection system. Just prior to entering the field of view, the units are spun and stopped so that, in the viewing field, only the solution is spinning, along with any particulate that may be present. Depending on the size of the container being inspected and the focal distance, a magnifying glass may also be part of the equipment.

When changing from a purely manual inspection procedure to an automated presentation device, the validation can be conducted using those statistical techniques presented later in this section. However, there are some very important factors that must be emphasized when making such a change:

1. Trained visual inspectors should undergo additional training to become accustomed to inspection with the presentation device.

2. The operating speed of the presentation device should be established based on the normal defect level present in those operations leading up to the inspection process. If there is a significant variation in the defect level, the inspectors may not be able to respond quickly enough.

3. The inspectors should be instructed to alert their supervisors if the defect level is significantly higher than normal, so the machine can be slowed to allow removal of all defective units.

4. The inspection process should be monitored by an in-process testing group using manual visual inspection techniques.

The full advantages of presentation devices cannot be accrued unless the filling/sealing process is well controlled with a low and consistent defect level.

C. Automated

In response to stringent quality requirements and the competitive economic climate, many firms are now using totally automated inspection equipment that employs electronic image or light-scattering techniques.

There are two types of machines currently available, with slightly different operating principles. The Autoskan Electronic Video Inspection System, manufactured by the Lakso Company, Leominster, Massachusetts, and the Particulate Detection System (PDA), developed by Schering Corporation and manufactured by Electro-Nucleonics, Inc., Fairfield, New Jersey, are two of the most widely known.

The two units are similar in the presentation method. The container is precisely spun prior to placement in the viewing field. The spin is designed to rinse the sides of the container and dislodge any particles to ensure that the particles are moving in the solution. The principles of detection are different, however.

In the Autoskan, the liquid in the container is illuminated from the bottom, using an adjustable, high-intensity fiber optic light source. The light will reflect off the particles moving in liquid. The machine rapidly records multiple video images in its memory. The first six images establish that a container is in place and the fill volume is correct. The last image of these six becomes the "master image" in the memory. The next 16 images of the container are placed in the memory and compared to the "master image." Any image that is different from the "master image" will cause the machine to reject the container automatically [31].

This entire process occurs in less than a second and is repeated for each container presented to the camera. Container imperfections do not affect acceptance or rejection because the container is stationary during the image-taking process.

The Particulate Detection System (PD-100) also utilizes light deflected by particles moving in the liquid, but its treatment is different. The container volume is uniformly illuminated by fiber optic light pipes arranged in the equivalent of vertical slits at a horizontal angle that optimizes forward scattering for the particulate size range of interest. The Particulate Detection System is designed to operate by evaluating redundant data. The image volume is monitored by two or more planes, depending on the container diameter. Each plane is subdivided into multiple slitlike rectangular units. In this system, particle size is related to the particle's transit time across the slitlike rectangular unit. The accept/reject decision is based on an analysis of the distribution of particulate transit times combined with the special signals generated by glass particles for each container. This combined description is compared with stored criteria based on manual inspection performance to accept or reject each container [32].

Despite the differences in detection principles, the two inspection machines can be validated in the same manner. The first step, as in any validation, is to optimize the operating conditions under which the containers are being inspected, i.e., rate of spin and light intensity. An excessive spin rate will create bubbles, which will result in false rejects, and an insufficient spin rate can prevent particles from being suspended in the liquid. Variability in light intensity will cause signal fluctuations that will be interpreted as rejects by the detection device.

D. Statistical Validation

The particulate inspection of a parenteral container is probablistic in nature. An inspector will not always make the same accept/reject decision each time he or she inspects a container. If an ampul undergoes multiple inspections, the ampul can be categorized by its frequency of rejection. If an ampul is rejected seven out of ten times it is inspected, the probability of rejection is 0.7.

If a large population of ampuls undergoes multiple inspections, we can categorize the ampuls in the population by their probability of rejection. At the extremes of the population are very, very good ampuls (0.0 probability of rejection) and very, very bad ampuls (1.0 probability of rejection).

The population is divided into three categories according to the ampul's probability of rejection:

Category	Probability of rejection (single inspection)
1. Accept zone	(0.00–0.30)
2. Gray zone	(0.31–0.69)
3. Reject zone	(0.70–1.0)

By comparing the performance of an inspection process in these categories, definitive statements can be made about the validity of an inspection process.

The ability of an inspection process to properly reject those ampuls in the reject zone is measured by the reject zone efficiency (RZE). The RZE is calculated by Eq. (6):

$$RZE = \frac{\text{no. of reject zone containers rejected in the inspection process}}{\text{reject zone population}}$$

$$= \frac{RZR}{RZN} \tag{6}$$

The ability of the rejection process to minimize the rejection of acceptable ampuls in the accept and gray zones is measured by the undesired rejected rate (RAG). This is calculated by Eq. (7):

$$RAG = \frac{\text{no. of accept and gray zone containers rejected in the inspection process}}{\text{population of accept and gray zones}}$$

$$= \frac{AGR}{AZN + GZN} = \frac{AGR}{AGN} \tag{7}$$

These two parameters, RZE and RAG, characterize the inspection process from security and discriminatory standpoints, respectively. As RZE increases, there is greater assurance that the production will meet quality standards. As RAG decreases, there is greater assurance that acceptable units are not being rejected and the inspection process is economically more acceptable. Experience has shown that RZE and RAG can be mutually optimized, resulting in a more cost-effective inspection process at an equivalent security level.

In comparing two inspection methods, there are two hypotheses that must be considered:

1. *Null hypothesis*: The two methods being compared are not different from each other.
2. *Alternative hypothesis*: The manual method is better than the automated method by a probability of 0.05 (ΔRZE).

If the null hypothesis is satisfied, ARZE > MRZE and the automated inspection procedure is acceptable for use in normal production. If the alternative hypothesis is satisfied, MRZE > ARZE + ΔARZE, the automated inspection procedure is not acceptable for use in normal production.

The values of N (total rejects from multiple inspections of the test population by each inspection procedure sufficient to satisfy the hypothesis with a 0.95 confidence level) are calculated based on an ΔARZE of 0.05. This is illustrated in Figure 11.

It is important to consider that using Tables 3–8, one can determine how may times the test population must be inspected in order to ensure that the hypotheses are satisfied for various types of inspection procedures.

Make the following assumptions:

1. The test population contains a reject zone population (RZN) of 50.
2. The reject zone efficiency (RZE) of both the automated and manual inspection procedures is 0.85. (Experience has shown this to be a realistic value for RZE.)
3. The two inspection procedures being compared are "single-pass."

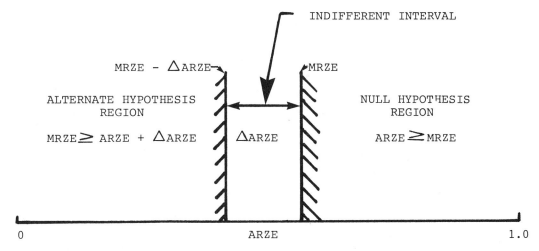

FIGURE 11 ΔARZE.

TABLE 3   One Pass of Standard Method M vs. One Pass of Method A

RZE = 0.050

MRZE$_1$	ARZE$_1$									
	0.70	0.71	0.72	0.73	0.74	0.75	0.76	0.77	0.78	0.79
0.70	1818	1800	1782	1764	1745	1726	1706	1686	1665	1644
0.71	1800	1782	1764	1745	1726	1706	1686	1665	1644	1623
0.72	1782	1764	1745	1726	1706	1686	1665	1644	1623	1601
0.73	1764	1745	1726	1706	1686	1665	1644	1623	1601	1579
0.74	1745	1726	1706	1686	1665	1644	1623	1601	1579	1556
0.75	1726	1706	1686	1665	1644	1623	1601	1579	1556	1533
0.76	1706	1686	1665	1644	1623	1601	1579	1556	1533	1509
0.77	1686	1665	1644	1623	1601	1579	1556	1533	1509	1485
0.78	1665	1644	1623	1601	1579	1556	1533	1509	1485	1461
0.79	1644	1623	1601	1579	1556	1533	1509	1485	1461	1436
0.80	1623	1601	1579	1556	1533	1509	1485	1461	1436	1411
0.81	1601	1579	1556	1533	1509	1485	1461	1436	1411	1385
0.82	1579	1556	1533	1509	1485	1461	1436	1411	1385	1359

p										
0.83	1556	1533	1509	1485	1461	1436	1411	1385	1359	1332
0.84	1533	1509	1485	1461	1436	1411	1385	1359	1332	1305
0.85	1509	1485	1461	1436	1411	1385	1359	1332	1305	1278
0.86	1485	1461	1436	1411	1385	1359	1332	1305	1278	1250
0.87	1461	1436	1411	1385	1359	1332	1305	1278	1250	1221
0.88	1436	1411	1385	1359	1332	1305	1278	1250	1221	1193
0.89	1411	1385	1359	1332	1305	1278	1250	1221	1193	1163
0.90	1385	1359	1332	1305	1278	1250	1221	1193	1163	1134
0.91	1359	1332	1305	1278	1250	1221	1193	1163	1134	1104
0.92	1332	1305	1278	1250	1221	1193	1163	1134	1104	1073
0.93	1305	1278	1250	1221	1193	1163	1134	1104	1073	1042
0.94	1278	1250	1221	1193	1163	1134	1104	1073	1042	1011
0.95	1250	1221	1193	1163	1134	1104	1073	1042	1011	979
0.96	1221	1193	1163	1134	1104	1073	1042	1011	979	947
0.97	1193	1163	1134	1104	1073	1042	1011	979	947	914
0.98	1163	1134	1104	1073	1042	1011	979	947	914	881
0.99	1134	1104	1073	1042	1011	979	947	914	881	847
1.00	1104	1073	1042	1011	979	947	914	881	847	813

N to satisfy H_0 and H_1 at $p = 0.05$ for two one-pass inspection systems. RZE_1's are shown: $N = RZN \times N_I$, where N_I is the total number of inspections performed. RZE for both hypotheses is 0.05.

TABLE 4　One Pass of Standard Method M vs. One Pass of Method A

RZE = 0.050

MRZE$_1$	ARZE$_1$									
	0.80	0.81	0.82	0.83	0.84	0.85	0.86	0.87	0.88	0.89
0.70	1623	1601	1579	1556	1533	1509	1485	1461	1436	1411
0.71	1601	1579	1556	1533	1509	1485	1461	1436	1411	1385
0.72	1579	1556	1533	1509	1485	1461	1436	1411	1385	1359
0.73	1556	1533	1509	1485	1461	1436	1411	1385	1359	1332
0.74	1533	1509	1485	1461	1436	1411	1385	1359	1332	1305
0.75	1509	1485	1461	1436	1411	1385	1359	1332	1305	1278
0.76	1485	1461	1436	1411	1385	1359	1332	1305	1278	1250
0.77	1461	1436	1411	1385	1359	1332	1305	1278	1250	1221
0.78	1436	1411	1385	1359	1332	1305	1278	1250	1221	1193
0.79	1411	1385	2359	1332	1305	1278	1250	1221	1193	1163
0.80	1385	1359	1332	1305	1278	1250	1221	1193	1163	1134
0.81	1359	1332	1305	1278	1250	1221	1193	1163	1134	1104
0.82	1332	1305	1278	1250	1221	1193	1163	1134	1104	1073
0.83	1305	1278	1250	1221	1193	1163	1134	1104	1073	1042
0.84	1278	1250	1221	1193	1163	1134	1104	1073	1042	1011

0.85	1250	1221	1193	1163	1134	1104	1073	1042	1011	979
0.86	1221	1193	1163	1134	1104	1073	1042	1011	979	947
0.87	1193	1163	1134	1104	1073	1042	1011	979	947	914
0.88	1163	1134	1104	1073	1042	1011	979	947	914	881
0.89	1134	1104	1073	1042	1011	979	947	914	881	847
0.90	1104	1073	1042	1011	979	947	914	881	847	813
0.91	1073	1042	1011	979	947	914	881	847	813	779
0.92	1042	1011	979	947	914	881	847	813	779	744
0.93	1011	979	947	914	881	847	813	779	744	709
0.94	979	947	914	881	847	813	779	744	709	673
0.95	947	914	881	847	813	779	744	709	673	637
0.96	914	881	847	813	779	744	709	673	637	601
0.97	881	847	813	779	744	709	673	637	601	564
0.98	847	813	779	744	709	673	637	501	564	526
0.99	813	779	744	709	673	637	601	564	526	488
1.00	779	744	709	673	637	601	564	526	488	450

N to satisfy H_0 and H_1 at $p = 0.05$ for two one-pass inspection systems. RZE_1's are shown: $N = RZN \times N_I$, where N_I is the total number of inspections performed. RZE for both hypotheses is 0.05.

TABLE 5   One Pass of Standard Method M vs. One Pass of Method A

RZE = 0.050

MRZE$_1$	ARZE$_1$										
	0.90	0.91	0.92	0.93	0.94	0.95	0.96	0.97	0.98	0.99	1.00
0.70	1385	1359	1332	1305	1278	1250	1221	1193	1163	1134	1104
0.71	1359	1332	1305	1278	1250	1221	1193	1163	1134	1104	1073
0.72	1332	1305	1278	1250	1221	1193	1163	1134	1104	1073	1042
0.73	1305	1278	1250	1221	1193	1163	1134	1104	1073	1042	1011
0.74	1278	1250	1221	1193	1163	1134	1104	1073	1042	1011	979
0.75	1250	1221	1193	1163	1134	1104	1073	1042	1011	979	947
0.76	1221	1193	1163	1134	1104	1073	1042	1011	979	947	914
0.77	1193	1163	1134	1104	1073	1042	1011	979	947	914	881
0.78	1163	1134	1104	1073	1042	1011	979	947	914	881	847
0.79	1134	1104	1073	1042	1011	979	947	914	881	847	813
0.80	1104	1073	1042	1011	979	947	914	881	847	813	779
0.81	1073	1042	1011	979	947	914	881	847	813	779	744
0.82	1042	1011	979	947	914	881	847	813	779	744	709
0.83	1011	979	947	914	881	847	813	779	744	709	673
0.84	979	947	914	881	847	813	779	744	709	673	637

0.85	947	914	881	847	813	779	744	709	673	637	601
0.86	914	881	847	813	779	744	709	673	637	601	564
0.87	881	847	813	779	744	709	673	637	601	564	526
0.88	847	813	779	744	709	673	637	601	564	526	488
0.89	813	779	744	709	673	637	601	564	526	488	450
0.90	779	744	709	673	637	601	564	526	488	450	411
0.91	744	709	673	637	601	564	526	488	450	411	372
0.92	709	673	637	601	564	526	488	450	411	372	332
0.93	673	637	601	564	526	488	450	411	372	332	292
0.94	637	601	564	526	488	450	411	372	332	292	252
0.95	601	564	526	488	450	411	372	332	292	252	211
0.96	564	526	488	450	411	372	332	292	252	211	170
0.97	526	488	450	411	372	332	292	252	211	170	128
0.98	488	450	411	372	332	292	252	211	170	128	86
0.99	450	411	372	332	292	252	211	170	128	86	43
1.00	411	372	332	292	252	211	170	128	86	43	0

N to satisfy H_0 and H_1 at p = 0.05 for two one-pass inspection systems. RZE_1's are shown: $N = RZN \times N_I$, where N_I is the total number of inspections performed. RZE for both hypotheses is 0.05.

TABLE 6   Two Passes of Standard Method M vs. Two Passes of Method A

RZE = 0.050

MRZE$_2$	ARZE$_2$									
	0.70	0.71	0.72	0.73	0.74	0.75	0.76	0.77	0.78	0.79
0.70	3564	3580	3592	3601	3607	3609	3607	3601	3590	3575
0.71	3580	3595	3607	3617	3622	3624	3622	3616	3606	3591
0.72	3592	3607	3620	3639	3635	3636	3635	3628	3618	3603
0.73	3601	3617	3629	3638	3644	3646	3644	3638	3627	3612
0.74	3607	3622	3635	3644	3649	3651	3649	3643	3633	3618
0.75	3609	3624	3636	3646	3651	3653	3651	3645	3635	3620
0.76	3607	3622	3635	3644	3649	3651	3649	3643	3633	3618
0.77	3601	3616	3628	3638	3643	3645	3643	3637	3627	3612
0.78	3590	3606	3618	3627	3633	3635	3633	3627	3616	3601
0.79	3575	3591	3603	3612	3618	3620	3618	3612	3601	3586
0.80	3555	3571	3583	3592	3598	3600	3598	3592	3581	3567
0.81	3531	3546	3559	3568	3573	3575	3573	3567	3557	3542
0.82	3501	3516	3529	3538	3543	3545	3543	3537	3527	3512
0.83	3465	3481	3493	3502	3508	3510	3508	3502	3491	3477
0.84	3424	3440	3452	3461	3467	3469	3467	3461	3450	3435

0.85	3377	3393	3405	3414	3420	3422	3420	3414	3403	3388
0.86	3324	3340	3352	3361	3367	3369	3367	3361	3350	3335
0.87	3265	3280	3292	3302	3307	3309	3307	3301	3291	3276
0.88	3198	3214	3226	3235	3241	3243	3241	3235	3224	3209
0.89	3125	3141	3153	3162	3158	3170	3168	3161	3151	3136
0.90	3045	3060	3072	3082	3087	3089	3087	3081	3071	3056
0.91	2957	2972	2984	2994	2999	3001	2999	2993	2983	2968
0.92	2861	2876	2889	2898	2903	2905	2903	2897	2887	2872
0.93	2757	2773	2785	2794	2800	2802	2800	2794	2783	2768
0.94	2645	2661	2673	2682	2688	2690	2688	2682	2671	2656
0.95	2524	2540	2552	2561	2567	2569	2567	2561	2550	2536
0.96	2395	2410	2423	2432	2437	2439	2438	2431	2421	2406
0.97	2256	2272	2284	2293	2299	2301	2299	2293	2282	2267
0.98	2108	2124	2136	2145	2151	2153	2151	2144	2134	2119
0.99	1950	1966	1978	1987	1993	1995	1993	1987	1976	1961
1.00	1782	1798	1810	1819	1825	1827	1825	1818	1808	1793

N to satisfy H_0 and H_1 at p = 0.05 for a two-pass inspection system. RZE_1's are shown: $N = RZN \times N_I$, where N_I is the total number of inspections performed. RZE for both hypotheses is 0.05.

TABLE 7   Two Passes of Standard Method M vs. Two Passes of Method A

RZE = 0.050

MRZE$_2$	ARZE$_2$									
	0.80	0.81	0.82	0.83	0.84	0.85	0.86	0.87	0.88	0.89
0.70	3555	3531	3501	3465	3424	3377	3324	3265	3198	3125
0.71	3571	3546	3516	3481	3440	3393	3340	3280	3214	3141
0.72	3583	3559	3529	3493	3452	3405	3352	3292	3226	3153
0.73	3592	3568	3538	3502	3461	3414	3361	3302	3235	3162
0.74	3598	3573	3543	3508	3467	3420	3367	3307	3241	3168
0.75	3600	3575	3545	3510	3469	3422	3369	3309	3243	3170
0.76	3598	3573	3543	3508	3467	3420	3367	3307	3241	3168
0.77	3592	3567	3537	3502	3461	3414	3361	3301	3235	3161
0.78	3581	3557	3527	3491	3450	3403	3350	3291	3224	3151
0.79	3567	3542	3512	3477	3435	3388	3335	3276	3209	3136
0.80	3547	3522	3492	3457	3416	3369	3316	3256	3190	3116
0.81	3522	3497	3467	3432	3391	3344	3291	3231	3165	3092
0.82	3492	3467	3438	3402	3361	3314	3261	3201	3135	3062
0.83	3457	3432	3402	3367	3326	3279	3226	3166	3100	3026
0.84	3416	3391	3361	3326	3285	3238	3185	3125	3059	2985

p										
0.85	3369	3344	3314	3279	3238	3191	3138	3078	3012	2938
0.86	3316	3291	3261	3226	3185	3138	3084	3025	2958	2885
0.87	3256	3231	3201	3166	3125	3078	3025	2965	2899	2826
0.88	3190	3165	3135	3100	3059	3012	2958	2899	2832	2759
0.89	3116	3092	3062	3026	2985	2938	2885	2826	2759	2686
0.90	3036	3011	2981	2946	2905	2858	2805	2745	2679	2605
0.91	2948	2923	2893	2858	2817	2770	2717	2657	2591	2518
0.92	2852	2828	2798	2762	2721	2674	2621	2561	2495	2422
0.93	2749	2724	2694	2659	2617	2570	2517	2458	2391	2318
0.94	2636	2612	2582	2546	2505	2458	2405	2346	2279	2206
0.95	2516	2491	2461	2426	2385	2336	2285	2225	2159	2085
0.96	2386	2362	2332	2296	2255	2208	2155	2095	2029	1956
0.97	2248	2223	2193	2158	2117	2070	2016	1957	1890	1817
0.98	2099	2075	2045	2009	1968	1921	1868	1809	1742	1569
0.99	1941	1917	1887	1851	1810	1763	1710	1651	1584	1511
1.00	1773	1749	1719	1683	1642	1595	1542	1483	1416	1343

N to satisfy H_0 and H_1 at p = 0.05 for a two-pass inspection system. RZE_1's are shown: $N = RZN \times N_I$, where N_I is the total number of inspections performed. RZE for both hypotheses is 0.05.

TABLE 8   Two Passes of Standard Method M vs. Two Passes of Method A

RZE = 0.050

MRZE$_2$	ARZE$_2$										
	0.90	0.91	0.92	0.93	0.94	0.95	0.96	0.97	0.98	0.99	1.00
0.70	3045	2957	2861	2757	1645	2524	2395	2256	2108	1950	1782
0.71	3060	2972	2876	2773	2661	2540	2410	2272	2124	1966	1798
0.72	3072	2984	2889	2785	2673	2552	2423	2284	2136	1978	1810
0.73	3082	2994	2898	2794	2682	2561	2432	2293	2145	1987	1819
0.74	3087	2999	2903	2800	2688	2567	2438	2299	2151	1993	1825
0.75	3089	3001	2905	2802	2690	2569	2439	2301	2153	1995	1827
0.76	3087	2999	2903	2800	2688	2567	2437	2299	2151	1993	1825
0.77	3081	2993	2897	2794	2682	2561	2431	2293	2144	1987	1818
0.78	3071	2983	2887	2783	2671	2550	2421	2282	2134	1976	1808
0.79	3056	2968	2872	2768	2656	2536	2406	2267	2119	1961	1793
0.80	3036	2948	2852	2749	2636	2516	2386	2248	2099	1941	1773
0.81	3011	2923	2828	2724	2612	2491	2362	2223	2075	1917	1749
0.82	2981	2893	2798	2694	2582	1461	2332	2193	2045	1887	1719
0.83	2946	2858	2762	2659	2546	2426	2296	2158	2009	1851	1683
0.84	2905	2817	2721	2617	2505	2385	2255	2117	1968	1810	1642

0.85	2858	2770	2674	2570	2458	2338	2208	2070	1921	1763	1595
0.86	2805	2717	2621	2517	2405	2285	2155	2016	1868	1710	1542
0.87	2745	2657	2561	2458	2346	2225	2095	1957	1809	1651	1483
0.88	2679	2591	2495	2391	2279	2159	2029	1890	1742	1584	1416
0.89	2605	2518	2422	2318	2206	2085	1956	1817	1669	1511	1343
0.90	2525	2437	2341	2238	2126	2005	1875	1737	1589	1431	1263
0.91	2437	2349	2253	2150	2038	1917	1787	1649	1501	1343	1175
0.92	2341	2253	2158	2054	1942	1821	1692	1553	1405	1247	1079
0.93	2238	2150	2054	1950	1838	1718	1588	1449	1301	1143	975
0.94	2126	2038	1942	1838	1726	1605	1476	1337	1189	1031	863
0.95	2005	1917	1821	1718	1605	1485	1355	1217	1068	910	742
0.96	1875	1787	1692	1588	1476	1355	1226	1087	939	781	613
0.97	1737	1649	1553	1449	1337	1217	1087	948	800	642	474
0.98	1589	1501	1405	1301	1189	1068	939	800	652	494	326
0.99	1431	1343	1247	1143	1031	910	781	642	494	336	168
1.00	1263	1175	1079	975	863	742	613	474	326	168	0

N to satisfy H_0 and H_1 at $p = 0.05$ for two-pass inspection system. RZE_1's are shown: $N = RZN \times N_I$, where N_I is the total number of inspections performed. RZE for both hypotheses is 0.05.

Then the N to satisfy the null and alternative hypotheses at p = 0.05 is 1104, which equates to approximately 22 inspections of the test population. A data base of 22 inspections by both methods is required to ensure that a correct evaluation can be made with a 0.95 confidence level.

To begin the validation, the test population must be established. In the experiments performed by Knapp, Kushner, and Abrahamson [33—36], a test population of 250 was constructed. It contained the following:

1. 125 ampuls randomly selected from a normal production batch.
2. 125 ampuls whose probability of rejection was 0.3 or greater. (These ampuls were selected rejects that were inspected by two senior inspectors a total of ten times.)

To ensure normal inspector responses, the proportion of reject zone containers in the test batch should be less than 25%. This may be lowered if the manufacturing process normally produces rejects in a range from 1 to 5%.

Once the test population is selected, there are some precautions that must be followed to ensure unbiased results:

1. The labels used to sequentially number the containers should be as small as possible.
2. A clerk (not an inspector involved in the test) is required to document the raw data.
3. The order in which the containers are presented to the inspector should be randomized.
4. The inspections should be performed at the same time of day, as fatigue is a large factor in the inspector's performance.

For the discussion here, we will concentrate on the evaluation of "single-pass" inspection procedures. The equations listed herein should be modified for each additional pass included in the inspection process.

For each ampul in the test population, there are two parameters that make up the data point:

1. P_m, the probability of rejection (one manual inspection)
2. P_a, the probability of rejection (one automated inspection)

Using the matrix form in Figure 12, we can group each parameter into 11 partitions, thus creating 121 data points. We can total the number of ampuls occurring at each data point.

We can now calculate the reject zone efficiency (RZE) for a single manual inspection (m_1) and a single automated inspection (a_1).

1. Total each column 2—12 and record the totals in row 12.
2. Total each row 1—11 and record the totals in column 1.
3. Calculate the reject zone population (RZN) for a single manual inspection by adding the values in row 12, columns 9, 10, 11, and 12. This is demonstrated by Eq. 8:

$$RZN = N(.7) + N(.8) + N(.9) + N(1.0) \tag{8}$$

4. Calculate the reject zone rejects (RZRs) for a single manual inspection (m_1) by multiplying the population (N) of each partition within the

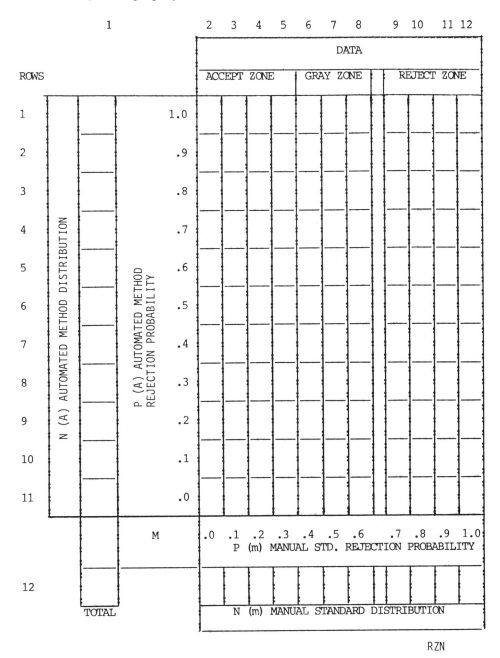

FIGURE 12   Matrix form.

reject zone (row 12, columns 9, 10, 11, and 12) by its respective
probability of rejection, $P(m_1)$, and then total the resulting product
from each zone. This is demonstrated by Eq. (9):

$$RZR(m_1) = 0.7N(0.7) + 0.8N(0.8) + 0.9N(0.9) + 1.0N(1.0)$$

$$(9)$$

5. Calculate the reject zone efficiency (RZE) for a single manual inspection (m_1) by Eq. (10):

$$RZE(m_1) = \frac{RZR(m_1)}{RZN}$$

$$(10)$$

6. Calculate the reject zone rejects (RZRs) for a single automated inspection (a_1) by adding the values in columns 9, 10, 11, and 12 for
   each row 1−11. Multiply each total by its respective probability of
   rejection, $P(a_1)$, via a single automated inspection. The total of the
   products can be shown by Eq. (11):

$$RZR(a_1) = (0.1) [N(0.1, 0.7) + N(0.1, 0.8) + N(0.1, 0.9)$$

$$+ N(0.1, 1.0)] + (0.2) [N(0.2, 0.7) + N(0.2, 0.8)$$

$$+ N(0.2, 0.9) + N(0.2, 1.0)] + \ldots (1.0) [N(1.0, 0.7)$$

$$+ N(1.0, 0.8) + N(1.0, 0.9) + N(1.0, 1.0)] \qquad (11)$$

7. Calculate the reject zone efficiency (RZE) for a single automated inspection (a_1) by Eq. (12):

$$RZE(a_1) = \frac{RZR(a_1)}{RZN}$$

$$(12)$$

If $RZE(a_1) > RZE(m_1)$, then the automated inspection method is more secure
than the current manual inspection method.

The same matrix can be used in the calculation of the reject rate in the
accept and gray zones (RAG) for both the manual and automated inspection
procedures.

1. Calculate the population of the accept and gray zone (AGN) for a
   single manual inspection (m_1) by adding the values in columns 2−8,
   row 12. This is demonstrated by Eq. (13):

$$AGN = N(0) + N(0.1) + N(0.2) + N(0.3) + N(0.4) + N(0.5)$$

$$+ N(0.6) \qquad (13)$$

2. Calculate the accept and gray zone rejects (AGRs) via a single manual
   inspection (m_1) by multiplying the population (N) within each partition
   of the accept and gray zones (columns 2−8, row 12) by their respective

probability of rejection, $P(m_1)$. The sum of these products is $AGR(m_1)$, as shown by Eq. (14):

$$AGR(m_1) = 0\ N(0.0) + 0.1N(0.1) + 0.2N(0.2) + 0.3N(0.3)$$

$$+ 0.4N(0.4) + 0.5N(0.5) + 0.6N(0.6) \tag{14}$$

3. The reject rate in the accept and gray zones for a single manual inspection, $RAG(m_1)$, is calculated by Eq. (15):

$$RAG(m_1) = \frac{AGR(m_1)}{AGN} \tag{15}$$

4. Calculate the accept and gray zone rejects (AGRs) via a single automated inspection (a_1) by adding the values in columns 2−8 for each row 1−11. Multiply each total by its respective probability of rejection, $P(a_1)$, via a single automated inspection (a_1). The total of the products can be shown by the equation:

$$AGR(a_1) = (0.1)\ [N(0.1,\ 0.0) + N(0.1,\ 0.1) + N(0.1,\ 0.2)$$

$$+ N(0.1,\ 0.3) + N(0.1,\ 0.4) + N(0.1,\ 0.5)$$

$$+ N(0.1,\ 0.6)] + (0.2)\ [N(0.2,\ 0.0) + N(0.2,\ 0.1)$$

$$+ N(0.2,\ 0.2) + N(0.2,\ 0.3) + N(0.2,\ 0.4)$$

$$+ N(0.2,\ 0.5) + N(0.2,\ 0.6)] \ .\ .\ .\ (1.0)\ [N(1.0,\ 0.0)$$

$$+ N(1.0,\ 0.1) + N(1.0,\ 0.2) + N(1.0,\ 0.3)$$

$$+ N(1.0,\ 0.4) + N(1.0,\ 0.5) + N(1.0,\ 0.6)] \tag{16}$$

5. The reject rate in the accept and gray zones for a single automated inspection, $RAG\ (a_1)$, is calculated by Eq. (17):

$$RAG(a_1) = \frac{AGR(a_1)}{AGN} \tag{17}$$

If $RAG(a_1) < RAG(m_1)$, the automated inspection method is more discriminating than the manual method.

It is important to note that the calculations presented here will provide approximate values, because we are grouping the data points into partitions. The exact values can be obtained by using the actual probability of rejection for each ampul in the zone of interest.

Other techniques have been utilized for the validation of automated inspection procedures, but none has a sound theoretical basis as exhibited by the comparison of RZE and RAG.

One of the techniques used is a graphical technique that compares the consistency and variability.

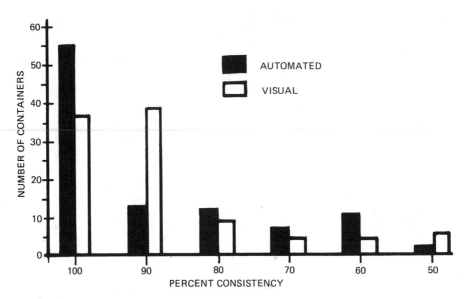

FIGURE 13   Consistency test.

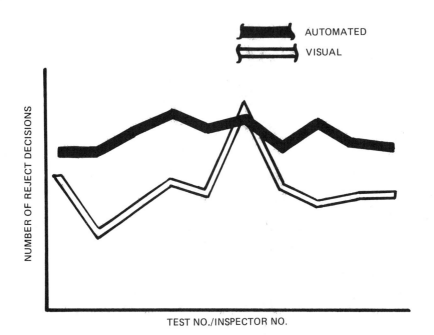

FIGURE 14   Variability graph.

Consistency	
100%	Sum of units rejected 100% plus units accepted 100%
90%	Sum of units rejected 90% plus units accepted 90%
80%	Sum of units rejected 80% plus units accepted 80%
70%	Sum of units rejected 70% plus units accepted 70%
60%	Sum of units rejected 60% plus units accepted 60%
50%	Sum of units rejected 50% plus units accepted 50%

When the histogram (Fig. 13) for each inspection method is plotted on the same chart, the automated inspection technique should show significantly more units at 100% consistency and fewer units at 90% consistency.

Also, the variation can be compared by plotting the percentage rejected for each inspector/test number. The automated technique should show a higher mean value and less variation when compared to the visual inspection technique (Fig. 14).

This technique does not really address the ability of the inspection procedure to discriminate bad from good, since it looks primarily for repeatability.

V. LABELING AND FINAL PACKAGING

The concept of validating labeling and final packaging is very difficult to put into actual practice in today's manufacturing climate. The variety of methods and equipment utilized to perform these tasks varies from hand application of labels to high-speed machines that label containers, place containers and literature into cartons, detect missing or incorrect components, and package into shipping cases at speeds of several hundred units per minute.

Validation is more successful with a process that is highly mechanized. The greater the human involvement, the less reliability can be guaranteed over the full duration of a process. This is a primary reason why in-process monitoring is critical to controlling any labeling and packaging process.

In this section, we will concentrate not on the validation of high-speed labeling and packaging equipment, but rather on the preparation of new equipment for introduction into the manufacturing process.

Why not validate high-speed, automated packaging equipment? Experience has shown us that these automated processes are very dependent on component quality, mechanical setup, and the experience and ability of the responsible mechanic. Validation of such systems is impractical.

Most pharmaceutical companies evaluate equipment before purchasing and receiving the equipment in their facility. However, these evaluations, although performed with actual components, are never performed under production conditions and never for a significant period of time. In order to prepare such equipment for introduction into the manufacturing process, there are three phases that must be completed once the equipment is installed in the facility. These three phases are normally referred to as Installation Qualification (IQ), debugging, and Operational Qualification (OQ).

A. Installation Qualification

Installation Qualification is primarily a tool to assist a project engineer in ensuring that those items which are necessary for a piece of machinery to operate in the pharmaceutical environment are in place. This includes the following:

1. Purchasing and design specification file
2. All appropriate SOPs and logs
3. Preventive maintenance program
4. Spare parts
5. Lubricants
6. Instrumentation list
7. Utility connections

The documentation completed by the project engineer during this phase will determine: (a) if the equipment purchased meets all required specifications; and (b) if the equipment has been properly installed.

The debugging phase is that period during which the project engineer has a free hand to operate the equipment in whatever manner he or she desires so that the machine performs all of the intended tasks. Any major modifications that must be made during this time must be documented and included in the IQ.

B. Operational Qualification

Operational Qualification (OQ) specifically tests each function of the machine to ensure that it will perform the intended tasks when properly set up and adjusted. As a minimum requirement, OQ normally includes three general categories called "SOP Verification," "Controls and Interlocks Verification," and "Commodity and Product Handling."

The SOP Verification requires the testing personnel to review the current, approved SOPs and witness the equipment/operating personnel functioning to verify that the SOP is properly written and accurate. This technique is commonly used by FDA inspectors during Good Manufacturing Practices (GMP) inspections.

The "Controls and Interlock Verification" requires a detailed evaluation of each control and interlock on the equipment to ensure that each is performing its intended function. The first step is to prepare a list of all "controls and interlocks" and should include such items as:

Bar code detectors
Print verification detectors
Missing component detection systems
Emergency stop buttons
Heat control indicators

These are just a few examples, but the list should include "controls and interlocks" necessary to ensure personnel safety when operating the equipment. To ensure that the various detection devices function properly, it will be necessary to prepare challenge commodities. In the case of a bar code detector, one can simply block all or part of the bar code of approximately 10 components, whether they be labels, cartons, etc. These modified components sufficient to operate the equipment for at least 1 hr. The testing personnel will monitor the equipment and verify that the equipment detects the modified commodity and reacts accordingly, i.e., alarms or cessation of the operation or both.

The ultimate test is the "Product and Commodity Handling." During this test, the equipment is operated at its maximum and minimum speeds for a minimum of several hours at each speed. Actual product and components should be used during these runs so that the resultant production can be sampled and tested by the in-process testing group to assure that the firm's Quality Assurance standards are met.

This testing regimen cannot be considered a validation because 3 hr of operation is not a sufficient period of time for a packaging operation. The primary difference between packaging equipment and filling/sealing equipment is the components the two equipment groups handle. The filling equipment handles rigid components, i.e., glass containers, rubber stoppers, and metal caps. The equipment can be precisely designed to handle these components because of the very small dimensional tolerances allowed for glass and rubber components. The opposite is true of packaging equipment, of which the worst offender is a cartoning machine, which must place literature (insert), a container, and sometimes an administration aid (syringe plunger rod) into a carton. The placement of these components into an open carton is the most pivotal point because the components are pushed from a moving partitioned conveyor belt into the opened carton, which is also moving.

Another factor that adds to the variability of such equipment is multiple vendors. In most cases, there are differences in commodities supplied by different vendors.

By following the testing outlined herein, we have prepared the equipment for production use, but we cannot guarantee the overall efficiency of the equipment or the package quality without statistical sampling. During the initial production, higher sampling levels or tightened inspections are recommended. As the equipment is used in normal production and mechanics become more aware of the fine adjustments required by such machinery, the efficiency will increase and the overall quality level will improve.

This is not to say that the mechanics and operating personnel should not be trained prior to OQ or production, but there is a certain familiarity that is necessary for a packaging system (equipment/personnel) to reach its optimum efficiency and quality level. This familiarity can be obtained only from operating the equipment over an extended time period.

VI. TRAINING

Training of personnel in the pharmaceutical industry is essential to the production of "safe, pure, and effective" drug products which are used in the maintenance of a healthy populace.

The Current Good Manufacturing Practices (CGMPs) [37], published September 29, 1978, require that "each person engaged in . . . [and] . . . each person responsible for supervising the manufacture, processing, packing or holding of a drug product shall have the education, training and experience or a combination thereof, to enable that person to perform the assigned functions."

The validation of a filling or packaging system is not valid unless the personnel operating the equipment during the testing have been properly trained. The personnel operating the equipment during this test period should be expected to operate this equipment once validation ends and normal production begins. If only your best employees were used during validation tests, you may enter the production mode blindly, only to discover significant problems.

Since filling and packaging equipment require more routine interaction with maintenance and operating personnel than an autoclave, the need for operator training and its impact on validation are even greater.

Training of maintenance and operating personnel cannot be accomplished solely by classroom lectures and demonstrations. However, classroom instruction does play an important role in personnel training. Its role is to provide a general introduction to the equipment, the operator's primary duties, the necessary safety precautions, and other portions of the manufacturing process that may interface with the area in which the operators are working.

The type of introductory training can be conveyed via various means, such as supervisory lectures, plant tours, films, and slide-tape programs.

Upon completion of the introductory training, these personnel are ready to participate in the debugging phase, which is the start of the final phase of training. With today's complex machinery, the maintenance and operating personnel must work with the equipment over an extended period of time to become proficient at their tasks. Normally, the equipment manufacturers will supply engineers and technicians to assist in the installation and initial debugging of the equipment. These people are the primary source of direct hands-on training for the maintenance personnel. But they can provide only the basics of operation, setup, and maintenance. Real working knowledge can only be gained by the experience of operating the equipment over an extended period of time.

Many times, project engineers underestimate the time and expense required to debug and validate such equipment. The personnel must be given the opportunity to gain some experience before Operational Qualification testing begins.

VII. GLOSSARY

A_2 Constant utilized in the calculation of upper and lower control limits for X

AGN   Population of the accept and gray zones

AGR   Number of accept and gray zone containers rejected in a single inspection

ARZE   Automated reject zone efficiency

AZN   Accept zone population

C   Capacitance

D_3, D_4 Constants utilized in the calculation of upper and lower control limits for R

ΔARZE   Differential automated reject zone efficiency

ΔP	Pressure differential between the two sides of a capillary opening expressed in dyne-cm^{-2}
F	Frequency
GZN	Gray zone population
I	Electrical current
L	Capillary length in centimeters
L_c	Label claim indicated on unit labeling
MRZE	Manual reject zone efficiency
n	Viscosity of test solution in dyne-sec-cm^{-2}
N	Number of times a container is inspected
P	Probability of rejection for a test container
r	Radius of capillary opening in centimeters
$\overline{R}$	Average of the ranges for a number of subgroups
R	Range of values in a subgroup
R	Resistance
RAG	Undesired reject rate in the accept and gray zones
$R(m_1)$	Number of times a test container is rejected via a single manual inspection
RZE	Reject zone efficiency
RZN	Reject zone population
RZR	Number of reject zone containers rejected in a single inspection
σ	Standard deviation
t	Time in seconds
T	Target fill for the setup of filler, measured in either weight or volume

ACKNOWLEDGMENT

Deep appreciation goes to my wife, Margie, who provided all of the necessary clerical assistance. Also, her love and encouragement were integral for the completion of the chapter.

T_C Threshold concentration.

V Voltage.

V Volume of liquid passing through a capillary of length L.

$\overline{X}$ Average of a subgroup of values.

$\overline{\overline{X}}$ Average of mean values from a number of subgroups.

$\circledinfty$ Voltage source.

REFERENCES

1. *The United States Pharmacopeia*, 20th Ref., 1980. Mack Publishing Co., Easton, Pa.
2. Unpublished Report, T–L Systems Corporation, Minneapolis, Minn.
3. Nicholas, R. J. 1980. A new concept for aqueous solution filling that is electronically instead of mechanically based. Paper presented to the Pharm. Tech. Conf., New York.
4. Juran, J. M. 1974. *Quality Control Handbook*, 3rd ed. McGraw–Hill Book Company, New York.
5. *Remington's Pharmaceutical Sciences*, 15th ed., 1975. Mack Publishing Co., Easton, Pa.
6. Crouthamel, T. G. 1981. Microfractures in parenteral glass ampuls. *J. Parenter. Sci. Technol. 35*: 18–19.
7. McVean, D. E., Tuerck, P. A., Christenson, G. L., and Cartensen, J. T. 1972. *J. Pharm. Sci. 61*: 1609.
8. Artz, W. J., Gloor, W. T., Jr., and Reese, D. R. 1961. *J. Pharm. Sci. 50*: 258.
9. Greiff, D., Melton, H., and Rowe, T. W. G. 1975. *Cryobiology 12*: 1–14.
10. Unpublished report, Nikka Densok Ltd., Tokyo, Japan.
11. Freiben, W. R., Folck, R. J., and Derisser, A. 1982. *J. Pharm. Sci. Technol. 36*: 112–116.
12. Federal Specifications, PP-C-186 C, November 10, 1976, Containers, Packaging & Packing for Drugs, Chemical and Pharmaceutical, Defense Personnel Support Center, Directorate of Medical Material, Philadelphia.
13. Konwaler, B. E. 1950. Pulmonary emboli of cotton fibers. *Am. J. Clin. Pathol. 20*: 385.
14. Jaques, W. E., and Mariscal, G. G. 1951. Study of incidence of cotton emboli. *Bull, Int. Assoc. Med. Museum 32*: 63.
15. Bruning, E. J. 1955. Uber Entstehung und Bedeutung intraarterieller Fremdkorperembolien der kindlicken Lunge. *Arch. Pathol. Anat. Physiol. Klin. Med. 327*: 460.
16. Sarrut, S., and Nexelof, Ch. 1960. A complication of intravenous therapy: Giant cellular macrophagic pulmonary arteritis. *Press Med. 68*: 375.
17. Von Glahn, W. C., and Hall, J. W. 1949. Reaction produced in pulmonary arteries by emboli of cotton fibers. *Am. J. Pathol. 25*: 575.
18. Garvan, J. M., and Gunner, B. W. 1963–1964. The harmful effects of particles in intravenous fluids. *Med. J. Aust. 2*: 140; 1(1).

19. Jaffe, R. B., and Koschman, E. B. 1970. Intravenous drug abuse, pulmonary, cardiac, and vascular complications. *Am. J. Roentgenol.*, *109*: 107.

20. Douglas, F. G., Kafilmout, K. J., and Pratt, N. L. 1971. Foreign particle embolism in drug addicts: Respiratory pathophysiology. *Ann. Intern. Med. 75*: 872.

21. Walter, C. W., Safety of large volume parenteral solutions. FDA Symp., FDA, Washington, D.C. p 83.

22. Silberman, J., Cravioto, H., and Feign, L. 1960. Foreign body emboli following cerebral angiography. *Arch. Neurol. 13*: 711.

23. Chason, J. L., Landers, J. W., and Swanson, R. E. 1963. Cotton fiber embolism. A frequent complication of cerebral angiography. *Neurology 13*: 558.

24. Adams, D. F., Tord, B. D., and Kosek, J. 1965. Cotton fiber embolization during angiography. A clinical and experimental study. *Radiology 84*: 678.

25. Jaffe, N. S. 1970. Elimination of particulate contamination from ophthalmic solutions for intraocular surgery. *Bull. Parenter. Drug Assoc. 24*: 218.

26. Ryan, P. B., Rapp, R. P., DeLuca, P. P., Griffen, W. O., Clark, J. D., and Cloys, D. 1973. In-line final filtration—A method of minimizing contamination in intravenous therapy. *Bull. Parenter. Drug Assoc. 27*: 1.

27. DeLuca, P. P., Rapp, R. P., Bivin, B., McKean, H. E., and Griffen, W. O. 1975. Filtration and infusion phlebitis: A double-blind prospective clinical study. *Am. J. Hosp. Pharm. 32*: 1001.

28. Lythgoe, R. J. 1932. Measurement of visual acuity, Special report no. 173. Medical Research Council, H. M. Stationery Office, London.

29. Blackwell, H. R. 1958. The effects of certain psychological variables upon target detectability, Engineering Research Institute Report 2455-12F, University of Michigan, Ann Arbor.

30. Knapp, J. Z., and Kushner, H. K. 1982. Particulate inspection of parenteral products: from biophysics to automation. *J. Parenter. Sci. Technol. 36*: 121.

31. Unpublished report, The Lakso Company, Leominster, Mass.

32. Knapp, J. Z., Kushner, H. K., and Zeiss, J. C., 1982. A validation procedure for the particulate inspection of parenteral products.

33. Knapp, J. Z., Kushner, H. K. 1980. Generalized methodology for evaluation of parenteral inspection procedures. *J. Parenter. Sci. Technol. 34*: 14.

34. Knapp, J. Z., and Kushner, H. K. 1980. Implementation and automation of a particle detection system for parenteral products. *J. Parent. Sci. Technol. 34*: 369.

35. Knapp, J. Z., Kushner, H. K., and Abramson, L. R. 1981. Automated particulate detection for ampuls with use of the probabilistic particulate detection model. *J. Parenter. Sci. Technol. 35*: 21.

36. Knapp, J. Z., Kushner, H. K., and Abramson, L. R. 1981. Particulate inspection of parenteral products: An Assessment. *J. Parenter. Sci. Technol. 35*: 176.

37. Current Good Manufacturing Practices for finished pharmaceuticals. 1978. *Fed. Reg. 43*(190), Sec. 211.25 (a) and (b).

22
Validation of the Lyophilization Process

THOMAS A. JENNINGS

T. A. Jennings Associates, Inc., Bala Cynwyd, Pennsylvania

I. INTRODUCTION

Under normal storage conditions, the formulation of aseptic pharmaceutical products, especially those using an aqueous base, may undergo a host of chemical reactions that can eventually lead to denaturation [1–6]. As a result of these reactions, the therapeutic value of the product is lost because of a significant reduction in the concentration of an active ingredient or the formation of an undesirable by-product. Depending on the kinetics of such reactions, the useful life of the pharmaceutical formulation may be limited to a matter of days or even hours. For these reasons, a stabilization process is necessary and often is the last step in the manufacture of an aseptic pharmaceutical formulation.

Freezing of the product is one means of obtaining long-term stability [1,5, 7,8]. By this means, the drug is separated into a matrix consisting of ice crystals and interstitial drug constituents. Stability of the product can be maintained as long as the storage temperature is low enough to prevent the interaction of free mobile water with the interstitial materials [7,9–11]. After thawing, the drug is ready to be administered.

A second drug stabilizing process is commonly known as lyophilization [1,12–15]. This process achieves stability by first forming a frozen matrix. Then, while the drug is maintained in a frozen state, the water is removed, at subatmospheric pressures, by sublimation and desorption. Long-term stability of the drug can be maintained at ambient temperatures provided the dried product is protected from water vapor, oxidizers, and light. The removal of the ice crystals generates a dried drug that has a highly porous structure and hence is lyophile characteristic, i.e., its rapid solubility in the original solvent [15].

Since the role of the stabilizing process is to ensure the continued safety, strength, quality, and purity of the drug until usage, the process must be validated; i.e., the process must be shown to be reproducible within specified limits. Lack of adequate controls of materials, process parameters, equipment, and instrumentation can lead to large variations in the properties of the final product. Such large variations not only will affect the product's quality and stability but also can affect the very financial well-being of the manufacturer through "lost batches" and a possible recall of a given product.

The remainder of this chapter considers the lyophilization process as a stabilizing process and a method for establishing the constancy for a material, process, or apparatus. Special emphasis will be given to the role that the process water plays in the lyophilization process and the effects that packaging materials can have on the long-term stability of the product. Means for validation of the freeze-drying equipment and its associated instrumentation will likewise be examined.

II. FUNDAMENTAL CONCEPTS

A. General Principles of Lyophilization

The lyophilization process is defined as one in which the product or formulation is first frozen and then the quantity of the major solvent system, generally water, is reduced, by sublimation and desorption, to levels that will no longer support biological or chemical reactions.

As stated in the above definition, the material must first be frozen. In doing so, the water is crystallized to ice and the drug is confined between the ice crystals. Except for the bound water, which may be necessary for the stability of the product [16–18], and some adsorbed free water, the freezing process serves to separate the solutes from the solvent. The resulting size and distribution of the ice crystals will determine the structure of the dried cake and its lyophile characteristic.

While being maintained in a frozen state, the pressure above the product is reduced to a value that results in the sublimation of water vapor from the ice surface. Sublimation results in the loss of both mass and energy from the product. Heat is applied to the product to maintain the sublimation rate but without increasing the product temperature to a point where a liquid phase or mobile water becomes present in the confined solutes. Drying of the product during the sublimation process is referred to as the primary drying phase [6,11,19].

When all of the ice has been sublimated, the temperature of the product can be increased and the remaining adsorbed water on the cake surface can be removed. This portion of the drying is referred to as the secondary drying phase [6,11,19]. The process is terminated when the moisture content of the product has reached an acceptable value that will produce a desired product stability. The dried product is then sealed so as to protect it from the environment.

B. Statistical Methods

In validating the lyophilization process, it must be shown that the properties of the key materials, various processes, equipment, and instrumentation perform within some defined limits. The function of these limits is to establish parameter boundaries outside of which the probability of finding parameter values is beyond normal chance. Such boundaries could be selected arbitrarily, but one would be hard-pressed to prove that such selected values are adequate to detect when a material property, phase of a process, or performance of the equipment or instrumentation is out of control. A more rational approach is to establish the boundaries based on a statistical analysis of those parameters found to produce an acceptable product. The following is a general discussion of key statistical aspects for determining and displaying the validation data.

1. Frequency Distribution

A frequency distribution is defined as an arrangement of data in a fashion that is independent of the sequence in which the data were taken [20]. The data are displayed in terms of the frequency in which a value or values within a given range appear in the data. Table 1 shows raw data, generated by a random-number generator, that simulates the moisture content in a lyophilized formulation [21]. By determining the number of data values that fall within a given 0.05 g range, e.g., 1.01–1.05, a frequency distribution can be generated for the data shown in Table 1. The frequency distribution is represented graphically in Figure 1 [21]. Examination of this figure shows that 66% of the data fall between the values of 0.91 and 1.10 and the data do not form what is known as a normal distribution [20].

2. Arithmetic Mean (Average)

An inspection of Figure 1 shows that the data have a tendency to group about a central value (1.03) within the range 1.01–1.05. This central value is generally referred to as the arithmetic mean or average [22] and is signified by $\langle \bar{X} \rangle_{av}$, where X is the variable and the bar (—) denotes a mean value. The arithmetic mean ($\langle \bar{X} \rangle_{av}$) is defined as

$$\langle \bar{X} \rangle_{av} = \frac{X_1 + X_2 + \cdots + X_n}{n} = \frac{\sum_{i=1}^{n} X_i}{n} \tag{1}$$

where the subscripts denote the sample number and n represents the total number of data values.

TABLE 1   Ungrouped Hypothetical Moisture Data in Terms of Water per 100 g of Lyophilized Product

0.98	1.17	1.01	1.10	0.96
1.01	1.11	0.94	0.97	1.06
0.93	0.95	1.03	1.00	1.05
1.21	0.95	1.18	1.18	1.04
0.97	0.89	1.24	1.08	0.86
1.09	0.87	1.05	1.05	0.94
1.13	1.17	1.10	0.91	0.89
0.97	0.92	1.23	0.87	1.01
1.42	0.96	0.99	1.07	1.18

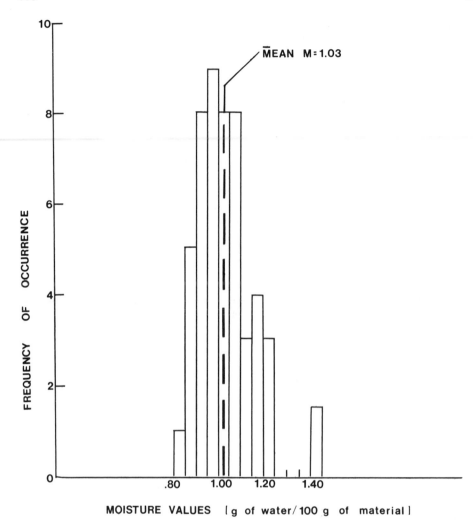

FIGURE 1 Graphic representation of the frequency distribution for the hypothetical moisture data.

3. Standard Deviation

As seen from Figure 1, about 60–70% of the data fell within the range 0.91–1.10; however, such percentages and limits are dependent on the width of the bars used to display the data. A more conventional means for expressing the grouping or the dispersion of the data about a central or mean value is the standard deviation (σ) [22]. The term σ is defined as the root-mean-square (rms) deviation of the data about its mean value, or

$$\sigma = \left[\frac{\sum\limits_{i=1}^{n}(X_i)^2}{n} - (<\bar{X}>_{av})^2 \right]^{\frac{1}{2}} \tag{2}$$

and can be defined as the square root of the mean of the squares minus the square of the mean. The mean $\langle \bar{X} \rangle_{av}$ and σ are expressed together as

$$\langle \bar{X} \rangle_{av} \pm \sigma$$

For the data shown in Table 1, $\langle \bar{X} \rangle_{av}$ and σ were found to be 1.03 ± 0.12.

4. Skew

Skewed data refers to any lopsidedness or deviation in the "normal" frequency distribution [23]. Examination of Figure 1 shows that the data tend to favor the right-hand portion of the frequency distribution. The degree that a distribution is skewed is determined by Eq. (3):

$$k = \frac{\sum\limits_{i=1}^{n}(X_i - \langle \bar{X} \rangle_{av})^3}{n\sigma} \tag{3}$$

For a normal or symmetrical frequency distribution, the value of k will approach zero; whereas if the distribution is skewed to the right, $k > 0$; and $k < 0$ when the data are skewed to the left. Application of Eq. (3) to the data shown in Table 1 gave $k = +0.79$ and agrees with the frequency distribution shown in Figure 1. The data values in Table 1 were randomly selected from an infinitely large "normal" distribution. Since the 50 data values of Table 1 came from a known normal distribution, the fact that the data are skewed must be a result of the sample size rather than the nature of the original distribution. The value of n should equal or exceed 250 in order to place any confidence that the observed skewed data are indeed a real representation of the distribution [23] and not an effect generated by the sample size.

5. Confidence Limits

When the sample size $n \ll 250$, the observed frequency distribution will most likely be skewed even though the sample was selected from a large population having a normal distribution ($k = 0$). Because of this, there will be some uncertainty regarding the values of $\langle \bar{X} \rangle_{av}$ and σ. It is therefore important to establish the limits about which the mean ($\langle \bar{X} \rangle_{av}$) will vary. This can be accomplished by considering the "probable error" [24] of the mean as

$$P.E. = 0.6745 \left(\frac{\sigma^*}{n^{\frac{1}{2}}} \right) \tag{4}$$

where σ^* represents the known σ for the distribution and the value 0.6745 corresponds to a probability value of 0.50. In other words, the P.E. represents the error $\langle \bar{X} \rangle_{av}$ will have with a probability of 0.50. The value of P.E. will be, as seen by Eq. (4), directly proportional to the probability factor and inversely proportional to the square root of the sample size n.

The confidence limits is thus defined as those limits, for a given probability, within which a mean value ($\langle \bar{X} \rangle_{av}$) will fall and is expressed as

$$\langle \bar{X} \rangle_{av} \pm \frac{j\sigma^*}{(n)^{\frac{1}{2}}} \tag{5}$$

where j represents the probability factor. The value of j for probabilities of 0.90, 0.95, and 0.99 are 1.645, 1.960, and 2.576, respectively [24]. When $n > 25$, then n is replaced by $(n - 3)$.

6. Control Charts

By the use of control charts [25], it can be determined if the observed values of $<\overline{X}>_{av}$ and σ will vary among themselves to a degree that is beyond normal chance. By this means, the control chart examines the data in terms of constancy. A typical control chart is illustrated by Figure 2 [21]. This figure shows the data represented by two charts. The upper chart is concerned with the average or mean value as a function of sample lots and the lower chart considers the variations in the standard deviation (σ), also as a function of the sample lots. Each graph has upper and lower control limits and a control line that represents the mean of means ($<\overline{X}>_{av2}$) or the mean of the standard deviation $<\sigma>_{av}$. Values of $<\overline{X}>_{av}$ or σ that fall outside the

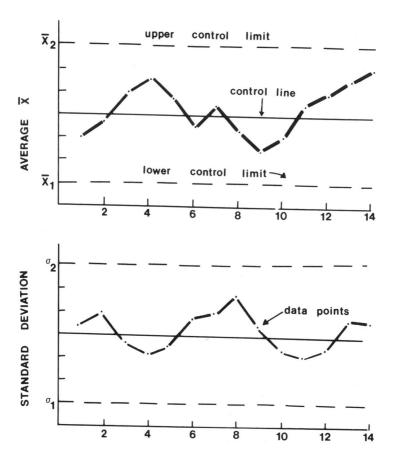

FIGURE 2   Typical control charts for 14 lots of a substance, where $<\overline{X}>_{av}$ denotes the arithmetic mean and σ the standard deviation.

control limits will show a lack of constancy in the property or process. The control charts are prepared as follows.

For j lots having n number of samples per lot and n > 25, the central lines, as seen in Figure 2, are determined from

$$\langle \overline{X} \rangle_{av2} = \frac{\sum\limits_{i=j}^{j} \langle \overline{X}_i \rangle_{av}}{j} \tag{6}$$

and

$$\langle \sigma \rangle_{av} = \frac{\sum\limits_{i=j}^{j} \sigma_i}{j} \tag{7}$$

while the upper and lower control limits are obtained by using the expressions

$$\langle \overline{X} \rangle_{av2} \pm \frac{3 \langle \sigma \rangle_{av}}{j^{\frac{1}{2}}} \tag{8}$$

and

$$\langle \sigma \rangle_{av} \pm \frac{3 \langle \sigma \rangle_{av}}{(2j)^{\frac{1}{2}}} \tag{9}$$

In using the above control charts, one should keep the following in mind:

1. When $\langle \overline{X} \rangle_{av}$ or σ values exceed or are less than the control limits, the control chart indicates only that the process or property lacks constancy and does not in itself indicate that the product is defective.
2. The lines used to connect the data points from lot to lot are used only to aid in displaying the data and do not serve to indicate a continuous function.
3. The sample size for each lot (n) is constant and equals or exceeds 25.
4. No confidence limits have been placed on the mean values. (Any use of a confidence level in the preparation of the control chart should be clearly indicated.)

C. Key Property Limits

The first step in the validation of a developed lyophilization process is the establishment of the key properties of the lyophilized formulation [26]. Such properties will then serve as a means for determining the constancy in the materials, the lyophilization process, and the equipment and instrumentation. The selection of the key properties will be considered first and then followed by the determination of the property limits.

1. Key Properties

Since the properties of the final product will serve as the basis for establishing if the process and its equipment show constancy, not only the number of properties, but also the nature of the properties must be considered. It is reasonable to assume that as the number of key properties used to characterize a lyophilized formulation having constancy are increased, so will the confidence in the validation also increase. For example, if one were to show that 100 properties of a lyophilized formulation for n number of batches are shown to fall within their control limits, there would be a high degree of confidence that the lyophilization process and the lyophilization equipment and instrumentation also show constancy. However, if only one property of the product were examined, such as color, then although the constancy of the process and the equipment may not have changed, the degree of confidence one would place in the constancy of the process would certainly be diminished.

While the number of product properties will certainly be an important consideration, the significance of the selected property must also be taken into account. In considering the stability and color of a product, one would place a greater weight on the constancy of the stability than on that of the color. This is not to imply that the color of a product should be ignored, but only that the stability generally carries more weight in the validation of a product than its color. It is recognized that each product will have its own set of key properties and that the weighting of the significance of a given property will vary from product to product. With this in mind, the following is a suggested method for determining the key properties and assigning their weight factors [21].

List Properties: Prepare a list of those properties of the product based on the criteria that the product would be rejected if the number of defects in this property were significant. Color may be a consideration in a clear container but of no real concern for an amber bottle.

Rearrangement: The list of properties are then rearranged in order of increasing importance. On such a list, color will most likely be higher on the list than stability of product.

Weight Factors: The properties are then numbered from the top of the list down. The list number of the property then serves as its weight factor. Table 2 [21] illustrates a possible list of weighted lyophilized properties for a product.

In considering the construction of a list like that shown in Table 2, one should consider all properties of the lyophilized product. Some properties, such as color, may prove to be difficult to assess. For example, the color white could be termed soft white, warm white, off-white, and even blue-white. The shade of white may be determined subjectively, and for that reason this parameter may not be an important consideration in the validation process. In considering not to include color as a key factor of the validation process, the confidence in the validation process will be affected. An estimate of the effect of the removal of a product property on the confidence (C) of the validation process can be determined from Eq. (10):

$$C = \frac{\sum\limits_{i=1}^{j} W_i}{\sum\limits_{i=1}^{n} W_i} \tag{10}$$

TABLE 2   Weighted List of Properties for
a Lyophilized Product

Weight factor	Property
1	Self-supporting structure
2	Color
3	Cake uniformity
4	Overall cake height
5	Gas release
6	Reconstitution time
7	Meniscus
8	Turbidity
9	Resistivity (+25°C)
10	pH (+25°C)
11	Moisture content
12	Active ingredient concentration
13	Stability (accelerated)
14	Stability (long-term)

In Eq. (10), W_j is the weight factor, n is the total number of properties on the list, and j is the number of weight factors used. Equation (10) is really the ratio of the sum of the weight factors used to the sum total of all weight factors. An inspection of this ratio shows that as j approaches 0, the confidence in the validation process will also approach 0 and the confidence will be greatest when j approaches n. If n were 10 for a product, the first two properties on the list could be ignored and the confidence would still be about 0.95. For an n value of 20, the first four properties on the list can be ignored and the confidence would still exceed 0.9. In either list, low confidence values would be generated if the last property of the list were ignored. The above provides a guideline for the selection of key product parameters to be examined in order to establish the validation of the lyophilization and its associated equipment and instruments.

2.   Key Property Limits

Once the key properties have been listed and an acceptable confidence level established, the next step is to demonstrate that the lyophilization process and its associated equipment and instrumentation produces a product whose selected product properties show constancy. The establishment of constancy requires that limits or control limits be determined for each of the properties. In order to determine the limits, the product properties are broken down into three classifications.

Class I: A Class I property is one in which a numerical value can be assigned to the property and, for any one lot, the property can be expressed as having a mean ($<\bar{X}>_{av}$) and a standard deviation (σ). The constancy of the property can be established by constructing a control chart as described above and illustrated by Figure 2. Properties that would be considered as Class I include cake height, reconstitution time, moisture content, active ingredient concentration, and resistivity of the reconstituted product. An example of a Class I control chart for the moisture of a hypothetical product is shown in Figure 3 [21]. The data were obtained from a random-number generator using a normal distribution [21] for a mean moisture $<M>_{av}$ of 1.00% H_2O and a σ of 0.10. The control chart was based on 14 lots with a sample size of n = 25. Examination of the chart shows that, even for a known normal distribution, there is considerable variation in ρ and σ with sample lot. The variation will become less pronounced as the sample size (n) is increased.

Class II: In this property class, only one or two values can be obtained for a given lot. The reason for such a low number could stem from the

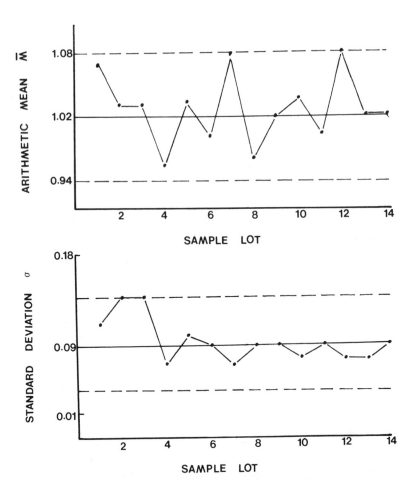

FIGURE 3   Control charts for the resistivity of a hypothetical product taken from a normal distribution having M = 1.00% H_2O and σ = 0.10.

complexity of the measurement, or the number of units required to determine a significant mean value could be excessively high. For example, assume in the case of accelerated stability studies that some 240 units are required to obtain one extrapolated stability time for a given storage environment. Then to obtain a mean stability time based on 30 determinations, some 7200 units would be needed. Such a large number of units may approach the total number of units in a lot. The control chart for a Class II function will consist of only one plot of the property value as a function of the sample lots. The control line is determined from the mean of property value for all lots and the control limits are defined as

$$\langle \overline{X} \rangle_{av} = \pm 3.25\sigma \tag{11}$$

where σ is the standard deviation for the mean value of $\langle \overline{X} \rangle_{av}$. A factor of 3.25 was arbitrarily selected and represents that the odds against one that a value of X from a normal distribution will be outside the limits defined by expression (11) will be about 4000, whereas, for a factor of 3 the odds against one would be only 369. Based on the above, it is reasonable to assume that

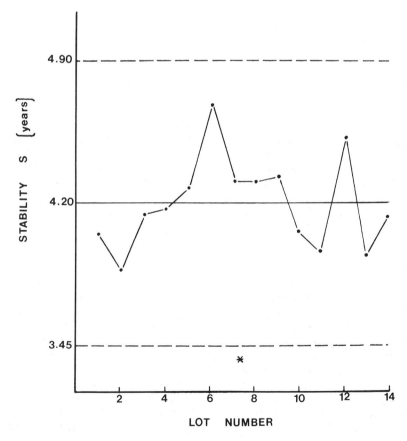

FIGURE 4 Example of a control chart for a Class II product property: Stability of a hypothetical product having a mean stability $\langle S \rangle_{av} = 4.25$ years and $\sigma = 0.2$.

any Class II property value that falls outside the limits defined by expression
(11) would show that there is a lack of constancy. An example of a control
chart for the shelf-life stability of a hypothetical product is shown in Figure 4
[21]. An inspection of this figure shows that the stability values fall about a
mean value of 4.18 years and the σ based on 14 lots was found to be 0.23. The
data values for Figure 4 were obtained from a normal distribution having a mean
value of 4.25 and a $\sigma = 0.20$. It is apparent that as the lot number increases
for the product, the value of the control line and the observed standard deviation will approach some constant value and thereby signify constancy by showing that the stability of the lots appear to be derived from the same distribution.

Class III: Class III is for product properties in which it is difficult to
assign a significant numerical value. In a sense the product is determined to
be either acceptable or not acceptable. A product property that would most
likely fit such a classification would be the turbidity of the reconstituted product. An acceptable turbidity may be one that is beyond the range of the measuring instrument. While there can be no control charts constructed for such
a property, one may arbitrarily set limits such as

$$\langle \bar{x} \rangle_{av} = \langle \bar{x} \rangle_{av} \pm 5\sigma \tag{12}$$

and thereby assign the odds against one that a container will not have an acceptable property limit to be 1×10^6.

III. MATERIALS

The materials used in the preparation of the formulation and the packaging
of the lyophilized product plays a major role in determining the nature of the
lyophilization process and the shelf life or stability of the dried product. The
chemical composition of the formulation can affect not only the structure of the
frozen matrix but also the primary drying phase through the thermal properties of the final formulation. This section of the chapter will briefly consider
(a) the key materials; (b) the role that such materials play in the lyophilization
process; and (c) the means for establishing the constancy of the materials with
respect to the lyophilization process.

A. Process Water

The process water is, for the most part, the major solvent medium of the formulated product. In this role, it forms a homogeneous system that allows for dispensing accurate weights of the pharmaceutical product. It is the formation of
ice that determines the structure of the matrix and affects such product properties as the reconstitution time. In a properly formed matrix, the ice crystals
and the interstitial materials will be uniformly distributed, while an improperly
formed matrix may be typified by a crust or glaze on top of the matrix. Such
a crust or glaze may result in a significant increase in the impedance to the
flow of water vapor from the product during the drying process. Since the
matrix structure can play such a major role in the drying characteristics of the
product, not only must the freezing of the product be carefully controlled, but
the formulation must be shown to have constancy with regard to the thermal
property known as supercooling. Figure 5 illustrates a frozen matrix having
a dual structure [21]. In region A, the matrix was formed by the supercooling

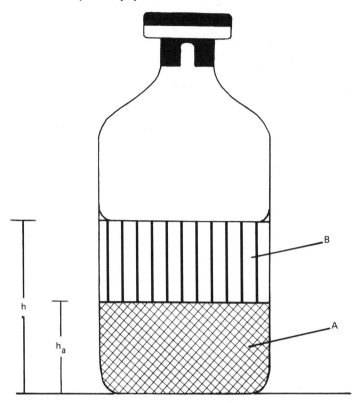

FIGURE 5 Illustration of differences in matrix structure, i.e., region A formed as a result of the supercooling of the formulation and region B resulting from slower ice growth; h represents the total cake height, and h_a indicates the height of region A.

of the formulation and the height of this region is indicated by h_a. The volume of the matrix shown by region B was formed by slower ice growth. The degree of supercooling of a formulation, and height h_a will be dependent on the supercooling properties of the process water and the manner in which the product was frozen [27].

The supercooling of the formulation can be ascertained by any one of three thermal analytical techniques: (1) thermal analysis using a single temperature sensor [9,19,28]; (2) differential thermal analysis (DTA) [9,18,28–34]; or (3) differential scanning calorimetry (DSC) [15,33–35]. While the analytical techniques may differ markedly, the results will be fairly compatible. Because the product container may readily affect the observed supercooling properties of the water or formulation, it is recommended that the supercooling analysis be conducted in a container that differs in composition from that used in the lyophilization process. Containers such as polyethylene and platinum may be employed for the analysis. Because the number of samples will most likely be less than 25, the limits for the control charts will be determined by expression (5).

B. Other Ingredients

The other components of a formulation often play an important role in determining the nature of the lyophilization process. These ingredients influence not only the thermal properties of the frozen matrix but also the very nature of the matrix structure. As a result, the cosmetic appearance, the manufacturing schedule, reconstitution properties, and even the stability of the final product will be dependent on the nature and concentration of these ingredients. Besides the active ingredient(s), the "other" ingredients may be in the form of [36–38]

> Organic compounds (sugars and starches)
> Inorganic compounds (sodium and potassium salts)
> Bulking agents (mannitol and lactose)
> Buffers (potassium phosphate and tartartic acid)

The thermal properties of the formulation most likely affected by the "other" ingredients will be the degree of supercooling; the degree of crystallization, i.e., the relative formation of ice in the formulation with respect to the amount of water present in the formulation; metastable states; and the melting temperature of the frozen matrix. Their effect on the structural, thermal, and drying properties of the frozen matrix should be well established before validation of the lyophilization of the formulation is undertaken. The thermal properties, supercooling, the degree of crystallization, and the presence of metastable states, can be ascertained by DTA analysis using methanol and water as reference materials. The melting temperature or eutectic temperature of the frozen matrix can be determined from either the D_2-product temperature function or from a combined D_2-product temperature function and DTA analysis [29].

Variations in the composition and concentration of the "other" ingredients can result in significant changes in the matrix structure and its thermal characteristics. These changes produce alterations in the drying schedule or in the nature of the final product, e.g., a loss of active ingredient or a change in pH, resistivity, reconstitution time, and an increase in turbidity. It is therefore essential to show constancy in the concentrations of the ingredients and in the electrical and thermal properties of the prepared formulation. Because a number of samples can be taken from the formulated product, properties such as concentration, activity, pH, and resistivity can be treated as Class I, whereas the thermal properties fall in Class II and turbidity in Class III.

By showing constancy in the supercooling properties of the process water and the properties of the final formulation, the validation of the process water and "other" ingredients are established. It is recommended that the constancy of the thermal properties of process water be determined on a regular basis. In this way, any lack of constancy in the thermal properties of the formulated product can be attributed to the "other" ingredients or the formulation process.

C. Packaging Materials

The product container and the closure play an important function in the lyophilization process. The function of these materials can be broken down into the following categories: (a) a vehicle in which the lyophilization process can occur, and (b) protection of the dried product from environment, i.e., moisture, microorganisms, and radiation, and a convenient means for reconstituting the materials while maintaining sterility. Because of the importance of these materials in the lyophilization process, it is imperative that constancy in the materials, separately and as a packaging unit, be established for each of the above categories.

1. Container

The container for lyophilized products is generally comprised of some composition of glass; however, other materials such as plastics are being considered [39,40]. While there will be some similarities between glass and plastic containers, this chapter will consider only containers of a glass composition. For most lyophilized formulations, there should be little, if any, chemical interaction between the container and product in the liquid, frozen, or dried state. Internal surface defects in the glass can, however, affect the degree of supercooling of the product and thereby alter the structure of the frozen matrix [41]. Such a change in the degree of supercooling results from the generation of sites where heterogeneous ice nucleation can occur. When this occurs, the height h_a of region A in Figure 5 will be diminished. Constancy in the product container with regard to its effect on supercooling can be demonstrated by a Class II control chart for the degree of supercooling of water for various container lots. Water rather than the formulation was selected as the supercooling medium so as to eliminate any effects that the "other" ingredients might have in altering the observed thermal properties. The degree of supercooling may be determined by analytical methods such as DTA or DSC.

2. Closure

The closure provides a means not only for protecting the final product from the environment but also offers a method for reconstitution, via a hollow needle, without disrupting the main sealing surfaces. The composition of the closures may vary from natural rubber to complex elastomer formulations. The Parenteral Drug Association, Inc. (PDA), has considered two areas of major concern regarding the closures, i.e., extractables and the performance and characteristics of the closures [42,43], and provides a test base for validating the closures. The PDA publications unfortunately did not consider the outgassing properties of the closures. This latter closure property has been shown to be a source of contamination for lyophilized products [2,44,45].

Outgassing of a substance [46], generally at subatmospheric pressures, involves the release of volatile matter. The nature of the released gases will be dependent on the composition of the substance, while the outgassing rate will increase with an increase in temperature [47]. Outgassing differs from permeability [2,42,46–48] in that the gases stem directly from the closure and are not dependent on the pressure drop across the closure. Gases such as water vapor, carbon monoxide, and carbon dioxide generally comprise the major components of the outgassing vapors, but higher-molecular-weight gas species have also been observed [44]. These latter vapors have not only been observed in the gaseous state but have been thought to be responsible for the formation of a tenacious transparent coating in the product container. When the coating forms on a glass surface, a solution of hot concentrated nitric acid containing a small amount of hydrofluoric acid was found necessary for its removal. The deposit of the coating on the lyophilized product resulted in an increase in the turbidity of the reconstituted product [44,45]. The presence of a coating, stemming from outgassing of the closures, can be easily detected by the reduction or the absence of a water meniscus [44]. In considering the validation of the closures, constancy should be examined for three outgassing parameters. The first consideration is the total outgassing rate (mTorr-liters/min) per closure and will be a Class II closure property. The second is the relative partial pressures of the major outgassing species, and this is also a Class II closure property. The last consideration is the presence of vapors that can form a deposit on a glass surface or on the surface of a lyophilized product and should be viewed as a Class III closure property. The total outgassing rate can be determined by placing a number of closures in a vacuum chamber and observing the increase in the chamber's virtual leak rate [46,50]. Examination of the gas composition during the outgassing rate determination with a mass spectrometer [44,46,50,51] can provide a measurement of the relative partial pressures of the outgassing species. The presence of vapors that can form a contaminating deposit is ascertained by the placement of closures, in their lyophilizing position, on clean empty glass containers and subjecting the latter to a pressure of about 100 mTorr and room temperature for a 24-hr period and then examining the container for the presence of a water meniscus.

3. Closure-Container Seal

The difference in values between real-time and accelerated stability studies may be a result of the effectiveness of the closure-container seal rather than differences in the analytical techniques or variations in the lyophilization process. For example, the moisture content in a product may have been measured to be 0.5% upon removal from the dryer; however, it may be found that the moisture content increased to 1.0% upon long-term storage. Should there be a strong dependency of the product stability with moisture content, then the difference in long-term and accelerated stability data would be attributed to defective seals rather than differences in analytical methods. In view of the above, validation of the lyophilization process requires challenging the effectiveness of the closure-container seal.

In challenging the effectiveness of the seal, the various means by which water vapor can enter the container must be considered. Water vapor may enter the container by three possible mechanisms, i.e., permeability, outgassing, and leakage at the closure-container interface. It may be argued that one only has to show that water vapor, by an increase in the weight of anhydrous calcium choloride [43], did not enter the container in sufficient quantity to alter the stability of the product. While certainly a reasonable method for establishing the effectiveness of the seal to water vapor, the above method does not lend itself to a 100% inspection of all the product containers after completion of the lyophilization process, nor does it provide any effective means for establishing if the source of the water vapor stems from one or more of the above moisture transport mechanisms. The total moisture transport mechanism may be expressed as

$$q = q_m + q_r + q_p \tag{13}$$

where

q_m = outgassing from the closure

q_r = the real leak rate of the seal

q_p = leak rate generated by the permeability of the water vapor through the closure

With the aid of Eq. (13), the transmission rate of water vapor for the closure-container seal can be established prior to the lyophilization of the formulation. This can be accomplished in the following manner:

1. Determine the outgassing rate of water vapor from the closures, by means of a mass spectrometer as described above.

2. By adding a quantity of helium to the gas used in backfilling the dryer chamber prior to stoppering, the real leak rate can be established by examining the sealed container for leaking helium.

3. From a knowledge of the outgassing rate of water vapor from the closure and an effective nondestructive means for detecting the presence of a real leak, the permeability leak rate, for a given storage temperature and humidity, can be established as follows. Place a quantity of containers, with a given amount of anhydrous calcium chloride, in a freeze-dryer with closures. Turn on the condenser system and reduce the pressure in the chamber to about 100 mTorr. Bleed back a mixture of dry gas and helium and stopper the containers. Remove any containers showing real leaks by the method briefly described above. Store the remaining containers in a controlled temperature and humidity chamber for a period of time and observe the increase in weight with respect to time. Since the containers having real leaks can be isolated, q_r can be set to zero and the permeability transmission rate of water vapor can be found from

$$q_p = q - q_m \qquad (14)$$

In order to show constancy in the closure-container seal, control charts should be established for q_m, q_r, and q_p. The control charts for q_p will be like those for a Class I property, while the control chart for the q_r rate will be a Class III, and q_m has been shown to resemble a Class II property.

IV. LYOPHILIZATION PROCESS

There are three fundamental steps in the lyophilization process: the formulation, the freezing or cooling function, and the drying schedule. Each step plays a significant part in determining the biological, chemical, and physical nature of the final product and for that reason must be considered in the validation process.

The basic parameters that are generally observed during the lyophilization process are concentration, temperature, pressure, and time. The common denominator found in each of the steps is time, and a process is generally defined as a change in concentration, temperature, and pressure as some function of time. An example of a time-dependent process temperature function is illustrated by Figure 6. The dots show observed temperatures for a given time interval, and the lines connecting the dots signify that the function is continuous. In order to show that the process has constancy, it must be shown that function falls within a given set of boundaries or control limits.

As in the case of the properties of a product, the various time-dependent functions can be grouped according to some classification system. A Class I function, for example, represents a function where a number of independent measurements of the process parameter can be made at any one time, while a Class II function stems from a single measurement of the parameter. The product temperature during the drying process represents a Class I function

because more than one product temperature is recorded for any given time
interval and the temperature may be represented as a mean value ($<T>_{av}$)
having a standard deviation (σ). An illustration of a plot of a mean product
temperature as a function of time is shown in Figure 7. The X's in this figure
are used to denote the mean temperature ($<T>_{av}$), and the length of the lines
above and below the X's signify (σ).

The σ's shown in Figure 7 are the same for each time interval, however, in
practice the σ is expected to vary quite appreciably with time. By use of
Eq. (1), the grand mean temperature ($<T>_{av2}$), for a given time (t), can be
expressed as:

$$<T_t>_{av2} = \frac{\sum_{i=1}^{j} T_{i,t}}{j}$$

(15)

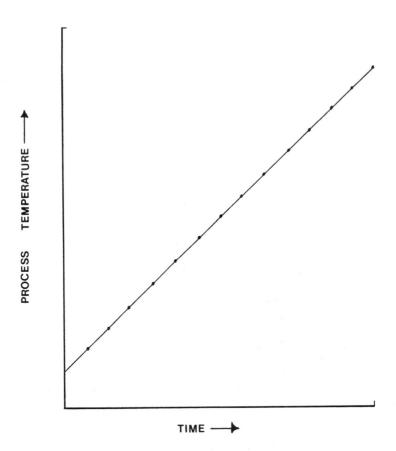

FIGURE 6   An illustration of a time-dependent process temperature.

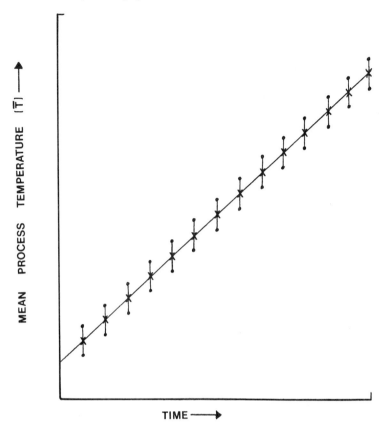

FIGURE 7   A plot of the mean temperature $\langle T \rangle_{av}$ and standard deviation as a function of time.

where j represents the total number of sample lots and $\langle X_{i,t} \rangle_{av}$ is the arithmetic mean for the ith lot at a time t.

The mean standard deviation for a given time t can be similarly expressed as:

$$\langle \sigma_t \rangle_{av} = \frac{\sum_{i=1}^{j} \sigma_{i,t}}{j} \qquad (16)$$

where $\sigma_{i,t}$ is the standard deviation for the ith lot of j total lots.

A time-dependent parameter control chart is illustrated by Figure 8. The central line represents the grand mean $\langle \overline{pH} \rangle_{av}$ while the control limits were obtained from expression (17),

$$\langle \overline{pH} \rangle_{av} \pm \frac{3 \langle \sigma_t \rangle_{av}}{j^{\frac{1}{2}}} \qquad (17)$$

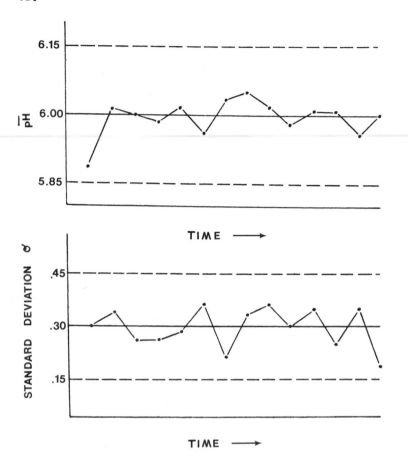

FIGURE 8   Control charts for the pH during the formulation of a hypothetical product, where dots indicate the pH of a given batch, the solid line designates the mean $\langle pH \rangle_{av}$, and the dashed lines indicate the upper and lower control limits.

with the control limits for σ_t determined from

$$\sigma_t \pm \frac{3 \langle \sigma_t \rangle_{av}}{(2j)^{\frac{1}{2}}} \tag{18}$$

Because none of the values of T_t exceeded the control limits, as defined by expressions (17) and (18), this part of the process shows constancy.

Time-dependent process parameter functions of Class II will result from but a single measured parameter value during a given process. An example of a Class II function is the pressure measured in a chamber. Placement of more pressure sensors throughout the chamber, assuming that the pressure is uniform throughout the chamber, would not in itself form a Class I function, and any derived mean or standard deviation would represent merely variations between measurements and not pressure variations within the chamber. A

Class II time-dependent function is one in which the observed value of the parameter is independent of the location of the sensor.

The central line for a control chart of a Class II function is defined as

$$X_t = \frac{\sum\limits_{i=1}^{j} X_{i,t}}{j} \tag{19}$$

where the term $X_{i,t}$ signifies the parameter X for the ith lot at a given time t. The control limits for the Class II function are determined from

$$X_t \pm 3.25\sigma_t \tag{20}$$

where σ_t represents the lot variations in X_t about a mean value of X_t.

A Class III function would again involve a process parameter that would extend outside the normal sensitivity range of the instruments. Although the actual value of the parameter can not be readily determined and control charts constructed, this does not mean that attempts to measure the parameter should be eliminated. For example, the presence of significant amounts of turbidity in a product would not only indicate that the process lacks constancy but also that the product is defective.

A. Formulation Function

The formulation is not only important to the preparation of the drug but also with respect to the lyophilization process. Variations in the low-temperature thermal properties of the product may be related directly to changes in the formulation protocol. For example, an increase in the temperature of the process water prior to formulating could result in a change in the size distribution of the clusters [16] in the water. The change in such a cluster distribution could alter the supercooling properties of the product and lead to a change in the matrix structure. The new matrix could differ so significantly with other product matrixes that the mean value of h_a of the dried product would fall outside the control chart (see Fig. 5) and the property be said to lack constancy. Besides temperature, other variations in the formulation process are concentration of the active ingredient and excipients, pH of the final product, and nature and quantity of the materials used to make the adjustment, nature and pressure of the gas above the solution during formulation, radiant energy present during mixing, composition of the mixing container, and time.

As it was in the case of the key properties of the lyophilized product, so is it important to establish the key parameters of the formulation protocol. The number of parameters will be dependent on the nature of the formulation process and the desired level of confidence. For example, a product that is prepared under what may be termed ordinary laboratory conditions would not require control charts for the nature and pressure of the gases above product. The method for the selection of key parameters and the establishment of the confidence levels has been described previously. Except for such parameters as radiant energy and container composition, which would be considered Class III parameters, the other formulation parameters will form Class II functions.

An example of Class II function is illustrated by Figure 8 [21]. The dots denote the observed pH value for a batch at a given time, while the solid line

represents the mean for a given time. The dashed lines indicate the upper
and lower control limits for a given time. Examination of the plot shows that
there is more spread in the pH values before a pH adjustment was made. The
figure also points out that the data be taken at discrete times during the
formulation process and the connecting lines are used only to aid in exhibiting
the data and not to indicate a continuous function.

B. Freezing Function

The freezing function, as already noted, plays a major role in the lyophilization process. The freezing function is defined as the variation of the product
temperature as a function of time. Figure 9 [21] illustrates a freezing function
that is made up of several stages. During the first stage, the entire product
is cooled to a temperature that is just above the equilibrium freezing temperature, i.e., that temperature where ice first starts to form. The importance
of this stage is to maximize the amount of solution that can undergo supercooling. In the second stage the product is frozen to a temperature that is about

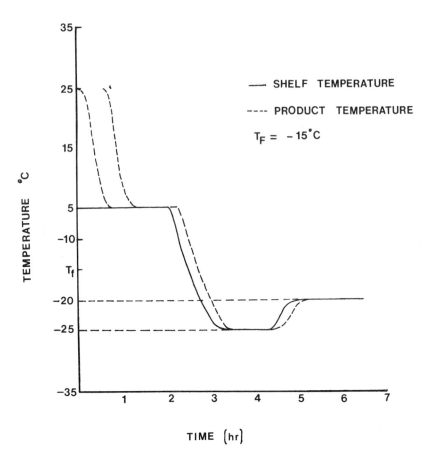

FIGURE 9   An illustration of a freezing function, where the solid line indicates
the shelf temperature and the dashed line is used to signify the product
temperature.

10°C below its matrix melting temperature as determined by a D_2 and DTA analysis. After ensuring that the product is completely frozen, the third stage of the freezing function increases the product temperature to ≈5°C below the melting temperature of the matrix. This third stage in the freezing function may also include thermal cycling of the product to remove any metastable states of water [11,15,29,41] or to induce crystallization of the interstitial materials [2,11,15]. It should be realized that a large number of freezing functions may contain only the second stage, and the illustration shown by Figure 9 is not meant to imply a general freezing function for all products.

Constancy in the freezing function, regardless of its form, can be established with the aid of control charts. The first control chart to be considered will be that of the change in the shelf temperature during the freezing process. Variations in the shelf temperature during the freezing process should be independent of the size of the batch or the loading schedule of the dryer. Large variations in shelf temperature could lead to some of the product undergoing several freeze-thaw cycles. Products that undergo such freeze-thaw cycles can experience a loss in the active ingredient concentration and changes in the structure of the matrix.

Since each shelf temperature will be an independent measurement, the control chart for the shelf temperature during the freezing function will be considered as a Class I time-dependent function. Such a control chart is illustrated by Figure 10 [21]. The dots represent the mean shelf temperature or the σ_t for a specific batch, the solid line (—) through the mean values serves to indicate the grand mean $<T_m>_{av2}$ of the shelf temperature for a given time, and the * is used to indicate the upper and lower control limits. In constructing a control chart like that shown in Figure 10, it is important to realize that the shelf temperature is the actual temperature of the upper surface of the shelf and not some measurement of the shelf heat transfer fluid as it either enters or leaves the shelves. Examination of Figure 10 shows that the entire batch was loaded on a cool shelf and the variation in shelf temperature was most pronounced during periods when there was a shelf temperature change.

In using the above freezing function, it is not considered necessary to construct a control chart for the product temperature, the reason being that as long as the shelf temperature shows constancy, the product temperature-time function must also have constancy. Such an assumption would not be valid if the product were loaded onto shelves whose temperatures were less than that of the melting temperature of the product matrix. In this case, it would be necessary to show that individual product temperatures on a given shelf, rather than a mean temperature, did not exceed the melting temperature of the matrix. While loading the product on very cold shelves may represent a simple cooling function, the validation of such a function can indeed become quite complex.

C. Drying Schedule

The drying schedule will commence at the completion of the freezing function. Because the ice structure may be temperature- and time-dependent, prolonging the freezing function may result in noticeable changes in the matrix structure and represent a lack of constancy in the product properties.

The drying schedule is comprised of two phases and is illustrated by Figures 11 and 12 [21]. The first of these phases involves the sublimation of ice from the matrix and is generally referred to as primary drying. In general, this

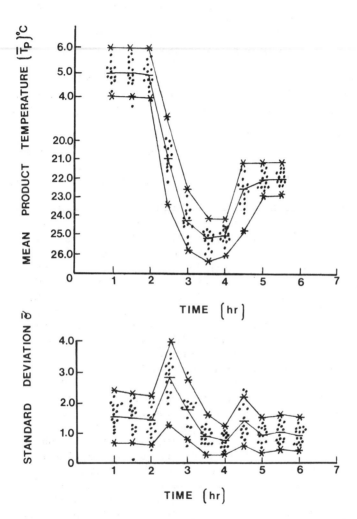

FIGURE 10   An illustration of possible control charts for the shelf temperature during the freezing of the product. The dots represent the mean shelf temperature or a value of σ for a specific batch. The solid line through the mean values indicates the grand mean and the *'s are used to designate the upper and lower control limits for a specific time.

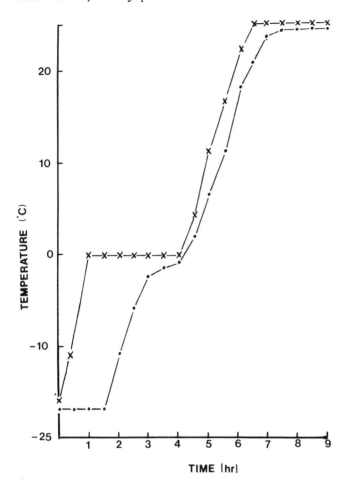

FIGURE 11   A plot of the mean shelf temperature, denoted by (×), and the mean product temperatures, indicated by (●), as a function of the drying time.

portion of the drying process is characterized by a fixed relationship among the shelf temperature, the product temperature, and the chamber pressure— see Figures 12 and 11. By holding two of these parameters constant, the third parameter remains fixed. Thus, by holding the shelf temperature and the pressure in the drying chamber within some set of limits, the product temperature, and therefore the sublimation rate, will remain fixed. It should be understood that the drying rate is dependent not only on the temperature of the product but also on the chamber pressure. By maintaining a given product temperature and increasing the chamber pressure, the sublimation rate will be decreased. It should also be understood that, if closures are used during the drying process, the product temperature must be determined with a closure positioned for lyophilization.

The second phase of the drying is called the secondary drying and will commence after completion of the primary drying, i.e., when the product temperature approaches the primary drying shelf temperature (see Fig. 11) and the remaining water is removed from the cake by a desorption mechanism. For a

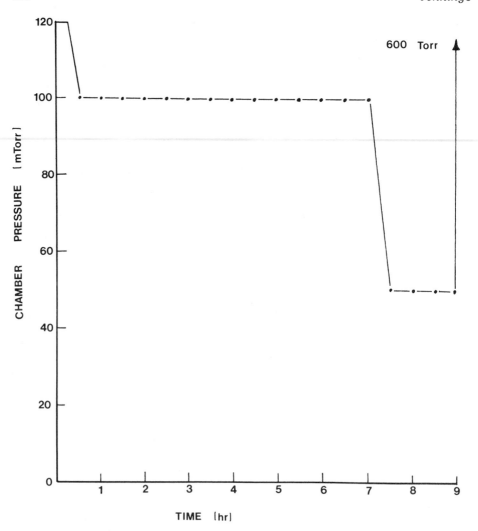

FIGURE 12   A plot of the chamber pressure during a drying schedule.

given chamber pressure P, the temperature difference between the shelf and product temperatures ($T_S - T_p$) will be dependent on the free water remaining in the product. As T_S approaches the maximum process temperature and $T_p \backsim T_S$, the residual moisture content in the product will be related to the total pressure and the partial pressure of water vapor (P_w) in the drying chamber. The former pressure may be ascertained by use of a total pressure gauge, whereas the latter is determined from a residual gas mass spectrometer.

In validating the drying schedule, it must be shown that the time dependency of T_S, T_p, and P exhibit constancy. Added confidence to the validation process will be gained if constancy can be shown in the P_w-time function during the drying schedule and in particular at the end of the secondary drying phase. The temperature-time functions will be Class I, whereas the pressure functions will be Class II. Figure 13 [21] illustrates a control chart for the

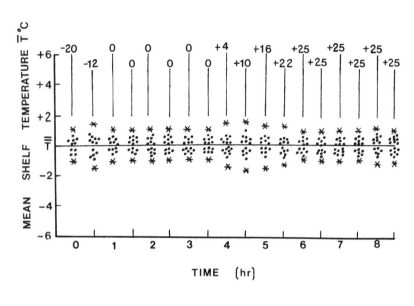

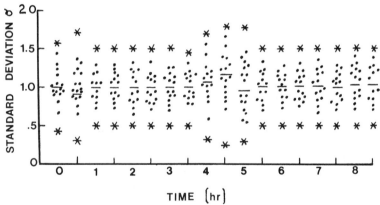

FIGURE 13 Control charts for the shelf temperature during the drying process, where $\langle T \rangle_{av2}$ represents the grand mean shelf temperature indicated by
the upper numerical value and (*) denotes the upper and lower control limits.

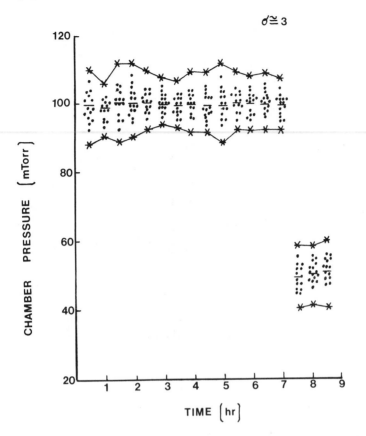

FIGURE 14   Control chart for the chamber pressure during a drying process, where the solid lines represent the mean pressure values and the *'s designate the upper and lower control limits.

shelf temperature during the drying process. Because of the wide range in temperatures involved in the drying process, a more convenient means of representing the control chart is suggested. Examination of this figure shows that the temperature ordinate consists of the grand mean $\langle T \rangle_{av2}$, represented by the solid line, and also upper and lower temperature scales. The actual T at any given time is designated by the upper numerical, and the * serves as the upper and lower control limits. The standard deviation (σ) plot differs slightly from that of the temperature in that the ordinate displays the scale of the values of σ and the solid lines represent the mean σ values for a specific time during the drying process. The control chart for the product temperature will be similar to that shown in Figure 13, while the control chart for the chamber pressure can be illustrated by Figure 14 [21].

V. EQUIPMENT

It must first be realized, when considering a piece of equipment used in the lyophilization process, that the validation must be performed with respect to the process and not with respect to the constancy of the equipment itself. Even a completely inoperative piece of equipment would show constancy, but its real value would be nil. Likewise, for example, vacuum freeze-dryers whose operating characteristics prevent duplication of established drying schedules will also be of little value. For this reason, the validation of the equipment should be based on the constancy observed during the lyophilization process and the properties of the final product.

The principal equipment associated with the lyophilization process includes the filling and stoppering machines, the drying trays, and the vacuum freeze-dryer. The following will briefly examine the role that each plays in the lyophilization process and consider the necessary control charts.

A. Filling Machine

The function of the filling machine is to dispense controlled amounts of the product solution into a container. The quantity of the solution added is determined either by volume or by weight. In either case, the actual amount of liquid dispensed must fall within some tolerance limits imposed by the product's specifications. While errors in the filling operation will have only a very minimal effect on the nature of the drying schedule, such errors may seriously affect the quantity of the active ingredient and thereby cause a serious loss of confidence by generating large errors in the stability data.

Because a number of independent measurements of the fill volume can be obtained, the control chart will be similar to the Class I chart shown in Figure 3. Since the fill volumes on the control chart will be mean values, it is highly unlikely that a mean value will approach or even exceed a control limit equal to the tolerance limits. Such results could be most misleading. For example, consider a 3.0-ml fill volume having a tolerance of ±0.3 ml. A control chart for such a filling operation is illustrated by Figure 15. This chart shows that the grand fill volume mean is 3.0 and the control limits are 3.06 and 2.97 ml, respectively. What is misleading is that the control limits are based on variations of means while the tolerance represents limits for a large population. Based on the indicated value of σ of 0.1, the probability of finding a fill volume outside the tolerance limits would be only one in 369. In order to increase the odds against one to a million, the value of σ would have to be reduced to 0.06.

B. Closure Placement

The placement of the closure on the container is perhaps one of the simplest operations in the lyophilization process but, nevertheless, an important step. A typical closure used in the lyophilization process contains a supporting structure that allows gases from the container to pass into the drying chamber via an aperture or slot [2,15,52]. Upon completion of the drying process, the seal is made by seating the closure on the rim of the container. Improper placement of the closure can result in an enlargement or a reduction of the aperture area. An enlargement of the aperture would reduce the impedance of the gas flow from the container. In a case where the impedance reduction is significant, the observed temperature of the product would be significantly lower than the product temperature. Not only could such a temperature reduction result in a decrease in the sublimation rate, but, if the closure were on a container monitoring the drying process, the resulting T_p could fall beyond the control limits of the control chart.

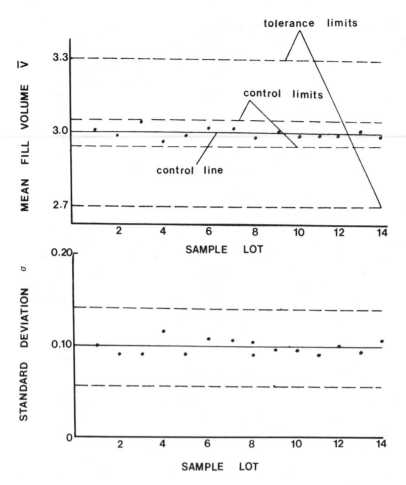

FIGURE 15   Control chart for a fill volume of 3.0 ml, tolerance limits of ±0.3 ml, and 25 samples taken per lot.

Excessive depression of the closure or the use of an improperly sized closure for the container can result in an increase in the impedance to the gas flow from the container. With such an increase in the impedance, the drying process is limited and the moisture content in the product greatly increased.

It is not possible to determine, once the closures have been seated, which of the closures were improperly positioned. The most effective means for preventing the above is a careful inspection of closures before they are placed in the dryer. Improperly positioned closures should be either removed or their closure properly positioned. When positioned correctly and loaded onto a tray, the closures will form a flat surface. Personnel operating the stoppering equipment and loading the freeze-dryer should be made cognizant of the importance of closure placement.

C. Drying Trays

Two types of trays are generally employed to contain the product in the dryer, full-bottom and bottomless trays. Full-bottom trays are generally fabricated

from a single sheet of metal such as aluminum or stainless steel. The choice
of tray composition is an important consideration. Aluminum trays offer light
weight and good thermal conductivity but suffer because aluminum is a relatively soft metal and dust may be generated when the trays are slid across
the shelf. Stainless steel is a much harder metal and there is less chance of
generating metal dust particles during loading and unloading operations. The
basic difficulty with stainless steel is its poor heat transfer properties. The
chief advantages for using such trays are (a) the ease with which the product
can be loaded into or taken out of the dryer; (b) less chance of breakage or
disturbing the position of the closures; and (c) only this type of tray can be
used to dry bulk materials in the present design of the vacuum freeze-dryers.
The basic difficulty with the use of full-bottom trays lies in their tendency to
warp with time. Tray warping can affect not only the drying schedule but
also the freezing function and manifests itself in a significant product temperature variation within the tray. A qualitative test for warped trays is to place
the tray on a flat surface and inspect light passing along the tray-surface
interface. Defective warped trays will be also apparent from a trend to increase the σ value for the product temperature during the freezing or the drying of the product. Should such a trend become apparent, it is recommended
that all of the trays be replaced before the lyophilization process is found to
lack constancy.

Bottomless trays are comprised of two sections, i.e., rectangular rim and
bottom. After the tray is placed on the shelf of the dryer, the bottom is removed by sliding it past the containers, thereby allowing them to come in direct contact with the shelf surface. The containers can be removed from the
shelf by slipping the bottom portion of the tray under the containers once
again. The rim of the tray stays in the dryer throughout the process and prevents the containers from moving about the dryer shelf. The chief disadvantage of this type of tray is that there is more handling, and the likelihood of
broken containers or spilled product coming in contact with the shelves is
increased. The principal advantage of this tray rests in that it, in itself, will
not interfere with the freezing or drying of the product and for that reason
need not be considered in the validation process except as a possible source
of biological or chemical contamination.

D. Freeze-Drying Equipment

The piece of equipment that will have the most pronounced effect on the lyophilization process is the vacuum freeze-dryer [53–55]. In general, the dryer
must perform three basic functions: (a) provide and maintain an environment
that is clean and free of any biological contamination; (b) have sufficient refrigeration capacity to freeze the product in accordance with the established
freezing function; and (c) be capable of maintaining the necessary shelf temperature, total chamber pressure, and partial pressure of water vapor throughout
the drying schedule. While the above represent three most important functions
of the dryer, validation of the dryer also requires that the dryer is maintained
with an effective testing and servicing program.

1. Environment

In the case of an aceptic product, the freeze-drying chamber must supply
an environment that is not only clean and free of any biological contamination
at the outset of the drying process but maintains such an environment throughout the entire drying process [50]. There are three possible sources of chemical

contamination that would result in the dryer being classified as unclean. The first of these sources is dust particles, which can stem from a number of sources. The first source could arise in the manufacture of the dryer. One obvious source of this dust is the grinding of the interior surfaces of the drying chamber in order to achieve a #4 finish. Fine particles from such grinding may lodge in regions where cleaning is difficult. A second source results from the resin coating that is sometimes used to coat the chamber walls and the shelves. Not only is it possible for this coating to be chipped off as a result of rough handling, but the resulting exposed metal surface may, in time, become a source of rust particles. Dust particles may also stem from the residuals left behind from a cleaning operation.

Dust particles in themselves are not a real threat to the quality of the product, provided that they do not become airborne and enter the product. However, such particles can become airborne during two phases of the drying schedule. Rapid evacuation of the drying chamber can create a turbulent atmosphere and thereby cause dust particles to be scattered throughout the dryer, while backfilling the chamber, prior to stoppering, may also represent a mechanism for generating airborne dust particles.

In validating the freeze-dryer, not only must it be shown that there are insignificant amounts of airborne dust particles in the dryer, but also that there is an effective means for their removal. Airborne dust particles in a dryer can be detected by filtering a stream of gas as it leaves the dryer. In order to perform this test, a white/black paper filter is attached to a port of the dryer such as a drain line. The dryer is pressurized to 1 psi and the port to the filter is opened. The gas is allowed to pass through the filter for 5 min. After the gas is turned off, the filter is removed and inspected for dust particles. The resulting filter should be retained as part of the batch record [21]. Should dust particles be present, then the dryer is cleaned and the filter test repeated. Dust particles are difficult to remove by normal techniques, and for that reason the vacuum cleaning of the dryer surfaces is sometimes necessary.

The second source of dryer contamination is nonatmospheric vapors in the dryer. These vapors, generally referred to as virtual leaks [46,50,56], may stem hydrocarbon vapors that have backstreamed from the vacuum pumping system, a leak in the shelf or condenser fluids, or residuals remaining from a cleaning or sterilization procedure. The presence of such vapors can be ascertained by first reducing the pressure in the dryer, with the condenser at ambient temperature, to about 200 mTorr and, after disconnecting the dryer from the pumping system, determining the rate of pressure rise (ROR_V) [46,50]. The source of the virtual leak(s) is determined by examining the composition of the gases in the dryer by means of a residual gas analyzer. The determined ROR_V and recorded mass spectrometric data should be entered into the batch record.

Real leaks differ from virtual leaks in that the former result from penetrations that permit atmospheric gases and other matter to enter the dryer [46, 50,56,57]. The introduction of gases into the dryer can seriously affect the chamber pressure during the drying process. As stated above, an increase in pressure could, depending on the shelf temperature, either increase the product temperature during the primary phase or reduce the drying rate. Other matter, depending on the diameter and length of the leak path, may include biological contamination. Since most of the surface area of a dryer processing aseptic products is contained in a nonsterile region, the presence of sufficient real leaks capable of transporting biological contamination would negate the sterilization process conducted prior to the loading of the dryer. The presence of real leaks in a dryer can be determined from examining the rate of pressure rise when the temperature of the condenser is less than $-60°C$ (ROR_r).

The actual location of the leak can be determined by probing the dryer with helium and at the same time examining the dryer for helium with a residual gas analyzer [46,50,57]. The ROR_r and the leak testing should be determined with the dryer clean and empty.

2. Refrigeration and Heating

The refrigeration and heating system of the dryer provides the necessary refrigeration to the shelves for the freezing function, sufficient energy to meet the shelf temperature requirement during the drying process (see Fig. 11), and the necessary refrigeration to operate the condenser.

The control charts shown in Figures 10 and 13 serve a dual purpose. It is not possible to show constancy in a process without also demonstrating constancy in the operation of the equipment. The fact that there is constancy in freezing function, as shown in Figure 10, must imply that the operation of the refrigeration system for freezing the product is adequate. Second, the constancy shown by Figure 13, the control chart for shelf temperature during the drying process, must also imply that the shelf heating and cooling system during the drying process is likewise adequate. The above does not negate the continued need for an effective equipment inspection and maintenance program, but it does demonstrate the futility of trying to validate the performance of an empty dryer.

Figure 14, an illustration of a control chart for the chamber pressure during the drying schedule, can be used to validate that the operation of the dryer's condenser system is performing adequately. This statement is based on the premise that if the condenser is *not* functioning adequately and the system is not free of significant real and virtual leaks, there would be a lack of constancy in the chamber pressure-time function. This does not imply that there is no need to record the condenser temperature during the drying process, but such recordings serve only to diagnose the performance of the dryer, not to validate its operation.

VI. INSTRUMENTS

Instruments play a major role in the controlling and monitoring of the lyophilization process. The constancy of the final product and the associated processes used to obtain the product are related directly to the nature and performance of the instruments. Because of the importance of the instrumental role, there is a need to show that the accuracy, precision, and in some instances the resolution of the instruments fall within a given set of specifications. The latter statement implies that the instruments used in the development of the lyophilized product should also be employed during the manufacturing process. Before considering the validation of the various instruments, it is best to consider the terms accuracy, precision, and resolution.

The accuracy of an instrument or measurement is defined as the degree of agreement between the measured value X_i and the true value X_0 [22,58,59]. It should be apparent that as X_i approaches X_0, the accuracy of the instrument increases or the error diminishes. The accuracy of an instrument is generally expressed in terms of the percent error of the reading, i.e.,

$$\text{accuracy} = \% \text{ error} = \frac{(X_o - X_i)}{X_o} \times 100\% \tag{21}$$

or

$$\% \text{ error} = \% \text{ fsd} \tag{22}$$

where fsd is the full-scale deflection of the meter.

The precision of an instrument refers to the repeatability of the measurement [22,58,59]. Precision refers to how closely the measurement falls about some mean value $\langle X_i \rangle_{av}$. The precision of an instrument will give a frequency distribution of measurements that are similar to that shown in Table 1 and illustrated graphically by Figure 1. The dispersion of the data points about $\langle X_i \rangle_{av}$ can be represented by the standard deviation (σ), and the measurement can be expressed as

$$X_i \pm \sigma \tag{23}$$

As the precision of the instrument increases, σ will approach zero.

While making measurements, two considerations should be kept in mind. First, a high degree of precision does not, in itself, ensure a high degree of accuracy. In such a case, the faulty instrument merely faithfully reproduces the same erroneous value. One should determine, if possible, the accuracy and precision over the entire useful range of the instrument. The second consideration is that the observed mean value $\langle X_i \rangle_{av}$ may represent an accurate measurement of X_i; however, $\sigma_x \gg 0$ would indicate poor precision [21]. Such an instrument would not be suitable to monitor and control a process if

$$\sigma_x \gg \sigma_i$$

where σ_i is the standard deviation for the ith process control. The effect of the above is to impose excessive control limits that would result in the data showing a lack of constancy. As a general rule, $\sigma_x < \sigma_i$ must exist in order for the control charts to have any significance.

Resolution is the smallest change indicated by an instrument [58]. With instruments that employ a meter movement, the resolution becomes quite apparent, but this is not always true of an instrument having a digital output display. Such an output may be a mean value, and the indicated resolution may represent values well beyond the capabilities of the instrument. For example, the resolution of an instrument may be in tenths (0.1) of a unit, while the display may indicate a resolution in thousandths (0.001) of a unit and thereby misrepresent the true nature of the measurement.

Throughout this chapter the validation of the lyophilization process was based on the constancy shown by the control charts for the various properties and parameters. In validation of the instrumentation, it must be shown that the accuracy, precision, and resolution of the instrument are sufficient such that the observed control charts represent variations in the measured parameters and not merely artifacts of the instrument itself. This section of the chapter will consider the effects that accuracy, precision and resolution can have on the determination of (a) the properties of the final product; (b) the formulation of the product; (c) the material, and (d) the freezing and drying process.

A. Validation of the Accuracy of the Instruments

The validation of the accuracy of the instruments can be determined by measuring a known quantity and determining if the measurement falls within the accuracy range prescribed by the manufacturer [17,58–61]. The accuracy of the instrument used to determine the resistivity of the reconstituted final product or the resistivity of the product solution during formulation can be determined by measuring the resistivity of known solutions of potassium chloride at 25°C [62]. If the observed measurement is not within the error limits, as given by Eq. (21), then adjustments to the instruments should be made and the measurements repeated with the known resistivity solutions. A record of the test method and results should be kept near the instrument. It is well beyond the scope of this chapter to consider all of the possible instruments that may be used in the lyophilization process or its validation. The accuracy of each instrument used to control the lyophilization process should be checked on a periodic basis.

B. Effect of Precision on the Control Charts

In validating the instruments, one must show that the precision is sufficient such as not to affect the variation in property as displayed in the control chart. The effect of the instrumentation of the results of the control chart can be shown by construction of a control chart for a known or control lot. The control limits for the latter control chart should fall well within the limits obtained for the product lots. The confidence in the results of the control chart for the product lots with respect to the control chart of the control lots can be expressed as

$$C_{cc} = \frac{(\sigma_p/(n_p)^{\frac{1}{2}} - (\sigma_c/(n_c)^{\frac{1}{2}})}{\sigma_p/(n_p)^{\frac{1}{2}}} \tag{24}$$

where σ_p is the mean standard deviation for a group of product lots having n_p samples per lot and σ_c is the mean standard deviation for a group of control lots having n_p samples per lot.

For equal groups of product and control lots and $n_c = n_p$, the confidence C_{cc} will approach 1 or certainty as $\sigma_p \gg \sigma_c$ and zero as σ_c approaches σ_p. By this means one can place a numeral value on the confidence of a control chart with respect to the precision of a given instrument. In the way of an example, consider the resistivity of a reconstituted product (that is electrically conductive) and based on 25 samples taken for each of the 14 lots. Examination of the results shows that the grand mean resistivity ($<\rho>_{av2}$) was 78.0 Ω-cm and the mean standard deviation $<\sigma_p>_{av}$ was 1.0 Ω-cm. The resistivity of a 0.1 M solution of potassium chloride (KCl) is 78.0 Ω-cm at a temperature of 25°C. A control chart, based on 25 samples of 14 solutions of KCl and using the same resistivity instrument as that used to measure the reconstituted product, is illustrated by Figure 16.

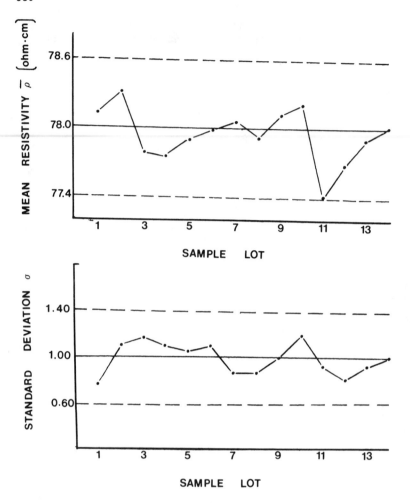

FIGURE 16   Control charts for the resistivity (ohm·cm) the 0.1 M KCl solution
at +25°C by random # generator $\bar{\rho} = 78.0$ ohm·cm, $\sigma = 1.0$.

An inspection of Figure 16 shows that the control limits for the KCl solutions were well within the control limits determined for the reconstituted
product. By using Eq. (24), the confidence value (C_{cc}) was determined at
0.82. With this illustration, it is seen that it is not sufficient merely to show
that the control limits for the control system falls within the control limits for
that of the product, but also some confidence value must be established such
that the variations in the data are known to stem from the process and not a
result of instrument fluctuations.

C. Resolution of the Instruments

The validation of the resolution of the instrument becomes of major importance
when the data are displayed in the form of a spectrum. In the lyophilization
process, the composition of the gases in the chamber during the drying process
is determined by means of a residual gas mass spectrometer [55]. The mass

analyzer not only determines the relative partial pressures of the common gases found in the dryer, i.e., water vapor (m/e = 17 and 18), nitrogen (m/e = 14 and 28), oxygen (m/e = 16 and 32), and argon (m/e = 20 and 40), but also fragments generated from vapors stemming from the vacuum pump fluid, shelf heat transfer fluid, condenser refrigerant, and sterilizing chemicals. The latter fragments may have m/e values ranging from 12 to >80. It is therefore necessary to show that the mass spectrometer is capable of resolving the m/e ratios of these fragments so as to identify their source. Since the absolute resolution is defined as the peak width at 10% of the peak height, the resolution of the mass analyzer, for a given sensitivity, is determined by sensing gases of a known composition, such as helium, nitrogen, and argon, and determining the resolution. It is generally necessary only to know the m/e value to the nearest unit; the value of the absolute resolution need not be less than 1.

VII. SUMMARY

This chapter considered the validation of the lyophilization process. The validation is based on the knowledge that the lyophilization process is established on known low-temperature characteristics of the product. Statistical methods were used to establish constancy through the use of control charts. The demonstration of constancy in the process materials, freezing and drying processes, the equipment, and instruments will be relevant only as long as there remains continued constancy in the properties of the final product. As demonstrated by broad scope of topics considered in this chapter, a rigorous validation of the lyophilization process can be costly and time-consuming; however, the basis for ignoring a given item lies in the effect its absence will have on the confidence that can be placed on the validation process.

REFERENCES

1. Rey, L. 1975. *Proc. R. Soc. Lond. B 191*: 9.
2. Amoignon, J. 1975. In *Freeze Drying and Advance Food Technology*, S. A. Goldblith, L. Rey, and W. W. Royhmayr, eds. Academic Press, New York. p 445.
3. Flosdorf, E. W., and Webster, G. W. 1937. *J. Biol. Chem. 21*: 353.
4. Seager, H., et al. 1979. *Manufacturing Chemist & Aerosol News*, January. p 40.
5. Rosenberg, G. I. 1964. In *Aspects Theoriques et Industriels de la Lyophilisation*, L. Rey, ed. Hermann, Paris. p 335.
6. Harris, R. J. C. 1954. In *Biological Applications of Freezing and Drying*. Academic Press, New York. p 87.
7. Greaves, R. I. N. 1964. In *Aspects Theoriques et Industriels de la Lyophilisation*, L. Rey, ed. Hermann, Paris. p 407.
8. Grief, D. 1975. In *Freeze Drying and Advance Food Technology*, S. A. Goldblith, L. Rey, and W. W. Royhmayr, eds. Academic Press, New York. p 73.
9. Rey, L. 1961. *Biodynamic 8*: 241.
10. Jennings, T. A. 1980. *J. Parenter. Drug Assoc. 34*: 109.
11. Rey, L. 1964. In *Aspects Theoriques et Industriels de la Lyophulisation*, L. Rey, ed. Hermann, Paris. p 23.

12. Jennings, T. A. 1979. In *Proceedings of the Second PMA Seminar on the validation of Sterile Manufacturing Processes: Aceptic Processing.* Pharmaceutical Manufacturers Association, Washington, D.C. p 161.
13. Garrell, R. K., and King, R. E. 1982. *J. Parenter. Sci. Technol.* 36: 2.
14. Couriel, B. 1977. *Bull. Parenter. Drug Assoc.* 31: 227.
15. Rey, L. 1977. In *International Symposium on Freeze-Drying of Biological Products*, V. J. Cabasso and R. H. Regamey, acting eds. Developments in Biological Standardization, Vol. 36. S. Karger, New York. p 19.
16. Meryman, H. T. 1966. In *Cryobiology*, H. T. Meryman, ed. Academic Press, New York. p 1.
17. Jewell, J. E., Workman, R., and Zeleznick, L. D. 1977. In *International Symposium on Freeze-Drying of Biological Products*, V. J. Cabasso and R. H. Regamey, acting eds. Developments in Biological Standardization, Vo. 36. S. Karger, New York. p 181.
18. Simatos, D., and Turc, J. M. 1975. In *Freeze Drying and Advance Food Technology*, S. A Goldblith, L. Rey, and W. W. Royhmayr, eds. Academic Press, New Y rk. p 17.
19. Jennings, T. A. 1980. *Drug and Cosmetic*, November, p 43.
20. Porter, W. R. 1982. *J. Parenter. Sci. Technol.* 36: 179.
21. Jennings, T. A. Validation of the Lyophilization. Seminar Notes.
22. Porter, W. R. 1981. *J. Parenter. Sci. Technol.* 35: 293.
23. *ASTM Manual on Quality Control Of Materials*, Special Technical Publication 15-C, 1951. American Society for Testing Materials, Philadelphia. p 26.
24. Ibid., p 42.
25. Ibid., p 59.
26. Rey, L. 1975. In *Freeze Drying and Advance Food Technology*, S. A. Goldblith, L. Rey, and W. W. Royhmayr, eds. Academic Press, New York. p xiii.
27. Stephenson, J. L. 1960. In *Recent Research in Freezing and Drying*, A. S. Parkes and A. V. Smith, eds. Blackwell Scientific Publications, Oxford, England. p 121.
28. DeLuca, P. and Lachman, L. 1965. *J. Pharm. Sci.* 54: 617.
29. Jennings, T. A. 1980. *Medical Device & Diagnostic Industry* 2(11): 49.
30. Rey, L. R. 1960. In *Recent Research in Freezing and Drying*, A. S. Parkes and A. V. Smith, eds. Blackwell Scientific Publications, Oxford, England. p 40.
31. Jennings, T. A., and Powell, H. 1980. *Medical Device & Diagnostic Industry* 3(3): 35.
32. Rey, L. R. 1960. *Ann. New York Acad. Sci.* 85: 510.
33. Maltini, E. 1975. In *Freeze Drying and Advance Food Technology*, S. A. Goldblith, L. Rey, and W. W. Royhmayr, eds. Academic Press, New York. p 121.
34. Wunderlich, B. 1982. *Am. Lab.*, June, p 26.
35. Gatlin, L., and DeLuca, P. P. 1980. *J. Parenter. Drug Assoc.* 34: 398.
36. Muggleton, P. W. 1964. In *Aspects Theoriques et Industriels de la Lyophilisation*, L. Rey, ed. Hermann, Paris. p 411.
37. Wang, Y. J., and Kowal, R. R. 1980. *J. Parenter. Drug Assoc.* 34: 452.

38. Bashir, J. A., and Avis, K. E. 1973. *Bull. Parenter. Drug Assoc.* 27: 68.
39. DeLuca, P. P., Papadimitriou, D., and DeLuca, P. P. 1982. *J. Parenter. Sci. Technol. 36*: 28.
40. Uotila, J. A., and Santasalo, N. T. 1981. *J. Parenter. Sci. Technol. 35*: 170.
41. DeLuca, P. P. 1977. In *International Symposium on Freeze-Drying of Biological Products*, V. J. Cabasso and R. H. Regamey, acting eds. Developments in Biological Standardization, Vol. 36. S. Karger, New York. p 41.
42. Motola, S., et al. 1980. *Technical Methods Bulletin No. 1.* Parenteral Drug Association, Philadelphia.
43. Motola, S., and Enzinger, R. M. 1980. *Technical Methods Bulletin No. 2.* Parenteral Drug Association, Philadelphia. p 21.
44. Leebron, K. S., and Jennings, T. A. 1981. *J. Parenter. Sci. Technol. 35*: 100.
45. Pikal, M. J., and Lang, J. E. 1978. *J. Parenter. Drug Assoc. 32*: 162.
46. Wilson, N. G., and Beavis, L. C. 1976. *Handbook of Vacuum Leak Detection*, W. R. Bottoms, ed. American Vacuum Society, New York.
47. Peacock, N. 1980. *J. Vac. Sci. Technol. 17*: 330.
48. van Amerongen, G. J. 1964. *Rubber Cehm. Technol. 37*: 1065.
49. Wood, R. T. 1980. *J. Parenter. Drug Assoc. 34*: 286.
50. Jennings, T. A. 1982. *J. Parenter. Sci. Technol. 36*: 152.
51. Kendall, B. R. F. 1982. *J. Vac. Sci. Technol. 21*: 886.
52. Hopkins, G. H. 1977. In *International Symposium on Freeze-Drying of Biological Products*, V. J. Cabasso and R H. Regamey, acting eds. Developments in Biological Standardization, Vol. 36. S. Karger, New York. p 139.
53. Morgan, S. L., and Spotts, M. R. 1975. *Pharm. Technol. 3*(3): 95.
54. Powell, H. R. 1977. In *International Symposium on Freeze-Drying of Biological Products*, V. J. Cabasso and R. H. Regamey, acting eds. Developments in Biological Standardization, Vo. 36. S. Karger, New York. p 117.
55. Le Floc'h, L. 1977. In *International Symposium on Freeze-Drying of Biological Products*, V. J. Cabasso and R. H. Regamey, acting eds. Developments in Biological Standardization, Vol. 36. S. Karger, New York. p 131.
56. Rowe, T. W. G. 1964. In *Aspects Theoriques et Industriels de la Lyophilisation*, L. ey, ed. Hermann, Paris. p 47.
57. MacKenzie, A. P., et al. 1977. In *International Symposium on Freeze-Drying of Biological Products*, V. J. Cabasso and R. H. Regamey, acting eds. Developments in Biological Standardization, Vol. 36. S. Karger, New York. p 151.
58. Erickson, W. L., and Wells, C. V. 1970. *Experimental Backgrounds for Electrical Instrumentation*, Laboratory Systems Research, Boulder, Colo. p 3.
59. Bremmer, R. E. 1982. *J. Parenter. Sci. Technol. 36*: 193.
60. Iverson, M. V., and Hartley, J. L. 1982. *J. Vac. Sci. Technol. 2*: 982.
61. Bills, D. G. 1977. *J. Vac. Sci. Technol. 16*: 2109.
62. Glasstone, S. 1960. *An Introduction to Electrochemistry.* D. van Nostrand Company, Princeton, N.J. p 37.

23

Retrospective Validation for Parenterals

JAMES P. AGALLOCO and JEANNINE A. DER BEDROSIAN*

E. R. Squibb & Sons, Inc., New Brunswick, New Jersey

I. INTRODUCTION

Retrospective validation is an oft-mentioned but poorly understood technique that utilizes statistical analysis of historical data for the purpose of documenting process control. While the term has been used widely in the literature, on responses to FD 483's, and in citations by numerous individuals, it is probably the least understood of all validation programs. This chapter will attempt to clarify some of the methods employed in retrospective validation, with particular emphasis on parenteral applications.

The basic technique behind retrospective validation is the assembly of in-process and/or end product test results to demonstrate that a specific manufacturing process is operating in a state of control. As such, it reflects an element of the Current Good Manufacturing Practices (CGMPs) that requires annual reviews of each product, which has long been a part of the regulations. Despite the clear mandate to perform annual reviews of processes, not all manufacturers perform these reviews using statistical methods. The emergence of validation has prompted firms to reemphasize the annual review and attempt to lend to that review a validation connotation. With the increased exposure that statistical review of processes has received, it would seem that the specific methods employed would have received equal attention. For whatever reason, this has not been the case, and the actual execution of the review has been almost totally ignored.

This chapter reviews the various statistical techniques that can be employed in retrospective validation and outlines some of the operational considerations that must be addressed.

II. CONTROL CHARTS

A. The X̄ Chart

The basic element of retrospective validation is the Shewhart control chart or X̄ chart [1]. A control chart is a graphical representation of analytical data

---

Current affiliation: Independent consultant, East Brunswick, New Jersey.

for a single test in sequential order. The $\overline{X}$ control chart is a rectangular grid that depicts the upper and lower control limits for the parameter (see Fig. 1). The value plotted may be the result of a single measurement, or it can be the mean value obtained from several individual measurements of a single lot. When utilized for process control (as was its original purpose), the control chart can aid the analyst in the rapid detection of process upsets, offsets, trends, etc., so that immediate corrective measures can be taken. In validation the application is somewhat different. The expectation is that the conventional process controls are adequate to ensure product quality; the validation control chart demonstrates that control by review of data over a period of time. This demonstration represents a validation of the routine production and quality control practices and proves the firm's ability to execute that process. Properly utilized, the control chart can serve both needs, the early detection of processing problems before they get out of hand and the periodic documentation needed to confirm process acceptability.

The control chart can be employed on a wide range of parameters relating to parenterals. Such items as potency, fill volume, pH, particle size, moisture, etc., should be obvious. The use of the control chart in these areas conforms closely with its application in other pharmaceutical and nonpharmaceutical applications, where it is desirable to easily monitor a specific dependent variable. Less apparent, but equally useful, applications would be particulate levels in finished products, environmental air quality (viables and nonviables), and HVAC system performance (temperature and relative humidity), all of which can be successfully charted for the rapid review and presentation of data. The utility of the control chart in these less familiar surroundings can provide unique insight into the effect of filling room rearrangements, filter changes on product, stopper formulation impact on particulates, or the ability of the sterile air systems to maintain the sterile environment air quality during

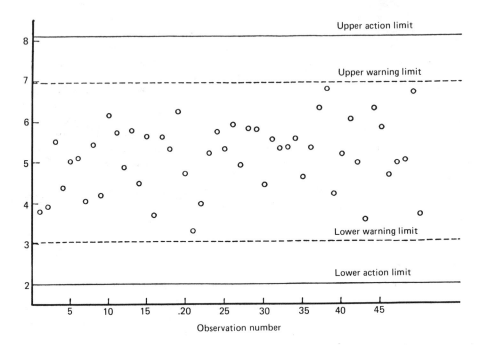

FIGURE 1 An $\overline{X}$ chart. (From Ref. 7.)

adverse weather conditions. See Figure 2 for examples of $\overline{X}$ control chart applications for parenterals.

B. The R Chart

The R chart (also developed by Shewhart) provides information concerning the variability or range (R) of values within a single lot (or sample), in contrast to the lot-to-lot variation depicted on an $\overline{X}$ chart. Here, the range between the highest and lowest values obtained during the testing of an individual lot is plotted sequentially with the range of values for each of several prior lots (see Fig. 3). Any lot evidencing a range of values (an R value) significantly greater than that demonstrated by the other lots may be suspect. The variables that can be reviewed in this manner encompass the full range of items reviewable on an $\overline{X}$ control chart. The unique applications outlined above for parenterals in the area of environmental air quality and particulate levels are well suited to this form of analysis.

C. The Cumulative Summation Chart

A useful adjunct to the Shewhart control charts is the cumulative summation (cum-sum) chart, where the difference between the value (individual or averaged) plotted on the $\overline{X}$ chart and the overall mean value for that process variable is determined and added (or subtracted) sequentially over time from the previous value to depict the cumulative deviations from the mean (see Fig. 4). This technique can provide rapid identification of the time frame in

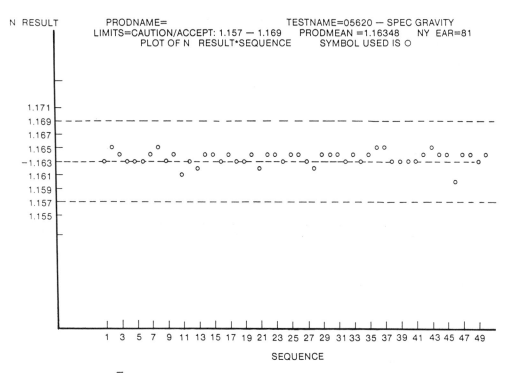

FIGURE 2 An $\overline{X}$ chart for a parenteral product. Graph of specific gravity results vs. time.

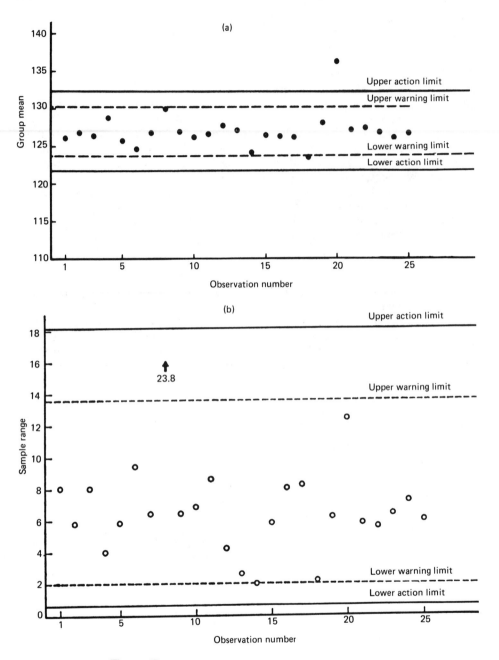

FIGURE 3   An $\overline{X}$ and $\overline{R}$ chart.   (From Ref. 7.)

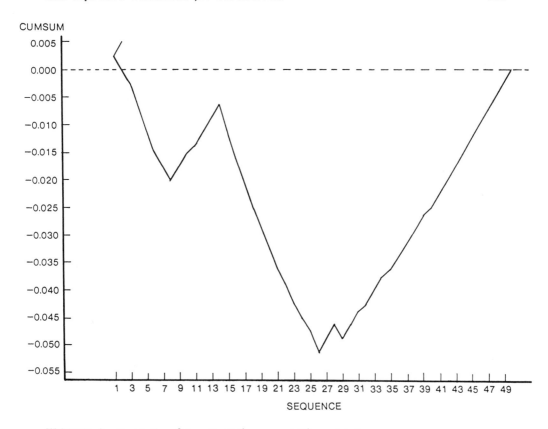

FIGURE 4 Example of a cumulative summation chart.

which a process shift occurs. Its sensitivity is such that shifts of less than 1% from the process mean can be readily detected. Care must be taken in the use of the cum-sum chart due to its high sensitivity. Minor shifts well within the control limits can sometimes be highlighted to the extent that their true value and relation to the limits is obscured, while the existence of a process shift (however minute) is overemphasized. Small deviations from the mean are usually more readily apparent on the cum-sum chart than on the $\overline{X}$ chart, but large deviations are more rapidly detected on the $\overline{X}$ chart since two to three observations are necessary to reveal a trend on a cum-sum chart. When used with care, the cum-sum chart can provide information about the subtle effects on a process brought about by seemingly insignificant changes in practice, layout, or materials.

D. Moving Average

A tool used with increasing frequency during retrospective validation efforts is the moving averages chart (see Fig. 5). Utilizing this method, the average of the first five sequential values is plotted as the first point on the chart, followed by the averages of values 2–6, 3–7, 4–8, etc. In this way a result is evaluated within the context of its neighboring values. This method provides a superior means to the $\overline{X}$ chart for detecting small deviations or trends,

```
                                    RETROSPECTIVE VALIDATION        14:45 MONDAY, MARCH 28, 1983   7

                        GRAPH OF        MOVING AVERAGES VS. TIME

        PRODNAME:                       TESTNAME=              ACLIMITS=CAUTION: 3.5-5.5/ACCEPT: 2.5-5.5   NYEAR=82

                     PLOT OF SEQUENCE*ACMOVAVG   SYMBOL USED IS *
                     PLOT OF SEQUENCE*MEANRES    SYMBOL USED IS !

   SEQUENCE ^           I                   I                                                I
            ^           I                   I                                                I
            ^           I                   I                                                I
            ^           I                   I                                                I
            ^           I                   I                                                I
          1 +           I                   I                        !                       I
          2 +           I                   I                        !                       I
          3 +           I                   I                        !                       I
          4 +           I                   I                        !                       I
          5 +           I                   I                        ! *                     I
          6 +           I                   I                        ! *                     I
          7 +           I                   I                        ! *                     I
          8 +           I                   I                        ! *                     I
          9 +           I                   I                        !  *                    I
         10 +           I                   I                        ! *                     I
         11 +           I                   I                        !*                      I
         12 +           I                   I                        !*                      I
         13 +           I                   I                        !*                      I
         14 +           I                   I                       *!                       I
         15 +           I                   I                       *!                       I
         16 +           I                   I                      * !                       I
         17 +           I                   I                      *!                        I
         18 +           I                   I                       *                        I
         19 +           I                   I                       !*                       I
         20 +           I                   I                       ! *                      I
         21 +           I                   I                       !   *                    I
         22 +           I                   I                       !  *                     I
         23 +           I                   I                       ! *                      I
         24 +           I                   I                       !*                       I
         25 +           I                   I                       *                        I
         26 +           I                   I                      *!                        I
         27 +           I                   I                      *!                        I
         28 +           I                   I                      *!                        I
         29 +           I                   I                      *                         I
         30 +           I                   I                      *                         I
         31 +           I                   I                      *!                        I
         32 +           I                   I                      *!                        I
         33 +           I                   I                      *!                        I
         34 +           I                   I                      *!                        I
         35 +           I                   I                      *!                        I
         36 +           I                   I                      *                         I
         37 +           I                   I                      *                         I
         38 +           I                   I                      *                         I
         39 +           I                   I                      *                         I
         40 +           I                   I                      *                         I
            ^           I                   I                                                I
            ^           I                   I                                                I
            ^           I                   I                                                I
            +-----+-----+-----+-----+-----+-----+-----+-----+-----+-----+-----+-----+-----+-----+-----+-----+-----+-----+-----+-----+-
           2.0   2.2   2.4   2.6   2.8   3.0   3.2   3.4   3.6   3.8   4.0   4.2   4.4   4.6   4.8   5.0   5.2   5.4   5.6   5.8   6.0

                                                      ACMOVAVG
```

FIGURE 5   Example of a moving average chart.

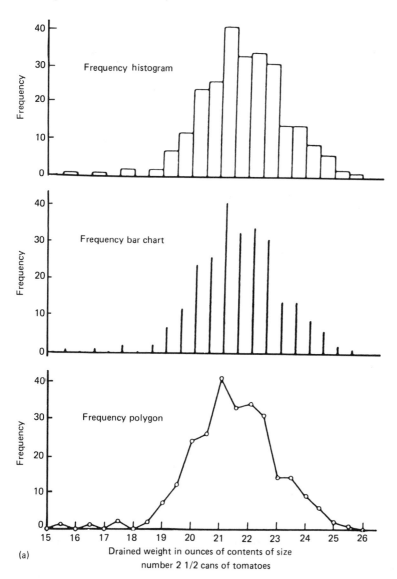

FIGURE 6 (a) Examples of other graphical techniques. Frequency distribution.

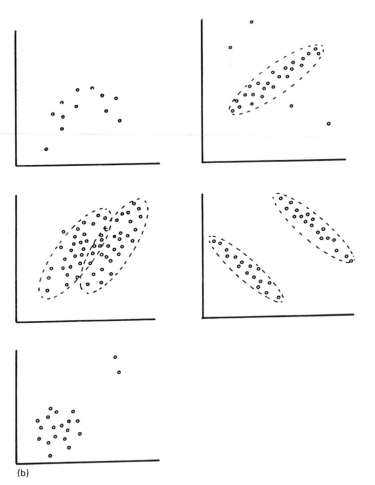

(b)

FIGURE 6 (b) X-Y diagrams. (From Ref. 3.)

but large changes are not always detected as rapidly. The advantage of the moving average chart over the cumulative summation chart is that extremes in values do not distort or "skew" the plot over a long period. Any individual value is used only in the calculation (averaging) of five points on the moving average chart, whereas an extreme value would have a cumulative effect on *all* points to follow on the cum-sum chart.

E. Other Techniques

There are other types of graphical and statistical methods for reviewing data for the confirmation of process stability. Techniques such as frequency distributions (for viewing the frequency of occurrence of each result) and X–Y plots (to depict the possible interrelationships between two variables) have been successfully utilized in the performance of retrospective validation. See Figure 6 for examples of the techniques mentioned above.

III. IMPLEMENTING A RETROSPECTIVE VALIDATION PROGRAM

There are as many possible approaches to retrospective validation as there are pharmaceutical firms in existence, but there are certainly more wrong ways to go about it than there are right ones. The authors have had success with the program outlined in this chapter. This is not to suggest that this is the only scheme by which retrospective validation can be achieved; it merely represents a suggested path for the beginning practitioner to follow.

A. Statistical Package

The easiest decision to make in retrospective validation is the decision to utilize a preprogrammed statistical package such as SAS or STATPAK (other programs are available as well) rather than developing one's own programs. These packages, which are available on most time-sharing systems, eliminate lengthy programming and allow rapid implementation of statistical methods for retrospective validation. Certainly, the statistical package will accelerate the validation effort, and the advantages of getting the program underway quickly offset any costs that might be incurred if the package must be purchased. In today's era of the computer, it is likely that the needed statistical tools will already be available in most firms.

B. Programmer

The availability of preprogrammed software enables the layperson to begin retrospective validation quite readily. However, to fully realize the potential inherent in this area, a competent programmer should be available to modify basic programs. As often as not, a company statistician is available, and in most cases this offers a distinct advantage, as the combined skills of programmer and statistician are needed to expand upon the basic output generated by the software. It should be recognized that a programmer/statistician is not a mandatory requirement for performing retrospective analysis, but the presence of a qualified individual can make the effort considerably easier and far more complete.

C. Data Assembly

In gathering the data for retrospective review, only two possibilities exist: The data are either available on a computer or they are not. Given the range of possible configurations the data may be in within a computer, it is almost a certainty that they must be rearranged to conform to the input needs of the statistical package. It is in this phase of the review that a programmer becomes necessary. In the event that the data are not available in a computer, the preparation of a data entry program is required. The data entry program should be tailored to fit the specific objectives of the firm, the data format requirements of the statistical package, and the technical skills of the person entering the data. In many of the available statistical packages, a data entry program is an integral portion, thereby eliminating the need for extra programming.

Regardless of the form in which raw data are retained, all data must be carefully reviewed prior to incorporation into the data sets for study. In many firms it is commonplace to find extraneous data within the compilation. This occurs when special testing is performed, resamples or retests are required, assays are performed in parallel using two similar (but slightly different) methods, and for numerous other reasons. All redundant and non-applicable data must be removed from the data sets to ensure that each lot is represented by a single value for each test under evaluation. (Note: In the event that variations within a lot are being studied rather than (or in conjunction with) lot-to-lot variations, the prior statement should be modified to read as follows: . . .each portion of the lot is represented by a single value for each test under evaluation.)

The elimination of data from consideration must be undertaken with care to ensure that data that rightfully belongs in the data set are not inadvertently discarded. This would discredit the entire program. For this reason a record of the raw data should be retained along with an explanation for why each portion of data was removed. When in doubt as to whether a particular piece of data should be retained, it appears to be prudent to keep it in the data set, thereby avoiding criticism of the program later on.

D. Data Presentation

When all data for analysis have been compiled in a computer-accessible file, additional precautions must be taken. Conventional statistical packages routinely condense the data when plotting charts if the number of items does not fit the output format required. This can cause a data set containing a large number of values to be compressed to fit a smaller-number character output, with each plotted point now representing either one or more pieces of data. For this reason the maximum number of points presented on a control chart sheet should not exceed the capabilities of the printer. Figure 7 illustrates a chart where the number of points plotted by the statistical program is excessive. The number of points must be further reduced to allow room for identification of the axes and titles. When the number of lots that must be studied in one data set exceeds these values and a single control chart is desired, the continuation of the chart onto separate sheets of paper can be considered. (The authors have had success with modifying the program to exchange the horizontal and vertical axes, allowing the computer to continue to plot points over several sheets. This type of alteration takes advantage of the fact that computer paper is conventionally joined at the top and bottom. The modification of the program to put data in this format is difficult and should be attempted only by an experienced programmer.)

E. Selection of Vertical Scale

In a manner similar to that for the compression of a data set to fit the selected output format, the conventional statistical package will select its own vertical scale unless the programmer defines a specific one for use with the data set. While this may appear on the surface to be an innocuous feature, it can prove to be extremely frustrating. This may cause an otherwise stable process whose data might approximate a straight horizontal line on the control chart to have its data "expanded" by the program to fill the entire vertical scale. Although this allows maximum resolution between the individual data points, it also serves to magnify the minimal differences (in numerical terms) between the points. Thus the apparent variation in the data set is greatly increased, when in real terms the process output is well controlled. By proper selection

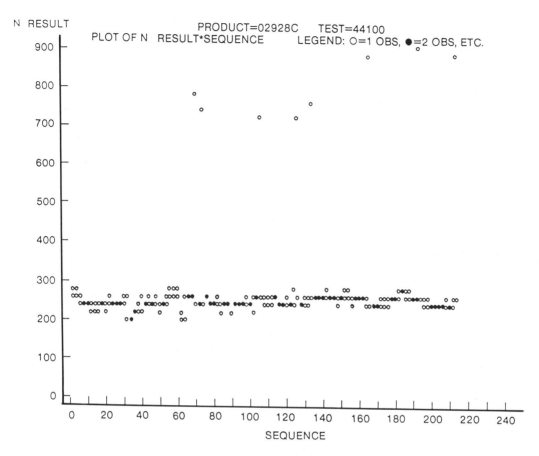

FIGURE 7   Example of improper charting techniques.

of parameters, an experienced programmer can override the statistical program and select a proper vertical scale. A practice that appears to be useful
in this case is to select a vertical scale that positions the majority of the data
in the middle third of the page. If the data is not completely screened prior
to this step, the existence of even a single point outside the programmer-
selected vertical scale will cause the program to compress the remaining data
into a narrow band virtually useless for validation purposes (see Fig. 7).
When a test has only an upper (or lower) limit, the scale selection should be
made such that the highest (or lowest) value is near the middle of the page.

F. Chart Preparation

The steps outlined previously will provide a sequential plot of the individual
data points on a vertical axis of appropriate size. The plots obtained in this
manner are not control charts in the strictest sense and, despite the considerable effort expended in their preparation, are inadequate for the purposes
of retrospective validation. A control chart must include additional elements
to fulfill the objectives of retrospective validation and to be a proper control
chart as developed by Shewhart. These include the following:

1. Headings

No figure or graph and certainly no control chart is complete without a heading. As a minimum, each chart should be identified with the following information: the product name (and strength, if necessary); the test plotted on that chart; and the time period from which the data is drawn. If desired, a number of other items can be added to increase the chart's utility, including notation of the product code number and test procedure number.

2. Control Limits

The most basic addition to the control chart is that of control limits. These should include both the alert and action limits (if both types are utilized) employed to control the process. A convenient practice is to include in the heading the numerical value of each limit. On the chart proper, the limits should be presented by a symbol other than that used for the individual points, and plotted in the appropriate positions on the chart.

The subject of how control limits are established and utilized in the routine release of manufactured products as well as for retrospective validation is one of considerable interst. The selection of process control limits is usually accomplished by one of two methods. The first approach is a rigorous statistical evaluation of process capability. Alternatively, the limits are determined by a less definitive projection of what process limits are sufficient to ensure end product acceptability. While it would appear that the statistical approach is overwhelmingly preferred, its actual implementation is less certain due to differences in lot size, equipment parameters, and the like. In the development of a New Drug Application (NDA), a pharmaceutical manufacturer identifies the process control and specification limits that will ensure product quality. In the course of developing the NDA, the manufacturer determines these initial limits from several sources. These may consist of process variability during the initial development and scale-up, process limits employed for similar products already in full production, and an awareness of what limits the reviewing agency will consider acceptable.

Common practice within the pharmaceutical industry is to pyramid control limits, i.e., to utilize narrower ranges at the early stages of production and for internal control, with a gradual broadening of the control limits as the product approaches the end product stages. The wider limits are those documented in the NDA and issued to the regulatory bodies. Once the limits have been established, the more stringent internal control limits may be adjusted as necessary to reflect actual performance.

All of the preceding discussion leads to what appears to be the major point at issue in historical data analysis: Some companies document process control range limits as those reflective of the filed specifications, while other firms employ those ranges that are indicative of process performance. Thus, one school employs those limits that are merely sufficient for the confirmation of product or process quality, while the second school employs limits at either 2 or 3 standard deviations (SD) from the true process mean. The more precise utilization of control charting for retrospective validation is certainly more statistically correct than the more convenient and less restrictive utilization of usually wider filed limits. A disadvantage of control limits that are statistically derived is evident in that use of 2 SD limits will accept only 95% of all historical data, while 3 SD limits will result in the acceptance of 99% of the values. In the final analysis, all firms that execute retrospective analysis employ filed limits to avoid unnecessary process adjustments and lengthy investigations.

Retrospective validation attempts to demonstrate that process quality can be maintained on a consistent basis over time. Regardless of whether regulatory limits or statistical control limits are plotted on the control chart, the objective of the analysis is to demonstrate that the process variability (within lots and between lots) is controlled such that virtually all of the materials produced will be acceptable for their intended use. This will result only if the process variability (as measured by the standard deviation) is sufficiently small and the parameter mean value can be maintained close to the intent. When process consistency is not maintained by routine process controls, retrospective validation will demonstrate (just as a proper prospective validation study would) that the process is not in a state of control.

3. Mean Value

A statistical review of data is considered incomplete unless a determination of the mean value for the data set is made. Where possible, this value should be presented in both numerical form and as a line in the appropriate position on the chart proper. Figure 8 provides an example of a control chart containing all the features described above.

4. Statistical Tables

A useful adjunct to the control chart (and a useful tool in its own right) is a statistical table that summarizes the individual results for each data point on the chart (including lot numbers, manufacturing date, etc.). These

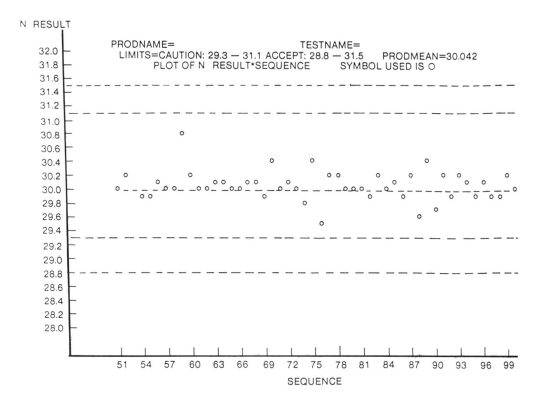

FIGURE 8 Example of proper charting techniques.

tables are arranged in the same sequential order as the data on the chart and present detailed data for each lot whose data appears in the table. Other useful statistical data summaries include tables of means, standard deviations, range, moving averages, etc. (see Fig. 9). The decision as to which of these elements to include is the prerogative of the individual developing the retrospective validation package.

G. Interpretation of Results

Once properly assembled control charts have been prepared, it might seem that the retrospective validation effort is complete. Unfortunately, a great deal of additional work may be needed to provide a fully usable retrospective validation package. When the assembled control charts demonstrate a well-controlled and stable process, all that remains is the preparation of the validation report.

If the data fails to present clear evidence that the process is in control, all is not lost. There are a number of external factors that can perturb the test results so that an apparent process upset may be evident, when in fact the process may be completely acceptable. Investigation into such areas as analytical test procedure changes, sample size adjustments, sampling plan revisions, process changes (however subtle), equipment modification, etc., can provide explanations for the apparent process instability. Recognizing that much of the work in the preparation of the control charts has been performed by either a programmer or statistician indicates that the information about the aforementioned external factors will either be of little value to him or will never have been available to him at all. A complete review of the potential causes must be carried out by persons knowledgeable in the specific area. If an external factor is identified that could have created the process perturbation, the chart may be divided into two (or more) separate charts reflecting the periods before and after the change. Each of these charts may demonstrate the required process stability. If the identification of probable

CODE & NAME	LIMITS CAUTION	ACCEPTANCE	NO. OF RESULTS	MEAN	MIN.	MAX.	STD DEVIATION
00960	388–412	388–412	8	398.0	395	400	1.6903
82990	0.0 – 0.75	0.0 – 0.75	8	0.1575	0	0.35	0.1159
83030	19.5 – 22.0	19.5 – 22.0	8	20.45	19.8	21.5	0.6990
83740	0.0 – 5.0	0.0 – 5.0	8	3.5250	3.0	3.9	0.2964
89910	97 – 103	95 – 105	8	100.425	98.4	104.3	2.1285

FIGURE 9   Sample statistical table.

causes proves fruitless, the only conclusion is that the process is not in a state of control. At this point the only recourse is an investigation of the process to identify factors creating the instability with concurrent development of a program aimed at their elimination. (This is beyond the scope of this chapter and will not be addressed here.) Since the data utilized to assemble the retrospective package represents the firm's in-process and end product test results, information concerning the process acceptability or unacceptability is not likely to be a total surprise. Retrospective validation, when properly executed, will confirm what any other form of validation will, that is, an unacceptable process is indeed unacceptable (and similarly, an acceptable process is in fact acceptable).

H. Documentation

Retrospective validation has many similarities to other validation programs, particularly in the need for accurate documentation of the validation. The individual pieces of documentation needed for retrospective review are described in detail below.

1. Validation Outline

The validation outline takes the place of the validation protocol ordinarily utilized. The outline should consist of the following elements:

1. A sample validation with copies of the original data as derived from the firm's records
2. A copy of the computer program utilized to process the data
3. A summary table of all the deleted sample data including the rationale for its exclusion
4. A sample validation report

Where possible, the validation outline is annotated to assist the reviewer in comprehending the package. The addition of comments to a computer program is readily accomplished and allows the individual reviewing the program to follow the logic employed. Once the validation outline has been completed, it will be reviewed by all concerned disciplines (in much the same way that a protocol is reviewed and approved) to ensure that it fulfills the validation objectives the firm has established. The validation outline serves as a guide to persons unfamiliar with retrospective validation and can be used to explain the procedures involved to FDA investigators.

2. Raw Data

Retrospective validation is unique in that there is no "raw data." All of the data utilized in its execution is already a part of the firm's records. All that should be retained in the validation files is a copy of all the intermediate versions of the data as it is processed into the final control charts. While this certainly doesn't fit the description of raw data, it will enhance any detailed review or investigation of the validation.

3. Validation Report

The focal point of any retrospective validation is the validation report, which documents the stability of the process under review. The report itself hinges upon the various control charts that demonstrate the ability of the process to consistently manufacture product within defined control limits. The report must include other elements to provide clarity of presentation as needed and to demonstrate that the data do indeed depict a process operating under proper controls. The suggested elements in the report not previously mentioned include the following:

1. A brief description of the process, with clear indication of where all in-process samples employed in validation were taken.
2. A copy of the various in-process and end product specifications utilized to monitor the product. (If the specifications are pyramided, then both specifications should be provided.)
3. A brief description of the various test methods for which data are tabulated. The analytical test procedures themselves must be validated; that, however, is beyond the scope of this chapter.
4. A complete listing of the various samples taken from the lot after completion of the manufacturing.
5. Other documentation as desired, such as detailed manufacturing instructions, standard operating procedures, test procedures, etc.

While the supporting information described above is recommended, there is one piece of documentation that should be considered mandatory: the statistical summary tables of data comprising the chronological results for each individual test. As mentioned earlier, these tables should be accompanied by a summary table including the following features: the number of tests in the table, the mean value of all results, the standard deviation about the mean, the minimum value, and the maximum value. Optional statistical measures that can be provided if desired are the standard error of the mean, the variance, and the coefficient of variation.

IV. CONCLUSION

As has been shown in this chapter, retrospective validation affords the opportunity to demonstrate process stability with data that have already been assembled. This form of validation offers a speed of execution that is a major reason for the widespread interest in the technique. There are a number of drawbacks that can diminish the utility of this practice.

On the surface it might seem that this form of validation is inexpensive, as virtually no new testing must be performed. The manipulation on a high-speed computer is very rapid. However, the number of calculations needed to execute even a small retrospective validation are surprisingly large, the data storage requirements are significant, and the connect time for outputting the reports will tie up a terminal almost full-time (if the programmer and/or statistician's time is included, that will also add to the total), causing the overall cost of executing a retrospective validation program to be far larger than might be expected. (For those skeptics who might think otherwise, contact your computer center and determine what the rates charged will be.)

A second consideration is the timeliness of the report. Given the speed of execution, it is possible to complete a retrospective validation in less than a week. The production of the next batch of the product will render that validation study obsolete, thereby tempting the practitioner to add that batch to the report. This requires that the entire report be redone. Every effort should be made to resist this temptation and allow the validation study to stand as is. Another name for retrospective validation is "historical validation." Employing this term, retrospective validation can then be placed in proper perspective. History deals with a fixed period of prior time and should not be confused with current events. Similarily, retrospective validation can be extremely effective if it deals with data drawn from a fixed period in the past. A potential solution is the completion of retrospective reviews on a periodic basis such that each product is subject to this form of validation on a regular basis. Recognizing that the speed of execution is rapid allows the firm to update the retrospective validation on any product in short order in response to an inquiry or FDA inspection.

The area of retrospective validation is one that is rapidly emerging, and for this reason the practitioner is reminded to stay abreast of current developments. Certainly no other area of validation holds more promise for the successful validation of all of a firm's products considering the relatively limited time and personnel required to prepare a retrospective validation study as compared to a prospective study. A second advantage is the simplicity of execution; there are no additional samples to be taken, no special testing, sophisticated measuring equipment, or new facilities needed.

REFERENCES

1. Simms, L. 1980. Process control, Conference notes and background material from 1980 Arden House Conference on Industrial Pharmacy, IPT Section of Academy of Pharmaceutical Sciences and Arnold & Marie Schwartz College of Pharmacy and Health Sciences, Long Island University, January 13—18, Harrison, N.Y.
2. Duncan, 1974. *Quality Control and Industrial Statistics*, 4th ed. Richard D. Irwin, Homewood, Ill.
3. Grant, E., and Leavenworth, R. 1980. *Statistical Quality Control*, 5th ed. McGraw—Hill Book Company, New York.
4. Simms, L. 1980. Validation of existing products by statistical evaluation, in *Proceedings of the PMA Seminar Program on Validation of Solid Dosage Form Process*, Atlanta, Ga., May 11—13.
5. Meyer, R. J. 1980. Validation of products and processes from a production, quality control viewpoint, in *Proceedings of the PMA Seminar Program on Validation of Solid Dosage Form Process*, Atlanta, Ga., May 11—13.
6. Ott, E. R. 1975. *Process Quality Control*. McGraw—Hill Book Company, New York.
7. Wetherill, G. G. 1977. *Sampling Inspection and Quality Control*, 2nd ed. John Wiley & Sons, New York.
8. *ASTM Manual on Presentation of Data and Control Chart Analysis*, 1976. American Society for Testing and Materials, Philadelphia.
9. *SAS User's Guide*, 1979 ed. SAS Institute, Cary, N.C.

24

Validation of Aseptic Filling Operations

JAMES P. AGALLOCO

E. R. Squibb & Sons, Inc., New Brunswick, New Jersey

I. INTRODUCTION

A facility used for the filling and processing of sterile dry powders and liquids probably represents the most diverse and complex area within the pharmaceutical production area. In addition to the modules and equipment, the facility may include a vial preparation system for cleaning, washing, and sterilization/depyrogenation of glass containers; filling equipment under laminar air flow; airlocks; autoclaves; ovens; closure sealing machines; conveyors; and the room(s) in which the equipment is contained. The environment as well as the personnel working in the area can have significant impact on the successful outcome of the operation. Some of the difficulties encountered during aseptic filling operations can be minimized by the careful design and location of equipment. Floors, walls, and ceilings must be carefully constructed for ease of cleaning and sanitization. Airlocks for the transfer of components, equipment, and entry of personnel contribute to the difficulties in maintaining aseptic conditions. The practices, procedures, and discipline maintained by the operating personnel cannot be overemphasized, since personnel are probably the primary source of viable and nonviable contamination in parenteral products.

All of the methods, facilities, and controls employed must be carefully defined, validated, and all operating parameters, procedures, and limits established. Equipment and controls must be calibrated and maintained to establish that they are in a state of control. They must be periodically reviewed to ascertain if there is a need for revalidation.

Previous chapters have described in detail the validation of specific equipment, processes and operations. Validation of liquid and powder filling operations with and without the use of a sterile medium process are described in this chapter.

II. GENERAL CONSIDERATIONS

The design and materials of construction for liquid and dry aseptic pharmaceutical operations have been described in previous chapters. Validation is a multidisciplinary effort dependent on extensive cooperation among Production, Quality Control, Engineering, and other groups. The performance of a successful aseptic filling validation is the culmination of a number of interrelated events. The facility design elements are important factors, and their influence on aseptic filling performance must be addressed.

A. Filling Room

The potential for microbial contamination in an aseptic processing area is quite large, and its minimization requires a properly designed filling room. The successful design must provide for ease of sanitization; air of appropriate quality wherever product or components are exposed; minimal manual manipulation of components and equipment; adequate temperature and humidity control to ensure personnel comfort in full sterile attire; and other aspects. The specific influence of any of these factors on a filling operation may not be obvious. However, it should be obvious that unless the facility design is comprehensive, some deficiencies will exist. Attention to the details of the design is necessary to ensure that the aseptic operations can be performed to reduce sources of contamination. Recognition that a media fill is one of the more difficult validation programs to execute should provide the practitioner with sufficient awareness that facility design factors are a major consideration for success.

A necessary step in preparing for aseptic filling validation is the satisfactory completion of all related validation programs. Particular emphasis should be given to the validation of the sterilization and/or sanitization procedures for materials, components, and product contact surfaces. In order to reduce the potential for the introduction of contamination, the concepts of sterilize-in-place and sanitize-in-place should be considered. The evolving techniques in this area afford the opportunity for increased assurance of sterility. The protection of items (not sterilized or sanitized in situ) during transport from the sterilizer to the filling room and through the manipulations necessary to ready the line for operation is another factor to consider in the selection of the methods and materials to be utilized. The validation programs should consist of the elements of installation qualification, operational qualification, and the functional validation of the process itself.

B. Related Validation Efforts

Prior to the execution of a validation program for aseptic filling, it is necessary that all equipment and processes are qualified or validated. These elements encompass cleaning and sanitation of the surfaces of the room (floors, walls, ceilings), sanitization of all surfaces of equipment (tanks, conveyors, turntables, closure machines, etc.) and tools. It is also essential that the air system for the room is qualified and that the air is of suitable quality. The pressure within the room must be within the operating parameters (previously established during qualification and validation of the aseptic processing area air system) in order to maintain the differential relation to adjoining rooms or hallways. Particulate counting for nonviable matter has been addressed in an earlier chapter, and acceptable established levels should be maintained. Viable counts should be within the established alert or action levels developed from trend data. Particulate contamination represented as a function of starting materials, and container and closure contribution, should also be assessed. Validation of other supportive processes (such as washing, steam sterilization, aseptic filtration, etc.), as addressed in previous chapters, must be established prior to commencing this operation.

III. VALIDATION

There exist several principal routes for the execution of a successful validation program for an aseptic filling operation. Some firms have chosen to employ media fill operations as evidence of their capability to fill a sterile product. Other manufacturers have determined that the media fill process, because of numerous inherent technical limitations, is not a viable alternative (see Sec. VIII). Still other firms have chosen to perform media fills for some processes, but not for others. The decision to utilize media is the major factor in the development of validation protocols for aseptic processes. Regardless of the outcome of the decision-making process, validation of the aseptic filling process is equally acceptable whether it is achieved with or without the use of media.

A. Validation Without Media

Representatives of the Food and Drug Administration (FDA) have stated that media fills are not required if the firm can demonstrate the acceptability of its aseptic procedures by other means. One approach that has been demonstrated to be successful in providing this assurance is the maintenance of Class 100 conditions wherever product or components are exposed to the environment. The demonstration of Class 100 must be continuous throughout the filling process and should encompass the key locations on the line such as filling and stoppering machines. Particle counting is performed in the room during operation, either with or without product. Monitoring without product is more often used to confirm environmental air quality for powder filling operations. For similar reasons, a number of firms that have elected to validate in this manner have adopted portable laminar-flow units for the transfer and loading/unloading of vials into lyophilizers.

A further enhancement of the nonmedia approach to validation includes the addition of microbial monitoring of the aseptic processing area's environmental air and exposed surfaces. This technique, in conjunction with nonviable monitoring, demonstrates that the areas of product and component exposure are free of viable organisms. Employing such a correlation of microbial and particulate monitoring data allows the firm, if it chooses to do so, to utilize the routine particulate count data as a substitute for the microbial monitoring in the area of concern. This can be further extended to include continuous multipoint particle counting in areas of product and component exposure. The firms that adopt this method are then able to confirm the acceptability of the critical areas on an ongoing basis. While the approaches outlined here are more prevalent in the validation of sterile dry powder filling methods, they are just as applicable to liquid fills.

B. Validation With Media

For those manufacturers who choose to utilize media in the validation of their filling operation, a number of methodologies can be employed. This section presents a selection of methods that can be adapted to suit the needs of the practitioner. Methods for liquid, powder, and freeze-dried products are described.

1. Liquid Fills

The objective is to confirm the acceptability of the liquid filling procedures to protect the formulation from adventitious microbial contamination. The practitioner must make a decision as to the number and size of vials and the percent contamination level deemed acceptable (see Table 1). The vials will be filled with a predetermined volume of sterile USP fluid soybean-casein digest medium (SCDM), stoppered and sealed.

Note: The selection of the acceptance criteria is a major responsibility of the individual(s) developing a media fill program. An expanded discussion of this issue is presented later in this chapter (see p. 663).

Verification of Media Growth Promotion Properties: Verification of the growth-promoting properties of the medium is performed as follows: The medium is perpared according to standard methods and sterilized as per the manufacturer's instructions. The sterile medium is filled into a predetermined statistically significant number of vials, and one-half of the vials are inoculated with *Bacillus subtilis* ATCC 6633 suspension adjusted to less than 100 colony-forming organisms per 0.1 ml. The remaining vials containing the test medium are inoculated with *Candida albicans* ATCC 10231 suspension adjusted to less than 100 organisms per 0.1 ml. The vials are stoppered, sealed with appropriate closures, and incubated at a predetermined temperature for a period of 7 days. A criterion that is often used is that the test medium is satisfactory if evidence of growth appears within 7 days in at least 50% of the inoculated vials representing each organism. Performance of media growth confirmation at this stage is optional. Media growth promotion properties in the actual vials are mandatory and are described later in the chapter.

Sterile Medium Preparation: The preparation of sterile USP SCDM is detailed below: A suitable holding tank is sterilized in a validated autoclave. The tank is removed from the autoclave into the aseptic area. The following sterilized parts are aseptically connected to the autoclaved tank: A bleeder valve and thermowell; a safety relief valve; a vent valve and vent filter assembly containing a 0.2-μm hydrophobic filter. (Alternatively, the tank and parts may be sterilized in place by steam.) The tank bottom outlet is aseptically connected to a sterilized filter holder equipped with a 0.2-μm membrane, in either cartridge or disk membrane configuration. The filter holder is aseptically connected to a water-for-injection (WFI) source. The medium is manufactured in the tank in accordance with the supplier's instructions. The medium is then filtered through a sterilized, 0.2-μm membrane filter into a sterile tank. The medium is sterilized by heating it to not less than 121°C for a minimum of 30 min, after which it is rapidly cooled to 25-30°C. The tank bottom outlet is aseptically connected to the inlet of a presterilized filter holder equipped with a 0.2-μm membrane or cartridge. The filter holder is then aseptically connected to the filling machine. Filter integrity tests are then performed. The medium is now ready for filling into containers.

Verification of Medium Sterility: The procedure outlined above closely follows that employed for the routine filling of products. As such, no sterility testing is conducted subsequent to the medium sterilization, but prior to media filling. If the medium is nonsterile prior to filling, the entire process will be found unacceptable. For this reason, several firms have chosen to hold the sterilized medium prior to filling in order to confirm its sterility.

TABLE 1 Probability of Detection of Nonsterility for Media Fills

X N	100	500	1,000	1,500	2,000	3,000	5,000	10,000	15,000	20,000	30,000
0.01	1.0	4.9	9.5	13.9	18.1	25.9	39.3	63.2	77.7	86.5	95.0
0.05	4.9	22.1	39.4	52.8	63.2	77.7	91.8	99.3	>99.9		
0.1	9.5	39.4	63.2	77.7	86.5	95.0	99.3	>99.9			
0.2	18.1	63.2	86.5	95.0	98.2	99.8	>99.9				
0.3	26.0	77.7	95.0	98.9	99.7	>99.9					
0.4	33.0	86.5	98.2	99.8	>99.9						
0.5	39.4	91.8	99.3	>99.9							
0.75	52.5	97.7	>99.9								
1.0	63.4	99.3	>99.9								
2.0	86.7	>99.9									
3.0	95.2	>99.9									
4.0	98.3	>99.9									
5.0	99.4	>99.9									
10.0	>99.9										

The probability of detection of nonsterility in a media fill is calculated using the following equation:

$$P = 1 - (1 - X)^N$$

where P is the probability, X is acceptable contamination rate, and N is the number of vials filled.

Once satisfied that the medium is indeed sterile, it can be used in the media filling with the assurance that any contamination detected is derived from the filling procedures.

Aseptic Operation: The vials and closures are cleaned and sterilized using standard operating procedures. The equipment filling parts and trays are cleaned and sterilized utilizing standard operating procedures as described earlier. A suitable liquid filling machine is employed, in which the standard fill rate is now maintained. Each of the sterilized test vials is filled with an appropriate volume of the sterile medium prepared as described above. The vials are stoppered and sealed. The medium-filled vials are collected in trays, covered, and each tray numbered sequentially. The trays are then inverted to assure closure contact with medium. Prior to incubation at the predetermined temperature, the trays are turned upright.

Verification of the Growth-Promotion Properties of the Filled Test Medium: Medium-filled vials are randomly selected from each tray of vials, and half of these vials are aseptically inoculated individually with a test inoculum adjusted to less than 100 organisms per 0.1 ml of *Bacillus subtilis* ATCC 6633 suspension. The remaining one-half of the selected medium-filled vials are individually aseptically inoculated with 0.1 ml of a *Candida albicans* ATCC 10231 suspension adjusted to less than 100 organisms per 0.1 ml. All the vials are incubated for a minimum of 7 days at the predetermined temperature. The test medium is satisfactory if evidence of growth appears within 7 days in at least 50% of the inoculated vials representing each organism.

Challenge Vial Incubation: The incubated vials (at the predetermined temperature) may be examined periodically until the fourteenth day. The number of vials, the number of each contaminated vial (if any), and the tray identification number of each contaminated vial (if any) are recorded. The contaminated vials should be carefully examined for evidence of vial/closure damage, and any damaged vials should not be considered in evaluating results. The undamaged vials are returned to the incubator and incubation is continued for subsequent visual examination following the fourteenth day of incubation.

The rate of contamination for each media fill is determined as follows:

$$\% \text{ contamination} = \frac{\text{number of vials with microbial growth} \times 100}{\text{number of vials filled} - \text{number of damaged vials}}$$

Evaluation of Results: If any of the medium-filled containers develop turbidity during the 14-day period, investigation should commence. This is accomplished by aseptically withdrawing a sample of the turbid medium from the vial and streaking it onto sterile plates of USP soybean-casein digest agar (SCDA). The plates are then incubated for 18–24 hr at a verified temperature and observed for growth as well as colony morphology. Gram stains are then prepared and evaluated. The initial observations should be limited to gross morphology and Gram-staining characteristics unless the media fill results indicate that further investigation is required.

2. Dry Powder Fills

The objective is to confirm the acceptability of the aseptic dry powder filling procedure(s) in protecting the product from adventitious microbial contamination. Glass vials will be filled with an appropriate volume of sterile liquid medium and then filled with a predetermined weight of a sterile dry powder.

The vials will be stoppered, sealed, and incubated. It should be noted that for a dry powder fill, two consecutive filling operations are performed, and the contribution of each of these steps may increase the potential for contamination. The method presented below is just one example of the approaches that can be utilized. Typical modifications to this procedure include employing only a simulation of the powder filling step; the addition of sterile media to the vials by use of a syringe through the stopper; and filling one of the dry components of the media in one step followed by the remaining medium components (including WFI) in the next step. These alternative procedures (and others not mentioned) are all capable of demonstrating process acceptability.

Selection and Sterilization of Powder: The validation of the aseptic dry powder filling process is identical to the procedure for aseptic liquid fills described earlier, except for an additional step, in which a sterile dry powder is added to the vial after the liquid fill is made. An appropriate dry sterile powder for use in validation studies is needed. Among suitable powders are lactose, mannitol, and polyethylene glycol 8000. Prior to employing any of the aforementioned powder materials, it will be necessary to evaluate the sterility, microbial growth-inhibitory characteristics, and solubility of these compounds after they have been exposed to a known level of gamma irradiation. The inert powder must be sterilizable in dry form, capable of being filled with a filling machine, soluble in liquid culture medium, and noninhibitory to microorganisms at the desired concentration. The dry powders are individually bagged in suitable containers (e.g., double heat-sealed polyethylene bags) and subjected to an exposure of 1.5–2.5 Mrad of cobalt-60. Each container of the irradiated powder is opened aseptically in the proper environmental setting. Samples are removed and are tested by the USP sterility test for a minimum of 7 days if desired. Another practice employed is to simultaneously expose a small sample of the dry powder in a suitable container together with spores of *B. pumilus* and open the container in the laboratory to be tested by the USP sterility test.

Inhibition Testing of the Irradiated Powders: For inhibition testing, the indicator organisms *Bacillus subtilis* and *Candida albicans* are employed, whereby the powders are individually tested for their potential to inhibit the growth of the indicator organisms. Each of the irradiated samples is suspended in sterile distilled water, and added to 100 ml of sterile SCDM at a final concentration of 1.0%, 2.5%, and 5.0% (w/v). Four tubes of each sample concentration are inoculated with less than 100 CFU of the challenge organisms. Two tubes are inoculated with *Bacillus subtilis* and two tubes are inoculated with *Candida albicans*. Control tubes are prepared by inoculating 100-ml tubes of SCDM (in duplicate), which do not contain the irradiated powder samples. All the tubes are incubated at a controlled temperature for 7 days and are inspected daily for visible evidence of growth. Growth must be evident in all tubes.

Solubility Testing of the Irradiated Powders: The solubility of the powders at a concentration of 5.0% is determined in SCDM. The amount of agitation required to solubilize the powders as well as the time and degree of solubilization should be noted. Any of the powders failing to dissolve completely require retesting at a lower concenteration.

Evaluation of Powders: Each of the powders must pass the USP sterility test after 14 days' incubation. The powders must not significantly inhibit the growth of the indicator organism. Growth must appear in the test tubes within 7 days, and the powder should be soluble in SCDM with a minimum of agitation required. Polyethylene glycol 8000, lactose, and mannitol can be sterilized when exposed to 1.5–2.5 Mrad of gamma radiation. It has also been shown that polyethylene glycol 8000, lactose, and mannitol were non-toxic to *Bacillus subtilis*, while only polyethlyene glycol 8000 and lactose were nontoxic to *Candida albicans* (mannitol exhibited slight inhibition of the growth of *Candida albicans*).

Powder Filling: The procedure previously described for aseptic filling of sterile liquid medium is employed for the validation of the aseptic dry powder filling with one addition. The inert powder (polyethylene glycol, mannitol, or lactose) is added to the sterile liquid medium-filled vial at a predetermined weight and the vials are then stoppered, sealed, and capped. (The sequence of filling can be reversed, although there have been reports indicating powder "blowout" when the vials are filled with liquid after the powder fill.) The treatment of the medium-filled vials and the evaluation of results are identical to the procedures outlined in Sec. 1.

3. Lyophilized Products

To confirm the acceptability of the freeze-drying (lyophilization) process, transfer, filling, and closure procedures in protecting products from adventitious microbial contamination is the objective of this test. The approach is similar to that employed for liquid fills except for the addition of the transport and freeze-drying steps. Two methods are presented, although other suitable procedures can be employed.

Method 1: An appropriate number of glass vials are filled to the proper level with sterilized water-for-injection, following which the filled bottles are subjected to the lyophilization process. The processed bottles are then filled with a known volume of a sterile liquid medium, sealed, and incubated as described previously. The routine and in-process environmental monitoring previously described are employed to ensure a continuing state of control. The freeze-dryer is sterilized utilizing a validated process.

Preparation of Sterile Water-for-Injection: Autoclave or sterilize in place a properly sized holding tank according to established procedures. If autoclaved, remove the tank from the autoclave into the aseptic processing area. The sterilized tank is then assembled as follows: A vent valve and vent filter assembly containing a 0.2-μm filter; a pressure gauge; a safety relief valve; and a bleeder valve and thermowell. The tank bottom outlet is connected aseptically to the outlet of a sterilized filter holder equipped with either a 0.2-μm membrane or cartridge. The required volume of water-for-injection is filtered into the tank. The WFI is heated to a minimum of 121°C for at least 2 hr. The tank contents are cooled to approximately 25–30°C. The tank may be, at this point, transferred to another aseptic processing area, such as the filling room. The bottom outlet is then connected aseptically to the filling lines, and the nitrogen line is aseptically connected to the sterilized vent filter outlet. (Note: If the filling operation employs a filter, then a presterilized filter holder equipped with an identical sterilizing membrane or cartridge is inserted aseptically between the tank bottom outlet and the filling line.) When ready to fill, the tank bottom valve and the tank vent valve are opened as well as the nitrogen line to the tank. The tank is pressurized with nitrogen to force the sterile water-for-injection through the filter into the filling machine.

The containers, equipment, filling parts, trays, and closures are cleaned and sterilized employing the established operating procedures. An appropriate number of glass vials are filled with a known volume of the sterilized WFI. The standard fill rate is maintained throughout the filling process. The sterile WFI-filled vials are collected in presterilized trays, covered, and each tray numbered sequentially. The filled trays are then transferred to either a prefreezer or to the freeze-dryer, in which the shelves are maintained at −10°C or lower. The routine number of thermocouples or thermistors are positioned in the vials to monitor the vial temperatures. The shelf temperature is maintained until the temperature sensors indicate the the temperature of the frozen solution is −10°C or lower. Those vials in trays frozen in a prefreezer with sensors in place are then transferred to the lyophilizer. The door to the freeze-dryer cabinet is closed and the chamber is evacuated. The absolute pressure is controlled at 300−900 μm of mercury (or as routinely performed) by bleeding 0.2 μm-filtered air or nitrogen into the chamber as required. After 2 hr, raise the vial temperature to 40−50°C (or as previously determined) and maintain the temperature for the duration of the cycle. At the completion of the cycle, follow standard operating procedures to bleed aseptically filtered air or nitrogen. The door is then opened, the trays removed, and the vials transferred to the filling line. Each of the vials is then filled with an appropriate volume of the sterile USP SCDM prepared as previously described. The medium-filled vials are plugged and sealed according to established procedures. The filled vials are inspected for closure or container defects. Each tray is inverted to ensure closure contact with the medium fill.

Method 2: This approach follows the procedure outlined for liquid-filled vials more closely than does Method 1. It does not provide the complete lyophilization process employed in that program. An appropriate number of vials are filled with SCDM utilizing the sequence described previously. One-third of the vials have their stoppers fully seated on the filling line and are used to confirm the adequacy of the filling process in preventing adventitious microbial contamination. The remaining two-thirds of the vials have their stoppers partially seated, are placed in trays, and are transported to the lyophilizer. The second one-third are loaded into the lyophilizer and have their stoppers seated inside the unit. This portion is utilized to confirm the adequacy of the practices involved in vial transport. The last one-third of the vials are then loaded into the lyophilizer. The freezing sequence is omitted and the chamber door is sealed. A vacuum of 24 to 25 in. of vacuum is drawn on the chamber, and this level is held for a minimum of 2 hr. Filtered air or nitrogen is utilized to break the vacuum. The stoppers are then seated within the cabinet. This portion is utilized to confirm the adequacy of the lyophilization procedures in the maintenance of product sterility. All the vials are removed from the aseptic area and sealed. The vials are inverted to assure medium contact with all internal surfaces and incubated. Due to the sequential nature of the process, care must be taken in the identification of the various portions of the vials.

Negative Controls: Approximately 1000 vials (or 10% of the total number filled) which have not undergone the freeze-drying process are sterilized according to normal practices and filled with an identical volume of sterile USP SCDM, stoppered, and sealed. These vials are transferred to numbered trays and inverted after inspection for closure or container defects.

Growth Promotion Test: As described previously, medium-filled vials from each of the trays are randomly selected (one or two vials each). One-half of the selected vials are individually inoculated with 0.1 ml of a *Bacillus subtilis* ATCC 6633 suspension containing less than 100 CFU per 0.1 ml. The remaining selected vials of test medium are individually inoculated with 0.1 ml of a *Candida albicans* ATCC 10231 suspension containing less than 100 CFU per 0.1 ml. The vials are incubated at the predetermined temperature for a period of 7 days. The test medium is satisfactory if growth appears within 7 days in at least 50% of the inoculated vials representing each organism. The medium-filled vials are incubated at the selected temperature. The vials are examined visually for growth, and the number of contaminated vials (if any) are identified. Contaminated containers (if any) should be carefully examined for evidence of container/closure damage.

IV. ENVIRONMENTAL CONTROL

The qualification and validation of the aseptic processing area are necessary prerequisites to the performance of an aseptic filling validation program. Conventional practice is the performance of environmental monitoring throughout the aseptic core on a routine basis, both at rest and during operations. During the performance of media fills, environmental monitoring gains increased importance in the review of data and resolution of problems. The subject of environmental monitoring for viable and nonviable particulates has been addressed elsewhere in this test. The key elements of a monitoring program are provided below by way of review.

A. Viable Particulates

Sources of viable organisms within the aseptic processing area are varied. The personnel working within the room are the major contributors, since the human body carries millions of organisms on its surface at all times. It is imperative that a comprehensive training program be established for the operating personnel in which hygienic practices are taught and the proper method of gowning is demonstrated. Adherence to the proper techniques on the part of the workers is essential if an aseptic environment is to be maintained. A formalized sanitization program for the aseptic areas must be employed, using a rigorous schedule, providing details of all measures taken to minimize organisms from floors, walls, ceilings, and equipment. A thoroughly developed disinfection program often includes rotation of agents on a periodic basis, comprehensive controls on the methods of application and preparation of the agent, and a complete understanding of the biocidal capabilities of the agent(s). An assessment of the indigenous bioburden at regular intervals (including seasonal variations) is employed to determine common as well as unusual organisms present within the facility. Monitoring of the aseptic (and for those firms that practice it, the nonaseptic) environment is accomplished by various techniques, including settling plates, Rodac plates, air samplers (Anderson, RCS, Sartorius, slit to agar), and swabs. Trend analysis profiles of the aseptic environment are employed to aid in problem identification.

B. Nonviable Particulates

Control of nonviables must be established and maintained throughout the aseptic environment. Federal Standard 209B is an established reference document pertaining to the maintenance of air quality. A criterion suggested by various regulators is to maintain a Class 100 condition over filling and sealing operations. At this time regulations have not been promulgated as to air class requirements. Instruments utilized to monitor the nonviable particulate levels include the Royco, Climet, Coulter, and other particle counters.

V. AREAS OF CONCERN

In the validation of most processes, the practitioner(s) must make decisions that will have significant impact on the level of assurance provided by the study. For instance, thermocouples may be calibrated to within 0.1, 0.2, or 0.5°C of the reference temperature; or 10, 20, or even 30 spore strips may be placed in an experimental load. The decision made will have a major impact on the ultimate credibility of the data generated. The authors believe that the validation of aseptic filling operations involves a number of variables whose selection can alter the evidence obtained. For this reason, and not for the purpose of setting policy or standards, we have included the following areas of concern to aid the practitioner in making his *own* decisions.

A. Acceptance Limit

Acceptance limits probably cause more discussion than any other media fill issue. Theoretically, a firm must determine two things: The confidence level that will satisfy itself and the percentage of nonsterile units it deems acceptable. These two variables can be utilized to calculate the number of vials that must be filled (see Table 1). The problem arises in the concept of allowing a media fill challenge to be acceptable if it contains a low percentage of nonsterile units. This small percentage (when compared to the 1 component in 10^6 utilized as the conventional criterion for terminally sterilized products) has been a concern of parenteral manufacturing and control personnel.

The difference between terminally sterilized and aseptically filled products is apparent in the uniformity of the terminal sterilization process (for vial, closure, and contents) as opposed to the diverse methods (dry heat, steam, filtration, sanitization, etc.) employed for the sterilization of the components for the aseptic filling process. The statistical probability of an organism being present in an aseptically filled product is contingent on the multiple independent sterilization processes employed and is totally unrelated to an organism surviving a terminal sterilization process. Therefore a lower acceptance limit is justified for aseptically filled products relative to terminally sterilized products. Current practices throughout much of the world employ the term "sterile" on the labels of products produced either aseptically or by terminal sterilization. The authors have been made aware that certain Scandinavian countries recognize the real differences in the level of sterility assurance provided by the two processes and as a consequence require non-terminally sterilized products to be labeled as "aseptically manufactured."

B. Multiple Filling Rooms

Where a firm has two or more identical filling rooms, it would appear that their equivalence could be readily demonstrated. However, for aseptic filling processes, the subtle differences from one room to another may be sufficient to upset the equivalence concept. One room may be at a slightly different temperature, or 12 ft farther from the steam autoclave. It would appear that aseptic filling validation should be performed on all filling lines within a facility on a rotating basis.

C. Slow Lines/Low-Volume Products

The unique aspects of slow-moving lines or low-volume products may present another problem to the performance of media fills. Many firms produce a larger than normal number of units in order to achieve a greater level of sterility assurance. The shortcoming in this situation is the length of time required to process the larger number of vials, which may be far in excess of the amount of time required for normal production. The equipment necessary to produce a 3000-vial media run may differ from that utilized in routine production of 25 vials, creating a difference in methods that can severely diminish the media fills utility as an evaluation tool. A media fill of 3000 vials may represent several years' production! This type of product is common in radioactive diagnostic products, where a lot may consist of as few as 10−20 vials and rarely exceeds 500 vials.

Where a production line operates so slowly that the output from a single shift is less than the desired number of vials, a situation analogous to low-volume production is encountered. There is a merit in extending the media run to provide the needed number of units. However, again the differences in equipment, technique, processing times, etc., can limit the utility of this approach.

A potential solution to both low-volume products and slow production lines is the summation of several small media runs into a single run for the purposes of evaluation. A series of media fills (produced as the normal product is manufactured, i.e., same speed, size, equipment, etc.) can be made and the total number of positives summed together. This total is divided by the total number of vials filled in all the runs to provide an overall percentage of non-sterile units. The individual fills can be performed on different days, shifts, etc., and can even be interspersed between production. This approach affords the desired level of assurance with only one serious drawback; the number of individual fills and the increased number of setups required increases the potential for failure.

D. Partial Fills

The need to fill a sufficient number of vials to provide the desired sterility assurance may mandate using a partial fill in the vial to conserve media, especially if larger-volume vials are employed. The filling line is operated at the same speed utilized during a full-volume fill. The partially filled vials must be rotated and inverted to ensure that the medium contacts the entire internal surface of the vial and closure prior to incubation. It is possible that anaerobes will not be detected in this situation due to the

---

*The substitution of N_2 for air may require the performance of parallel challenges to ensure that both aerobes and anaerobes can be adequately detected. Other options to be considered when anaerobes are present are changes in media on a rotating basis. If nitrogen is used routinely during production, it should be utilized during the media filling trials.

presence of additional air in the headspace of the vial. The use of a
filtered (0.2 μm) nitrogen purge may be considered to circumvent this
possibility.*

E. Anaerobes and Aerobes

Any medium testing program should provide for detection of contamination
from either aerobic or anaerobic organisms by the use of appropriate media
and incubation methods. The use of a filtered nitrogen purge may be required to ensure anaerobic conditions. Consideration can be given to this
if the sterility test results, bioburden data, and/or environmental monitoring have detected the presence of anaerobes (see footnote p. 664.)*

F. Medium Choice

Confirmation of the selected medium's ability to support the growth of the
indigenous organisms found during environmental monitoring must be performed. A useful approach would be the utilization of the more prevalent
environmental contaminants in the medium growth-promotion tests, which
must be conducted on each lot of medium.

G. High-Speed Lines

Three thousand vials may represent only a minor portion of the filling
line's output during a single shift. Suggestions have been made where
the line is run at full production speed for brief intervals during the shift.
This type of procedure limits the amount of activity in the filling room
during the course of the media fill program and therefore is not indicative
of actual production. A practice that is often utilized on high-speed lines
is the recycling of vials through the filling line to simulate the production
of a large number of units. If recycling is employed, care must be taken
to ensure that recycled vials are not filled with medium, as this represents
a far greater level of exposure. The increase in handling over normal
operations, does reduce the chance for success for a media fill challenge
performed in this manner.

An alternative to this approach is the filling of the media vials at the
start of the shift in one continuous operation. This practice attempts to
draw on the increased likelihood of contamination from the setup and initial
machine adjustments. The typical high-speed line is heavily automated,
thereby diminishing the potential for contamination during operation and
increasing the potential for contamination during the setup/startup phase,
which is more complicated than that required for a less automated line.

H. In-Process Media Fills

A technique that has been adopted by a number of firms is the performance
of the media fill immediately after the completion of the regular filling process
without an intervening cleaning operation. This affords the opportunity to
monitor the line at its full operating performance. The direct linkage of the
filling process for the product with that of the media fill will complicate the
interpretation of the appropriateness of the lot itself in the event of a media

process failure. In addition, if the product contains a preservative, is bacteriostatic, or is inhibitory to the growth of organisms, any product that remains in the filling system after the product fill and becomes a contaminant in the medium may invalidate the media fill challenge.

I. Environmental Testing

A successful media fill run provides assurance of the filling line's ability to produce a sterile product at the time of the trial. An unsuccessful fill affords the firm an opportunity to resolve potential problems, provided that the environmental screening performed is adequate to reveal the source (or sources) of contamination. Insufficient monitoring of the environment affords the firm little or no opportunity to resolve media fill problems. The relatively short duration of the media fill operation implies that a single monitoring might be adequate. However, the realization that the initial setup/startup of the line contributes significantly to the potential for contamination suggest that monitoring during this phase may prove valuable. During the course of the actual media fill, environmental samples (primarily microbial) should be taken frequently. If the speed of the line is such that multiple samples cannot be taken sequentially, then simultaneous sampling of multiple locations can be employed. The utility of environmental monitoring in media fill problem solving can be significant.

J. Incubation Period

It should be recognized that the length of incubation may not be adequate to reveal very slow-growing organisms. There have been reports of organisms that have gone undetected in routine sterility testing for periods longer than 14 days. If such an uncommon organism is the contaminant in a medium fill, a 7- or even a 14-day incubation may be inadequate. The recognition that such organisms exist raises questions concerning current practice in both sterility testing and media fills. There are no quick answers to the question as to how long a media fill or a sterility test should be incubated. The longer the period for which it is held, the more definitive the results. Nevertheless, with the current state of technology, 7 to 14 days' incubation is appropriate to accomplish the stated objective.

K. Incubation Temperature

The selection of an incubation temperature is an area that often receives little or no attention. The fact that some organisms will grow only at particular temperatures increases the concerns that must be addressed in the identification of the incubator temperature setting. The information gained from the environmental monitoring (during routine production, sterility testing, and media filling) need to be considered in the determination of the incubation temperatures to be employed.

L. New Facilities

It is common practice to perform aseptic filling validation during the startup phase of a new parenteral facility. The desire to validate the facility rapidly may result in all runs being scheduled over a relatively short time period. This can lead to an inadvertent bias in the results by the compression of all

the runs into a period of a week or two. A more comprehensive practice is
to perform the runs over a 1- to 2-month period. Additionally, the runs
should be performed by a variety of personnel on all operating shifts. The
aseptic filling room team is, of course, staffed with the personnel who will
operate the room during production, and not with a startup crew comprised
of different individuals, and certainly not with production supervisors or
forepersons.

M. Vial Size

The variety of vial sizes filled on most sterile filling lines raises questions of
whether all vial sizes must be tested on each line. It has been suggested
that a "worst-case" vial be utilized in the validation program. The selection
of the "worst-case" vial may present additional complications: Should the
worst-running product be utilized, the slowest-running vial, the most involved process, or some other criteria? A possible choice appears to be the
container/closure system that has the poorest sterility record based on end
product sterility testing over prior years. Some firms have chosen to perform media fills in all container sizes filled on each line, an extremely costly
and time-consuming approach. For new facilities where there is no experience
with the vials to be filled on a particular line, the vial sizes tested may cover
the extremes of size run on that line.

N. Suspension Products

It has been indicated that solution products, dry fills, and freeze-dried products must all be addressed in the performance of media fills. A neglected
application for media fills is the sterile suspension, which ordinarily includes
significantly different filling setups from those utilized for solutions. Where
the setup for a suspension differs from that used on solution products on a
line, that setup must also be evaluated.

O. Opaque Containers

A number of manufacturers routinely fill sterile solutions (primarily ophthalmic
products) into opaque containers. This adds an additional complication in
that the examination of the containers after incubation is severely hampered.
A common practice for this type of product is to perform pour-outs of the
vials after the incubation period is over to identify contaminated units. Of
necessity, this greatly reduces the speed of testing and decreases its reliability, particularly if slow growers are commonplace. When this type of
examination is performed, it is essential that the persons performing the pour-
out inspection be carefully trained to prevent false negatives. The simplest
solution, though not always available, is the utilization of an identically configured container that has adequate clarity for postincubation inspection.

P. Manufacturing

Despite the widespread application of media challenges to aseptic filling operations, there has been only limited extension of this form of challenge to manufacturing operations. The formulation of parenteral products can involve any
number of steps in which there is a real potential for microbial contamination.
Operations such as sterile solid blending, suspension preparation, pH

readjustments, and even final batch sampling prior to filling all provide a
potential for contamination. Many firms produce sterile solids with a large
number of product exposure situations. While media challenges for these
operations have yet to be devised, it raises an area of concern never before
addressed with media challenges. Such challenges appear not to be practical
at this time.

VI. MEDIA FILLS AS A PROBLEM RESOLUTION TOOL

Once a media filling has been performed and the results of all vial and environmental testing become available, the assembled information must be carefully reviewed in order to gain the full benefits of the program. The data
review should include data from other than the media fill proper, such as
the routine environmental monitoring performed during product filling operations and during sterility testing, as well as the characterization information
obtained on product sterility failures (see "Evaluation of Results" in Sec. III,
B, 1). A cross correlation of the various possible test results can be utilized
in the identification of the causes for the failures (see Table 2). Outlined
below are suggested troubleshooting approaches to be utilized to resolve the
difficulties encountered:

1. Media fill contaminant same as sterility test contaminant: Increase
    media fill vial quantities and routine filling environmental monitoring
    to identify the source of contamination. Review environmental data
    obtained during line setup.
2. Media fill contaminant same as media fill environmental contaminant:
    Cause identified.* Increase routine environmental monitoring to deter-
    mine if the contamination potential exists during routine filling opera-
    tion.
3. Media fill contaminant same as routine environmental contaminant:
    Possible cause identified.* Increase media fill environmental monitoring
    (in the same location) to confirm the contamination source.
4. Sterility test contaminant same as media fill environmental contaminant:
    Possible cause identified.* Increase routine environmental monitoring
    (in the same location) to confirm the contamination source. Increase
    the number of media vials filled to confirm.
5. Sterility test contaminant same as routine environmental contaminant:
    Cause identified.* Increase media fill environmental monitoring (in
    same location) and number of media vials to confirm.
6. Sterility test contaminant same as sterility test environmental contami-
    nant: Sterility test voided. Investigate sterility testing procedures
    and room sanitization/sterilization methods to eliminate cause.
7. Media fill environmental contaminant same as routine filling environ-
    mental contaminant: Increase the number of vials in the media fill in
    order to determine the product risk potential. Review monitoring

---

*While environmental testing can detect organisms, it does not provide infor-
mation regarding their exact location or source. The identification of the
specific factor(s) creating the contamination should be the objective of an
intensive investigation to pinpoint the probable cause.

TABLE 2

Media fill troubleshooting	Sterility test contaminant characterization	Media fill environmental contaminant	Routine filling environmental contaminant	Sterility test environmental contaminant
Media fill contaminant characterization	Increase media environmental filling environmental to isolate cause.	Cause identified? Increase filling environmental to determine product contamination potential.	Possible cause identified? Increase media fill environmental to confirm cause.	N/A
Sterility test contaminant characterization		Possible cause identified? Increase filling environmental to determine if product contamination potential exists. Increase media vial number.	Cause identified? Increase filling environmental to isolate positive factor.	Sterility test void.
Media fill environmental contaminant characterization			Increase media vial number to determine risk potential. Review environmental practices.	Review environmental practices.
Routine filling environment characterization				Review environmental practices.

techniques for possible problem. Review personnel practices, gowning, sanitization, and sterilization.

8. Media fill environmental contaminant same as sterility test environmental contaminant and routine filling environmental contaminant same as sterility test environmental contaminant: Check environmental monitoring methods and techniques closely for problems. Review personnel practices, gowning, sanitization, and sterilization.

The accumulated data must be carefully assessed to provide insight into what elements of the operations are the sources of microbial contamination. While the outline presented above covers many of the possible contamination combinations, it is by no means complete. Caution must be exercised in the resolution of sterility failures, whether for product or media fills. However, this approach can afford good opportunity for sterility problem resolution.

VII. CONCLUSION

Media fills can be compared to a symphony. The individual musicians can practice their own score time after time, in much the same way a steam autoclave can be qualified and validated (or revalidated). Despite all the time the musicians spend practicing separately, they must work well together, if one is to experience the symphony as it was written. Similarily, the various operations needed to produce a sterile product must be in concert if a media fill is to be acceptable. It is only when all the individual elements are in harmony that the performance of a symphony or the execution of a media fill can be considered successful.

An aseptic filling validation program provides the management of a sterile production facility with a two-edged sword. For those operations that are not properly designed, operated, and controlled, a successful validation can prove to be quite elusive, while for those facilities whose methods and practices are acceptable, success is a routine event affording excellent assurance of the operation's acceptability.

VIII. APPENDIX: TECHNICAL LIMITATIONS OF MEDIA FILLS

The chief arguments employed against a media fill program are the following:

1. Sterility can never be substantiated by nondestructive means. To presume that any sterility test will confirm that the next unit of the same or any other lot is sterile is fallacious. The media fill, like any other sterility test, cannot provide overall assurance that any product will be truly sterile.

2. The success or failure of a media fill has little or no bearing on a facility's ability to produce a sterile product. All a media fill demonstrates is the suitability of the procedures used to fill media, not product. The differences in fill volume, viscosity, lack of preservatives, bulk sterilization methods, and equipment are sufficient cause to preclude the projection of the media fill results onto product manufacturing.

3. A related argument centers around the human manipulations necessarily performed prior to the start of and during filling operations. The ability of the operator to perform these operations successfully (or unsuccessfully) is

not a good indicator of his or her performance on the next (or previous) filling-line setup or operation. Coupling this with the expected variations in human performance from individual to individual indicates that the media fill provides little or no assurance of the suitability of the aseptic processes.

4. The sensitivity of the media to contamination is so great that practices which would be acceptable if employed with a product (whose growth promotion capability may be nil) may become suspect, thereby creating unnecessary precautions, which are required only for the media fills.

5. The complexity of the sterile filling operation is such that operations/ movements that seemingly have no impact on the media fill can cause a failure and discredit an otherwise acceptable procedure and/or facility. The identification and elimination of the cause for the failure will be expensive and time-consuming and in all probability unsuccessful (especially if the cause is not readily apparent).

6. Many products, due to their inherent inhibitory characteristics, will not support the growth of organisms. This phenomenon occurs primarily with antibiotics. However, other types of products, because of the solvent system, sugar content, or other formulation aspects, can behave similarily. If a product of this type becomes contaminated with an organism, it is unlikely that the product vial will become nonsterile. An identical contaminant entering a media-filled vial will result in growth and subsequent detection of the organism.

7. The use of media in the evaluation of a powder and/or freeze-drying filling operation may involve the adaptation of conventional practices to accommodate the media. The differences in procedure introduce a greater potential for contamination above that experienced in product filling operations. The additional operations may serve to discredit an otherwise acceptable operation.

BIBLIOGRAPHY

Anisfeld, M. A., and Lovejoy, C. 1978. Design for a small-volume parenteral manufacturing facility. *J. Parenter. Drug Assoc. 32:* 285.

Austin, P. A., and Timmerman, S. W. 1965. *Design and Operation of Clean Rooms*, Business New Publishing Co., Detroit.

Byers, T. E. 1978. GMPs and design for quality. *J. Parenter. Drug Assoc. 32:* 22.

Dirksen, J. W., and Larsen, R. V. 1975. Filling vials aseptically while monitoring for bacterial contamination. *Am. J. Hosp. Pharm. 32:* 1031.

Griffin, J. C., and Pauli, W. A. 1976. Design concepts for a sterile products production facility. *Bull. Parenter. Drug Assoc. 30:* 293.

Health Industries Manufacturing Association. 1978. Microbial control in the manufacturing environment. *HIMA Report 78:* 4.3.

Herwarth, W. R. 1972. Environmental control in parenteral filling operations. *Bull. Parenter. Drug Assoc. 26:* 147.

Kiritsky, P. A., and Engvall, R. 1973. Sterile filling facility—Its design, construction and operations. *Bull. Parenter. Drug Assoc. 27:* 279.

McQuillen, D. F. 1981. Design and testing of pharmaceutical sterile rooms. *Pharm. Technol. 5*(11):44.

National Aeronautics and Space Administration. 1967. Standards for clean rooms and work stations for microbially controlled environments. NHB 5340.2.

Parenteral Drug Association. 1980. *Validation of Aseptic Filling for Solution Drug Product*, Technical Monograph No. 2.

Parenteral Drug Association. 1984. Validation of aseptic drug powder filling processes, Draft Report.

Pharmaceutical Manufacturers Association. 1978. *Proceedings of the PMA Seminar Program on Validation of Sterile Manufacturing Processes*, International Conference Center, Reston, Va., March.

Pharmaceutical Manufacturers Association. 1979. *Proceeding of the Second PMA Seminar Program on Validation of Sterile Manufacturing Processes: Aseptic Processing*, Atlanta Hilton, Atlanta, Ga., March.

Raiman, H. L. 1974. Panel discussion: Environmental sampling in an aseptic environment. I. Microbiological environmental monitoring. *Bull. Parenter. Drug Assoc. 28*: 253.

Sherman, N. E. 1974. Panel discussion: Environmental sampling in an aseptic environment. II. Particulate contamination control. *Bull. Parenter. Drug Assoc. 28*: 260.

Tetzlaff, R. A. 1981. Informal notes taken at ISPE symposium on Validation of Aseptic Processes, Governours Inn, Raleigh, N.C.

Tetzlaff, R. A. 1983. Aseptic process validation. *Particulate and Microbial Control 2*: 24.

World Health Organization. 1977. Technical Report Series, No. 530.

25

The Regulatory Aspects of Validation

RALPH BADAGLIACCA

Pfizer Inc., Brooklyn, New York

Throughout this book, the term *validation* occurs repeatedly. The authors have exercised their prerogatives in defining it. Their interpretations, in principle, are very similar, and the meaning of validation is implicitly understood.

However, the evolution of the term as it is currently used has been a gradual process. In the pharmaceutical industry its meaning is generally understood. The intent of this chapter is to present, briefly, the history of process validation and to reference a number of relevant publications on the subject. Since there is an overlapping of the practices and principles involved in the validation of aseptic and nonaseptic manufacturing practices, both phases of validation are discussed.

The Federal Food and Drug Act, enacted in 1906, said nothing about validation, nor did it contain an inspection requirement. With the passage of the Federal Food Drug and Cosmetic (FD&C) Amendment of 1938, factory inspections were authorized, which increased the Food and Drug Administration's authority considerably. The FDA's authority was expanded further by the 1962 amendments, which allowed FDA inspectors to examine records pertaining to prescription drugs. In 1962, Current Good Manufacturing Practices (CGMPs) became part of the act. The term "validation" was undefined until many years later. Although the term appears in the *Current Good Manufacturing Practices (CGMPs), Human and Veterinary Drugs*, published in September 1978 [1], it did not contain a definition. However, Subpart F, Production and Process Control, Section 211.100(a), states: "there shall be written procedures for production and process control designed to insure that the drug products have the identity, strength, quality and purity they purport or are represented to possess," which *implicitly* mandate the validation process to be instituted. Sections 211.100(a) and (b) yield an interpretation of retrospective validation [1]. This paragraph requires that control procedures shall validate the performance of manufacturing processes. (For a thorough explanation of retrospective validation and a definition of validation terms, see Ref. 2.)

T. E. Byers, formerly Associate Director for Compliance, Bureau of Drugs, FDA, at a meeting of the Proprietary Association in October 1974 [3] discussed "Design for Quality." He discussed the need to build quality into a product

by design rather than by testing. The provisions of the CGMPs were considered "as they reflected 'design'."

> The most important aspect of the production of drugs, in which design
> plays a part, is in the areas of production and control procedures. In
> order to assure products of uniform quality, purity, and performance, it
> is essential that such a process be defined with a great deal of specificity
> and that the adequacy of each step of such a process be challenged to
> determine its adequacy . . . we are using a new term in our consideration
> of the manufacture of pharmaceuticals within the agency, that is, qualifica-
> tion of the process. . . . In the case of control procedures including the
> analytical procedures, adequacy of such procedures must be established
> prior to the qualification of any process or product.

The February 1976 Proposed Rules [4] for updating the CGMPs mention
the term "validation" with regard to "acceptance criteria . . . for each product . . . and statistical data derived from validation studies to determine
the variability of the manufacturing process . . . in-process procedures are
properly validated . . . validation of any sterile process." No definition of
the term is provided. At a meeting in Arlington, Virginia, in April 1976 [5],
Mr. Byers reiterated the idea that "we must give more attention to the role
of the design function. . . . In our compliance programs, we shall be giving
more attention to the adequacy of validation data developed by the manufacturers for their products and processes. Failure to have such validation
data, in our opinion, constitutes a failure to comply with Current Good Manufacturing Practices and regulations." Then he continued, "we are looking at
the matter of drug product quality from a prospective viewpoint . . . especially in the case of parenterals; where finished product testing does not
adequately or even minimally give an assurance of sterility. . . . Here we
are talking about such things as heat penetration and heat distribution studies
in the case of sterilizing equipment." Finally, the "adequacy of processes"
was mentioned, and that included "facilities, equipment, records, personnel,
and testing procedures." The die was cast—a manufacturer had to have
validation data for his processes, and failure to have them could result in
regulatory consequences.

Industry's concern, in 1976, was that there were neither regulations nor
guidelines to direct the manufacturer as to what constituted adequate validation data. Everything in the manufacturing process could require validation.
The thought was expressed that these ideas had been an inherent part of
Current Good Manufacturing Practices and FDA regulations.

In June 1976, GMPs for Large Volume Parenterals (LVPs) were proposed
[6]. These proposed regulations were very explicit. For the first time,
limits were promulgated for lethality factors, the laminar flow of air, heat
distribution, heat penetration, as well as for air and water quality. Although
never approved, they nevertheless have had a significant effect on manufacturing processes [7].

In these proposed LVP GMP regulations, the word "validation," although
cited, was not defined in regard to systems. In Paragraph 212.182, it is used
generically, in discussing "corrective action . . . including validation of the
effectiveness of the action." In Paragraphs 212.243, 212.244, and 212.245,
sterilizer validation is outlined in specific detail. The term "validation" was
still undefined.

In June 1976, more explicit criteria were outlined by R. E. Shepherd, Senior Drug Investigator, FDA, at a meeting of the Parenteral Drug Association [8]. A systems evaluation approach to inspections was described that included:

> GMP's, the scientific method and common sense . . . a basic set of criteria is used to evaluate the cause and effect relationship of production and quality control operations and procedures to the quality of the finished product. . . . Included in this set of criteria are: sterility, pyrogenicity, particulates, potency, and stability. . . . In a systems inspection, we are looking for protocols which were used as the basis for the testing, evaluation and qualification of each of the systems used in the operations . . . systems which are evaluated would include: water, compressed air, sterilizers, heating-ventilation and air condition systems (HVAC), container closure systems, laboratories, and production processes.

Some specific details were given by Mr. Shepherd:

> In evaluation of sterilization systems, either steam under pressure or ethylene oxide gas, we will be looking for validated sterilization cycles, and the use of these cycles during production runs. In the validation process for steam under pressure systems, we will be evaluating reproducible heat distribution runs in the empty and loaded vessel; reproducible heat penetration studies, with thermocouples located in the coldest spot in the product containers, determined by thermocouple studies; use of biological indicators during these runs; venting procedures and sterilization times and temperatures for each product and container size for each autoclave, which has been determined from heat penetration and heat distribution base line data and biological data relating to the known microbiological product load and microflora.

Mr. Shepherd continued:

> When processing sterile products by aseptic technique, the control and monitoring of the environment along with the sterilizing process is one of the important attributes of the validation process.
>
> The inspection team is looking for manufacturing processes and quality control procedures which can be shown, by documentation, to be under control at all times, and that products produced under these conditions are safe and meet appropriate established standards.

Many LVP and SVP (small volume parenterals) manufacturers took heed and followed the suggestion that protocols were required that "should be the end result of scientific input from engineering, production, and quality control" [8]. Companies established committees to evaluate the systems, developed protocols, and accumulated validation data on systems that were already in use. To validate the basic systems would take time, energy, and effort, plus the expenditure of resources to establish that the systems were "doing what they purported to do." For new products, the design aspect would be emphasized during the development stage. Eight years after the publication of these proposed LVP GMP regulations, they are still not final! However, validation studies are being performed, classes on the subject matter are being conducted routinely, and numerous papers, manuals, and books have been written on the subject.

After the proposed LVP GMPs were published [6], it appeared that FDA inspectors employed them as their guidelines during their inspections of both LVP and SVP facilities. This matter was discussed by B. Loftus, former Director of the Division of Drug Manufacturing, Bureau of Drugs, FDA, in his regulatory review in June 1981 [9], as follows:

> Ted Byers and I told industry symposium after symposium that the proposed LVP regulations were not de facto regulations . . . rather, we said they were simply guidelines . . . FDA professionals sat with representatives of the LVP manufacturers . . . that resulted in the LVP regulations proposed and published . . . the entire industry opposed the concept of a compulsory minimum F_0 of 8. Mr. Byers embarked on an intensive campaign to sell the concept of process validation.

Almost a year earlier (in September 1980 [10]), Mr. Loftus felt that "the proposed LVP regulations have done yeoman service for both FDA and industry . . . the LVP industry took the (proposed) regulations very much to heart . . . the proposed regulations have had a phenomenal effect on the small volume parenterals (SVPs) industry. Whether SVP companies were moved to action because they saw the proposed LVP regulations as already enforceable, the SVP industry has certainly improved."

In October 1976, in a letter "to all manufacturers of injectable drugs" [11], the FDA noted that the validation of manufacturing processes was not "limited only to single-dose aqueous solutions of injectables for human use, containing 100 or more milliliters, the so-called large volume parenterals." The letter stated:

> Since their inception in 1963, the current good manufacturing practice regulations for all drugs, both human and veterinary, have specified that production and control procedures shall include all reasonable precautions to assure that the drugs produced have the safety, identity, strength, quality, and purity they purport to possess. With particular regard to sterility, the regulations require that appropriate precautions be taken to minimize microbiological and other contamination in the production of drugs purporting to be sterile; and there is a requirement of adequate in-process controls. These requirements imply the necessity that every sterilization process be validated to assure that it will produce sterile drugs, whether they be packed in small volume or large volume containers, whether they be single dose or multiple dose, and whether or not they contain preservatives.
>
> . . . finished product sterility testing of samples will not, in itself, assure that the lot from which the samples were taken is sterile. The process must be validated or the product is deemed adulterated under Section 501(a)(2)(B) of the Federal Food, Drug, and Cosmetic Act." [This section refers to CGMPs.]

Subpart F. Section 211.113 of the proposed revisions of the Current Good Manufacturing Practice regulations for Human and Veterinary Drugs, published in February 1976 [4] in the *Federal Register*, contains the following language: 'Appropriate written procedures shall be established and followed prescribing precautions to prevent microbiological contamination in the production of drug products purporting to be sterile. These precautions shall include validation of any sterilizing process.' The text is new; but the validation requirement, better stated in the proposal than before, has been in effect for years.

There must be assurance of the effectiveness of the sterilization process, whether the process depends on terminal sterilization or aseptic assembly of previously sterilized components. Effective depyrogenation procedures must also be employed when applicable.

With this letter, validation became a part of the regulatory process, (by implication). The proposed revisions to the GMPs were cited (as though they had become an established fact), and the validity of the sterility test, in use for many years, had a shadow of doubt cast over it.

When the so-called umbrella CGMPs (because of their comprehensive nature) were issued in September 1978 [1], the word "validation" was cited in Paragraphs 211.68(b) (computer data), 211.84(d)(2) (component testing, containers and closures), 211.113(b) (sterilization processes), and 211.165(e) (test methods). Manufacturers' doubts and questions were further clarified, in some detail, in the preamble to the CGMPs (Paragraphs 239, 242, 249, 305, and 393).

So, within two years, the word "validation" became a household word to the pharmaceutical drug manufacturer. The validation process was applied, initially, to sterilization cycles, since they were so critical to parenteral drug manufacturing: " . . . the agency had to do something following the LVP accidents of the late sixties and early seventies [9]. Sterility problems caused the FDA to emphasize the control of microbial contamination.

No regulations have been officially published, specifically for "process validation," a matter often associated with nonaseptic dosage forms. In May 1980, the Pharmaceutical Manufacturers Association presented a seminar on Validation of Solid Dosage Form Processes, in Atlanta, Georgia [12]. Emphasis was placed on product uniformity within the lot and between lots within certain defined limits. The validation approach for oral dosage forms could be accomplished by the accumulation and statistical interpretation of data derived from final dosage form testing. In-process studies could be helpful in the evaluation of new products or processes. File data could be of value in a validation program for older products. Lot release statistical data could be analyzed for continuous process validation.

Finally, in the FDA's 1978 Compliance Program No. 7356.002 [13], Chapter 56, Drug, Product Quality Assurance (subject "Drug Process Inspection"), the term "validation" was defined as follows:

A validated manufacturing process is one which has proved to do what it purports or is represented to do. The proof of validation is obtained through the collection and evaluation of data, preferably, beginning from the process development phase and continuing through into the production phase. Validation necessarily includes process qualification (the Qualification of Materials, Equipment, Systems, Buildings, Personnel), but it also includes the control of the entire process for repeated batches of runs.

With aseptic systems validation clearly outlined, the FDA began to focus on process validation. In a talk before the Parenteral Drug Association [14], C. G. Broker, Bureau of Drugs, FDA, gave the following definition for process validation: "Process validation is the documentation and evaluation of evidence to provide a high degree of assurance that the process under consideration will, with proper control, consistently produce a drug product meeting the desired quality attributes."

With this definition, it would appear that validation of the attributes of all drug products could be accomplished retrospectively, whereas with parenteral products, aseptic systems validation was a prospective procedure.

In March 1983, the FDA made available the draft of a Process Validation Guideline [15]. In March 1984, an updated draft version [16] was issued. It appeared that these draft guidelines were an invitation to industry to consider process validation as a requirement of the Current Good Manufacturing Practices Regulations for Finished Pharmaceuticals, 21 CFR, Parts 210 and 211. In addition, it read "This guideline states principles and practices of general applicability that are not legal requirements but are acceptable to FDA [16]." It continued:

> Assurance of product quality is derived from careful attention to a number of factors including selection of quality parts and materials, adequate product and process design, control of the process, and in-process and end product testing . . . each step of the manufacturing process must be controlled to maximize the probability that the finished product meets all quality and design specifications. Process validation is a key element in assuring that these quality assurance goals are met. It is through careful design and validation of both the process and process controls that a manufacturer can assure that there is a very high probability that all manufactured units from successive lots will be acceptable. Successfully validating a process reduces the dependence upon intensive in-process and finished product testing.

A definition is provided: "Process validation is a documented program which provides a high degree of assurance that a specific process will consistently produce a product meeting its pre-determined specifications and quality attributes."

The FDA presented the idea "that the manufacturer prepare a written validation protocol which specifies the procedures (tests) to be conducted and the data to be collected. The purpose for which data are collected must be clear, the data must reflect facts, and the data must be collected carefully and accurately. The protocol should specify a sufficient number of replicate process runs to demonstrate reproducibility."

The draft guidelines proposed "a full challenge of the process . . . worst case conditions . . . suitability of materials, the performance and reliability of equipment systems, buildings, and the competence of personnel . . . qualifications of each system." The elements of process validation to be evaluated are enumerated: prospective validation (product specifications, equipment and process, timely revalidation, documentation) and retrospective validation.

The Pharmaceutical Manufacturers Association reacted to the 1983 draft guidelines [17] by asking for a glossary of definitions on general principles of process validation. Many readers found the draft confusing and subject to different interpretations. It objected to the failure of the draft guideline to make distinctions between validation approaches to sterilization and non-sterilization processes. Industry is concerned that FDA inspectors and plant managers be clear on what constitutes a validation violation. In "A Suggested Lexicon" [2], K. G. Chapman, Chairman of The Pharmaceutical Manufacturers Association Validation Advisory Committee, has provided a definition of terms for use in the discussion of process validation. This fulfills a need for

industry and the FDA to be speaking the same language. The document has
been acknowledged repeatedly by the FDA. B. Loftus "recommended that
process validation be defined as 'establishing documented evidence that a
process shall do repeatedly what it purports to do'" [15].

The FDA held a public workshop in New Brunswick, New Jersey, in
June 1984 [17] to discuss the draft proposed guidelines issued in March 1983
and March 1984. The Pharmaceutical Manufacturers Association (PMA) took
issue with many of the ideas presented in the two documents. The PMA contends that, except for aseptic processes, prospective validation can be adequately replaced, effectively, by retrospective and concurrent approaches.
Representatives of industry objected to: the need for three replicate studies,
the need to validate every process, the use of "worst-case" terminology, and
the need for periodic revalidation. The FDA conceded that the use of retrospective and concurrent validation, the adequacy of end product testing, and
the inclusion of a lexicon in the guidelines are vital to process validation.
The PMA also contends that buildings, product specifications, equipment,
suitability of materials, which are part of the GMP requirements, are elements
that are related to, but are not validation issues. The FDA has stated clearly
that guidelines are statements of general principles. FDA guidelines are very
specifically defined but are not legally binding. They represent how firms
can comply with regulations.

E. Fry, Director of Drug Quality, Compliance, FDA, commented at the
June 1984 workshop that retrospective validation was included because it was
recognized that many products on the market in 1976 came from unvalidated
processes, and it was not the FDA's intent to have all such products recalled.
(See Ref. 18 for Mr. Fry's comments on Process Validation.)

At a subsequent workshop held in October 1984, *F-D-C Reports* [19]
stated that:

> PMA voiced concern over an emphasis in the draft guidelines on prospective
> as opposed to retrospective validation methods. The agency, PMA con-
> tended, should broaden its view of retrospective validation to recognize
> its relative advantages, and to reflect the well established, contemporary
> industry practice of using retrospective approaches that have considerably
> wider applicability than the prospective approach, which is more suited to
> sterilization processes [19].

In April 1984, the FDA made available its Draft Guideline for Submission of
Supportive Analytical Data for Methods Validation in New Drug Applications
[20]. The guideline was intended to "provide directions and suggestions to
drug applicants for the presentation of data, assembly of information, and
submission of materials to the Food and Drug Administration (FDA) concerning regulatory specifications and methodologies as required by 21 CFR
314.50(e)."

Methods validation was to be carried out *after* the New Drug Application
(NDA) has been submitted, or it might be requested and performed during
phase III of the IND. "Validation" (their quotation marks) may range from
the "step-by-step repetition of an assay procedure to more elaborate studies
that include assessment of accuracy, precision, specificity, sensitivity, and
ruggedness of the method and purity of reference standards." Specific instructions were given for samples submission. "Samples of impurities, pre-
cursors, or degradation products must be submitted if limit specifications
exist, or if they are critical to the assessment of the performance of assay or

identity tests." The information requested included synthesis of the drug, synthesis of the reference standard, and tests for its purity.

Reproducibility day by day, lab to lab, technician to technician, and column variability data are required. This draft guideline leaves nothing to the imagination, and even lists "examples of Common Problems That Delay or Prevent Successful Validation." It goes into considerable detail on how to define a particular high-performance liquid chromatographic column. The FDA provides a list of everything that is required without specifying the sources for obtaining this information. Vanderweilen and Hardwidge [21] give a summary of the testing for accuracy, reproducibility, and sensitivity of assays and suggest how to design experiments to test the validity of a method.

With regard to computerized systems, a 25-page booklet, *Guide to Inspection of Computerized Systems in Drug Processing* [22], is used by FDA Investigators to cover the subject of CGMPs for Validation of Computer Systems.

Compliance Program C.P. 7356.002 (October 1978) defined validation: "a validated manufacturing process is one which has been proved to do what it purports to do" [13]. The definition was dropped in the October 1982 Compliance Manual [22]. The FDA offered the above as one definition of validation. Compliance Program 7356.002A, *Small Volume Parenterals* [23], is closely related to validation. It encompasses recommendations for air quality, media fills, sterility retesting, pyrogen testing, particulate matter detection, water sytems, and computer systems. An interesting aspect of this manual is that FDA personnel are instructed that the use of the term "inadequate," when employed with regard to validation, is to be fully explained.

In June 1984, Robert L. Sorensen, Assistant to the Chief, Manufacturing Review Branch, Division of Drug Quality Compliance, at a validation seminar [24], presented a number of FDA observations. He addressed some of the strengths and weaknesses observed during the FDA's evaluation of written validation protocols. He updated the current validation practices, made recommendations on sterile parenteral systems protocols, and made the point that "the basic principles and concepts will apply across the board."

Mr. Sorensen said that: "Validation must do two things. The validation protocol must prove that the process works properly and secondly, it must prove that the process is reproducible, that it will operate properly time after time after time."

It is necessary to be "clear and concise. Specify exactly what you are validating, what data will be necessary to validate the process, keeping in mind that you will have to demonstrate why the data that you have obtained does in fact validate what you wanted it to." Mr. Sorensen cited those systems where failures are repeatedly seen: environmental control, water systems, sterilization systems, and aseptic filling operations.

Mr. Sorensen covered the "defective" processes, including lyophilization, in very specific terms. He made recommendations for viable contamination levels, air quality, pyrogenicity of water for final rinse of containers and closures, etc. On media fills, he cited levels for contamination that should be sought. These suggested levels appear to be more stringent than those currently used in the industry; some are in disagreement with published recommendations [25]. Finally, he discussed the concepts of performing revalidation studies.

The U.S. pharmaceutical industry is indeed heavily regulated by compendial bodies. Fortunately, FDA principals have proven to be receptive to the discussion of mutual problems. We expect this dialogue to continue in the future.

REFERENCES

1. Human and veterinary drugs, Good Manufacturing Practices and proposed exemptions for certain OTC products, *Fed. Reg. 43*, Part II, No. 190, September 29, 1978, pp 45013—45089.
2. Chapman, K. G. 1983. A suggested validation lexicon. *Pharm. Technol. 7* (8):pp 51—57.
3. Byers, T. E. 1974. Design for quality. Presented at the Manufacturing Controls Seminar, Cherry Hill, N.J., October 11.
4. Proposed rules, Current Good Manufacturing Practice in manufacturing, packing, or holding, human and veterinary drugs, *Fed. Reg. 42*, Part II, No. 31, February 13, 1976, pp 6878—6894.
5. Byers, T. E. 1976. Drug product quality as viewed by the Food and Drug Administration. Presented at the Conference on Quality Programs and Government Regulations, Arlington, Va., April 13.
6. Proposed rules, human drugs, Current Good Manufacturing Practices in manufacture, processing, packing, or holding of Large Volume Parenterals and request for comments regarding Small Volume Parenterals, *Fed. Reg. 41*, No. 100, June 1, 1976, pp 22202—22219.
7. Chapman, K. G. 1984. The PAR approach to process validation. *Pharm. Technol. 8* (1): 22—36.
8. Shepherd, R. E. 1976. FDA inspections of Large Volume and Small Volume Parenterals manufacturers. Presented to the Meeting of the Parenteral Drug Association, Chicago, June 25. *Bull. Parenter. Drug Assoc. 30* (5): 209—213.
9. Loftus, B. T. 1981. Regulatory review. *Pharm. Technol.*, June, pp 41—46.
10. Loftus, B. T. 1980. Regulatory review. *Pharm. Technol.*, September, pp 38—49.
11. Byers, T. E. 1976. Notice: To all manufacturers of injectable drugs, October 29.
12. Final Program, Parenteral Manufacturers Association Seminar on Validation of Solid Dosage Form Processes, Atlanta, Ga., May 11—13, 1980.
13. FDA Compliance Program. No. 7356.002, Chapter 56, Drug, Product Quality Assurance (Drug Process Inspection), October 1978.
14. Broker, C. G. 1981. Validation in perspective—1981. Presented at the Spring Meeting of the Parenteral Drug Association, Philadelphia, March 20. *J. Parenter. Sci. Technol. 35* (4): 167—169.
15. FDA Communication. 1983. Draft guideline on general principles of process validation.
16. FDA Communication. 1984. Draft guideline on general principles of process validation. March.
17. *The Gold Sheet*, Quality Control Reports, Vol. 17, No. 7, July 1983.
18. Fry, Edmund M. 1984. Process validation policy. *Die Pharmaceutische Industrie 46* (6): 601—609.
19. *F-D-C Reports*, October 29, 1984, p T&G-7.
20. FDA Communication. 1984. Draft guideline for submission of supportive analytical data for methods validation in new drug applications.
21. Vanderweilen, A. J., and Hardwidge, E. A. 1982. Guidelines for assay validation. *Pharm. Technol. 6* (3): 66—76.
22. FDA. 1983. Guide to Inspection of Computerized Systems in Drug Processing.

23. FDA Compliance Program Guidance Manual, Program 7356.002A, *Small Volume Parenterals*, October 1, 1982.
24. Sorensen, R. L. 1984. Draft guideline on general principles of process validation. Presented to the International Society of Pharmaceutical Engineers, Teaneck, N.J., June 11–12.
25. Parenteral Drug Association. 1980. *Validation of Aseptic Filling for Solutions, Drug Products*, PDA Technical Monograph No. 2.

26
Validation: Where To?

THEODORE E. BYERS

Byers Enterprises, Alexandria, Virginia

The role of a seer is indeed a hazardous one. As I take this role in this chapter I would like the result to be twofold: a forecast of how things could be, and a forecast of how things are likely to be in regard to validation during the next several years.

The two institutions that will determine the place of validation in the production of parenterals in the future are those that are making such determinations now, namely, the pharmaceutical industry and the Food and Drug Administration (FDA). If the history of the recent past is any indicator, it is unlikely that industry and the public will reap the full benefit of application of the concept and principles of validation in the production of pharmaceuticals.

On the one hand, the Food and Drug Administration is reluctant to change its way of doing business. This is evidenced by the new drug requirements with regard to manufacturing processes and quality control. At the present time and probably in the future, the FDA requires a full description of manufacturing and quality controls as a part of *all* New Drug Applications (NDAs) and Abbreviated New Drug Applications (ANDAs); in addition, and this is a more burdensome problem, *all* changes in such procedures, with few exceptions, require approval by the FDA before they can be implemented. This procedure flies in the face of logic, and it is accepted that good manufacturing practice and the current Good Manufacturing Practice (GMP) regulations require that all such procedures and changes in procedures must be validated by the manufacturer.

On the other hand, there seems to be a great deal of reluctance within the industry to fully accept and implement validation to its fullest extent. The current situation reminds me of an experience I had during World War II. I was stationed in the Aleutian Islands as chief of a radar station designed to act as the guidance system for coastal defense artillery. The commanding officer, a World War I "retread," was reluctant to use this new instrument, saying he wouldn't fire at anything he couldn't see. One day during a visit of the commanding general, a target practice was scheduled. Just as the target was being towed onto the range, the weather closed in and the target was not visible to the optical range finders. The unit commander was about to call off the practice when the general ordered the guns to fire using radar only. The result was a direct hit on the first salvo, something that had never occurred using optical instruments. Perhaps the reader can relate this incident to a practice in industry where some still rely more on end product testing than validation. Sometimes validation is more on target than test results (e.g., sterility testing).

In considering the directions validation will take for you or your firm, two factors are important: perspective and motivation. One must keep in perspective the concept and role of validation. Perhaps a repetition of some definitions of validation would be helpful. Validation is defined as:

1. A scientifically designed program to prove that a process consistently does what it is designed (intended) to do
2. The attaining and documenting of sufficient evidence to give reasonable assurance, given the current state of science and the art of manufacturing, that the process under consideration does and will do what it purports to do or is expected to do
3. A formal program to demonstrate that a specific product can be reliably manufactured by the designed process

In further defining validation, a Compliance Program issued by the FDA entitled "Drug Process Inspection" is of great value. This document defines "a validated manufacturing process" as one that has been proved do do what it is purported or represented to do. The proof of validation is obtained through the collection or evaluation of data, preferably from the process and developmental phase and continuing through into the production phase. Validation necessarily includes process qualification (the qualification of materials, equipment, systems, building, personnel) but it also includes the control of the entire process for repeated batches or runs. Supporting data usually include challenges to the system, which may include challenge organisms and/ or multiple tests of the systems themselves and also in-process and finished product testing. Where the pertinent attributes and variability can be readily measured by in-process and, in particular, in-product testing, the proof of the validation rests primarily, but not solely, in the evaluation of the results of such testing. Where the state of the art is such that certain attributes cannot be adequately measured by reasonable finished product testing, then the proof of validation of the process is determined by the proof or qualification of each and the totality of the various systems, such as water and air; equipment, such as sterilizers; materials, such as ingredients; personnel, such as operators and supervisors; and the manner in which they are controlled during the operation of the manufacturing process.

In a further attempt to put validation into proper perspective, let us suggest a sequence of events in a very basic qualification and validation setup.

1. Establish the desired attributes. These attributes include physical as well as chemical characteristics. In the case of parenterals, these desirable attributes should include stability, absence of pyrogens, and freedom from visible particles.

2. Acceptance specifications for the product should be established in order to uniformly and consistently attain the desired product attributes. The specifications should be derived from testing and challenge of the system on sound statistical basis during the initial developmental and production phases and continuing through subsequent routine production. In order to assure a high degree of sterility assurance in a parenteral drug product, release

specifications may include a combination of factors including limits on pre-sterilization bioburden, documented delivery of and established F_0 and sterility testing.

3. The process(es) and equipment should be selected to achieve the product specification. For example, in selecting a filter to be used to achieve a sterile liquid, product specifications would include absence of microorganisms and absence of particulates and fibers. Therefore, filters for this purpose should be selected with consideration of pore size, fiber shedding characteristics, and filter media migration. The selection of suitable processes and equipment may be made with the participation of many people from a variety of disciplines within a firm. For example, Design Engineers, Production, and Quality Assurance people may all be involved.

The process should be defined with a great deal of specificity, and each step of the process should be challenged to determine its adequacy. These aspects are important in order to assure products of uniform quality, purity, and performance. For example, in the production of parenteral solutions by aseptic filling, the significant process steps to define and challenge would include the sterilization and depyrogenation of containers/closures, sterilization of solutions, and the filling and sealing of containers.

In the establishment of a manufacturing process for a specific product, it is not sufficient merely to make a pilot batch of a product using procedures that were either established for another product or were conceived, and then assess the adequacy of such a process by merely testing portions of the finished product to see if they conform to acceptance specifications. For example, if a heat sterilization procedure using an established time/temperature combination was determined to be adequate for a given product, it would be sufficient to assess the adequacy of that process for an entirely different product by merely subjecting a pilot batch to the same time/temperature treatment and testing selected samples for sterility.

Here, there is no one group in a firm, unless it is a very small firm, that has sole responsibility. We are talking about the various disciplines within the firm, including the design people, engineers, production people, and the quality assurance people. A very important aspect of the selection of equipment and the operation of equipment is that in order to have a sound basis for validation, one must be certain that the performance characteristics are repeatable throughout the use of such equipment and that adequate monitoring of the operation of the equipment is written into the manufacturing process, since it is obvious that the process may not be under control if the equipment varies in its performance and that variance is not detected and either corrected or determined to be insignificant.

4. Making certain that a system of quality assurance is in place that requires revalidation of the process whenever changes are made in any of the attributes of the product, its formulation, and/or equipment or process used. Tied to this—and this is especially important to people involved in Quality Control—is the need for adequately and appropriately specifying methods of testing and analysis. Some of the weaknesses that have occurred and that are occurring today, not only in the matter of assuring quality through validation, but in assuring the stability of the product through its shelf-life expectancy, has been in the area of specific testing methodology.

Now most of what I said above would be in a setting of a prospective look either at an entirely new product being introduced by a firm or at a change in the manufacturing process of an old product. But one may very well ask, what about the many products that we currently have on the market which, with the evolution of the concept of validation, may not have kept up. Your files are a rich source of data which may enable you to take a retrospective look, and enable you to at least in some large measure to validate the adequacy of your processes. Perhaps there is process data such as records of time, temperature, and pressure of autoclaves demonstrating that these pieces of equipment are operating and have been operating uniformly, delivering a uniform condition of sterilization to the products being sterilized in this equipment. In addition, if a firm has been maintaining and controlling the environment in which you are producing these products, both those subjected to terminal sterilization and those aseptically filled, they may very well have in their files data that will greatly reduce the amount of additional validation procedures to be carried out. I believe that as one looks at this data, if there have not been changes in the manufacturing process or where there have been changes in the process those changes have been adequately documented in the record, one can analyze this data and make a determination of what expected variance would be for various dosage forms. In addition, you may have such things as dissolution tests, which demonstrate that the physical characteristics of the product are not varying to a degree that would cause concern. Let me emphasize here, however, that in looking at this data, it is not enough to say that all products meet compendial specifications or your own specifications on a batch-by-batch basis, that is, using a standard of go, no-go, pass vs. reject, since hopefully you have already done that in carrying out your functions as the Quality Assurance department.

In the specific area of parenteral drug products, in addition to the activities of the FDA concerning finalization of the Large Volume Parenteral Good Manufacturing Practices, both the Parenteral Drug Association (PDA) and the Pharmaceutical Manufacturers Association (PMA) have been quite active in working on guidelines and/or definitions of validation and validation practices for terminally sterilized parenterals. The PDA has just recently published a document entitled "Validation of Steam Sterilization Cycles." I believe that, in general, this is an excellent document, and suggest that if you are interested, as most of you are, you contact the PDA and purchase copies of this document. In the document, the PDA divides the matter of validation of systems as follows:

1. *Laboratory studies*, in which they determine bioburden and then use the bioburden data as well as other values to calculate the probability of survival and the F_0 value required for sterilization.
2. *Plant studies*, or process studies in which they start out with calibrations of the temperature monitoring equipment, what they call certification or qualification of sterilizers, proceed into heat distribution studies, and in a corollary way, cold spot studies. They then go into heat penetration studies, use of biological indicators, and evaluation of these results.
3. *Overkill approach to sterilization validation*: This is a particularly interesting topic and merits special consideration where the products being sterilized are heat-stable and the overkill approach can thus add an additional safety margin.

The FDA has been taking the position particularly in cases of products purporting to be sterile that the process by which they are produced is not considered "adequate" unless such process has been adequately validated. In keeping with this position of written documentation, it follows that a process has not been validated unless documentation to that effect exists. In this regard, the FDA has in the past and is currently taking action to stop production of small-volume parenteral solutions in the absence of such validation.

From the above, one thing becomes clear: Validation has been an integral part of manufacturing assurance of quality and regulatory approach by the FDA for many years. There are many approaches to validating processes, and these approaches depend on the process and product in question. However, one thread runs through all considerations of validation: Validation is a systematic approach to quality assurance from the development to the marketing of a product. As such it cannot be treated as an isolated or separate activity. Validation is not the responsibility of any one scientific discipline within a firm. It requries the active participation of every element, including Engineers, Production, Product Development, and Quality Control personnel.

Let us now turn to what I term "motivation." What the future holds for validation will depend on a large part on the desires of the industry. If a firm makes use of the concept and tools of validation, the result can only be an increased assurance of quality and, in many cases, savings in capital as well as operating cost.

On the other hand, if validation is treated as a separate entity and just another "empire" or "fiefdom" of any one organizational unit, whether it be Production, Product Development, or Quality Control, full benefits will not be realized. One type of behavior that will have to be overcome is the continued reliance on finished product testing as the main tool of quality assurance. The idea of testing quality into a product is not consistent with the concept of validation. In the case of parenteral products this is especially true. As the FDA recently stated in speaking of validation:

In validating the adequacy of a process intended to yield a sterile drug product, end-product sterility testing is generally of limited sensitivity and reliability in characterizing with certainty the absence of microorganisms in each unit in a lot. (The sterility test in the United States Pharmacopeia/National Formulary—USPXX/NFXV—for instance, is only capable of detecting a contamination level of 10% when the test is conducted nine times out of ten.) In this example, relatively little significance should be placed on end product sterility test data for purposes of validation. Therefore, greater significance should be placed on data concerning such elements as water and air systems, equipment such as sterilizers, materials such as ingredients, personnel such as equipment operators and supervisors, and the manner in which production controls are exercised during the entire manufacturing process.

If we consider validation in the proper perspective and are motivated to use validation to its fullest benefit, the following should occur:

1. Validation will be integrated into the activities of each firm. Appropriate scientific disciplines will be utilized in the design and construction or modification of facilities and processes. Standard operating procedures will be established to implement validation. Validation terms will be established.

2. Industry and the FDA will continue to cooperate in review and implementation of plans for construction of new facilities or modification of existing facilities. Inspections of new facilities will be "segmented" where possible to reduce time from completion to approval.

3. New technology such as computer-controlled processes and equipment will assure that all units were produced under designed conditions, and this fact will be documented.

4. A shift in priorities and activities of Quality Control and Quality Assurance units will occur. This shift will be from finished product testing to support of validation activities. Routine finished products testing for sterility and pyrogens will cease. Inspection for particulates will be reduced due to improvement in process and environmental controls.

5. The FDA will give more recognition and attention to validation in determining compliance with GMPs. Hopefully, relief from the requirement of preapproval in ANDAs and NDAs for manufacturing process and controls will be granted except in the case of new and unique processes or dosage firms.

6. Industry groups such as the Parenteral Drug Association and the Pharmaceutical Manufacturers Association will continue to produce guidelines in the area of validation. The industry groups, along with academia, (e.g., Purdue University, University of Georgia, and University of Wisconsin), will expand seminars and training programs. A means of providing "hands-on" training for FDA personnel in industry will be found.

So—Validation: Where to? The answer to this question is for you. Where do you want to go? The safe course, is as always, to stand pat. This course won't make it today. For most of us, whether we are willing or unwilling participants, we are being pushed into fuller use of validation concepts and practices. Those who treat validation as an opportunity for improvement both in the quality and efficiency of their firm's operations will be the winners. Many of those who don't will be, at best, merely survivors. It would be unrealistic to believe that the full benefits of validation will be realized in the near future, but I believe that, in a large part, they will.

Index